The Pentagon Paradox

The Pentagon Paradox

The Development of the F-18 Hornet

James P. Stevenson

Distributed by:
Airlife Publishing Ltd.
101 Longden Road, Shrewsbury SY3 9EB, England

Stevenson, James Perry.
The Pentagon paradox : the development of the F-18 Hornet / James P. Stevenson.
p. cm.
Includes bibliographical references and index.
ISBN 1-55750-775-9
1. Hornet (Jet fighter plane)—History. 2. United States—Armed Forces—Procurement. I. Title.
UG1242.F5S754 1993
358.4'383—dc20 93-35642
CIP

Printed in the United States of America on acid-free paper ♾

9 8 7 6 5 4 3 2

First printing

For
Sara, Genevieve, and Anna
and
those quiet but honest government employees
who believe that the government should work the way their
9th grade civics teacher told them it worked.

Contents

Preface

This book began out of an insult. It was originally conceived as a buff book, one designed to be similar to two previous books I had done on the F-14 and on the F-15. Someone told me that I should interview Col. Everest Riccioni, who had retired from the Air Force and was working at Northrop.

When I met "Rich," as everyone called him, he was standing in front of his desk. He had the happy swagger of a St. Bernard puppy, even while standing still. Almost instantly, he said: "I read your F-14 book and I read your F-15 book. They're both full of shit. Now if you want to know what's really going on, I'll tell you. Otherwise, get the hell out."

I answered before the full force of the insult took effect. "Yes, I want to know," I said.

"O.K.," Rich said and walked to the door of his office. He leaned outside and said to his secretary, "Hold my calls *for the day*." It was only a little after 10:00 A.M.

He settled back into his seat. I asked, "O.K., so what's wrong with my books?"

"Well, let's just take an example. How about your statement that the F-15 can go Mach 2.5? That's what you said in your F-15 book, isn't it?"

I nodded.

"Who told you that?" asked Riccioni.

"McDonnell Douglas and the Air Force."

"Well, there's truth, the whole truth, and nothing but the truth," Riccioni said. "What you got was *some* truth."

"Why would they lie to me?" I asked.

"Well," Riccioni said, "that is a separate issue. Let's establish that you did not get the whole truth. Then I'll tell you why."

Rich reached back and picked up a document.

"Do you know how to read one of these?" he asked. I did. He was showing me a flight profile of the F-15 in a document purporting to be a collection of high-speed test runs of the F-15 at Edwards Air Force Base in California. Rich pointed to a particular page. "What does this say?" he asked. The profile he was pointing to said it was for a maximum speed run. "Note the equipment on the F-15," Riccioni said, showing me that this particular test run was performed with four Sparrow missiles, four Sidewinder missiles, gun, and ammunition. "So what is the maximum speed?" Riccioni asked. I measured across and then looked down at the Mach scale. It showed that the maximum speed was slightly shy of Mach 1.8.

I looked up. Riccioni could see the confusion on my face.

"Look," he said, "the F-15 *can* fly Mach 2.5. But to do it, the Air Force had to take off all of the tactically relevant weapons—the Sparrows, the Sidewinders, the gun and the ammo. Then they flew it to altitude. Then they topped it off with fuel and ran it out to Mach 2.3. Next the pilot had to hit the V_{max} button which permits the F-15 to continue to Mach 2.5. At that point two significant events took place. First, the F-15 was out of fuel so it had to land immediately. Second, upon landing the engines had to be replaced because the V_{max} switch allows only an additional 5 minutes before the engines have to be overhauled. So I guess in a sense the F-15 is a Mach 2.5 airplane, if you want to build them for air shows. However, Mach 2.5 has no tactical significance.

"So you see, they did not exactly lie to you, but they did not tell you the whole truth. You were lucky. Usually they will simply lie.

"Now you want to know why they lie?" Riccioni asked.

I nodded.

"Money and career. For the aerospace companies there are literally billions of dollars at stake. For the military officers assigned to the Pentagon, advancement is a function of how well they help their respective service increase its share of the defense budget."

Riccioni admonished me to challenge everyone and everything I would hear in the future. In return, I told Riccioni I would not even accept what he said. "Good," he added. "I particularly want you to check what I say."

I left Riccioni's office with my world somewhat shaken. Prior to my visit, when I saw stars or gold on a flag-ranking officer, I submitted to a sense of respectful deference. After my iconoclastic visit to Riccioni, I began my conversion to requiring substantiation of what anyone told me. I knew then that this would not become another buff book. Still I had some doubts about the degree of the problem in spite of what Riccioni said.

Shortly after my visit to Riccioni, I was in the Pentagon and overheard an Air Force colonel telling a story in which he was ordered to do a series of tasks that were so offensive, I blurted out, "Oh, come on. I can't believe they would make you do that."

The colonel pivoted on his feet in a snappy right-face, put his finger in my chest, and said:

"Listen, son. I was an operator in the Air Force for 22 years. I was proud of my service, proud of my men, my experience, and most importantly, of myself. But as a result of spending two years in this building, when I leave, I'm going to have to [perform an unnatural sexual act] just to gain my self-respect."

Maybe things were worse than Riccioni claimed.

One refreshing aspect of my walk through the procurement maze was the occasional individual who would speak up and say, "But the emperor has no clothes." John Boyd and Pierre Sprey were two who saw more naked kings than most people. Based on Riccioni's revelation that some individuals would lie, I challenged and checked everything that Riccioni, Sprey, and Boyd told me. I never found an inconsistency.

When I met Chuck Myers, and later Chuck Spinney, I had the same experience. Sometimes we might disagree over whether the glass was half-full or half-empty. But when they said a four-inch glass had water at the two-inch level, they were always correct.

Unfortunately, *some* of the officers and civilians in the Department of Defense and military services in the defense procurement business would tell me the glass had three and seven-eighths inches of water in it when there was not enough water to measure. In some cases the water was filled with another substance that Sprey liked to call balonium, unavailium, or unobtainium.

Sprey was the toughest critic of all, attributing evil intent to most false statements. At the other extreme, some flag officers said that procurement officials were doing the best they could with the information available. I concluded the truth was somewhere in between. There are individuals who intentionally lied to perpetuate their positions, careers, or the cause. But in the majority of cases, the lie was merely repeated by trusting subordinates. This naive attitude is reflected in a comment one Navy civilian made to me. I had asked him several times about the truth of a particular statement. He kept insisting that it was true. I kept insisting on proof. Finally, in exasperation, he said, "My admiral told me and I don't believe he would lie." That was his proof. Chances are his particular admiral did not lie; but somewhere along the communication chain, someone did.

My experiences with most military and civilian officials in the defense procurement industry has been positive. I hope the reader will not come away from this book believing, as one retired three-star admiral did after reading it, that I "seem to think all naval officers are crooks—particularly flag officers." My father was a naval officer, and most of my friends are or were naval officers. I spent six fantastic years as the editor of the Navy Fighter Weapon School's *Topgun Journal*. I learned firsthand about the high quality of the majority of naval officers.

What I do believe is that *some* naval officers, flag or otherwise (not to mention Air Force, Marine, and Army officers, and civilians) lose sight of their fiduciary responsibility to the taxpayer. The law puts certain burdens on individuals within this society to ascertain information which they may not have. It is illegal to receive stolen property that one knew was stolen or *should have known* was stolen, *even if one did not actually know.* A naval officer who works on a program that requires taxpayer money is a fiduciary. Therefore, he or she has an even higher level of responsibility than the average citizen does to determine if property was stolen. So when the admiral mentioned above says he believes that "people were making honest decisions based upon the best info available," I can only respond by saying that while the information may have been the best available, in some cases, *some* officers *should have known* that they needed better information and not made representations to Congress until they had it.

I have been asked why I used the "F-18" designation instead of the "F/A-18" designation on the cover. I take issue with the use of the "F/A-18" designation, for what I believe are some very sound reasons.

First, there is a governing body that is in charge of designations. That body is the Department of Defense (DoD), which is a higher authority than the Department of the Navy. The operative DoD instruction is Inst. 4120.15-L, "Model Designation of Military Aerospace Vehicles," February 1993.

The DoD Instruction lists the *Hornet* under two categories: *fighter* and *attack*. Under *attack* the *Hornet* is listed as the A-18 and the FA-18 (not F/A-18). Under *fighters* it is listed as the F-18. The FA-18 designation is not a typo—the Instruction 4120.15 states that in using the FA-18 designation, the "A" is the primary mission and the "F" is a modification of the primary mission.

Originally Vice Adm. William D. Houser, DCNO (Air), sent a message that the designation F-18 would be used for the fighter version and A-18 for the attack version.[1] The change to the use of "F/A-18" was

1. Houser to CNO, "Memorandum for the Chief of Naval Operations," Memo 05/187 (30 October 1975).

done with the recognition that it was in violation of the regulations.

On 5 September 1978, Vice Adm. F. C. Turner, DCNO (Air), wrote the commander of the Naval Air Systems Command responding to the commander's recommendation that the Navy use "F-18A for the multimission, common VF and VA, USN and USMC Hornet."[2] Turner said: "Your recommendation was based on *conformance with existing regulations.* My choice, F/A-18, would be based *not* so much *on conformance with existing directives* as with the necessity to designate this aircraft so that it truly reflects its multimission nature. *Certainly the designation F-18 is in consonance with the tri-service instruction.* . . . I prefer to continue [with F/A-18] even though it may be one that receives its legitimacy through use rather than directive."[3] (Emphasis added.)

In other words, Admiral Turner wanted to use F/A-18 regardless of what the DoD instruction said. This example of thwarting higher authority is one of many that I discovered in researching this book. If Admiral Turner were familiar with the DoD definition of a "fighter" from which the "F" designation is derived, he would have known that the definition for "fighter" is multimission already. The definition follows:

> **Fighter**—Aircraft designed to intercept and destroy other aircraft or missiles. Includes multi-purpose aircraft *also designed* for ground support missions such as *interdiction*, and *close air support.*
>
> **Attack**—Aircraft designed to find, attack, and destroy enemy land or sea targets using conventional or special weapons. This symbol also applies to aircraft used for *interdiction* and *close air support* missions.[4] (Emphasis added.)

In other words, the definition of a "fighter" includes the definition of an "attack" aircraft, which makes the use of both the "F" and the "A" in F/A-18 redundant.

DoD Instruction 4120.15-L states that the use of the designations listed in the document is *mandatory*. Either DoD has the right to designate aircraft or it does not. If it does, then the next question is why would I or my publisher, the Naval Institute Press, want to perpetuate a violation of an act committed with requisite knowledge that it constituted a violation?

---

2. Turner to Commander, Naval Air Systems Command, "Memorandum for the Commander, Naval Air Systems Command." Ser. 506C5/781084 (5 September 1978).

3. Ibid.

4. DoD Inst. 4120.15-L (AFR-82-1 [18 May 1990], AR 70-50, and NAVAIRINST 8800.3)

I will feel that the book is a success, despite whatever errors may have crept in, if it will stimulate debate. The egregious behavior I mentioned above extended to an attempt to interfere with this book. No less than the Navy F-18 program manager asked my publisher to "review" the book because he believed that it contained false and misleading information. There is a certain irony that in an attempt to perpetuate his position—whatever his mind-set—a naval officer would want to in any way interrupt the first amendment, that amendment he swore an oath to defend with his life. "They'll review it, all right," said a friend, upon hearing of the request. "They'll find so many things wrong with your manuscript that it will never see the light of day."

Fortunately, cooler heads prevailed. I particularly admire the Naval Institute's executive director, Capt. James Barber, USN (Ret.), for politely refusing the Navy's request to "review" my manuscript. For all I know, Barber may totally disagree with what I have said. He, no doubt, remembers his oath and recognizes that rebuttal is a superior response to repression.

Acknowledgments

This is the most difficult part of the book to write, or not write to be exact. I would like to give credit to literally hundreds of military and civilians who wanted this story told. Unfortunately, giving them credit is difficult. Most of them would jeopardize promotions or even lose their jobs if I acknowledged their help.

It is frustrating to me to not give them a justly deserved thank you, however. So, to all of you who were so helpful, I give you my sincerest thank you. I admire your willingness to attempt to tell a story.

A special thank you for all of the kindness from the people at Nisus Software.

Chapter 1

A Frame of Reference

Technology, it seems, can be worshipped, enjoyed, respected, admired—even loved. It may provide job opportunities or reasons for not doing the job. As institutions face the confusion of the modern era, their leaders may find it easier to seek after a new bid of hardware rather than confront underlying problems. It is quite clear that many modern organizations find their attention dominated by gadgetry which by-passes consideration of mission or purpose. While in some cases the technology is appropriate, in others what develops is an inappropriate fixation technology—technomania—with a corresponding technopathology contaminating administrative structures.

Frederic A. Bergerson
The Army Gets an Air Force

The F-18 Hornet slid over the land that several millennia before had invented the wheel, the first written law, and the battle chariot. Small momentary mounds rose from the desert, hidden hummocks offering an empty salutation from lost cities with famous names: Ur of the Chaldees, Sumeria, Babylon, Ashurbanipal, and Nineveh. This was the womb of civilization, Mesopotamia—the basin in which the first Neanderthal men chose to form cities.

The Tigris and Euphrates Rivers emptied into the Persian Gulf after traveling hundreds of miles from the northwest, coming closest together near modern-day Baghdad. The rivers were navigational marks for the F-18 pilot. If the wind had not blown, if time had stood still, he might have seen the tracks left in the sand by Cyrus of Persia and Alexander the Great when they used horse and chariot to generate wholesome fear in their concurred masses. In 39 days he would see tanks execute these same tactics.

But this early afternoon on January 18, 1991, Lt. Nick "Mongo" Mongillo of VFA-81 was cruising at 31,700 feet at Mach 0.88, almost 90 percent the speed of sound. In five minutes he would travel the distance Alexander could have traversed in a day. And whereas Hammurabi had wedged pliable clay with reeds to introduce the first written law, the F-18 used megabytes of data to cross-corollate and update the integrated flight control systems so that the F-18 could accurately navigate to a point on the desert where it could establish a law of its own.

This F-18 was on a bombing mission, but at the first challenge from enemy fighters, Lieutenant Mongillo would only have to flip a few switches on his stick and throttle to quickly transition to the air-to-air mode. It was a good idea.

"Bandits two-oh-six 20 miles," a warning from one of the many omniscient electronic airborne observation aircraft interrupted whatever thoughts the pilot had. Lieutenant Mongillo's mission had just switched from air-to-ground to air-to-air. For the next few minutes, he forgot about his bombing mission until he became the first Navy pilot in Operation Desert Storm to shoot down an Iraqi MiG.

When Jack Krings took the F-18 Hornet for its first flight on November 18, 1978, 12 years and 2 months prior to Lieutenant Mongillo's MiG encounter, his mission as a test pilot was clear.* The Hornet's mission as a fighter was not. The F-18 Hornet did not evolve as a response to a set of needs generated by the U.S. Navy after much deliberation. Rather, the F-18 resulted from a continuing debate in Washington, D.C., over what works and what doesn't in aerial warfare.

The argument is essentially this: The established military position states that technology will save us from our potential adversaries who will always outnumber us. The minority argues that history disputes such optimism, that numbers have always played the dominant role in successful warfare, as General Custer learned at Little Bighorn. Nothing frames the argument better than two separate studies done by the U.S. Air Force approximately 13 years apart.

THE WELCH TAC AVENGER STUDY

Shortly after the U.S. Air Force awarded the F-15 Eagle contract to McDonnell Douglas in December 1969, the F-15 began experiencing political difficulties. This was nothing new; all aircraft programs experience problems in Congress. But the F-15 Eagle was no ordinary airplane. It was the first jet that the U.S. Air Force had procured with air combat maneuvering (dogfighting) as part of the design requirement.† Furthermore, it was the most visible, not to mention

*Jack Krings was not actually the Chief Test Pilot, whose duty it was to make the first flight. Krings had been the McDonnell Chief Test Pilot but had just been promoted to Director of Flight Operations, which put him in charge of all test pilots, including incoming Chief Test Pilot William Brinks. One of Krings's first actions as the new director was to rewrite his job description so that he could grab the historically significant honor of making the first flight. He then turned over the duties to Brinks.

†Some students of air warfare believe that the F-86 was the first. Although it performed credibly in Korea, the requirement for the F-86 was generated as a high-

most expensive, program that the Air Force had developed in a long time. Consequently, when the congressional attacks on its rising cost escalated, the Air Force's institutional immune system went on full alert.

The responsibility to develop a counter to this swell of negative publicity fell on the solitary star-laden shoulders of Brig. Gen. Ben Bellis, Commander of the F-15 System Program Office, known as the SPO. Bellis turned to the Air Force's Studies and Analysis group for help. Fortunately, he found the ideal man in Lt. Col. Larry Welch. With Welch's help, and a computer program called TAC Avenger, Bellis developed a series of briefings within the Air Force in preparation for his presentation on Capitol Hill.

Concurrent with the F-15 development, the Air Force was also developing a new heat-seeking missile known as the AIM-82. This paper missile had a 50 degree off-boresight capability (the ability to look 50 degrees to the left, right, up, or down from its centerline) and large fins so that it could practically look and turn up its own tailpipe. Apparently it occurred to Welch that some analysis showing an exchange ratio between the F-15 with the AIM-82 missile and a potential threat would show Congress why money should be no object when dealing with the powerful combination of the AIM-82 and the F-15 Eagle.

While Lieutenant Colonel Welch was doing his exchange ratio analysis (expressed as the number of enemy aircraft shot down for every loss—sometimes called a "kill-loss" ratio), he must have considered the fact that it had to be significant enough to support the high cost of the F-15, but believable. After all, the kill-loss ratio for all of World War II was 1.6-to-1; Korea 6.2-to-1; and Vietnam 2.5-to-1.[1]

Yet some isolated cases were much better, such as the Navy's 19-to-1 kill-loss ratios with F6F Hellcats against the Japanese in World War II.[2] When Welch developed his model of one F-15 Eagle with the heat-seeking AIM-82 missile against one MiG-21 with an AIM-9D Sidewinder equivalent, he had the benefit of the history of these ratios.*

With Welch's analysis done and overhead viewgraphs prepared, Brigadier General Bellis began his presentation to General Furgerson, Commander of the Air Force Systems Command. From Furgerson, the presentation would soon go before Congress to prove the value of the F-15.

altitude interceptor.

*All historical analyses reveal that one-versus-one analysis *never* characterizes aerial combat, which is almost always N aircraft versus M aircraft. (Statement made by E. E. Riccioni to the author.)

When Bellis came to the viewgraph (see table 1-1) that showed the kill-loss ratio between the F-15 and the MiG-21, an air of strained incredulity filled the room. Bellis was offering an unheard of kill-loss ratio. He wanted General Furgerson to believe that Larry Welch's analysis proved that for every F-15 Eagle the U.S. Air Force would lose, it would shoot down 955 MiGs! That is to say, Welch's analysis showed a 955-to-1 kill-loss ratio or a 1,500 percent improvement over any other aircraft in any previous conflict.

General Furgerson's response was short and to the point. He said, in essence: "Ben, if I believed your story—which I don't—but if I did—well, then we'd only need three F-15s: one in Europe, one in the Pacific, and one in the U.S. to train in. Now take that god-damn brief and burn it!"[3]

Table 1-1
AIM-82A Program
Air Combat Effectiveness Analysis
Exchange Ratios

	Threat MiG-21F AIM-9	Threat MiG-21F AIM-82/30°	Threat MiG-21F AIM-82/50°
F-15			
AIM-9J	18-to-1	1-to-2.3	1-to-8
AIM-9E (X)	22-to-1	1-to-1.6	1-to-6
AIM-9K/50°	245-to-1	1.7-to-1	1-to-2
AIM-82/50°	**955-to-1**	6-to-1	**1.4-to-1**
F-4			
AIM-9J	1-to-6	1-to41	1-to-159
AIM-9E (X)	1-to-4.7	1-to-20	1-to-39
AIM-9K/50°	1.2-to-1	1-to-2.3	1-to-5
AIM-82/50°	**5-to-1**	1.8-to-1	1-to-1.4

SOURCE: U.S. Congress. Senate. *Impact of Technology on Military*. . . P. 180

These are the data from the infamous slide created by Larry Welch. Note how little credit the U.S. Air Force gives to its new design, the F-15. According to this analysis, if the F-15 and the MIG-21 both have the same missile—the AIM-82 with 50 degree off boresight capability (the degrees from the centerline of the missile)—the Air Force will lose one F-15 for every 1.4 MiG-21s it shoots down. If the U.S. Air Force had accepted these data, it might have avoided the need to develop the F-15 because it could achieve a 200 percent improvement over its Vietnam exchange ratio simply by adding the AIM-82 missile to its existing F-4 Phantom. (Emphasis added. The original slide used the shorthand 18/1 in lieu of 18-TO-1.)

THE BURTON AIR-TO-AIR STUDY

In the early 1980s another Air Force officer was doing analytical studies and delivering briefings in the Pentagon. Col. Jim Burton took it upon himself to investigate the lessons of history in order to develop realistic future air-to-air missile requirements. His briefing, entitled "Letting Combat Results Shape the Next Air-to-Air Missile," investigated 27 years of actual combat, from the Formosa Straits to the 1982 Middle East Air War. Burton examined the azimuth and range of more than 2,000 firings, which included guns, heat-seeking missiles, and radar-guided missiles. (He counted each gun trigger squeeze as a firing.)

Burton was curious to see how well each system performed, in particular the radar-guided Sparrow missile. After all, the U.S. Air Force's tactical air doctrine was based on shooting down enemy aircraft beyond visual range. So the beyond-visual-range Sparrow missile was bound to make a good showing somewhere along the way. What he discovered surprised him.

Colonel Burton found that in the history of air-to-air warfare, at least during a 27-year period, there were only four beyond-visual-range radar-guided missile kills.* These performance results translate into a probability of kill (P_K) of .002, or two-tenths of 1 percent.

These two analyses, one based on the theoretical, the other on actual combat, sum up the nature of the debate. Should American fighter design be driven by the eternally optimistic theory that sophisticated,† that is, more complex, technology will negate the effects of being outnumbered, or should we evolve our design requirements from combat-derived criteria and build greater numbers of less complex aircraft.

It may be hard to understand that an entire doctrine—that of developing planes with a beyond-visual-range capability—could be based on a system that has demonstrated such poor results. But keep in mind that in large organizations, precepts are self-perpetuating. Anyone who challenges the system is blackballed; when they help to preserve it, they are rewarded. Lt. Col. Larry Welch is a classic example. He went on, in the spirit of the Gilbert and Sullivan operetta *H.M.S. Pinafore,* to become a four star general and Air Force Chief of Staff, the number one position in the U.S. Air Force.

Col. Jim Burton is also representative. For his missile analysis and other fine work, the Air Force tried to retire him many times. They were ultimately successful. Burton was removed because of his participation in the M-2 live-fire test. He was concerned that validation models did not accurately predict combat results.

If it surprises anyone that a system would attempt to rid itself of an individual who delivers the truth, it should not. After all, if General Motors was willing to pay Ross Perot $700 million merely to prevent his further criticism of its upper management, is it any wonder that the U.S. Air Force, a more bureaucratic institution,

*Burton defined beyond visual range as five miles.

†The *American Heritage Dictionary of the English Language* (Third Edition) p. 1,719 defines sophisticate as: "Very complex or complicated. . . ."

would silence one of its own at the trivial cost of excommunication?

The history of the F-18 is the story of the ebb and flow of two views—one claims that sophistication will expand capability, the other that simplicity will lower costs and allow us to increase the number of tactical fighters. Inherent in this second view is the belief that developing sophisticated aircraft has not increased their capability. This historical investigation looks at how the F-18 addresses this continuous debate. The data collected during my investigation tend to support what can only be called the Pentagon Paradox:

Benefits are inversely proportional to the promise.

I refer throughout this discussion to many U.S. Air Force documents in addition to U.S. Navy data. For the purpose of this history, it makes little difference whether one looks at the U.S. Air Force or the U.S. Navy when attempting to gain insights on the sophisticated technology mindset that exists. Their institutional attitudes toward sophistication are virtually identical. They differ when it comes to the actual procurement, but not with respect to their belief in the promise of technology, particularly technology that will allow pilots to destroy other aircraft beyond visual range with radar-guided missiles or to drop bombs with the accuracy of a Nintendo game. But while they are similar in their faith in technology, the U.S. Air Force has generated, collected, or preserved more information.

There is a connection between the U.S. Air Force and the U.S. Navy with respect to the F-18 Hornet. Whereas the F-18 in its current form is a U.S. Navy airplane, its heritage comes from the U.S. Air Force. But that is not the whole picture. The genesis of the F-18 came from a combination of supporters from the Air Force, Navy, and civilians within the Office of the Secretary of Defense. It is reasonable, therefore, when airing the debates that led up to the procurement of the Hornet, to include the comments of both the Air Force and Navy regarding the nature of what a fighter in the tactical air force should look like. References to the tactical aircraft of both services and the doctrine that surrounds them is commonly referred to as TacAir.

Quantity versus Quality

The debate has developed buzz words that act as shorthand for the two positions. The two arguments are encapsulated most often in the phrase Quality versus Quantity.

In essence, the argument of the quantity group is that for the same money, we could have more of the less complex, or less sophisticated, fighters. They would be easier and less expensive to support; their readiness would increase; and there is no historical evidence that the more sophisticated aircraft are better at their primary mission, destroying other aircraft in the air, or their secondary mission of dropping bombs.

The quality faction argues that requirements cannot be made in a vacuum, that we must keep up with the potential threat, and that as the sophistication of the threat increases, so must the sophistication of our tactical aircraft. This usually puts an inordinately heavy emphasis on air-to-ground capability.

The criteria and hardware normally associated with quality fighters have the following characteristics, as outlined in Kross:

- Sophisticated radars to search for targets beyond the range of the pilots' eyesight, (beyond-visual-range, or BVR)
- Beyond-visual-range missiles
- Complex avionics
- High [maximum] speed capability, usually in excess of Mach 2
- Long range on internal fuel
- Multimission capability

The quantity versus quality debate centers on weapons system performance, cost, and supportability.* [4]

THE MILITARY KNOWS BEST

One might reasonably ask at this point, why question the military? After all, presumably they understand best what is needed to do their job effectively. Indeed, some generals openly advocate this sentiment. Gen. Robert D. Russ, summed it up in the April 1981 issue of *Air Force* Magazine. "What we should do is put a moratorium on the debating and, instead, direct our attention to accelerating the development and procurement of quality aircraft, avionics, and weapons systems."[5]

The military's high tech advocates attempt to substitute logic with *argumentum intimidatum*, to convince us that the military planners know what's best. But if the generals and admirals know

*Kross's book, *Military Reform: The High-Tech Debate in Tactical Air Forces*, is the best summary of both sides of the debate, and comes down on the side of the quality advocates.

Kross defines supportability as

- **Readiness**: the capacity to perform one's mission when directed to do so. This is synonymous with preparedness.
- **Sustainability**: staying power in the combat environment. The capability to remain combat ready for a required period.
- **Reliability**: the inherent capacity of given equipment to remain in working order for the necessary period. The opposite of equipment failure.

best, then why blunders such as the surprise at Pearl Harbor, the fallacious belief in unescorted manned bomber in World War II, (not to mention the claim that we would not need to commit soldiers to that War), the draw in Korea, the loss in Vietnam, the raid on Iran, the *Mayaguez* Incident, and the DIVAD, to name a few?

One explanation of the lack of foresight implicit in these events might be that our preconceptions limit what we see. For example, Chinese astronomers saw and identified stars, planets, and comets centuries before their Western counterparts. What prevented Western astronomers from seeing these same heavenly bodies? Their religious beliefs asserted that the sky was fixed and immutable. Likewise, the military has doctrines and dogma that create preconceptions about the benefits of complex technologies. Billions of dollars have been spent on electronic solutions for problems for which electronics may not have been the solution.

As an example, the size and shape of U.S. fighters begins and ends with a design that accommodates the 36-inch diameter radar antenna. Smaller designs have been rejected solely because they could not accommodate the 36-inch radar dish. Conventional wisdom states that this 3-foot dish is necessary in order to have the necessary radar range.

One of the drawbacks to a large radar dish is that it increases the frontal area of the aircraft. This increases drag and generates a requirement for a bigger, more powerful—and more complex—engine. Yet in spite of the bigger engines, the drag is so great that aircraft that are supposed to have great performance differences do not. The F-15, for example, at 10,000 feet of altitude is only a few knots faster than the F-5E, an aircraft one-third its size and price, and carrying 40 percent of the F-15's thrust.

The larger dish increases the radar image size of the aircraft, thus making it easier to detect by a smaller radar system in a smaller fighter. It also increases the visual signature for passive acquisition. The larger radar antenna also improves passive radar detection.[6]

This spiraling technology was set in motion by the theory that beyond-visual-range radar-guided missiles would make dogfights a thing of the past. Yet despite the technological advances, Burton's analysis indicates that only four beyond-visual-range radar-guided missile kills were on the scoreboard through 1982, the year after the F-18 was procured.

One of the fundamental reasons for the beyond-visual-range failure comes from the fact that our fighters cannot tell the good guys from the bad. Former Tactical Air Commander Gen. William Creech admitted in 1981 congressional testimony that the critical Identification Friend or Foe (IFF) has never worked. Identification Friend or Foe, which is usually referred to by its initials IFF, is the critical piece of equipment required for pilots to electronically differentiate enemy from friend. The IFF equipment interrogates other aircraft through the on-board radar, much like the transponder systems used in the air traffic control system throughout the United States. Air combat tactics have been developed from the inception of the beyond-visual-range missile as though the IFF would work. In Desert Storm and as recently as post–Desert Storm violations of the no-fly zone below the 32nd parallel in Iraq, it still did not work. As a result, before a pilot could fire at a target he had to get a second opinion which in those cases was a clearance from a multimillion dollar supplement to the IFF known as the E-3 AWACS. Until the Gulf War, American fighter pilots were restricted to using the beyond-visual-range Sparrow missile only when they had *visually* identified the target.

Even if the IFF worked perfectly, the radar-guided missile does not seem to do well in the real world environment of the air-combat arena. In Vietnam, the kill-loss trend was, during the period prior to the development of the F-18, on the decline. In June 1965 the exchange ratio between U.S. and Vietnamese fighters was 1-to-1. By June of 1967 the ratio had increased in the United States's favor to 3.77-to-1. By March of 1968 the trend had dropped to 2.39-to-1. What drove this average down was the fact that between July 1967 and March 1968, the United States destroyed 27 MiGs but lost 24 in the process, for an exchange ratio of 1.13-to-1. Of even greater concern was the fact that between June and December 1967, MiG-21s shot down six American aircraft without suffering any losses. For the April 1, 1965, to March 1, 1968, period both the U.S. Air Force and the U.S. Navy had similar overall exchange ratios of 2.39- and 2.4-to-1 respectively.[7]

Thus, TacAir fighter design criteria—large, drag-ridden fighters—carried weight, maneuvered with drag, and fired beyond-visual-range missiles *within* visual range at a cost of billions of dollars in excess of what it could have been if the fighter had been designed to carry only within-visual-range missiles such as the Sidewinder. Moreover, Sparrows don't work well when fired within visual range. The U.S. Navy, for example, fired 50 Sparrows in a row in Vietnam without a hit.

Although not readily apparent, the Probability of Kill (P_k)—the military manner of stating a percentage of kills resulting from missiles

Table 1-2
Missile Results 1965 to Spring 1968 by Missile and Year

	Fired	Kills	P_k(%)
Sidewinder (AIM-9B)	**175**	**28**	**16.0**
1965	8	2	25.0
1966	55	10	18.2
1967	105	16	15.2
1968	7	0	0.0
Sparrow (AIM-9D, E)	**224**	**20**	**8.9**
1965	3	0	0.0
1966	22	2	9.1
1967	161	15	9.3
1968	38	3	7.9
Falcon (AIM-4D)	**43**	**4**	**9.3**
1965	0	0	0.0
1966	0	0	0.0
1967	26	1	3.8
1968	17	3	17.6
Gun (20MM)	**N/A**	**34**	
1965	N/A	0	
1966	N/A	5	
1967	N/A	27	
1968		2	

SOURCE: Goartz, "An Analysis of Air-to-Air Missiles. . ." p. 59
The AIM-4 Falcon missile was the most maligned of all missiles during the 1965-68 period, yet paradoxically, it had better results than the Sparrow.

fired—decreased over time during the first phase of the Vietnam Air War. (The first phase of the Vietnam Air War was from April 1965, when the first air-to-air kill occurred, to November 1968 when President Lyndon Johnson called a halt to the air war.

Table 1-3

	Missiles Fired	Missile Kills	Missile P_k(%)	Gun Kills	Total Kills	Gun Kills as a Percentage of Total Kills
1965	11	2	18.2	0	2	0.0
1966	77	12	15.6	5	17	29.4
1967	292	32	11.0	27	59	45.8
1968	62	6	9.7	2	8	25.0
Total	**442**	**52**	**11.8**	**34**	**86**	**39.5**

SOURCE: Goartz, "An Analysis of Air-to-Air Missiles . . ." p. 59
The gun was an effective means of killing enemy aircraft with almost 40 percent of the kills to the gun's credit during this April 1965-March 1968 period.

As a result of the poor performance during this period, the U.S. Navy, led by Capt. Frank Ault, generated a study to correct these poor results. The product of this study was unofficially known as the Ault Report. Among its recommendations was the creation of a graduate school for fighter pilots, known as Topgun. Ironically, the Navy had omitted the gun completely in the design of the F-4 Phantom. The irony results from the fact that a significant number of MiGs were destroyed by guns (see fig. 1-3).

Figure 1-1
Missiles Fired in Vietnam and the Resulting Kills

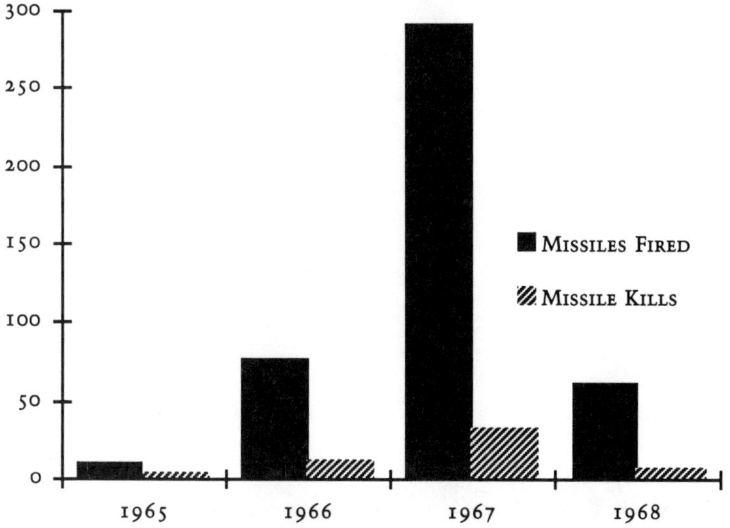

SOURCE: Goartz, "An Analysis of Air-to-Air missiles . . ." p. 59
The number of missiles fired over the course of the first phase of the Vietnam Air War showed that the effectiveness of the missile did not increase. These data are from the period April 1, 1965, through March 1, 1968. President Lyndon Johnson called a halt to the Vietnam Air War in November 1968.

These kinds of errors in judgment caused a bipartisan Congress, heated by the press, to attack our military commanders in the late 1970s and mid-1980s. The group was collectively know as the Military Reformers. One measure of this increasing attack on the military was, ironically enough, the Pentagon Bookstore.

Although the bookstore has always carried a title or two critical of the defense industry, the shelves reached a critical mass denigrating the military's judgment during this time. Several of the books were by military and civilian Department of Defense (DOD) employees.[8] Franklin Spinney's book argued, among other things, that aircraft unreliability combined with budgeting fantasies had led the U.S. military into a state of unreadiness that could not have been done better by our adversaries. Richard Gabriel, an Army reserve major, described in his book why the U.S. military had not had a victory since World War II.

Not only were the Pentagon bookshelves crying for reform, so were otherwise prodefense publications. *Aerospace America* published an article in its August 1985 issue entitled "Avionics Unreli-

Figure 1-2
Probability of Kill (P_k) For All Missiles Over Time in Vietnam

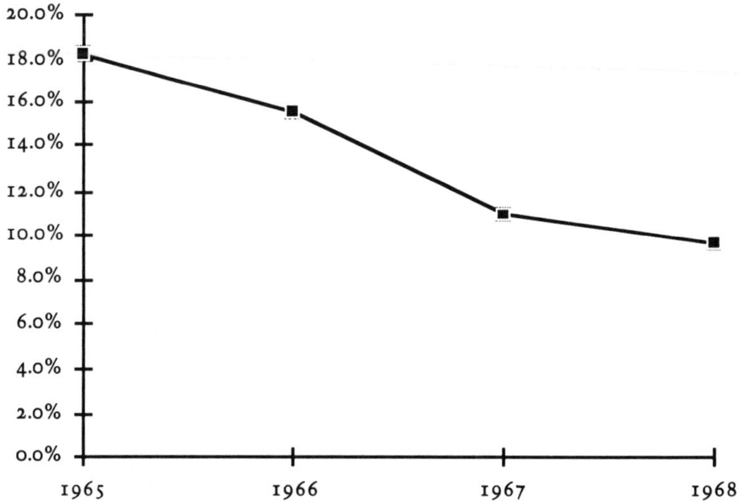

SOURCE: Goartz, "An Analysis of Air-to-Air missiles . . ." p. 59
These data are for the period April 1, 1965, through March 1, 1968.

ability Turns Fighters Into Shop Queens."[9]

The DIVAD Program serves as living testimony of the degree to which institution momentum can perpetuate a bad idea. The DIVAD Program cancellation was unprecedented. Never before has a program gone so far (the Army spent four years, $1.8 billion, and received 65 units) and been cancelled. The Bradley Fighting Vehicle, designed to protect soldiers from light-gun fire, was marked as another candidate.[10] During tests of resistance to small-arms fire, the vehicle experienced a meltdown, the opposite result it was designed for.

Naturally, Congress became involved in this criticism of the military. If one accepts the comments of Les Aspin, then Chairman of the House Armed Services Committee, the criticism is justified.* [11]

GROUPTHINK

The reasons for the criticism are not just of recent origin. The U.S. Air Force and Navy have made their share of historical mistakes.

Air power advocates prior to World War II said, for example, that because the bomber was so lethal, we would never have to commit

*Aspin issued a press release and supporting documentation stating that the Reagan administration spent $1 trillion, with little improvement in military readiness. Aspin went on to become the Secretary of Defense under President Clinton.

Figure 1-3
Gun Kills as Percentage of All Kills In Vietnam

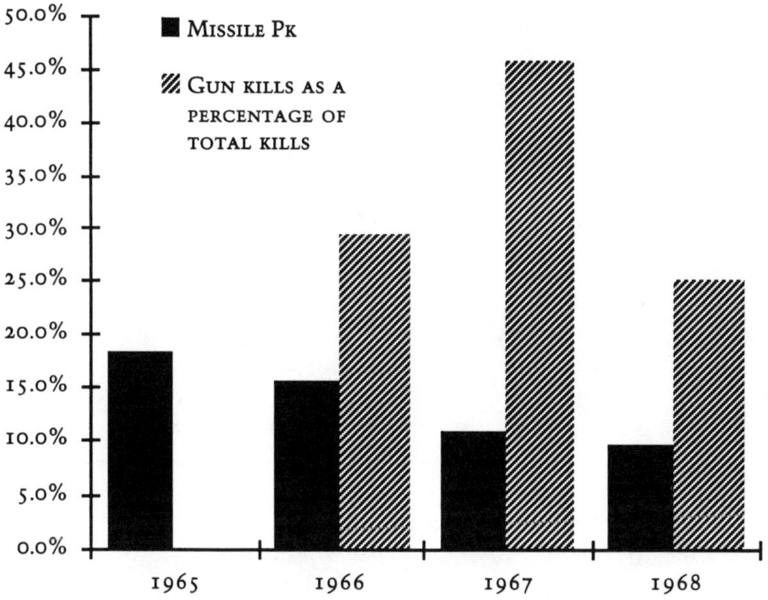

Source: Goartz, "An Analysis of Air-to-Air missiles . . ." p. 59
These data are for the period April 1, 1965, through March 1, 1968.

foot soldiers to a land war or develop escort fighters for the upcoming war brewing in Europe. Foot soldiers would stay home because bombers would destroy the enemy's war-making capability and eliminate the enemy's will to fight. History dispelled that notion.[12]

Equally misguided was the concept that bombers were so fast, heavily armed, and armored, that the enemy fighters lucky enough to catch them would be destroyed. The idea of the self-defending bomber formation died along with approximately 20 percent of the bombers on the first two long-range raids into the heart of Germany in late 1943. As Gen. Haywood S. Hansell, one of the planners, stated after the war:

> The fanatical belief of the bombers in their own defensive fire power was not so much a choice and election to operate unescorted as it was a conclusion that fighters could not be built with sufficient range to accompany them. . . . We had a tendency to build our doctrine around the drawing-board designs and the expected performance of aircraft still in the design stage. On this basis we unquestionably magnified our expected capabilities and minimized our limitation. . . . Our doctrine held that bombers in proper formation could conduct a running fire

> fight and preserve themselves against fighter attacks. *Unquestionably this was based on hope and not on existing fact.* (Emphasis added.)* [13]

The current military groupthink syndrome is based on three fundamental beliefs. The first is, as Spinney states, the "faith that advancing technology will make the future different from the past." The second is the attrition mindset. This concept is based on the notion that the side that can inflict the largest body count or destroy the most targets wins. History again disproves this concept. The third notion is the false belief that war is a manipulable, deterministic process that can be centrally controlled.† [14]

This reliance on hope, rather than experience, in spite of overwhelming evidence to the contrary, has all the characteristics of a syndrome Irving Janis calls the Groupthink Syndrome.

It was this groupthink syndrome that rendered the Navy vulnerable to the sneak attack on Pearl Harbor. The Navy failed to prepare in spite of the fact that the leaders had sufficient information that indicated a Japanese attack.

Indeed, the Korean War, the War in Vietnam, not to mention the *Mayaguez* Incident, the raid on Iran, and the specific failures in Granada are all testimony to the fact that the military fails as regularly as most large institutions—if not more so. And when they fail they constantly complain that their failures are due to the interference of civilians.[15]

Groupthink caused the French prior to World War II to rely on the Maginot Line to make their country safe from Germany. The Maginot Line was a concrete fortress that ran virtually the length of the border between France and Germany. Its purpose was to prevent a repeat of a German invasion, which they experienced in World War I. It would be impossible to penetrate due to its size and firepower—in short its technology. In spite of the fact that France had larger numbers of troops and equipment, their mindset was such that they relied on the technological achievement of the Maginot Line—to their detriment. The French, like others before and after, wallowed in the complacency that their technology would save them. Had the French questioned the technology, they might have

*This is a classic example of technology shaping strategy, just like the technological belief in beyond-visual-range changed our current air-to-air doctrine.

†The *American Heritage* dictionary defines Determinism as

> "The philosophical doctrine that every event, act, and decision is the inevitable consequence of antecedents, such as physical, psychological, or environmental conditions, that are independent of the human will." p. 359.

realized how easily the Germans could circumvent it, which they did.[16]

Even the Israelis are not immune to groupthink. Their reliance on their own version of the Maginot Line along the Suez Canal—the Bar Lev Line—combined with their belief that the Egyptians would never invade Israel without first establishing air superiority, caused Israel not to go on alert prior to the 1973 war, in spite of absolute confirmation of when and where the Egyptians would strike.

On a more tactical level, groupthink allowed an ad hoc committee of U.S. tactical air planners to recommend removing the gun from the F-105 based on their belief in the technological promise of the future, which said that there would never be another dogfight. (This same thinking omitted the gun altogether from the design of the F-4 Phantom.) Fortunately, the F-105 recommendation did not prevail.[17] Ironically, the F-105 would get credit for over 20 kills in Vietnam with the 20-mm cannon—and these F-105 wings would fall under the command of two of the same generals who made the recommendation to remove the F-105's guns.*

The U.S. Air Force resisted the P-51 in favor of the P-47, an airplane that weighed and cost virtually twice as much and that could not accompany bombers all the way to the target, the purpose for which it was designed. Paradoxically, the P-51, which was designed and procured outside the system, could.

In spite of a history of incorrect decisions, TacAir thinking during the time leading up to the F-18 procurement was characterized by a dogmatic certainty:

> We know what kinds of forces and systems are required if we are to successfully confront a numerically superior, highly capable adversary on a sophisticated battlefield—we know that requires quality systems. And if some people want to equate quality with sophistication, that's fine, because sophistication is a relative term. In this case, relative to the enemy we face and the mission to be accomplished. During the Korean War, some people considered the F-86 too sophisticated when compared with some of the aircraft it was to replace. But it certainly was not too sophisticated when compared with the MiG-15 that it had to find, engage, and defeat over the Korean peninsula. The same parallel can be drawn with the F-15. Compared with the F-4 it may be more sophisticated, but not when viewed against the MiG-23 Flogger or MiG-25 Foxbat that it must outfly and outfight.† [18]

*The report was signed by, among others, Maj. Gen. B. K. Holloway and W. W. Momeyer, both of whom would find under their chain of command the F-105s during the Vietnamese conflict.

†General Russ's reference to the F-86 as not being "too sophisticated . . . to find [MiG-15s]" is today's rhetoric applied to yesterday's history. The inference is that because the F-86 was sophisticated, it could find MiG-15s. However, it was not the

Groupthink dies hard, even when there is the benefit of hindsight. Larry Welch, when asked whether he was involved in the 955-to-1 analysis on the F-15, said: "I don't remember the numbers, but you can get those kind of numbers if you—we—often got those kinds of exchange ratios as you ran the F-15 and the super weapons against those kinds of airplanes [MIGS]."[19] Nevertheless, when the author expressed incredulity at the 955-to-1 exchange ratio, Welch said, "Well, I suggest you abandon the numbers, I don't believe them. That's just—that's just what comes out of analysis. When you put those things on charts, after you do some analyses, even when you are young and foolish."[20]

"Quality School" of the Defense Planners

One of the biggest reasons TacAir planners advocate quality is that they don't believe they will ever receive large numbers, even if they opted for them. Many believe that the number of aircraft they are allowed to have is fixed, and not a function of the budget. Possibly because of this belief, the planners attempt to get the "best." This belief that the military can only procure a fixed number of aircraft is a carryover from the 1920s when the military did work with a fixed-force concept. This TacAir mentality is memorialized in a 1986 McDonnell Douglas advertisement headline that begins, "We'll never outnumber them . . . ."

Even those TacAir planners who do not believe that the number of fighters is fixed by statute are quick to state that the fixed numbers are a function of manpower recruiting, fuel limitations, retention, and readiness costs. And the "best" had better get better, because as these planners point out, in 1980 the Russians spent $50 billion more on defense than the U.S.* As a result, they turned out a new tactical aircraft every six to seven hours, or 1,300 each year. In essence, the quality school states that we have to keep up with the competition, whose increasing sophistication is characterized by improvements in equipment that expands their night and all-weather capability.

The quality school states that in addition to their increased capability to defeat the enemy through the beyond-visual-range weapon system, they also have proven the ability to sustain a high wartime tempo. They point to the F-15 Eagle as an example. The F-15's avionics system has, they claim, a mean time between failure (MTBF) almost 100 percent better than the F-4. They also add that the F-15

F-86's sophistication that found MIGS, it was the pilots' eyes.

*Spinney, a Pentagon analyst, notes that there is no way of accurately calculating this number.

is maintainable. Only 20 percent of its downtime is due to sophisticated systems. The other 80 percent is due to systems and subsystems common to all aircraft. As Larry Welch described it, "There is nothing that makes it inherently unable to fly high sortie rates. [More people and more parts is] just part of the price of that kind of capability. The problem is that it's possible to buy that kind of an airplane and forgo the support capability. And the fact that it is possible to do that means that there are choices made to do that. And that's an extremely unfortunate choice."[21]

The quality school believes in taking advantage of all the technology that American ingenuity has generated. Again General Russ summarizes the quality school position.

> The quality school desires to capitalize on the vast U.S. industrial base and to modernize our tactical fighter force by pursuing continued and sustained sophistication of our systems. These advocates point out that over the years our technological superiority has allowed us to design, develop, and deploy highly capable aircraft, avionics systems, and weapons that are recognized as superior to those of our adversaries. This school believes that we should continue to rely on technology and capitalize on technological opportunities. They stress that this approach has served us well in the past, not only in terms of military capabilities and hardware, but in civilian applications as well. They point to the advances made in hand calculators, digital watches, and computer chip technology as evidence.* [22]

If there is any fundamental TacAir position on sophisticated aircraft, it is related to alleged need for night and all-weather capability. At least these are the conditions used to justify and perpetuate the beyond-visual-range missile capability. As Larry Welch maintained, the issue in developing fighters is a function of combat relevancy.

> You have to start with the principle that says any capability is relevant only if it can be brought to bear on the condition of combat. That's number one. So, if the condition of combat has to do with night or in Europe, under layers of clouds, or between layers of clouds, under those kinds of conditions, then the only systems that are relevant in that situation are airplanes that can operate under those circumstances. And that happens to be right now an airplane with a pretty good radar. . . . So the first thing is, I wouldn't argue that you couldn't have a cheaper airplane and make it do that job to some degree. And, if indeed, you could have 2,000 of those things, and you had a place to put them,

*Chuck Myers's reaction to General Russ's comment in which he states that U.S. technology has "served us well *in the past*," is that U.S. and Allied forces defeated the Axis powers through force *depth* not sophistication or technology. Germany, Myers comments, had a vast technological lead over the USSR and the U.S. The air interdiction in Normandy was successful because of the thousands of sorties and airplanes we had everywhere at once. We generated them from 300 grass fields not 16 concrete palaces. (Statement by Chuck Myers to the author.)

and you could bring 'em to bear, and somebody had the stomach for buying them for you, then that would be an interesting trade-off.[23]

In pursuing the concept of an all-purpose aircraft, one that will dogfight, work in all types of weather, as well as bomb, one inevitably comes face-to-face with what TacAir planners call the Force Multiplier. This is a word of art used to define the all-purpose aircraft with increased sophistication that has been advocated in both services since the pre–World War II era. Yet the idea caused the same problems then that it does now.

> It is rather difficult to understand how aviation experts could have taken this [all-purpose] proposition seriously, since all experiments with multiplace pursuit, going back to World War I, had been unsuccessful. Perhaps one reason for the support of the idea was the fact that it appeared to the General Staff to be a possible means of reducing the number of Air Corps types, a policy consistently encouraged by the War Department in the interest of standardization, quantity production, and economy.[24]

Nevertheless, the U.S. Navy continues in its defense of the all-purpose aircraft.

> The argument for the all-purpose fighter starts with the geography of air superiority.* Most experts agree that the best way to gain air superiority is to destroy the enemy's fighters on the ground, where they are presumably most vulnerable. To do this, the fight should be fought over the enemy territory. To get there, a long-range, well-equipped, well-defended fighter is required. This implies a large and heavy airplane, long on range and weapons but short on maneuverability. If the enemy's ability to produce airplanes is modern, he can build smaller, short-range, but highly maneuverable fighter aircraft. Our fighter, encumbered with

*Air Superiority is a term that is thrown around with a lack of precision. Many use it to imply a total control of the air environment. The *U.S. Air Force Dictionary* gives a more precise definition. In ascending order, from some control to total control, here are the definitions:

Air superiority. That superiority in air power or air control, local or general, held when an air force has greater combat effectiveness than that of an opposing air force, esp. if the degree of this superiority permits the conduct of air operations without prohibitive interference by the opposing air force. Air superiority technically covers several degrees of greater combat effectiveness than an enemy possesses, from bare superiority up to and including air supremacy.

Air supremacy. That degree of air power or air control, local or general, held when an air force can impose its will upon any hostile air force at any time or any place within the realm of control; the highest degree of air superiority. "Air supremacy" implies the existence of a hostile but ineffective air force; if no such force exists, "control of the air" is preferred.

Control of the air. 1. A kind of control by which a nation is able through its own relative strength to maintain a dominant position with respect to air power and national air capacity, and to exert through this strength desired influence on the actions of another nation or nations either in peace or war. 2. In a restricted sense, the physical control of airspace through the use of military air vehicles.

weight, must rely upon better weapons systems, better training, or better tactics to achieve air superiority. This in turn, implies more sophistication, perhaps a two-man crew, more complexity and better safety features.

Throughout this argument, the fighting has always taken place over enemy homeland, not friendly bases. If a scenario is selected which reverses this situation—putting the friendly forces in a defensive posture—the arguments for the multimission fighter is based upon its better weapons and systems, its longer combat times, and its integrations within overall defensive command and control systems. . . .

In Vietnamese skies, the multi-mission F-4 Phantom reigns supreme over MiG-17s and MiG-21s.* [25]

"QUANTITY SCHOOL" OF THE LIGHTWEIGHT FIGHTER MAFIA

The quantity school believes that numbers contribute to the friction of war. They resent the use of the term "quality versus quantity" because it suggests that greater numbers of aircraft necessarily mean lower quality.†

Quantity school advocates argue that the "quality" the Defense Planners claim will benefit us has not advanced our ability to destroy other aircraft in the air or targets on the ground. Meanwhile, the cost of fighters has increased astronomically. Former director of Defense Research & Engineering (DDR&E) William Perry summed up the increase: "As we progressed in the last thirty or forty years in the design of airplanes, they have become substantially more sophisticated, substantially more complicated, than airplanes built in the 40's and 50's. In fact, the fire control system of an airplane today cost probably 10 times as much as the entire airplane cost in the early 40's."[26]

The quantity advocates are quick to point out that this ten-fold increase in avionics systems cost has generated hardly any increase in beyond-visual-range radar-guided missile kills (for which the avionics were primarily designed) but, instead has produced the barren results that Colonel Burton exposed. They also add that this increasing expense is responsible for the decreasing size of our forces.

*In other words, no matter what the tactical environment, the Navy can always justify an all-purpose fighter.

While O'Rourke may believe that the F-4 Phantom reigned supreme in Vietnam, the North Vietnamese never launched more than 11 MiG-21s at one time. (Statement made by E. E. Riccioni to the author.)

Chuck Myers also expressed surprise at O'Rourke's "reigns supreme," with, "I'll be damned. The F8U had a much better kill ratio which would have been even better if they had a gun that *worked*." (Myers's comment to the author.)

†The concept is sometimes referred to by the legal maxim *expressio unis est exclusio alterius*—the expression of one thing is the exclusion of the other.

Quality advocates, on the other hand, cite inefficient production runs as the cause of high unit cost. However, advocates of increased numbers believe that this stands the argument on its head. "The argument that modern fighters seem more costly than they really are because of the penalties imposed by uneconomic production run . . . confuses cause and effect. It is not . . . that modern aircraft are so costly because fewer are built [but] that fewer are built because modern aircraft are so costly."[27]

According to Norman Augustine's Law Number 16, "In the year 2054, the entire defense budget will purchase just one aircraft. This aircraft will have to be shared by the Air Force and Navy 3-1/2 days each per week except for leap year, when it will be made available to the Marines for the extra day."

One of the major contributors to the increasing cost of military fighters is the "requirement" for high speed. The F-15 is an excellent example. Its high speed requires such items as variable ramp inlets

Figure 1-4
Ultimate Cost of a Tactical Fighter

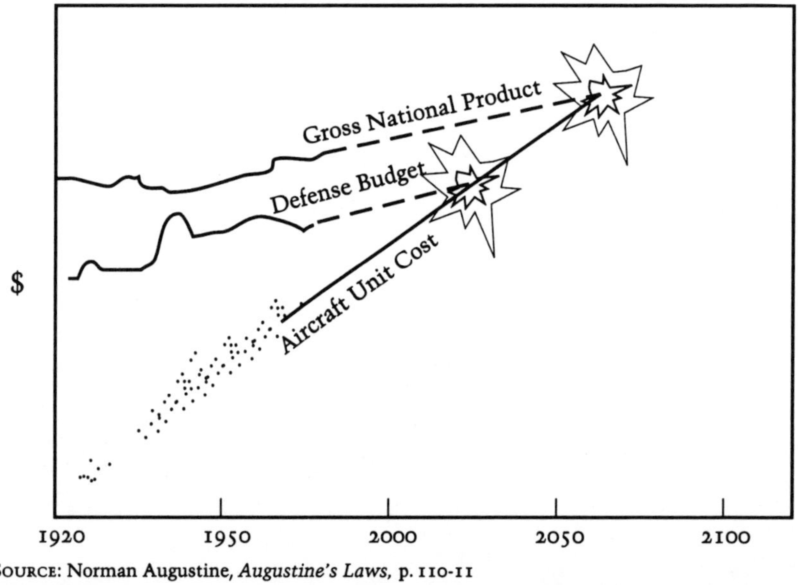

SOURCE: Norman Augustine, *Augustine's Laws*, p. 110-11

and exotic leading edge and engine metals. The irony, or tragedy, is that in spite of the money spent in the design, development, and production for high speed—what Larry Welch calls the "combat relevant" environment, that is, one in which the full complement of fuel and missiles are required—the result is a difference of only 60 knots at sea level.

Table 1-4
Comparative Speeds (In Mach) of the F-5E and F-15A in Combat Configuration* at Altitudes (in Feet)

	Sea Level	5,000	10,000	15,000	20,000	25,000	30,000
F-5E	1.00	1.03	1.07	1.12	1.18	1.275	1.4
F-15	1.07	1.11	1.165	1.25	1.345	1.465	1.6
F-15 faster by	0.07	0.08	0.09	0.13	0.16	0.19	0.20

SOURCE: U.S. Air Force test reports
*4 Sparrow and 4 Sidewinder missiles for the F-15; 2 Sidewinder missiles for the F-5E

In spite of the billions of dollars spent in order to allow the F-15 Eagle to fly at two and a half times the speed of sound (Mach 2.5), the fact is that since 1972, when the F-15 began flying, over 99 percent of its flight time has been below the speed of sound (Mach 1).* Furthermore, it cannot achieve the Mach 1.2 airspeed at sea level called for in the original specification.

ROOTS OF THE LIGHTWEIGHT FIGHTER CONCEPT

The principal architects closest in time to what became known as the Lightweight Fighter (from which the F-18 evolved) were a group known as the Lightweight Fighter Mafia.† The goal of making a fighter lightweight was based on the irrefutable fact that lower weight equals lower cost (not to mention better maneuverability) and, hence, more fighters for equal cost.‡ The group acquired the Mafia name because their efforts were seen everywhere and they were difficult to stop.

The group consisted of John Boyd, Pierre Sprey, and Everest Riccioni. Many would include Chuck Myers even though in the beginning he was outside of government and did not operate sub rosa in his attempts to win converts.

Myers's origins in the lightweight fighter movement can be traced to his efforts with an alliance of former and active-duty U.S. Air Force and Navy fighter pilots, civilians in OSD, and the aerospace industry who, in the 1961-65 period, launched a crusade to correct the growing deficiency in the United States' air superiority fighter mission capability. This alliance became known as the Air Superiority Society and was jokingly referred to by its acronym ASS. (Female associates were known as ASSETS.)

*Pratt & Whitney data from F100 engine flight recorders located on every Nth aircraft.

†When the term Lightweight Fighter is capitalized, it refers to the designs and ultimately the winners of the Lightweight Fighter competition. The two winners were the YF-16 and the YF-17. All other references to the term lightweight fighter mean a fighter that is significantly lighter than its contemporaries.

‡Boyd defines maneuverability as the ability to change altitude, airspeed, or direction in any combination.

These early lightweight fighter advocates were handicapped by the nuclear mindset of individuals in the procurement systems at the time, which embraced a nuclear war deterrence philosophy. This blinded the decision makers to any possibility of air-to-air combat as a subset of airpower.

If chronology sets the measure of merit, then C. E. ("Chuck") Myers, Jr., probably rates as the granddaddy advocate of the pre-Vietnam lightweight fighter concept. Myers was hired by Lockheed Aircraft company in the fall of 1961 because of his flying experience. Myers had been a pilot for the U.S. Army Air Forces in World War II, flying B-25s. After a college education from the G.I. bill, he became a naval aviator and flew F9FS from the carrier *Bon Homme Richard* in the Korean War. The Navy then sent him to its test pilot school, which launched him on a career as a professional test pilot, eventually flying for General Dynamics at Edwards Air Force Base. He would fly most of the nation's advanced fighter and attack airplanes and helicopters during his career.

In spite of Chuck's extensive experience, Lockheed was not exactly sure where to place him. His first job in Lockheed Burbank was in marketing, gathering competitive intelligence. He became a roving resource-at-large within the organization. Early in Myers's employment, Lockheed was competing for the TFX. He was asked to attend an internal briefing on their TFX proposal. Myers recalls: "I watched the presentation. The DOD requirement produced an airplane that was pushing 80,000 pounds—almost two and a half times heavier than a World War II B-17—and was expected to perform five separate missions: air superiority, close air support, all-weather attack, nuclear attack, and all-weather intercept. What's more it was going to do it for two different services."[28]

During this interview with Myers, I asked him why he thought it was wrong for a contractor to provide what a military service wants. After all, I asked, is it up to the contractor to tell the military what kind of aircraft the service should have? Isn't this relationship like a customer with a prostitute: You may not approve of the request, but when the customer says I want this, that, and the other thing, the prostitute's job is to provide it. Myers replied without hesitation: "That was a bad analogy because a hooker can do all that!"

In the early 1960s Myers became active in trying to sell the U.S. Air Force on the need for an air superiority fighter. He did this for two reasons. First, Lockheed had the only aircraft—the F-104 Starfighter—that could, with some improvements, handle the air superiority mission. Second, Myers deemed it necessary for the general

Source: C. E. Myers
Chuck Myers in February 1974 at Nellis Air Force Base with the U.S. Air Force Agressor squadrons.

staff of the U.S. Air Force to understand the nature of the air-combat arena in *non*-nuclear war and to begin to create appropriate forces.

> I was trying to sell the F-104 in an environment in which the Air Force thought the solution to everything was the F-111, which would solve the air superiority problem by killing the enemy air force on the ground. I was fortunate because I was paid to evangelize for the F-104, which was the only airplane at the time that could possibly address the air superiority mission. My personal goal was to educate the general staff on the nature of air combat and the characteristics of an air superiority fighter force. Part of the task was to educate Washington about the differences in the various missions. There were four missions, as I saw them: all-weather air intercept, close air combat, deep strike, and close air support.[29]

Myers was fortunate that along the way he caught the attention of J. Ray Donahue. J. Ray, as Myers calls him, flew in World War II and at this time worked for Litton. And J. Ray knew everyone. Myers recalled:

> J. Ray didn't call anyone "general." He knew them all by first name. It wasn't General Momeyer, who at that time was head of requirements, it was "Spike." J. Ray took me under his wing and would walk me into generals' offices around the Pentagon or around the country, usually with no notice. Once we were in, J. Ray would do the socializing, ask about the wife and kids by name, and say something along the lines of "This is Chuck Myers. He has something important to say and I think you should hear it." They always gave us a cordial reception even though much of what I said was blasphemous relative to existing doctrine.

Myers was particularly startled by the lack of understanding of the nature of air warfare on the part of the Department of Defense's upper management. This was illustrated by a meeting he had with the Assistant Secretary of Defense for Systems Analysis, Dr. Alain Entoven.*

> There I was at the top of the Marriott in the Windjammer Club overlooking National Airport and having a martini and a crab salad, jawboning about air combat with the nation's senior "whiz kid" —Alain Entoven. He said to me, "I just came from a most perplexing meeting. They were arguing about whether a fighter aircraft needs a gun. They were unable to explain why they needed a gun, it got to be a very emotional debate."
>
> In an attempt to help, I unfolded one of the cocktail napkins and drew the following diagram for him. (Fig. 1-5.)

Figure 1-5

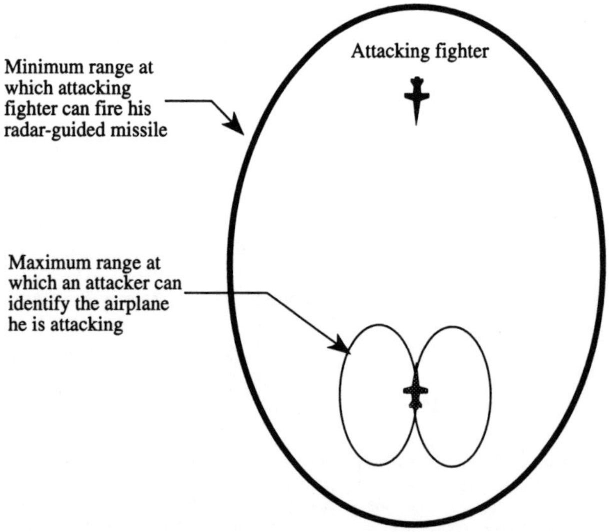

*Systems Analysis would be renamed as Program Analysis & Evaluation.

What Myers illustrated for Dr. Enthoven was that a missile attack require that the pilot make the decision to launch before he can know whom he is shooting because the missile minimum launch range always exceeds the visual identification range. To fire closer than this minimum point would mean that the missile would not work. "The pilot had to visually identify the airplane he was attacking, Myers told Dr. Enthoven, because the promised capability to do that through electronics known as IFF (Identification Friend or Foe) had never worked. Even if it could, it would not be able to resolve the question, particularly in a close-in chaotic situation."

As a result, Myers added, when you have to get close, the best weapon is a gun.* Myers continued. "Dr. Enthoven said to me, 'That seems perfectly logical. Why didn't they tell me that.' I thought about a poem written by Bernie Lay in the 1930s in which he explained that pilots are inarticulate. It wasn't that the whiz kids were screwed up. We aviators were doing a poor job of explaining the problem of air-to-air combat. I immediately converted the cocktail napkin into a colored vu-graph and included it in my briefings."

Myers was a prolific briefer and memo writer. When he wasn't face to face with a group of generals or admirals he was sending them memorandums on his thoughts of what a fighter should look like. One of the generals who listened to Myers was Maj. Gen. Arthur Agan, who at that time was the Assistant Deputy Chief of Staff for Plans and Operations. Chuck convinced him to convene a panel of World War II and Korean Aces in December 1964 in an attempt to further define and resolve the problem.[30] As a result of this gathering of eagles, a concept paper was written that corroborated the need for a dedicated air superiority fighter.

Figure 1-6

SOURCE: C. E. Myers
This is a facsimile of a patch created during the time the Air Superiority Society was active attempting to explain the benefits of a close-in maneuvering weapon.

*Chuck Myers memorialized some of his early efforts for a gun-fighting fighter in his 1963 paper on the requirement for a "close-combat cannon equipped **fighter**."

During one of Myers's many trips, he and marketing engineer William S. Reed, himself a former Air Force fighter pilot, visited Rear Adm. Thomas J. Walker, who was the Deputy Commander for Joint Task Force 2 at Sandia Base, New Mexico. In a follow-up thank-you letter, Bill Reed suggested that Admiral Walker might want to get a copy of "Energy Maneuverability Theory (U)" by John R. Boyd, Maj., USAF, and Thomas P. Christie, Proj. Scientist.* "This report, classified secret, develops a method for comparing fighter plane performance, the beauty of which is that it puts down on paper the performance criteria that fighter pilots know intuitively but find hard to explain. It also compares U.S. and foreign aircraft on the basis of Energy Maneuverability. Major Boyd has briefed many people on his theory, including the President's Scientific Advisory Council."[31]

Within a few months of this meeting, in April 1965, the U.S. Air Force lost two F-105s in Vietnam. They were shot down by gunfire from MiG-17s. The Air Force rushed into production with a definition of air superiority. Right after it came out, General Agan sent Chuck Myers a copy, with the following note: "We have succeeded in publishing an Air Superiority paper. Because of your interest in this matter, I am enclosing a copy so that you may see the outcome of our efforts in this regard. We are continuing our fight for air-fighting capability in our aircraft. I appreciate your interest and help in this regard."[32]

This air superiority paper was important because the U.S. Air Force was developing its next "F" designated aircraft (which at that time was a concept known as the FX for Fighter Experimental) that went on to become the F-15 Eagle. The air superiority paper, coming from the Chief of Staff of the Air Force, was designed to set the tone for development. It said in part:

> 1. The air superiority element of airpower needs to be more clearly understood and more positively considered in our plans, our definition of force characteristics, and our conduct of operations. The following Air Force doctrine on air superiority is provided as guidance to all members of the United States Air Force.
>
> 2. *Definitions*
>
> a. Air Superiority is "that degree of dominance in the air battle of one force over another which permits the conduct of operations by the former and its related land, sea, and air force at a given time and place without prohibitive interference by the opposing force."

*Donahue and Myers had discovered John Boyd at Eglin Air Force base and had begun a continuing dialogue with him.

b. Air Supremacy is "that degree of air superiority where the opposing air force is incapable of effective interference."

Like all concepts, this document was interpreted according to the filter through which it was read. Lightweight fighter advocates focused on paragraph 8.

8. To assure that we can gain air superiority we must provide and train the proper forces. We must be prepared to win air superiority. We must not assume it. We need at least one—preferably two or all three—of the following interdependent advantages: *numerical superiority*; tactical superiority (including training) and technical superiority (e.g., aircraft performance). (Emphasis added.)

But for the old guard, who were raised under the concept of massive retaliation, bombing the enemy was still the only answer.* Consequently, their filters let them focus on paragraph 10, which began: "10. Enemy airpower is destroyed in two ways: in the air and on the surface. Both methods are essential parts of counterair operations and should be carried out concurrently."[33]

Many of the generals and admirals that Myers met with were still under the impression that nuclear strike was the best method for achieving air superiority. What Myers thought he had to do was somehow distinguish the missions that a fighter aircraft had to perform and then show that each mission required, for optimum performance, a different airframe design and weapons system.

Myers was working with a definition of a fighter similar to the one found in the 1956 edition of the *U.S. Air Forces Dictionary*, which defines fighter as "a combat airplane designed primarily for intercepting and destroying other aircraft in the air." Myers would emphasize the words *in the air* by quoting Baron Von Richthofen: "The mission of the fighter pilot is to roam over the battlefield and shoot down anything he sees—anything else is rubbish!"

Contrast that definition for fighter with the F-111A, which had no capability to shoot down other aircraft in the air. Indeed, the F-111A's design and role was, from inception to function, exactly as the B-47, B-52, and B-58. The F-111A was a pure nuclear bomber.

In an attempt to sort this out, Myers wrote numerous lucid papers on air combat and mailed them to key decision makers. In one such paper Myers noted the inconsistency between the mission and designation. The text below within brackets is the author's.

There are four basic missions for which general purpose fighter and attack aircraft were designed, procured and/or are used. Unfortunately,

*Massive retaliation was a foreign policy term that meant, regardless of your transgression we will apply nuclear bombs as a response.

one cannot categorize an aircraft by virtue of the official DOD designations. . . .

Toward the goal of acquiring useful equipment and developing an effective air force, the writer has prepared a brief description of the characteristics which contribute to excellence in each of the four mission categories:

1. Close Air combat (Dogfighting)
2. Close Air Support [required coordination with Army ground troups.]
3. Deep Strike Interdiction [B-17 missions in WWII]
4. All Weather Intercept. . . .

1. *Dogfighter* (F^2)

*Stealth:** The most valuable characteristic for air-to-air combat is the degree of invisibility to visual, IR and radar acquisition systems. Size and proper selection of paint are primary contributors to stealth.

Cockpit Visibility: It is of great advantage to be able to see (easily) out of the cockpit. Obstructions to visibility should be minimized. The pilot who makes the initial visual sighting should win the contest if he chooses to fight.

Wing Loading:† Below 60 pounds per square foot.

Thrust to Weight:‡ In excess of one at full internal fuel.

Radius of Action: Legs enough to reach the fight he can win. Extra range may only result in burial further from home.

Cost: Low enough to afford large numbers and permit much training. Air combat effectiveness is directly related to training.

Speed: V_{MAX} [maximum speed] should be a product of optimized air fighting performance.

Weapons: Optimized for effectiveness inside 3000 feet slant range during rear hemisphere attacks. Low enough in cost to afford much training and high expenditure of rounds (missiles or guns).

Maintainability: Very low (high sortie rates required).

Crew: One.[34]

*This is the first reference the author can find to stealth as it applies to a fighter aircraft. Myers, when we worked for the Department of Defense some years later, renewed his efforts on stealth, which led to the F-117, an aircraft that migrated from his "Close Air Combat" intent to "Deep Strike Interdiction," the conventional wisdom solution to air superiority. It also differed in size and complexity from what he originally proposed as a stealth fighter.

†Wing loading is determined by dividing the weight of the aircraft by the wing area. Wing loading is important because it is a large contributor to turning ability: lower wing loading contributes significantly to tighter turns.

‡Thrust-to-weight ratio is the thrust of the engine in pounds divided by the weight of the aircraft in pounds. For example, if an F-4 Phantom weighs 45,000 pounds and is powered by two J79 engines which have 17,900 pounds of thrust each, the thrust-to-weight ration is determined in the following manner:

$$\text{Thrust-to-weight ratio} = \frac{(2)(17,900)}{45,000} = \frac{35,800}{45,000} = 0.795$$

Myers wanted thrust-to-weight greater than 1.0 because greater thrust-to-weight increases acceleration.

Figure 1-7

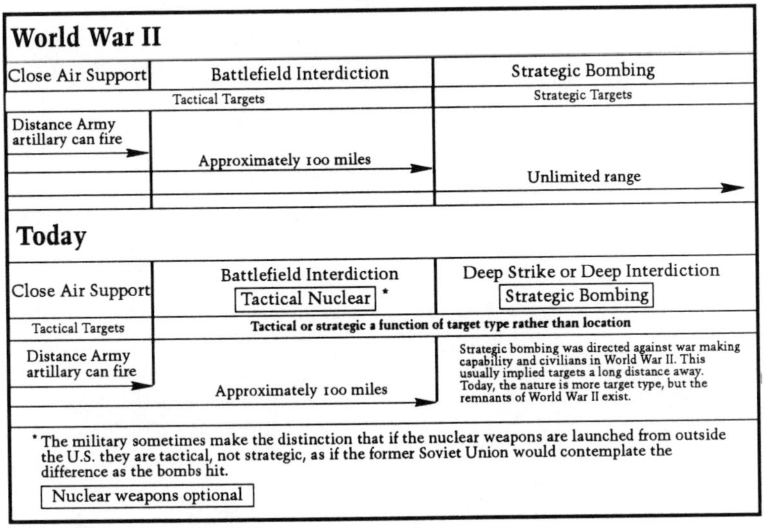

During World War II, the terms close air support, battlefield interdiction, and strategic bombing were associated with distance. While that is still true to a great extent today, strategic bombing is also applied to specific targets regardless of their distance and to all targets destine to receive nuclear bombs.

Myers went on to describe the other missions. One thing was clear from his treatise: each mission required a separate airframe and avionics. In addition to Myers's many arguments for an air superiority fighter, he, through his friend in the Office of the Director of Defense Research and Engineering (DDR&E) Dr. Tom Cheatham, lobbied the Air Force Chief of Staff to rescind John Boyd's orders to Okinawa.[35] Boyd was sent instead to the Pentagon to help rescue the evolving FX, the predecessor to the F-15. If Boyd, Sprey, and Riccioni were to get credit for painting the *Lightweight Fighter*, Myers prepared the pigments, stretched the canvas, and was instrumental in creating an audience for a private showing.

John Boyd's original work focused on global analyses of fighter performance comparisons and more recently on research into what does and does not work in warfare. Sprey's work was on the weapons system's performance, with inroads into cost and supportability and, most importantly, a summary of what criteria are important in air-to-air combat. Riccioni and Myers made major contributions in getting the Lightweight Fighter procured. Combined, these individuals represent the quantity school mentality.

If the quantity school is about anything, it is about using numbers to make up for our inability to predetermine the outcome of conflict. If conflict resolution were as predictable as the TacAir planners

SOURCE: *Dallas Life* Magazine
John Boyd (standing) and Pierre Sprey discussing early battles over the development of the F-16.

believe, then a football coach could assign blocks for each player, with every hike resulting in a touchdown.

Such is not the case. War is filled with what Clausewitz called friction. The elements of friction that contribute to war (or football) are physical danger, extraordinary demands for exertion, chance, uncertainty in information, and the enemy's unpredictability.[36]

In John Boyd's work on what does and does not work in conflict, we begin to get enriched insights into why numbers are important.[37]

But how can Boyd's concepts be turned into criteria for a fighter? According to Sprey, a look at history will show that the fighters that performed better adhered to Boyd's concepts, or rather allowed the pilots to slide through the four steps of observation, orientation, decision, and action.

When Is a Fighter a Fighter?

Before we can ask, "What makes a great fighter?" we have to answer, "What is a fighter?" The definition varies according to whom you ask. For many, the idea of a fighter is exemplified by the P-51 of World War II, which truly reigned supreme in the air-to-air combat arena. For others, however, a fighter is exemplified by the P-47 because of its ability to destroy aircraft as they sit like sunning lizards on the tarmacs.

Defining terms like "fighter" appears to answer a fundamental need in communicating, as Chuck Myers found in talking to senior defense management.* But classification, like all human urges, is subject to distortion—accidental or intentional. In 1962 Secretary of Defense Robert McNamara merged the designation systems of the U.S. Navy and U.S. Air Force into a common system in order to avoid confusion. Prior to his action, the McDonnell Douglas Phantom II, famous for its Vietnam action, was known in the Navy as the F4H-1; in the U.S. Air Force as the F-110. You can imagine the confusion in Congress. But while McNamara's scheme solved some problems, it was flawed in several areas. In the grand scheme, it did not demand precision from those charged with defining the designations. This failure led to further confusion.

Discipline in assigning designations such as fighter, bomber, battleship, or aircraft carrier was better during World War II. Then, a designation for "battleship" conveyed an immediate understanding of the ship's approximate size, range, armor, and armament. Indeed, even the mention of the a ship's name—such as the USS *New Jersey*—was usually enough to evoke a vision of the vessel, because battleships, like other naval ships, were named in a codified manner. For example, battleships were named after states, submarines after fish, cruisers after cities, aircraft carriers after famous battles or vessels, and so forth.

Today, designations no longer provide such clarity. One of the most distorted designations is the term "fighter," abbreviated with the letter "F." As mentioned earlier, the *U.S. Air Force Dictionary* defines *fighter* as "a combat airplane designed primarily for intercepting and destroying other aircraft *in the air*." (Emphasis added.) But using that definition for fighter, how is it that the F-111A had no capability to shoot down other fighters in the air? On the contrary, the F-111A's design and role was, from inception, to function exactly

*Carl Linnaeus, the eminent eighteenth-century Swedish botanist, spent a lifetime developing a classification system for plants. He divided them into categories known as kingdom, phylum, family, genus, and species. Military services, responding to this same human penchant for order, have classified their soldiers' rank, formations, and equipment since the time of the Roman Empire with terms like legion, centurion, cohorts, and more recently into lieutenant, captain, major, general and so forth. In today's Army we see terms like squad and platoon; in the sea-going Navy, destroyer, cruiser, and submarine; and for the flying services, we differentiate aircraft with terms like fighter, attack, bomber, trainer, cargo, and transport. All of these terms have a single purpose—to deliver complex ideas with a single word.

as a nuclear bomber. If the term *fighter* can meander from describing an aircraft whose essence is to destroy other aircraft in the air, such as the F-16, to describing a pure nuclear bomber, such as the F-111A, then the term fighter lacks sufficient differentiation to be useful.

Converting fighters into bombers was the result of the Tactical Air Command's fight for budget share. After the Russians dropped their first atomic bomb, the Strategic Air Command's bomber force received increasing portions of the Air Force budget that previously had gone to the Tactical Air Command (TAC). Recognizing that if it did not have bombers it might become obsolete, TAC evolved its requirements from air-to-air to nuclear air-to-ground, while keeping the "F" designation on its aircraft. Thus, Congress thought it was procuring a balanced arsenal; instead, it was funding a duplicitous Air Force.

One adroit congressional manipulator was former Chief of Naval Operations Arleigh Burke, a master at the bellows of wordsmithing. During a particularly difficult time in the procurement process of a forthcoming Navy guided-missile destroyer program, Admiral Burke's aide asked him how he would ensure success. Burke, knowing that the image of a smaller, less expensive ship might find easier passage, told his aide Ray Peet that he would rename a forthcoming destroyer, which Burke mistakenly believed was a cruiser, as the DLGN *Bainbridge*, the first of the guided missile frigates.

The frigate designation procured the funding, but for reasons not entirely clear, the designation was eventually changed to cruiser. The Air Force's Tactical Air Command has also created new designation confusion. Recently it named its latest air-to-ground airplane the F-117. The added touch was to skip the F-19 designation that resided between the McDonnell Douglas F-18 Hornet and the Northrop F-20 Tiger II. Skipping numerical sequences shows a lack of discipline, but designating a fighter as a combat aircraft that cannot fit the mission definition is pure distortion. In the tradition of the F-111A, TAC has refused to give the F-117 an air-to-ground specific designation, such as "A" for "attack." Any other designation would have been more accurate than "fighter" because it has as much fighter capability as the F-111A, which has none. The F-117 carries neither gun nor missile.

No doubt the justification the U.S. Air Force would give for naming the F-117 is shrouded by the American flag. If pressed, the Air Force will probably point to the good job it claims the F-117 did in Operation Desert Storm. While the stealthiness and accuracy of the F-117 are debatable, the distorted designation is not.

In an ideal world we would seek clarity by asking for the official government definition. However, there is not much help there, as the Pentagon lexicographers tried to provide something for both the P-51 (air-to-air) and P-47 (air-to-ground) orientation. Here are the definitions for both fighter and attack aircraft effective May 18, 1990.

> **Fighter-**Aircraft designed to intercept and destroy other aircraft or missiles. Includes multi-purpose aircraft also designed for ground support missions such as interdiction, and close air support.
>
> **Attack-**Aircraft designed to find, attack, and destroy enemy land or sea targets using conventional or special weapons. This symbol also applies to aircraft used for interdiction and close air support missions.[38]

In other words, the definition of a "fighter" includes the definition of an "attack" aircraft. Thus, for the purposes of defining what Boyd, Sprey, Riccioni, and Myers were attempting to introduce into the U.S. Air Force, consider the *Air Force Dictionary* definition of a fighter, which is "a combat airplane designed primarily for intercepting and destroying other aircraft *in the air*," or, as Myers calls it, a Fighter-Fighter.

What Makes a Great Fighter—in Priority Order

Sprey maintains that there are four criteria that represent victory in air-to-air combat. In order of importance they are (1) obtain the first sighting, (2) outnumber the enemy in the air, (3) outmaneuver the adversary to gain firing position, and (4) have the ability to achieve split second kills.[39]

Obtain the First Sighting

American fighter pilots have a saying, "first sight wins the fight." History shows that 65 to 85 percent of the pilots never saw the aircraft that shot them down. As the former editor of the *Topgun Journal,* the author asked hundreds of pilots over a six-year period what single advantage they would like to have, that is, longer-range missile, more guns, better maneuverability, etc. To a pilot they all said, "the first sighting." This is a concept upon which both American and Russian pilots agree. The Russian corollary is "the first to spot the enemy wins!"[40]

From World War I to the post-Korean era, the relative size of fighter aircraft remained virtually constant. Thus, comparative size has not played a part in the discussions on fighter combat. Who saw whom first was more a matter of sun position or eyesight. Fighters could visually acquire each other at virtually the same time. Vietnam changed all that. (See fig. 1-8.)

Figure 1-8
Visual Signatures of Fighter Aircraft

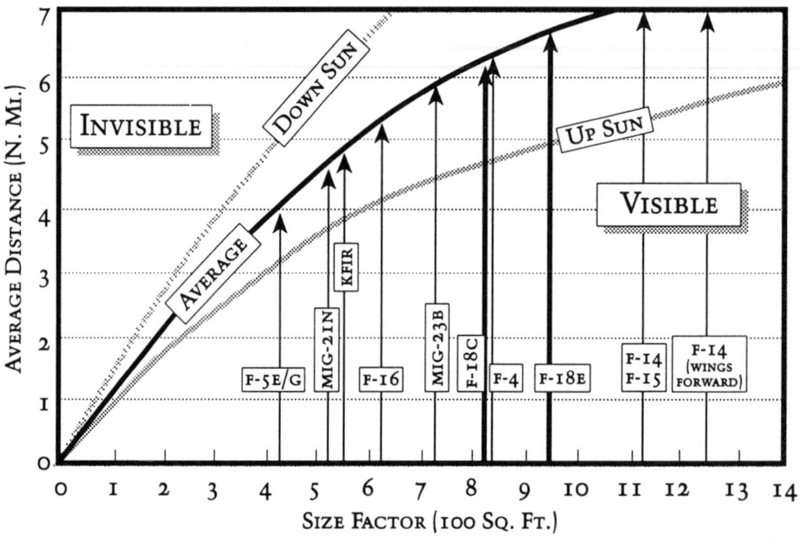

SOURCE: Northrop Corporation

This chart show the maximum viewable surface of an assortment of fighter aircraft. As the size of the aircraft increases, the distance at which the first sighting occurs increases. It is possible for the F-5, for example, to keep an F-15 constantly in view while remaining invisible to the F-15 pilot. Note that the F-18E can be seen further away than the F-18C.

In Vietnam MiG-17s and MiG-21s were visually acquiring F-4s before the Phantoms sighted the MiGs. (Of course, the black smoke from the J79 engine acting as a pointer to the F-4s did help.) In Vietnam and since there has been such a disparity in size between U.S. and threat fighters, that the military is using camouflage paint schemes in an attempt to hide fighters. The F-15 Eagle rolled out in a paint scheme called Air Superiority Blue, a requirement generated by Riccioni.[41] The military has also considered other approaches at camouflage, such as the attempt to distort the aircraft's aspect with the Ferris air-to-air paint scheme.[42]

Naturally, the quality school would argue that the reason for the disparity in size is to accommodate the sophisticated radars that provide an extension of the pilot's eyesight so that he can see the other plane first. Unfortunately this is often not the case.

Radar operates much like a flashlight. If you think of a policeman walking down a dark alley looking for a suspect, you understand the nature of radar. The question you have to ask is, Who will see whom first? Will the suspect see the light from the flashlight before the policeman sees the suspect? In almost all cases the answer is yes. The reason is one of physics.

Light, like radar, becomes less intense the further it travels. If the suspect is far enough away, the light will not have enough power to reflect off his clothes. However—and this is the important part—the light will be powerful enough to stimulate the suspect's eyes, which will allow the suspect to see the policeman coming long before the policeman can spot the suspect. It is for this reason that pilots often turn off their radar. They don't want to be as obvious as the policeman in a dark alley.[43] Fighters have equipment called Radar Warning and Heading gear (RHAW, pronounced Raw Hah) that works like the eye. That is why they can "see" radar long before radar can them.

Unlike a flashlight—which the policeman can shine in all directions—radar is normally limited on a fighter to 60 degrees in azimuth. Consequently, even if one accepts that the radar does provide an extension of the pilot's eyes during the observation phase of an engagement, it still leaves a large blind area—one the quality advocates thought not important until Vietnam proved otherwise. As a Russian colonel points out: "A Sabre [an American F-86 fighter, which saw action in Korea] pilot had a 360° field of observation. But the pilot and system operator of a Phantom, to quote observers, 'had a clock which indicated only from 9 to 3.' This meant that in contrast to the Sabre, the Phantom was blind to the rear, and the pilot could search only in the forward hemisphere."[44]

What makes matters worse, unlike the policeman who can rely on his eyes to accurately interpret what he sees when he does get a reflection from his flashlight, the pilot's functional equivalent for eyes, the IFF (Identification Friend or Foe) is useless—*and the Russians know it*, as this quote from a Russian journal testifies:

> The detection system, however, did not distinguish a target against the earth's background, the IFF system did not reliably identify the target, and the warning system gave a warning on every aircraft coming into its effective range, including a friendly aircraft.
>
> After two friendly aircraft were downed in initial engagements, the U.S. pilots ceased to have faith in the imperfect equipment and established identification of a detected target visually. But this required permitting the adversary to approach to a range corresponding to the pilot's visual acuity.[45]

Even if the IFF did work, the Vietnam Air War experience shows that 82 percent of all contacts were visual. Or looking at it another way, only 18 percent were made with *any* radar. This point is important, because latter-day apologists say that the radar assists in the previsual area. But experience refutes this last-ditch attempt to justify the expensive flashlight. Of the acquisitions made by radar, only 16 percent were made by the radar on board the aircraft. In other words, only 2.8 percent of all contacts in Vietnam were made by the airplanes' on-board radar. And yet, between 1955 and the early 1970s, the Department of Defense spent over $10 billion on radar alone.[46]

Whenever the quality school is confronted with data that refute some previous position, such as the fact that radar has not delivered the promise, they quickly run to the spook side of research and development and confidently maintain that all has been fixed. "We now have a fix with new technology," is the refutation war cry. The fix of the 1980s was called Combat Tree; but, according to Col. Jim Burton, that did not work either.[47] At least one U.S. Navy pilot, Lt. Mark Foxx, told a Tailhook Symposium audience that in Desert Storm he would not rely on anything other than a visual identification. Fox got credit for the second Navy MiG kill in the gulf.

Outnumber the Enemy in the Air

Sprey's second criterion goes to the very heart of the debate of quantity versus quality. While most advocates of the quantity position would point to many historical examples as proof of their position, military analysts have tried to quantify this most subjective form of battlefield ballet—the aerial dogfight. The only method since World War I for determining who won in mock dogfights was who shouted the loudest or who held the higher rank in the postfight debriefing sessions. Sixty-three years later, the Department of Defense sponsored the aerial wargame designed to take the subjectivity out. The name of this exercise was AIMVAL/ACEVAL.*

The AIMVAL/ACEVAL test took place between January and October 1977. It had two purposes. The first portion of the test—AIMVAL—was to test five missile concepts; the second portion of the test —ACEVAL—was designed to examine how force size ratios would affect the outcome of an aerial dogfight. In short it was designed to prove the point that Sprey maintains is the second most important criterion in winning in air-to-air warfare—a concept that Air Force Gen. Bruce Holloway observed from World War II. "In World War II, we did not gain air superiority in any major theater of operations until we had achieved numerical superiority in fighter aircraft."[48]

The good guys in AIMVAL/ACEVAL, called the Blue Force, were made up of F-14s and F-15s. The Red Force, simulating MiG-21s, were composed of F-5Es.

*The acronym comes from AIM—Air Intercept Missile; VAL—EVALuation. The ACE stands for Air Combat Evaluation because the term "ace" is given to fighter pilots who have destroyed at least five enemy aircraft in the air.

In the ACEVAL portion, the Blue Force aircraft carried AIM-7F Sparrow medium-range, semiactive, radar-guided missiles, AIM-9L heat seeking, short-range Sidewinder missile, and 20-MM guns. The Red Force had the same short-ranged Sidewinder and the 20-mm gun.

The force size ratios went from the Blue Force having twice as many aircraft as the Red Force to just the opposite, or Blue Force ratios of 2-to-1 going to 1-to-2. The maximum number of aircraft used was eight, four-versus-four, which created a force ratio of one-to-one. In an attempt to quantify the effect of force size ratios, the Department of Defense devised the ACEVAL portion of the AIMVAL/ACEVAL test. However, the trends were basically the same for both AIMVAL and ACEVAL. Even the invalid data exhibited the same trends. Within the visual arena, the test was realistic. Lt. Col. Bob Fay of the Joint Test Force testified: "It wasn't actual combat. We think it came as close as we could to actual combat without firing the hardware."[49]

Lieutenant Colonel Fay went on to testify that the visual identification requirement that was imposed on AIMVAL/ACEVAL is also a requirement of the real world. To keep the pilots honest, that is not taking shots at an airplane unless they knew it belonged to the opposing force, phony aircraft were thrown into the test. Nevertheless, both Red and Blue Forces managed to fire at the "keep 'em honest" aircraft a significant percentage of the time.[50] One Red Force pilot, James McKinney, said that he visually identified an F-15, and fired his weapons, only to find out later that it was an F-4 Phantom.[51]

SOURCE: U.S. Navy
The F-14 Tomcat with six Phoenix missiles was designed to eliminate the need for a dogfighting.

McKinney's statement raises a question: If he could mistake an F-4 for an F-15—two visually distinctive aircraft—and the IFF still does not work (which it doesn't), can we expect the air-combat arena to head in any direction other than a close-in encounter during the next conflict? Desert Storm, at first glance, would tend to contradict this notion. But as the Pentagon Paradox poses, things are not always as they appear.

Defenders of the F-14 and F-15 claim that the AIMVAL/ACEVAL tests were artificial because the F-14 and F-15 were constrained to the 30-mile test circle. More importantly, they complain that the F-14s and F-15s were required to visually identify the Red Force aircraft which took away their real advantage, the beyond-visual-range capability of the medium range Sparrow missile for the F-15 and both the Sparrow and the Phoenix for the F-14.

What the AIMVAL/ACEVAL revisionists fail to mention is that the visual identification rules of engagement were thoroughly discussed before the test began. The Red Force argued that if the Blue Force could fire beyond visual range, then the Red Force should be permitted to carry radar warning and homing (RWAH) equipment, which all MiG-21s have. The radar warning equipment would tell a Red Force pilot if he were a potential target for a radar missile and permit him to take evasive action. During the work-up phase prior to the actual test, the Red Force used a modified Fuzz Buster. The modification cost approximately $100. It was so successful that the Blue Force complained and the Red Force had to stop using it because radar warning receivers held the potential of revealing how easily radar missiles could be defeated and were therefore not permitted.

Instead, the Blue Force was so certain that the exchange ratio would be one-sided that they permitted visual rules of engagement. (Ironically, these rules also simulated real combat experience.) Optimistic Air Force analyses (from the same group that gave us the 955-to-1 ratio) predicted a 78-to-1 exchange ratio between F-15s with Sparrow missiles and F-5ES with Sidewinders* Before the AIMVAL/ACEVAL test Air Force officials believed that the F-15s should be outnumbered two to one in order to make the test fair for the F-5ES.

Latter-day rhetoric aside, the F-14s and F-15s were able to fire their Sparrow and Phoenix missiles beyond visual range. In the four versus four engagements in which the F-15s did poorly, the rules of engagement required that only one F-15 have a visual confirmation

*Riccioni believes that the same TAC Avenger program was used.

that the opposing forces were F-5ES. The other three F-15s were then free to fire from any distance beyond visual range.

John J. McGrath, a spokesman for McDonnell Douglas Corporation, builder of the F-15, defended the poor AIMVAL/ACEVAL results, and in the process tried to rewrite history. "The F-5E excels by design as a dogfighter, so when the F-15 is handicapped by the rules and comes out with a kill-loss ratio of 2 to 1, we think that's pretty good."[52] McGrath is mistaken. The F-5E was not designed to dogfight, but to intercept.* Ironically, the first aircraft to be designed as a dogfighter was the F-15.

The real value of low cost-fighters becomes more obvious when one looks at the exchange ratios when the F-15s were outnumbered two to one, that is, four F-5ES and two F-15s. (This is important because for equal dollars the U.S. could purchase three or four F-5ES for every F-15.) Under these two-to-one force ratios, the exchange ratio fell nearer 1-to-1.

And that was only, according to Chuck Myers, because the Blue Force was able to reconstitute F-15 pilots—they were able to come back and fly the next day. During the initial engagements, the exchange ratios so favored the F-5ES that it caused one journalist to succinctly state: "It takes little more than a back-of-the-envelope calculation to conclude that the success of an air campaign under these [outnumbered] conditions hangs by a perilously thin thread. Anything less than kill ratios close to the best achieved in USAF's history and an equally prolific sortie rate might spell failure."[53]

It appears that one of the benefits of numbers is that they contribute to friction. AIMVAL/ACEVAL showed that as the total number of aircraft increased—even though the force ratios remained the same, for example, one versus one growing to four versus four, the exchange ratios for the sophisticated Blue Forces decreased and tended toward one-to-one. "The best [explanation] we could come up with is that we think there is more confusion and decreased coordination as the numbers increased on the part of Blue and Red."[54]

Figure 1-9 shows that even though the ratio of red versus blue aircraft remains the same, the exchange ratio drops as the total number of aircraft increases. In a sense, one might call this the fighter friction chart.

It is interesting to note that the quality school, which historically has relied on tests rather than combat experience to justify its so-

*An interceptor, according to the *Air Force Dictionary*, is a fighter aircraft "characterized by a high rate of climb, high speed, high ceiling, effective armament, and relatively short endurance."

phisticated solution, found little solace in the AIMVAL/ACEVAL results. Nevertheless, the quantity school chose not to rely heavily on these test results.

Using history, Pierre Sprey points out that 2,000 P-47s and P-51s ground down 70 vastly superior ME 262 jet fighters. The protectors of the conventional TacAir wisdom say that while this 30-to-1 ratio would create similar results today, America is not outnumbered by more than 2-to-1.

These TacAir planners do not believe, as do the quantity advocates, that developing sophisticated aircraft could put them in the same position that Germany found itself in with superior but outnumbered fighters. The real issue, they believe, is

> how well the 2,000 P-51s and P-47s . . . would have done against 1,000 ME 262s (a 2-to-1 ratio). German fighter ace Adolf Galland [chief of the German Air Force] would have been satisfied with only 350 ME 262s, from what he said in the final days of the war: "We need quality of performance, if only to restore in our force the sense of superiority, even if our numbers are smaller. For example, to give some idea of values: at this moment I would rather have one ME 262 than five ME-109s."[55]

But all this presupposes that Hitler intentionally procured small numbers of the ME 262, which is not true. The advocates of sophistication claim that it was Hitler's procurement of large numbers of other fighter aircraft that prevented him from having the first operational jet, the ME 262, in large enough numbers to make any difference in the air war.

The argument implies that the Germans made the conscious decision to opt for quantity instead of quality embodied in the ME 262. Such an inference stands the argument on its head. On the contrary, the ME 262 was delayed because of technical problems—just as today's sophisticated aircraft are—and not with production problems. When the technical problems were reduced, the ME 262 was produced as rapidly as possible.

However, as the number of Allied aircraft swelled, the Germans did not respond with force multipliers, as the TacAir planners like to describe U.S. technically advanced aircraft. Instead, Germany went in the direction of even greater numbers, with such extremely lightweight aircraft as the Bachem Natter and the HE 162 People's Fighter.[56] Both of these aircraft were chosen because they were inexpensive, could be built with unsophisticated labor, and were, therefore, affordable in large numbers.

Both the Germans and the Americans attribute the winning of the Air War in Europe to the massive numbers of aircraft that the

Figure 1-9
Exchange Ratios versus Force Ratios AIMVAL/ACEVAL

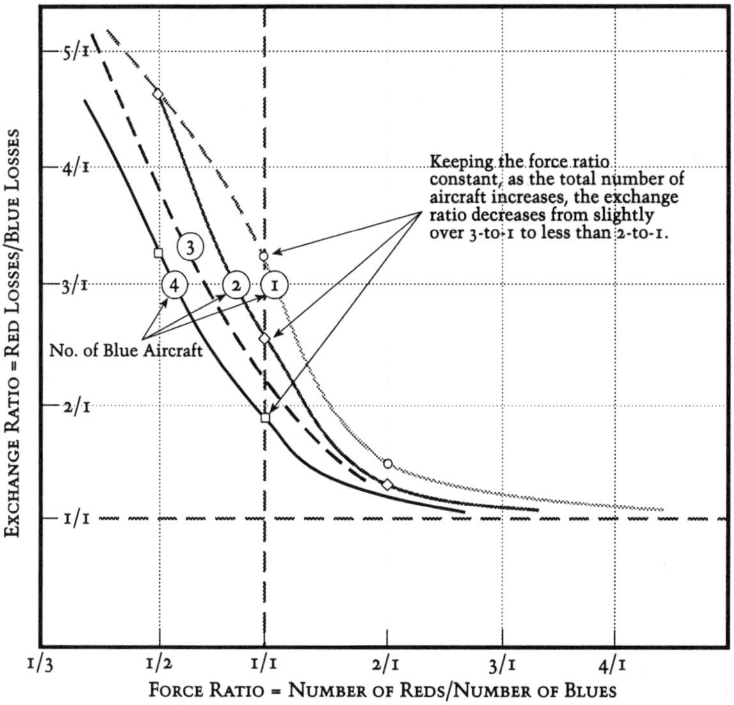

SOURCE: AIMVAL/ACEVAL Tests

Moving from the upper left to lower right along these curves shows a change in kill-loss, or exchange, ratios listed on the left-hand vertical axis. More importantly, however, note that if you hold the force ratio constant (see Force Ratio 1:1) that is, both sides have the same number of aircraft, then the exchange ratio drops from 3.2:1 to 1.8:1. As the force ratios begin to approximate what the TacAir planners claim our potential adversaries have, the exchange ratios approach parity.

U.S. and the Allies threw against Germany. Adolf Galland's major concern for the rapid development of the ME 262 fighter was the air superiority of the Allies due to the increased range and "overwhelming number of American fighter escort."[57]

The technological increase between the ME 262 and the P-51 or P-47 exceeds any differences that exist between current U.S. tactical air forces and those of any other nation. And yet, the Germans, with the ME 262, were able to generate only a 1.5-to-1 kill-loss ratio against the superior numbers of U.S. fighters. While Adolf Galland may have been satisfied with only 350 ME 262s, they would have generated only 525 kills, leaving another 1,475 fighters to deal with. Even with the force ratio of 2,000 P-51s and P-47s against 1,000 ME 262s, the Germans would have had to deal with the 500 left.

The reason that current quality school planners do not relate to the use of history is that they are hostages of the Groupthink Syndrome. Setting aside the undisputed technological superiority of the ME 262, TacAir planners conclude that in comparing the remainder of the tactical air forces in World War II, the U.S. won the war by procuring the most advanced aircraft at the time. Former Air Force Chief of Staff Larry Welch reflects this view:

> Somehow [people] have the impression that in World War II we had thousands and thousands of very simple airplanes and that's why we won the war. But the fact is the most effective airplanes in World War II were the most sophisticated. . . . The P-51, the P-38, the P-47, the later Spitfire. So today we look back at those airplanes and we say, "My, look at those simple airplanes." By the technological standards of that day, those were the most sophisticated, most capable airplanes that the United States and Great Britain knew how to build. And they were better, they were more sophisticated than the airplanes that were built by the adversary.[58]

Welch's two main points—that our frontline fighters of World War II were our most sophisticated and that they were more sophisticated than our adversaries—are somewhat misleading. The real issue is what the U.S. Army Air Force wanted prior to the friction of war, versus what they evolved into once the flak started to fly.

Originally they wanted some very sophisticated aircraft. One design the Army Air Force wanted, for example, was the functional equivalent of a flying naval destroyer. Bell Aircraft offered a design that was to protect the bomber like the destroyer protects the battleship or aircraft carrier. From their attempt evolved the XFM-1 Airacuda. As Ben Kelsey, charged with fighter procurement at Wright Field during the beginning of World War II, explained it: "There is a weakness in the philosophy. This is the numbers racket that we used to feel so bad about. If you have three articles, 'gnats' if you will, they are just as annoying as one large 'wasp' and you do have to knock down three of them. Just one won't do."[59]

The fact that the P-51, the most successful fighter in World War II, was not only that era's lightest fighter—and not, as Larry Welch suggests, the most sophisticated of the day—is a testimony to the tenacity of the lightweight fighter union within the Army Air Force. Most of the benefits of lightweight fighters—lower cost, greater numbers for equal dollars, and higher performance—were known as far back as World War II.

Larry Welch is correct when he says there were thousands of sophisticated fighters in World War II. However, sophistication is always relative to other contemporary aircraft. Of the three principal fighters—the P-38, P-47, and P-51—only the P-38 and P-47 could be called sophisticated, which reinforces the lightweight fighter advocates' point. Since the P-38 was pulled out of the European theater because of its inability to cope in the air-to-air environment; and because the P-47 was relegated to the air-to-ground task of close-air support due to its inability to fly fighter escort with the bombers to the targets and back; and because the Congress of the United States wanted to award the P-51 the congressional medal of honor for its war-making capability, it's safe to say that the P-51 is another example of the lightweight fighter demonstrating in the real world of combat that less sophistication and less cost equate with greater capability.

Larry Welch is trying to imply—by linking "better" and "sophisticated" in his statement, on page 42—that U.S. aircraft were better because they were more sophisticated. Welch is obviously ignoring the fact that just before World War II "the RAF, the Russians, the Italians, and the USN still were buying wire-braced, fabric-skinned, wood-framed biplane fighters. In August 1939, when every operational shipboard fighter in the inventory of the U.S. Navy was a biplane, the Germans began testing the world's first turbojet-powered airplane."[60]

Lightweight fighter advocates will concede that, in applying the definition of sophisticated outlined above, the less successful fighters—the P-38 and P-47—were the more sophisticated. But a quick look at the kill:loss ratios shows that the German fighters were hardly less capable.

Sprey's criterion makes the point that the real issue is to outnumber the threat *in the air*. This is a feat made more difficult because the sorties per day per $1 million in constant dollars had declined from 2.1 to 0.1.

*Outmaneuver to Gain Firing Position**

It is common knowledge that the German Air Force increased the sophistication of its air force toward the end of World War II. However,

*The term maneuverability is one that one must be understood to appreciate the subtleties of air-combat maneuvering, or dogfighting. John Boyd provides a working definition: Maneuverability:—the ability to change altitude, airspeed, and direction in any combination.

Turn rate, turn radius, and g all contribute to maneuverability. Once again Boyd provides some appreciation for their meaning:

Turn radius: Represents how small an area or volume in which a directional change can be achieved.

Turn rate: represents how quickly a directional change can be achieved.

g: represents directional change as an acceleration perpendicular to present line of flight.

because the American pilots had four to five times the training in particular aircraft and three times the total training as the German pilot, the *United States Strategic Bombing Survey* concluded that "the deterioration of quality of German pilots appears to be the most important single cause of the defeat of the German Air Force."[61]

Table 1-5
U.S. Army Air Force Exchange Ratios
Major Theaters in World War II

	Kills	Losses	Exchange Ratio
Mediteranean & North Africa	7,003	6,731	1.04-to-1
Western Europe	13,623	11,687	1.17-to-1
Japanese	8,899	4,530	1.96-to-1
Total	**29,525**	**22,948**	**1.29-to-1**

SOURCE: *Armed Forces Journal International*, May 1974, p. 30

Training is a function of aircraft availability and direct costs. It's no secret that more complex aircraft are more expensive to maintain and, consequently, tend to be less available for training, unless the budget is unlimited. But not everyone agrees.

The Korean Air War provides an opportunity to examine some examples of this argument. Kross gives the institutional TacAir position:

> The TACAIR Planners believe the Reformers even misread the lessons of the F-86 in Korea. The Reformers cite the F-86 as the last great fighter built by the United States, but in Korea, the F-86 was actually the most sophisticated fighter of its day—a relatively expensive winner that achieved a 10-to-1 kill ratio over the less costly and far simpler MiG-15—the cheap loser. The MiG-15, like the Zero of World War II, would fit the Reformers' classical mold of a fighter.
>
> The F-86's 10-to-1 kill ratio should be examined more closely, say TACAIR Planners. In the first part of the war (June 1950 to December 1952) when Russian "Honchos" flew with the North Korean MiGs, the kill ratio was only 4.9-to-1 in favor of the F-86. When the Russian pilots were pulled out in January 1953, the kill ratio soared to 20-to-1 in the last six months of the war.[62]

The fact that the exchange ratio grew in favor of the United States after Russian pilots left makes the quantity school's point. Training made a 400 percent difference. Add to this the fact that when one compares the statistics of the MiG-15 with the F-86, the MiG-15 comes out the clear winner. The MiG-15 was faster, could climb higher, turn tighter—by any criteria, the MiG-15 was better than the F-86. Yet it is this same one-dimensional threat comparison that the TacAir planners typically use to justify a new aircraft or at least claim one aircraft's superiority over another. In other words, given only the specification sheets of the two aircraft, the TacAir planners would conclude that the MiG-15 was the more sophisticated or capable aircraft. Ironically, the F-86 prevailed—and it did so for a very low-technology reason.

The pilot could see out of the cockpit, while the view from the MiG-15 was tantamount to looking through a coke bottle. Thus, Boyd's first requirement of the OODA loop, observation, put the MiG-15 pilot at a disadvantage: the MiG-15 cockpit had poor visibility; the F-86 had excellent visibility. Poor visibility obstructed the MiG-15 pilot's view and made the sequential orientation, decision, action part of the OODA loop difficult.*

The difference, according to Colonel Boyd, was also due to a another factor—full power hydraulic flight controls. Such controls permitted the American pilots to roll more quickly. As a result, the pilots of the F-86 could maneuver in either direction more quickly than the MiG-15 pilot. While the MiG-15 pilot would try to follow an F-86 roll to the left, the F-86 was completing his roll and reversing to the right before the MiG-15 was completing his left-hand roll. By repeating the process, the F-86 could force the MiG-15 pilot out in front for the kill.

The difference in speed through which an adversary and an American could cycle through the OODA loop is a function of, according to Boyd, increasing the number of states with which the enemy commander must deal, maximizing his confusion. Boyd calls this "entropy,"a term physicists use to measure confusion in a complex process. Technology can go either way on this. In some cases it may help raise an opponent's entropy; in other situations it may raise one's own entropy even more. For example, increasing numbers of aircraft in a dogfight lowered the exchange ratio favoring F-14s and F-15s in the AIMVAL/ACEVAL tests even though the simulated threat aircraft (F-5Es) were considered less capable.

Kross makes Sprey's third argument, which is to out-maneuver the enemy to gain gun-firing position, when he makes reference to the difference in exchange ratios between two separate groups of pilots. The fact that the exchange ratio could change so dramatically due to the change in the amount of fighter pilots' training is testimony to the fact that the pilot makes the most significant difference.

One of the biggest impediments to training is available flight time. Fighter squadrons are constantly complaining about running out of fuel allocations for training. Ironically, while F-14 fighter squadrons at NAS Miramar in the early 1980s were hovering around

*Any student of aircraft design need only reflect on the transition from the greenhouse look of, for example, the P-40, early P-47s, and P-51s against the later style of bubble canopy, with the corresponding transition back to poor visibility, in such aircraft as the F-4 Phantom, F-8 Crusader, and F-105.

the 20 hours per month mark, a large percentage of the instructors at the Navy Fighter Weapons School averaged 45 to 60 hours per month.[63] The fundamental reason for insufficient training flight time is the high cost of training in complex aircraft.

The other reason for a lack of training is the poor readiness rate of military fighters. The poor readiness of American tactical air forces is well documented. And yes, while it is possible to generate high sortie rates with complex aircraft, short of an all-out effort such as Desert Storm the cost is something none of the services can endure for long. As a result, one heard this kind of testimony at congressional hearings in the early 1980s:

> Currently we have sufficient pilots in every squadron to fully man the F-15 units. We would like to have a mix of about 40 percent experienced pilots and about 60 percent inexperienced pilots. Experience is determined by the total amount of flying time an individual has, and the total amount of fighter time he has.
>
> Whether a man can fly to the maximum performance is a matter of what kinds of standards you set down. We set down three levels of standards. The minimum standard is what the pilot has to do to be able to be considered mission capable. At this level he is capable of shooting down another fighter in a one-to-one flight. As he progresses and gets more flying time, the scenario in which you employ him gets more difficult. It may be a one-to-one, one-to-three or what we call a one-versus-many, where one airplane attacks four or more airplanes. When he is proficient you progress him into the second level. Then you progress him into the third level which is force-on-force.
>
> So I would say that 95 percent of our people are at level one, maybe 50 are at level two and a few are at level three. You always have and you need young pilots coming into the squadron. I think the current F-15 force is balanced and very capable.

It is difficult to understand why a desired goal by the Air Force would be to have 60 percent of its F-15 pilots inexperienced. However, this may be an acknowledgment of reality: low sortie rate airplanes create low time, inexperienced pilots. F-5E pilots who are able to fly more often routinely defeat F-15 pilots. The difference in monthly flight time accounts for the paradoxical exchange ratio. It is ironic, if not sad, that the inability to fly these complex planes—due to their expense—prevents adequate training and negates the very advantage they were designed to produce.

But lack of experience due to limited flight time is not the only contributor to an aircraft's poor maneuvering in combat. The size and shape of the initial design is a large contributor, and has been for a number of years. The continuous increase in fighter size has been a function of accommodating the desire to increase the diameter of the radar antenna, which sizes the remainder of the aircraft.

Increasing size and its negative side-effect, has been recognized since World War II.

Achieve Split Second Quick Kills

Air combat presents random firing opportunities by an enemy that seldom cooperates. In Vietnam Col. Robin Olds had one of the rare opportunities to fire at the North Vietnamese head on with a Sparrow missile in Operation Bolo. After the initial successful achievement by U.S. forces, the Vietnamese never attacked head on intentionally. As a result, the North Vietnamese flew up from behind the American fighters, thus forcing the encounter into a dogfight.

Dogfights require quick-responding weapons. For that reason, the Navy Fighter Weapons School developed a nine-second rule—never fly in one direction for longer than nine seconds, otherwise, you become predictable. If an enemy were to realize this and implement this rule, we would have more trouble using our radar-guided missiles because predictability is what radar and radar-guided missiles need.

Because the AIM-7F Sparrow missile requires illumination from the launching aircraft during the entire course of its flight, the Sparrow often creates an environment that will increase the likelihood of getting shot. Pilots call this "killed while killing." *Aviation Week & Space Technology* summarized the problem this way:

> On a recent simulated exercise in Denmark, the wing learned repeatedly that holding on a target while waiting for the AIM-7F . . . radar missile to reach its destination often put the F-15 in jeopardy. "The best thing would be to fire, then sweep into the flow of traffic," Capt. David Pomerenke said. "With the AIM-7F you have to wait 20-25 sec. with beyond-visual-range rules and 10-20 sec. for closer-in targets. . . .
>
> "There's a risk of losses when engaging large numbers of enemy aircraft at short range and, with the AIM-7F, you have to remain predictable while keeping the target illuminated."[64]

CONCLUSION

The military mindset that has prevailed since the early 1920s has dominated the procurement process and disrupted innovation. Attitudes like "the new missiles . . . will revolutionize warfare" and "our technology is what will save us," by former R&D czar William Perry (who became the Deputy Secretary of Defense in the Clinton administration) and Secretary of Defense Harold Brown permeate the procurement process.[65]

This aspect of groupthink, that missiles are the savior of future air-to-air battles, dies hard. For example, Larry Welch, who repudiated the 955-to-1 exchange ratio of the AIM-82, held on to the concept in the end.

> Exchange ratios, by themselves, don't tell you anything about kill rates. Kill rate is how many of those guys, how many of that guy's airplanes that I can kill that are coming at my air fields, or they're coming at my ground forces today. What do I have, what do I have to destroy to spoil his raid. What do I have to destroy to save my ground forces today. And the fact that I get very high exchange ratios is uninteresting to me if, while I'm doing that, I can't kill enough of his airplanes for my ground forces to survive and enough of his airplanes so that I can operate off my airfields tomorrow. It could get marvelous exchange ratios in the air, and if my kill rates aren't very high, then I lose the war. And that's why, when we talk about having the capabilities that are relevant to the situation, you've go to be able to extract the kill rates from those low altitude penetrators at the time that they choose to penetrate, or no matter how wonderful your dogfight comes out, you lose the war.
>
> And at 955-to-one—I can think of a situation where 955-to-one would be the ratio.[66]

If the tenacity with which Larry Welch stuck to his 955-to-1 position comes as a surprise, then consider Maj. Gen. Perry McCoy Smith's comments. They are relevant for several reasons: Smith is a retired Air Force general, he was a student of the process, and he was a consultant for CNN during the Gulf War.

> Once a military doctrine is established it is difficult to change, especially if technological advancements in weaponry seriously bring into question a doctrine upon which a specific military is based. . . . And if service doctrine is questioned by members of that service, there is a tendency for the leadership to brand the critics heretics, especially if the doctrine is ordinarily designed to justify fully the services's attempt to obtain or maintain exclusive control over certain missions. . . .
>
> When doctrine becomes dogma, all kinds of counter-dogma signals can be ignored. If the lessons of the Battle of Britain could be ignored, if the high losses in bombardment aircraft whenever they were seriously opposed by German fighters in the early, unescorted daylight raids in 1943 could be discounted, if it took the loss of 60 aircraft on a single mission over Schweinfurt in August 1943 and 60 more over Schweinfurt in October 1943 finally to convince all the Air Corps leaders that unescorted bombardment against defended targets was self-defeating as well as suicidal, then is there any reason to believe that attitudinal changes among the American public and in the War Department would have permitted a different Air Force to develop?[67]

If the reader finds the evidence presented here paradoxical, the enigma continues. The paradox is wrapped up into an almost religious belief. In fact, the U.S. Air Force likens doctrine to a religious belief. "Although 'doctrine' does not, of course, have the same spiritual origin and emotional connotation that 'religion' has, the two might be compared in development."[68] As a result, realilty often is overlooked by the otherwise vigilant military officers.

The military tries to explain away the quantity advocates as a group of effete intellectual analysts who have not "been there," referring to actual aerial combat. Ironically, the most vocal advocates for increased numbers of tactical aircraft are also the most competent military tacticians, the Air National Guard.[69]

The Air National Guard not only qualifies as an authorative source for the quality versus quantity argument, but in many respects it is more qualified. It consistently betters its full-time Air Force counterparts in competitive exercises. The Air National Guard rejects the concept of force multipliers and the attrition warfare mentality that goes with it. The Air Guard believes in maneuver warfare and has the numbers of aircraft to support it. To the Air Guard, the ideal fighter would be the less sophisticated F-16A or an austere version of the Northrop F-20 Tigershark.* Three reasons are given to support this belief:

> 1. Numerical inferiority. Despite claims to the contrary, this problem cannot be answered by "force multipliers" which rely heavily on high technology systems of questionable reliability. A more realistic answer to the number of Soviet fighters likely to be found in the battle area is more friendly fighters.
>
> 2. Beyond Visual Range capability. To a large degree, projected exchange rates are predicted on the Beyond Visual Range capability of friendly fighters, particularly the F-15. Rules of engagement of previous wars haven't allowed these shots and it seems unlikely, given the circumstances likely to accompany future conflicts, that they will ever be permitted other than on a case-by-case basis.
>
> 3. Exchange rates. There is a mounting volume of evidence, including Air National Guard experience, that our current exchange rate projections for the newer fighters, such as the F-15, bear no resemblance to reality. Exchange rate projections tend to consider only quantifiable data and then, only the quantifiable data that the person making the projection finds helpful in making their point. Unfortunately, many of the realities of war are not so easily quantifiable, but have held true since the Spad: (1) the pilot is the most important single factor in any aerial engagement; (2) surprise is what determines most kills; (3) sound tactics can overcome aircraft inferiorities; and (4) one versus four, or one versus six isn't a great place to be no matter how great a fighter you happen to be flying.[70]

The history of the F-18 is a study of the bureaucratic debates over what fighters should do, how much they should cost, and how many the Navy should have. The requirements that drove these debates were based in part on the philosophies already discussed, as

*The numerical designation of the F-5G Tigershark was changed to the F-20 on November 23, 1982, to create the appearance that the Tigershark was a completely new aircraft. It was, at first, merely an F-5E with an F404 engine.

well as the perceived mission of both the Air Force, the original procurer of the F-18 prototype, and the Navy. Only with an understanding of the Navy's mission can one begin to understand its approach to fighter aircraft requirements and why it rejected an Air Force-designed airplane.

Chapter 2

The U.S. Navy Mission

Historically, the close of every major war in this century has seen the participating nations caught in a strange dichotomy. While generally lauding the performance of their aviators, they have also disdained air-to-air combat as obsolete and sought systems to obviate the need for air combat. It has been with tragic irony that each air war has begun with an agonizing relearning process for fighter crews and hurried adapting of weapons systems back to the arena they were designed to eliminate.

Commander Ron "Mugs" McKeown, USN
Commanding Officer
Navy Fighter Weapons School (Topgun)
Testimony before the Senate Committee on Armed Services
Spring 1973

Neither the F-18 Hornet nor the U.S. Navy would exist if it did not have a mission. The Navy's mission, like the F-18's, has changed over time. During the period of debate on the F-18, the Navy saw itself primarily providing America freedom of the seas while denying them to any potential enemy. Its secondary mission was to impose the United States' will on countries that the Navy can reach from its aquatic sanctuary.

The Navy has fulfilled its mission through sailing ships, battleships, submarines, and aircraft carriers. Submarines with ballistic missiles can reach most of the world, battleships can impose U.S. will along the coastline, and the aircraft carrier can reach the areas in between. Since World War II the aircraft carrier has been the fundamental unit around which the U.S. Navy performs its two missions of sea control and power projection, through aircraft such as the F-18.

The division of labor between the U.S. Navy and other U.S. military services has evolved by agreement and through interservice rivalry and jealousy. Missions currently belonging exclusively to the U.S. Navy, such as antisubmarine warfare, once belonged to the U.S. Army Air Force. On the other hand, the U.S. Navy once had a secondary mission to participate in continental defense, a mission performed today exclusively by the U.S. Air Force.[1]

During the developmental F-18 period, the Department of Defense called for cooperation between the U.S. Navy and the U.S. Air Force in time of war. The Air Force has primary responsibility in a NATO European War; the U.S. Navy was expected to control the Mediterranean and seal off the Greenland-Iceland-United Kingdom line. With this under control, the Navy would participate in the ground campaigns, with close air support and battlefield interdiction.[2]

The Navy's role in close air support and battlefield interdiction is well codified.[3] The Navy is also required to support the Marines "until Marine Air is established ashore in support of their ground troops."*[4]

The Navy and Marine Corps air wings are task oriented as opposed to the wing concept of the U.S. Air Force, which had been aircraft-type oriented. The typical U.S. Air Force wing contained three squadrons of a single type of airplane. Each squadron consists of 24 aircraft for a total of 72. The Navy and Marine Corps wings, on the other hand, have several types of aircraft. Table 2-1 lists the composition of Navy and Marine Corps air wings.†

Typically, the U.S. Navy will have 11 squadrons and a total of 89 aircraft on board an aircraft carrier. Between 1975 and 1980 the U.S. Navy planned to have a total of 12 active air wings and 2 reserve air wings. Only 27 percent of the air wing was dedicated to the fighter mission, the purpose of which is to provide defense for the aircraft carrier as well as escort and defend the attack aircraft as they ingress and egress the target.

During World War II the percentage of fighter composition increased

*At one time the U.S. Marine Corps provided its own close air support from the sea from the smaller Escort Carriers (CVE). The Marines advanced the idea of supporting troops with their own aircraft from their own aircraft carriers in 1926. From 1931 to 1934 the Marines operated from carriers. By 1934 the Marine Corps recommended carriers for the sole purpose of supporting amphibious landing units. The Marine Corps possessed its own escort carriers late in World War II but failed to capitalize on the mission.

> The truth is that the top Marine aviators didn't pay enough attention to (1) close support, (2) amphibious landings, (3) a combination of the two. They were too deeply interested in shooting enemy planes out of the wild blue yonder, so they lost sight of their primary mission. They stopped being amphibious enough to forget Roy Geiger's blunt statement in 1939: "The primary reason for the Marine Corps' having airplanes is their use in close support of ground troops." This resulted in (1) Marine aviation being laid open to the charge that it was duplicating Army aviation and (2) the Navy grabbing off the mission of supporting troops during amphibious landings. (Citation omitted.)

†The Air Force changed its orientation in September 1991 to combine dissimilar aircraft in the same air wing.

as the war progressed. In 1942 the percentage of fighters on the aircraft carrier averaged 25 percent, similar to today's complement. This had increased to 70 percent by the end of the war.[5] The threat to the aircraft carrier increased the Navy's need for carrier defense. Toward the end of World War II, the Japanese attacks required maximum fighter effort to keep the aircraft carriers in operation.

In spite of the need to defend the aircraft carrier, the purpose of carrier aviation is not to defend itself, but to use its attack aircraft to maintain control of the seas or project power ashore. But since the end of World War II the fighter mission has received the most publicity.

Table 2-1

U.S. Navy Aircraft Carrier Air Wing Aircraft Composition

	Function	No. of Squadrons	No. of Aircraft
F-4, F-14, F-18	Fighter	2	24
A-7, A-18	Light Attack	2	24
A-6	Medium Attack	1	10
KA-6D	Tanker	1	4
S-3A	ASW (fixed wing)	1	10
SH-3H	ASW (rotary-wing)	1	6
EA-6B	Electronic Warfare	1	4
E-2	Airborne Early Warning	1	4
F-14 TARPS	Reconnaissance	1	3
	Total	11	89

U.S. Marine Corps Air Wing Aircraft Composition

	Function	No. of Squadrons	No. of Aircraft
F-4, F-18	Fighter	4	48
A-4, A-18, AV-8A	Light Attack	2-3	46
A-6	Medium Attack	1-2	17
KC-130	Tanker/Transport	1	12
EA-6B	Electronic Warfare	1	10
RF-4	Reconnaissance	1	7
OV-10	Observation	1	12
AH-1	Attack Helicopter	1	24
CH-53, CH-46, UH-1	Transport/Utility Helicopter	1	13-14
	Total	18-21	302

SOURCE: Senate Appropriations Subcommittee on Department of Defense. *Department of Defense Appropriations for Fiscal Year 1981*. Hearings "Part 1—Posture Statement."

The Navy's concern for the carrier's defense spread to the defense of the task force and convoys that might accompany it. As early as 1946 the Navy began studies on vertical-rising aircraft that could fly from ships and submarines. In 1949 the Navy opened a competition for a Naval Convoy Fighter, designed to take off vertically from various merchant and naval ships. The two winners in the competition were the Convair XFY-1 Pogo and the Lockheed XFV-1.

The turning point in carrier and task force defense came with the radar-guided missile. Although the Navy began the Sparrow missile program in 1946, they did not incorporate the Sparrow III missile into an aircraft design until the advent of the McDonnell F4H-1 Phantom II, which first flew in May 1958.

The Phantom II aircraft began as a design study after McDonnell lost the day fighter competition against the Vought XF8U-1 in June 1953. The McDonnell design carried several designations during its design evolution: F3H-G/H, AH-1, and finally the F4H-1. The final designation changed from attack to fighter after the Navy briefed McDonnell that the Navy wanted a carrier-launched interceptor that could fly 250 miles, loiter for two hours, and return with a total cycle time of three hours. Grumman Aircraft competed with their XF12F design, which they called the Task Force Defense Fighter.[6] Neither aircraft was equipped with a gun.

The Navy debated whether the carrier defense fighter should be a subsonic or a supersonic platform. A subsonic aircraft could carry a larger-diameter radar and search for and detect targets further away. A supersonic aircraft required less frontal area for high speed but could fly faster to meet the enemy further away. These arguments continued as the Navy accepted the F4H Phantom II and prepared to build a follow-on to it.

The Navy issued a Request for Proposal on December 10, 1959, for its next fleet defense fighter. The Douglas F6D Missileer, a subsonic design with a five-foot radar antenna, won the competition. The Missileer design carried the Bendix/Grumman Eagle missile, which the Navy had awarded previously to Bendix in December 1958.[7]

The Eagle missile's range was greater than 130 miles. The Navy required the F6D to patrol 150 miles from the ship with supersonic missiles. This combination of subsonic aircraft and extra-long-range missile was in contradiction to the supersonic F4H Phantom II concept. The Navy was divided on the Missileer because it was a single-mission concept. Those opposed thought it was too slow to survive; proponents felt that the long range of the 60-inch antenna could overcome the slow speed.[8]

The concept of putting performance in the missile and not the airplane was verified in analytical studies done in the early 1950s. The Eagle-Missileer concept resulted from this analysis as the most efficient and cost-effective way to defend the fleet.[9] The Deputy Chief of Naval Operations (Air Warfare) at the time reflected the Navy's views:

> Aside from the technological and cost problems, the very high mach

> interceptor armed with a short range missile is faced with an almost unsolvable intercept problem by virtue of the high speeds and short time involved. To provide for the necessary time for solution of the problem, it is readily apparent that the next interceptor weapons system development must include the capability of acquiring the target at extended range.
>
> This in turn dictates an airborne interceptor missile with increased speed and range performance. Add to this the ability of the missile fighter to track more than one target and [fire] the missile simultaneously and you have the basic ingredients of our follow-on interceptor concept.
>
> When it comes to task force defense, however, we have been considering another concept. With radar missile development what it is, why must we bore supersonic holes in the air for air defense?[10]

As the Eisenhower administration waited for President Kennedy to assume office, Secretary of Defense Gates deleted the funding for the F6D Missileer aircraft in the FY 1962 budget, but he left the Eagle missile intact.[11]

Two months later, in February 1961, the Douglas Aircraft Company offered the Navy a reason to resurrect the F6D Missileer. They acknowledged that the primary purpose of the aircraft carrier was to project power on land or at sea, but they tried to show that the F6D could defend the carrier and also fulfill the primary mission of the carrier.

> The prime mission of the carrier task force is attack. The level of attack is strongly influenced by the number of aircraft required for Fleet protection. If these aircraft can be given an attack capability without appreciable compromise, the offensive strike force is greatly augmented, and justification for the cost of defense is enhanced. . . .
>
> Based on a typical complement, estimated by the Navy . . . a 36-percent level of defense requirement permits a 57-percent offensive complement. When air superiority has been established, using the F6D in the attack role will increase the level of attack to 72 percent. . . .
>
> By also utilizing the F4H for short radius attack missions, a maximum of 87 percent of the complement may be operated as attack aircraft.[12]

Douglas Aircraft's attempt to reinstate the F6D Missileer was fruitless. By the time of their presentation, the new Secretary of Defense, Robert McNamara, had assumed office. He saw that both the Navy and the Air Force were asking to procure two new airplanes, both called "fighters." The Air Force wanted an airplane to replace its F-105, which it was using as a pure nuclear bomber; the Navy wanted a fleet defense fighter with long-range missiles to replace its F4H Phantom II, which had been designed as a pure inteceptor. Although these two aircraft had entirely different missions, McNamara believed that the Air Force and Navy could operate with a common aircraft. From this emerged the multipurpose, multiservice Tactical Fighter

Experimental, or TFX.*

> When I became Secretary of Defense . . . I learned that the Air Force was developing plans for a tactical fighter that would ultimately replace the F-105. At the same time, the Navy was designing a second tactical fighter to replace the F4H in its fleet air defense role. These two planes would have many common missions and require many similar operational capabilities. After consultation with my military and civilian advisors, and independent study, I became convinced that one tactical fighter could be developed that would meet both the Navy and Air Force requirements. Accordingly, I directed that the Air Force re-orient its program with Navy participation, to achieve the goal of a common fighter.[13]

The Navy began a seige to destroy its version of the TFX, known as the F-111B. The Navy would have no part of an airplane created by the Air Force. The Navy focused on the sacrosanct area of carrier suitability to kill the F-111B, a maneuver it would resurrect a decade later to prevent the Air Force–designed YF-16 from being imposed on it.

The F-111B had areas of superior performance over the F-4 Phantom II. The F-111B's landing speed was slower—an important characteristic of carrier suitability—and its loiter time was longer than the Phantom's. But when the Navy compared the F-111B's performance to the Navy's unrealistic requirements, the F-111B did not measure up. And the Navy insisted that the Air Force make the F-111B live up to the Navy's requirements. When the Air Force could not, the Navy used these data to kill the F-111B. The F-14, a Navy-developed airplane, would not bear this same burden.

The Navy continued to degrade the F-111B, criticizing it for not meeting the wind-over-deck requirement, which is the amount of wind needed over the aircraft carrier to take off and land. The F-111B was deficient by seven knots, but compared to the original specification, the F-111B was deficient by only one knot and was 11 knots better than the F-4 Phantom II.†[14]

*McNamara may have believed that the two missions were similar because they were both called fighters. On the other hand, the promises of Douglas Aircraft with the multipurpose proposal of the F6D may have led McNamara, and those who advised him, to believe that one airplane could serve all purposes. The history of the TFX and the events surrounding the program are well documented. See, Robert F. Coulam, *Illusions of Choice: The F-111 and the Problem of Weapons Acquisition Reform* (Princeton: Princeton University Press, 1977).

†Thresholds and goals are distinct contractual requirements. The goal is a desired point; a threshold is supposed to be the minimum acceptable criteria. Theoretically, if the contractor goes below the threshold, the contract will be cancelled. It seldom happens because the military service that judges the performance also creates the program. For example, the specification for the F-15 Eagle's air superiority combat radius had a goal of 260 nautical miles and a threshold of 240 nautical miles.

SOURCE: Grumman
The Grumman/General Dynamics F-111B.

As the Navy increased its attempts to destroy the F-111B, the U.S. Air Force began studies in 1965 on an aircraft known as the Fighter Experimental, or FX. This began as another overweight fighter like the F-111A—the Air Force version of the TFX—but quickly evolved into a 90,000-pound dogfighter. At the same time, the U.S. Navy began its own studies for an airplane to replace the F-4 on the assumption that it would be stuck with the F-111B. The Navy airplane was called VFAX for *V* (heavier than air) *F*ighter-*A*ttack *E*xperimental, but originally the A was bigger than the F.* The roles were reversed in the FX: the primary mission for it was air superiority; its secondary mission was air-to-ground.

In the summer of 1966 McDonnell Aircraft Company offered a variable swept version of the F-4 that did not carry Phoenix missiles.[15] The McDonnell Aircraft variant of the F-4 signaled the beginning of F-111B alternatives. Although the Navy did not take the variable sweep F-4 design seriously, it welcomed the momentum. When the Navy believed it could eliminate the F-111B with a follow-on aircraft

Actual flight tests showed less than the 240 nautical miles. Yet the F-15 was not cancelled. If the Department of Defense had been trying to impose the F-15 on the U.S. Navy, the Navy would have killed the F-15 for missing the threshold by one nautical mile.

*The Navy uses the V to indicate heavier than air. Blimps are designated with a Z and helicopters with an H.

(in spite of the fact that it carried two fewer of latter-day versions of the Eagle missile, called the Phoenix), it accelerated its internal studies. The Navy's systems analysis division led the examination to determine the most cost effective fleet air defense system. The division was instructed by the Secretary of Defense not to consider carrier suitability in its analysis. It told the Secretary of the Navy that *if* the F-111B could get on and off the carrier, it was the most cost-effective system, adding that the AWG-9 weapons system and the Phoenix missile were without equal.[16]

Because the Secretary of Defense prohibited the Navy's systems analysis group from commenting on the F-111B's carrier suitability, the group touted the weapons system and the missile. As a result, the Secretary of the Navy told Secretary McNamara that the Navy should examine another aircraft as an insurance policy. This was the VFAX concept.[17] Grumman Aerospace Corporation responded to the VFAX momentum in October 1967 with an unsolicited proposal to replace the F-111B. In November the Chief of Naval Operations and other high-ranking Navy officials began serious arrangements to eliminate the F-111B.[18]

At the beginning of 1968 Secretary McNamara was still under the delusion that the F-111B was a viable aircraft for the Navy. In January he told Congress: "When the F-111B is introduced into the fleet, it will be used for long range fleet air defense and the F-4 for escort of attack aircraft. . . . The Navy is presently studying the next generation of fighter aircraft (VFAX) for the air superiority and escort missions"[19]

Although McNamara believed that the common F-111 was intact, its inevitable death was giving life to the Air Force's FX and the Navy's VFAX. Dr. John S. Foster, Jr., Director of Defense Research and Engineering, told Congress on February 7, 1968, that there was "unanimity among the services and OSD that both new fighters, the Air Force FX and the Navy VFAX, should be optimized for air-to-air combat."[20]

Dr. Foster spoke of the FX and VFAX as though they were one aircraft. When asked by Congress about the FX and VFAX commonality, Dr. Foster replied that since aircraft were becoming so expensive, there would be enormous savings from a common aircraft. He added that the differences between air superiority and fleet air defense might require a separate airframe, but there would be many benefits from common avionics and engines.[21]

The Navy perceived that it was dangerously close to becoming involved in another common aircraft program. Both services were advocating that air superiority was the primary mission of their

SOURCE: McDonnell Aircraft Co.
McDonnell Douglas submitted a variable sweep F-4 proposal for the evolving VFAX aircraft, later designated VFX, designed to eliminate the F-111B.

respective fighter designs. The Office of the Secretary of Defense had already designated the Air Force as the executive service on the FX-VFAX joint engine program.

This was different from the TFX/F-111 debacle. During that time the Air Force wanted a nuclear bomber to follow the F-105 and the Navy wanted a fleet defense fighter to follow their F4H-1 Phantom II interceptor. The FX-VFAX designs had a common mission, which made the argument for a common aircraft more plausible.

There was now a greater justification for the two services to end up again with a common aircraft. The Navy had already taken the position that the Phoenix missile and the AWG-9 fire control system were without equal. If the F-111B were allowed to exist, it would be the logical platform for the Phoenix missile. This would allow the remaining VFAX aircraft to assume the air superiority mission. However, the Air Force had already said that the FX was an air superiority aircraft. It would be only logical to merge the two fighters into a common design, something neither service could tolerate.

Consequently, the Navy had to eliminate the F-111B so that the VFAX would become the new home of the Phoenix missile system.

The Navy believed that if it could justify the need for the 8,000-pound Phoenix weapon system, the FX/VFAX design requirements would diverge.*[22]

The Navy successfully eliminated the F-111B in July 1968 and offered an alternative concept. Instead of a fighter-attack aircraft, the Navy omitted the attack portion and offered a combination air superiority-fleet air defense aircraft called the VFX. The Navy intended to use the VFX as a dogfighter; it decided to introduce the VFX in three phases.

In the first phase, the Navy would take the existing AWG-9 concept and the two Pratt & Whitney TF30 afterburning turbofan engines (originally designed without afterburners for the F6D Missileer) and put the new Grumman airframe around them.† It designated this airplane the VFX-1, which became the F-14A Tomcat. The Navy planned to introduce the VFX-2, or F-14B, later with the F401 engine. (The F401 was the common engine developed with the Air Force under the Joint Engine Program along with the FX's F100 engine.) The F-14B would have been the version designed to dogfight. The VFX-3 was to have been the F-14C, the B version with new avionics.[23]

The Navy justified its substitution of the F-14 for the F-111B because it claimed that the F-111B was not carrier suitable and because it needed an airplane that could dogfight. Yet with the exception of the F-14's alleged dogfight capability, the F-111B was actually superior in many areas. It was cheaper by almost half, it had a better loiter time, came closer to meeting its loiter requirement than the F-14 did in meeting its loiter time, and the F-111B's loiter requirement was higher. The F-111B's launch and recovery wind-over-deck requirement was slightly less than the F-14's, but the F-14 requirement was designed around a missile load 4,200 pounds lighter. As of 1964 the F-111B carrier landing speed was 11 knots slower than the Tomcat's.[24]

The Navy argued that the F-14's lower performance in some areas was due to the higher dogfight requirements. Yet the Navy canceled the F401 engine that would have given the F-14Bs dogfighting capability. While the Navy justified the F-14 on the basis of certain

*Ironically, the Air Force originally wanted the AIM-7G Sparrow, which operated in the K band frequency. The Navy wanted to operate its radar in the X band frequency. The Navy's VFAX was a multipurpose aircraft, but the X band was optimized for air-to-air. The Air Force's FX was allegedly a pure air superiority aircraft but the K band frequency was a compromise between air-to-air and air-to-ground. (Statement made by John Boyd to the author).

†The TF30 had never flown with an afterburner on it. This would prove to be a technological nightmare.

deficiencies in the F-111B as well as the need for a dogfighter, it exacerbated the F-111B's deficiencies and withdrew the dogfight requirement when it killed the F-14B.

The F-14A is not an incompetent dogfighter. However, many pilots complain that it is underpowered. Senior Navy officials defend the lack of power by attributing it to the relative lower thrust of a turbofan engine while in military or intermediate power. Yet these same officers did not bother to justify the F-111B's lack of power even though the engines were identical.[25]

The Navy used its specifications to kill the F-111B program, despite the fact that the F-111B came closer to meeting specifications the Navy imposed on an Air Force–originated design than the F-14 did in meeting its specifications. Notwithstanding the fact that the F-14 performed more poorly against its set of performance criteria than did the F-111Bs, these differences did not cause the Navy to cancel the F-14. On the contrary, because of its rabid assault on the F-111B, the Navy was irrationally committed to the F-14 program.

The Navy's fanaticism for its own concepts would repeat itself when Congress would again try to force the Navy to procure an Air Force fighter, the YF-16. With the F-14 the Navy finally had an aircraft designed specifically to defend the fleet, something it had worked on since the end of World War II. The F-14 represented the ultimate solution. It could track 24 targets at once and fire six missiles against the most threatening targets. But the most menacing foe the Navy would face was not incoming planes or missiles but the F-14's escalating cost and dwindling numbers.

The rising cost of the F-14 meant that the Navy would face the possibility of buying fewer of them. Whenever a military service faces this decision, it usually begins considering less expensive alternatives to maintain an adequate quantity of airplanes.

While the Navy did not consider less expensive airplanes, the Office of the Secretary of Defense did. Its studies of the problem of shrinking numbers and rising costs indicated that there was a definite relationship between the size, weight, and cost of aircraft. But the mere mention of a lighter weight fighter implied lower quality to many Naval officers.

Ironically, the Navy demonstrated the value of the lightweight concept when it built scores of lightweight aircraft carriers as well as the quintessential lightweight fighter, the Grumman F8F Bearcat, under the exigencies of World War II. With the rising cost of the F-14, lightweight fighter proponents would resurrect the arguments that preceded the F8F Bearcat.

Chapter 3

Cost, Numbers, and the Lightweight Fighter Concept

The Chief of the Air Corps made no secret of the circumstance that the funds appropriated by Congress sometimes bought fewer aircraft than intended in the original estimates for the simple reason that manufacturers turned up at the last minute with superior aircraft of radically improved performance—at a higher price. To ignore this advanced equipment would be to arm the nation with weapons less than the best.

The technical services are never satisfied with anything less than a perfection which is always unobtainable. The best is the enemy of the good. If we are to avoid the catastrophe of "too little and too late," there must be a decision as to production types. Germany has demonstrated that thousands of imperfect tanks on the battle field are better than scores of perfect tanks on the testing ground.

Buying Aircraft: Materiel Procurement of the Army Air Forces
I. B. Holley, Jr.

The dilemma the military faced on the eve of World War II was whether to have more of the less sophisticated, less expensive and in the minds of some, less capable fighters, or fewer of the more complex, more expensive but in the minds of others, more capable fighters. Its decisions are an epitaph of history, and as it wrestled with the issues, it faced the same dilemmas that the U.S. Navy and the U.S. Air Force faced when they were making decisions on the aircraft that led to the F-18 Hornet.

As the threat of World War II escalated from a possibility to a probability, the weight of fighter aircraft declined, and as fighters lost weight, they gained capability—not only individually but collectively. The lightweight fighter was ubiquitous, gave military commanders more options, and ultimately created larger exchange ratios against enemy fighters than did its more adipose stablemates. Fighter aircraft like the P-51 Mustang, F8F Bearcat, and F-16 Falcon are examples of fighters that are lighter than their contemporaries, are less expensive, and have greater performance. Because fighter aircraft of lower weight can have increased performance, can cost less, and can create a larger force, these three benefits are embodied in the term "lightweight fighter." (Throughout the text the term "lightweight fighter" refers to the generic concept. When capitalized,

"Lightweight Fighter" refers to the program from which the YF-16 and YF-17 aircraft evolved.)

The arguments for lightweight fighters—lower cost, greater performance, and increased numbers—were as relevant in World War II as they are today. Consequently, on the eve of World War II both the Army and the Navy were actively investigating the benefits of lightweight fighters.

As Hitler invaded Poland, American intelligence reported that Germany had an air force of approximately 8,000 aircraft. The United States, on the other hand, had barely 2,400.[1] Germany had a three-to-one advantage over the United States, a ratio that some military planners claim existed between the Warsaw Pact and NATO during the conceptual phase of the F-18.

Then as now, however, the American military proclaimed that America had technological superiority. The Army Chief of Staff claimed in 1938 that American planes were "equal, if not superior to any in the world." This rhetoric was a continuation of a theme offered by the Secretary of War four years earlier when he said that the U.S. combat aircraft were "superior to those of other countries."[2]

American defense planners have always faced the dilemma of whether to put money into quantity or quality. Without the pressures of war, they have spent money on increasing complexity. Yet when the military believed that the potential threat equaled U.S. technology, the emphasis shifted to quantity. For example, Assistant Secretary of War Louis Johnson, said in 1938: "Recent advances in other countries have equalled if not exceeded our efforts. We have known for some time that the foreign nations far surpassed us in the number of military aircraft at their disposal but we also knew that we led the field technically. It now appears that our research and development programs must be accelerated if we are to regain our position of technical leadership."[3]

The rhetoric on the eve of World War II and the defense debates of today are a matched set: maximizing advanced technology of each individual aircraft. But when the number of enemy aircraft begins to dominate, the military begins a parallel sales campaign to have an equal number of aircraft to match the enemy's. To a technocrat, there is never enough technology; to a tactician there is never enough aircraft. The fulcrum for this seesaw has always been the defense budget.

Regardless of how much the military planners resist the concept of a fixed budget, only a finite amount of money exists from which to procure military equipment. The reality of the fiscal constraints causes planners to attempt to squeeze more out of fixed budgets. Unfortunately, the unit cost of American fighter aircraft has increased so much that the promised performance cannot possibly keep pace with the increase in cost.

By any standard, modern aircraft are expensive. The cost of fighters in 1973 was eight times as expensive per pound as in the 1940s; four to five times as expensive per pound as in the 1950s; and twice as costly as those of the 1960s. These prices per pound are for production cost only. Development costs have escalated even more steeply.[4]

In 1943 the Army Air Force spent $2.47 billion to purchase a dozen different types of aircraft at an average cost per airplane of $99,400. In 1975 the U.S. Air Force requested $1.07 billion to purchase 98 aircraft for the same purpose with an average cost of $10.9 million per plane. While the Navy's F-14 Tomcat cost 190 times more than the F4U Corsair, which had the same mission as the F-14, the CVN 70 nuclear-powered aircraft carrier cost only 18 times as much as the *Essex*-class aircraft carrier of World War II.[5] The U.S. Army Air Force's lightweight fighter of World War II, the P-51 Mustang, cost approximately $54,000. In fiscal year 1990 dollars, the P-51 would cost $370,200. If the U.S. Air Force were to resurrect its Korean MiG killer, the F-86 Sabre, it would cost the Air Force $1.5 and $2.5 million in flyaway and program costs respectively. Based on 1990 fiscal year dollars, the Navy could buy a squadron and a half of 18 F-86's for the price it pays for each F-18 Hornet.

To suggest that the U.S. Navy procure 18 F-86s for the cost of one F-18 would be blasphemous. Yet, when the F-14 Tomcats first flew against Navy-owned F-86s, the F-14 pilots lost many engagements. F-14 advocates argue that in these encounters, the F-14 was not allowed to use its long-range Phoenix or Sparrow missiles. The visual identification requirement would appear to preempt that possibility. The point that lightweight fighter advocates make, however, is that no Tomcat driver could handle 18 F-86s regardless of whether he could use his missiles or at what range. And that's what equal dollars would force him to face.

The debate on numbers versus sophistication has been continuous in the military establishment. One view holds that because it is impossible to plan on the exact nature of a conventional war, it is better to have a multipurpose aircraft that can do three missions reasonably well, than to have an aircraft that can do only one mission in a superlative manner. The counterview says that it is better to make an airplane do one job well because its lower cost allows for greater numbers, which gives the battlefield commander additional options. As this quote from World War II shows, the debate has raged for some time.

> It is a fundamental law of nature that when an object is increased in size its weight increases faster than its surface area. A handy rule of thumb is that if the size is increased 2% the weight will increase 3%.
>
> Thus it follows that if we build a large airplane precisely similar to a small airplane the structural weight of the large airplane will increase more than did the wing area. Carrying this to the extreme, it would appear that if an airplane were built large enough it could not carry its own weight, let alone any useful load. . . .
>
> In the small fighter airplanes the weight law makes itself felt in requiring greater structural complexity as the size of the airplane increases, and this involves more difficult manufacturing and greater expense.
>
> The most frequent reason why weight is added to a fighter airplane is to increase the military load. . . . It will also take the form of more structure to support the increased military load. Whatever form it takes, it harms the performance and it reduces the maneuverability.
>
> The advantages of specialization now become apparent, and possibly need some emphasis. . . . [O]ne may build a fighter having long range and great fire-power and adaptability to a great variety of purposes, but one must be prepared to pay the penalty in poorer performance and poorer maneuverability. Likewise one may sacrifice range and retain the fire-power and the performance; this is the familiar "interceptor" type. Or one may sacrifice speed in favor of range and takeoff, which is the pattern for Naval carrier-based aircraft.[6]

Both Germans and Americans attribute the winning of the air war in Europe to the massive numbers of aircraft that America and the Allies threw against Germany. Chief of the German Air Force Adolf Galland's major concern for the rapid development of the ME 262 fighter was the air superiority of the Allies because of the increased range and "overwhelming number of American fighter escort."[7]

In spite of the superiority of the ME 262 once it did fly, it was not such a menace that it could cope with the numerous Allied fighters. Gen. John C. Myer, USAF, a World War II ace, described the relative capability of the P-51 and the ME 262 this way:[8] "The 262 couldn't out-turn the Mustang. But it didn't need to. Think of it this way. If one was starting with these two fighters from the same point on the outside of an apple, for a theoretical analogy, the 262 couldn't out-turn the Mustang but it was so much faster that it could fly the outside of it about as fast as the P-51 could fly the line cutting straight through it. He had the initiative and could go around and get into position for a pass while staying outside our gun range."*

*Ironically, Myer would later attempt to kill the Lightweight Fighter.

As a result of flying against the technologically superior ME 262, General Myer concluded that "eight P.51S were the equal of one ME. 262 if each knew of the other's presence."[9]

Lightweight fighter advocates point out that the ME 262 versus the P-51 exemplifies their argument. The ME 262 was a quantum leap in technology over the P-51, new technology versus old, jet versus piston. Today, no nation has a fighter that equals the technological leap that the ME 262 represented over the P-51. But in spite of this difference in capability, the larger numbers of the less sophisticated P-51S so totally dominated the environment that the ME 262 was unable to exact a better than 1.5 to 1 exchange ratio against the "inferior" Mustang, an exchange ratio poorer than the 2.5:1 ratio the Navy said was unacceptable in Vietnam.

The lightweight fighter advocates maintain that there is no historical evidence of a more sophisticated fighter being worth the difference in cost. Yet in spite of its extensive evidence favoring increased numbers of less complex airplanes, the military continues to resist the benefits history gives to lightweight fighters.

The Navy resisted converting from sail to steam for 30 years in spite of the obvious advantages.[10] Military officers are aware of the problem as evidenced by Maj. Gen. Perry McCoy Smith's comment, "once a military doctrine is established it is difficult to change, especially if technological advancements in weaponry seriously bring into question a doctrine upon which a specific military is based. . . ."

Current doctrine and dogma in the U.S. Navy and U.S. Air Force state that sophisticated technology will remedy America's numerical inferiority. Lightweight fighter advocates maintain that the increase of sophistication in today's fighters is as faulty a decision as the military's belief prior to World War II that the bomber was invincible and would not need fighter escort. In light of today's Navy and Air Force resistance to lightweight fighters, it is ironic that the two most capable fighters in World War II were lightweight fighters.

The benefits of the lightweight fighter concept were not lost on the designer of the P-51, Ed Schmued. While Republic Aviation was proposing an 11,500-pound XP-47B design, Schmued's XP-51 flew in October 1940 with a gross weight of only 7,965 pounds. The addition of the Merlin engine, the engine that made it famous, increased the weight to only 8,350 pounds. Schmued said that unnecessary Army Air Force regulations kept the P-51 heavier than necessary.[11]

Another lightweight fighter success story belongs to the U.S. Navy with the development during World War II of the Grumman F8F

Bearcat, which was designed to fly from the evolving smaller aircraft carriers. The Navy began World War II with seven large fleet aircraft carriers (CV) but toward the end of 1942 had only two operational carriers. Fortunately, the Navy had begun a program to supplement the conventional-size aircraft carrier with the smaller *Independence*-class light aircraft carrier (CVL) and the still smaller escort, or Jeep, carriers (CVE). The Navy built the CVE's originally to provide anti-submarine protection while escorting convoys of ships to Europe. Escort carriers evolved from that mission until they became part of the fleet air defense of the larger aircraft carrier and ultimately were used as offensive weapons.

Figure 3-1

World War II Aircraft Carrier Growth

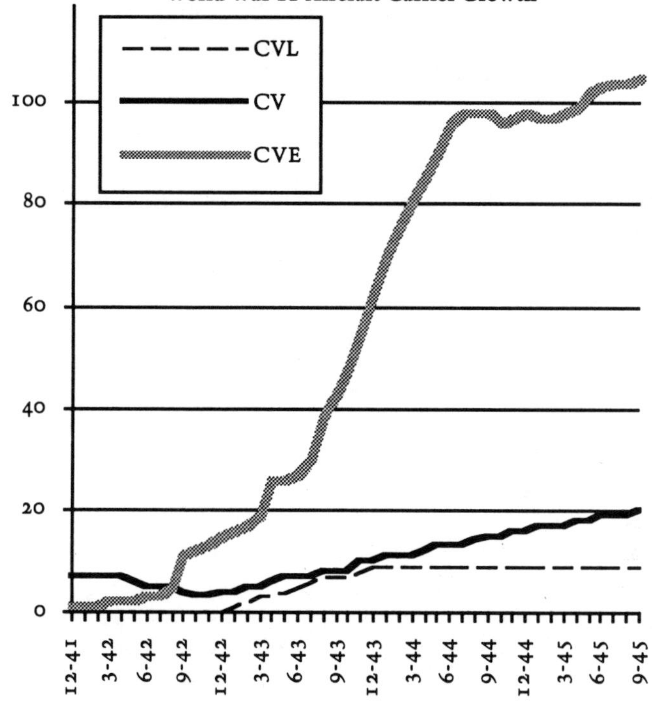

SOURCE: Ernest J. King, *U.S. Navy at War: 1941–1945*, p. 287.
The pressure of war caused the Navy to purchase more of the smaller CVE class carrier than the larger CV-class carrier.

The Navy built these smaller escort carriers because, as with lightweight fighters, it could build more of them more quickly. Between July 1, 1941, and July 1, 1943, the large *Essex*-class carriers increased in number (including combat losses) only 16 percent. As fig. 3-1 shows, the escort carriers, on the other hand, increased in numbers 1,700 percent. The trend during World War II was to build smaller but more numerous aircraft carriers. On July 1, 1945, the Navy owned 20 large *Essex*-class aircraft carriers, 5 light carriers, and 70 escort carriers. The pressure of war had changed the Navy's prewar position of a few large carriers to numerous small carriers.

Current large aircraft carrier proponents argue that the lightweight aircraft carriers (of the CVL or CVE class) are not suitable because, among other reasons, they cannot withstand the battle damage they would be likely to encounter. During World War II, however, the U.S. Navy lost no CVLs and only six escort carriers, one more than it lost of the large carriers.

Wartime trends caused Grumman Aircraft Engineering's founder, Leroy Grumman, to begin thinking about a new fighter for the Navy. In July 1943 he was conscious of the expanding escort carrier (CVE) program. Although he was partial to large twin-engine airplanes, he recognized the benefits of the escort carriers as well as their inability to carry the larger twin-engine aircraft. Grumman also recognized the need for good visibility from the cockpit and the need for a small-size aircraft.

He penned his thoughts to his chief designer, W. T. Schwendler. Grumman wanted to see if his idea for putting an F4F Wildcat-size body around the F6F Hellcat's engine was feasible. He assumed that the new airplane would have greater performance than the F6F. Grumman's memo to Schwendler is the genesis of the F8F Bearcat. His memo records both the Navy's and Grumman's rationale for building a lightweight fighter.

July 28, 1943

Memo to Mr. W.T. Schwendler

Our present development program for complete new designs of airplanes (consisting of XF7F and XTB2B) is subject to criticism from the following standpoints. It is based on airplanes becoming very much larger and heavier and also upon the general acceptance by the Bureau of twin engine types.

Controversial as to Size and as to Twin-Engine

Both of these airplanes are enormous, - in comparison to types now in service. There is little doubt that this increase in size is justified for land based operation. However, the practicability of airplanes of this size for carrier operation is not as yet proved. Furthermore, regardless of our feeling as to the advantages of twin engines, the Bureau has not as yet accepted this whole heartedly. After cessation of the war, it will be impossible to prove out in Service our ideas as to the real value of these design in Wartime, - and we will therefore be in a position of having to accept the Bureau's opinion as to whether or not such large airplanes, or even twin engine airplanes are suitable for the Navy's use. Although the Navy has been obliged to operate from land bases in Wartime, they have not as yet ordered combat type planes purely for land work. Peace time orders will be tied in to carrier operations more than ever.

Small Converted Carriers

The small converted carriers are doing a good job. They are still being built by the dozen. Because they are so numerous and cheap, they can be used where a large carrier would not dare operate for fear of risk of loss. In this respect they may prove more practical than the large carrier.

The Navy will undoubtedly retain and operate most of these after termination of the War. Their problem will be to procure suitable planes of small size for these carriers.

Proposed Addition to Experimental Design Program

A small fighter plane, which could (without question) be used on large or small carriers, and with a performance superior to the F6F, would be a valuable addition to our experimental program, - if for no other reason than to keep all our eggs out of one basket.

What I have in mind for a starter is as follows:

(a) Airplane -same size and dimension as "Wildcat".
(b) Gross Weight - 8,500 Pounds (Normal).
(c) Engine - 2800 - 2 Speed.
(d) Armament - 4 (50 Caliber - (rapid Fire Type)) with 250 rounds each.
(e) Fuel - Internal Protected Fuel Approximately 170 gallons
(f) Other Features - Blister Type of Cockpit Canopy
(g) Other Deviation from "Wildcat" -
Complete change in Landing Gear to obtain proper tread and propeller clearance.
(h) Performance - Superior in every way to "Hellcat".
(i) Loadings 8500/2100 = 4.+ Lbs/Horsepower
8500/200 = 33 Lbs/Square Foot

Advantages of Inclusion in Experimental Program

Many Bureau Officers have expressed interest in a small fighter. Roy Simpler who commanded a "Wildcat" Squadron in Pacific, and is now in Bureau, brought up the subject only last week. No one in Bureau would be basically against such a project.

Recommendation

It is recommended that a design study be made along lines proposed above, before approaching Bureau, to determine limitation to Useful Load. Recommend that this study be given priority over the Jet Propulsion Studies.

[Signed L. Grumman]

P.S. In order to check Bureau tendency to overload, this design should be sold as a "converted-carrier" fighter.

SOURCE: Grumman

This memo is significant for several reasons. First, looking at the date of the memo and comparing it with the first flight of the F8F shows with what speed an aircraft can be procured if the pressure of war is on. Second, Leroy Grumman penned a comment that Riccioni would make later when he stated that the small carriers could operate where the others would not "for fear of risk of loss." Third, Leroy Grumman remarked on the value of numbers of smaller carriers versus fewer large carriers, an argument that would resurrect itself in the early 1970s when the Navy discussed Sea Control Ships. Fourth, Grumman used the subterfuge of "converted-carrier" fighter to prevent the Navy's perpetual tendency to make heavyweights out of bantamweight fighters. (Emphasis in original.)

The Bearcat represented the quintessential lightweight fighter concept. It was a lighter airframe around an existing engine, resulting in improvements in almost all performance parameters. Unlike the lightweight versions of the P-51, the F8F did not suffer in range or endurance. With the exception of a slightly lower cruise speed and an 8 percent higher landing speed, the Bearcat outperformed the F6F Hellcat in every area. The most impressive improvement was the 100 percent increase in climb rate.

The threat to the aircraft carrier escalated as the war progressed. The Navy responded in two ways. The first was to approve the Grumman F8F Bearcat proposal in late 1943. The second was to increase the percentage of fighter aircraft on each aircraft carrier (see fig. 3-2).

The Bearcat was designed against a requirement to take off from the smaller escort and light carriers placed around the heavy carriers to protect them from the incoming air raids. These smaller carriers loaded with Bearcats were conceptually similar to the contemporary concept of the Aegis air defense radar network of surface-to-air missiles loaded on destroyers that surround today's aircraft carrier.

The U.S. Navy resorted to a lightweight fighter design under the pressures of war, yet resisted the benefits of lightweight fighters in peacetime. The use of smaller, more numerous, relatively lightweight escort and *Independence*-class aircraft carriers raises the obvious question: why didn't the Navy build greaater numbers of heavy carriers and propose heavier, multipurpose fighters, such as the F7F

Tigercat and the proposed 48,000-pound Grumman XTB2F-1, to fly from them? The answer seems to be that under the pressure of *actual* combat, the Navy chose to go for numbers.

Figure 3-2
The Evolution of
World War II Carrier Air Group Aircraft Composition

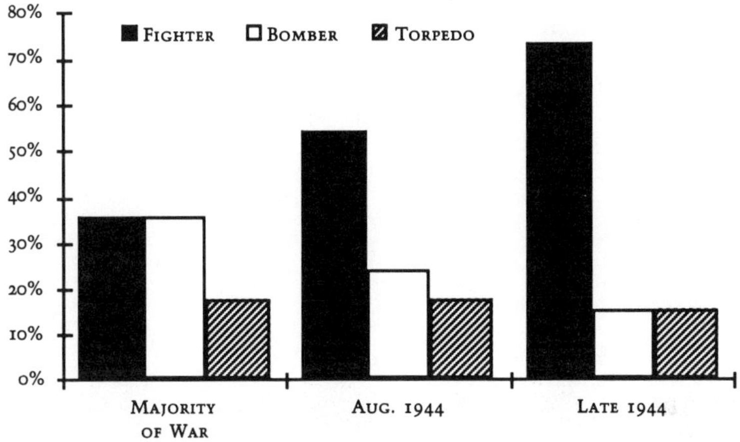

SOURCE: Anderton, *Hellcat*, pp. 50-51

SOURCE: Northrop
During the mid-1950s, Northrop Corporation developed some proposals for lightweight fighters specifically designed to fly off the escort (CVE) carriers.

Lightweight fighter proponents did not fade away after the end of World War II. Their constituency increased and ultimately created the proposal for the Lightweight Fighter competition that pitted the YF-16 against the YF-17, from which the F-18 evolved. Kelly Johnson, the designer of the F-104—the quintessential lightweight fighter of the 1950s and 1960s—would be responsible in the early 1970s for creating the Lightweight Fighter competition.

Chapter 4

Vietnam: Old Lessons Relearned

Even the best cookery book is no substitute for even the worst dinner.

Aldous Huxley
from the foreword of
The First and Last Freedom
by J. Krishnamurti

On April 4, 1965, during a bombing run on the Than Hoa Bridge, North Vietnamese MiG-17s shot down two F-105s. As a response, General McConnell, Air Force Chief of Staff, issued a document entitled, "Air Force Doctrine on Air Superiority."[1] This document, (which grew out of Chuck Myers's early work discussed on page 26 above) became a catalyst for some of the first studies on a design then known as the FX, which evolved into the F-15.[2] The Hornet's lineage is an uninterrupted flow from this first fighter engagement.

Air Force conventional wisdom cried out for a large, complex, F-111 type fighter to respond to the sophisticated F-105's destruction by two simple, gun-firing MiG-17s. When the F-15 ultimately evolved as an airplane of approximately half the weight of the F-111, many people felt that the F-15 had become a "lightweight fighter."

To the lightweight fighter advocates, however, the evolving F-15 design was still overweight, too expensive, and unable to accomplish the mission. Chuck Myers captured the essence of the arguments against a large F-15 in a memorandum written two months before the Air Force announced the winning F-15 contractor.

> The Air Force . . . has narrowed the competition for the F-15 to three contractors.
>
> Unfortunately, all three have designed aircraft which bear little resemblance to air superiority fighters.

The fault lies mostly with the Air Force in that it would never bring itself to overcome the appetite for sophistication and technology. All the popular notions such as (1) two engines are necessary (2) long range on internal fuel is required (3) no respectable fighter should have less than a 2.5 Mach placard (4) long range radar is useful and (5) inertial navigation [the U.S. Air Force regards] as a must.

Simplicity is not yet accepted as an important characteristic for a combat air-to-air fighter. Few people give full consideration to operations under a desperate wartime situation wherein the USAF is under constant pressure from enemy air, ground forces, and Communist agents.

Airplane size is not yet accepted as a prime fighter design characteristic. Combat exercises and tests at Nellis have highlighted the impact of being half the size of your adversary; perhaps there are those who have not been made aware of the value of stealth.

The importance of numbers has been completely disregarded even though experience and analysis supports that quantity is the most important element in a war environment.

Last minute adjustments and concessions are being made in an attempt to keep the F-15 under the 40,000 pound target weight. However, this effort will bear little fruit. Nothing short of a severe change in the stated requirement and removal of the unrealistic design restraints can save the program from producing another "technology display."

The disturbing aspect of the situation is that the F-14 and F-15 airplanes will absorb such vast quantities of money that it will be quite impossible to develop and procure an air superiority FIGHTER of proper character.* [3]

Chuck Myers contributed to the ultimate development of the Lightweight Fighter from several vantage points. He had worked outside the Defense Department for a major aerospace manufacturer and had consulted with several others.

Yet, even before Myers wrote his F-15 comments, Col. John Boyd and Pierre Sprey were working actively to prove what the Air Force conventional wisdom would not accept: smaller aircraft had better performance in almost all categories.

Sprey and Boyd were joined by Everest Riccioni, another Air Force colonel. Riccioni's efforts would become instrumental in creating the environment for the Lightweight Fighter. Many Air Force officers believed that Boyd, Sprey, and Riccioni were in a conspiracy to impose a less capable fighter on the Air Force. Consequently, they dubbed them the Lightweight Fighter Mafia. To many, Myers was

*Myers's prediction was correct. The F-15 weighs more than 40,000 pounds in the lightest version. McDonnell Douglas and the Air Force are producing an F-15E version that weighs closer to 70,000 pounds.

Myers is probably responsible for the first use of the word *Stealth*. He would go on later to immortalize the concept with the initial proposal under *Project Harvey* which he conceived as an ultra-light weight fighter but which the U.S. Air Force evolved into the F-117 bomber.

an unindicted coconspirator.

If any one individual was capable of leading a group of insurgent bureaucrats to impose an unwanted airplane on the U.S. Air Force it was John Boyd. Boyd has been likened to a military Moses because of his leadership qualities; and just as Moses parted the Red Sea, the mere mention of Boyd's name would part a roomful of generals. His competency commanded the respect of his superior officers but his integrity was often at odds with generals whose position on issues was based on the party line.

Nevertheless, Boyd had the flying experience to support his theories on the advantages of lightweight fighters. He spent a short combat career in Korea. Its brevity is a tribute to his ability to teach tactics and air combat maneuvering skills. His ability to consistently defeat World War II aces in mock dogfights made him more valuable at the training command. Later, he became known as "40-Second Boyd" because flying his F-100 Super Sabre he could defeat anyone within 40 seconds.

As an instructor at the Air Force Fighter Weapons School, Boyd flew two to three sorties per day for almost five years. He analyzed his responses to his opponent's maneuvers. As a result, he was the first to question the high-g maneuver as the universal countermove. He developed the soft maneuver analysis and began using the vertical dimension. Boyd published many articles during his tour as a tactics instructor at Nellis AFB but his enduring work was a catalog of maneuvers and countermaneuvers entitled "Aerial Attack Study."[4] All of this he accomplished at or below the rank of captain.

As a major, John Boyd, along with Tom Christie, a civilian Air Force employee, developed his celebrated energy-maneuverability theory, the first quantitative global analysis by which one could accurately compare one aircraft against another throughout their performance envelopes. As an expansion of his energy-maneuverability theory, Major Boyd showed that simple "S" curves could degrade the kill probability (P_K) of missiles. As a result, he forced the overly optimistic missile manufacturers to reevaluate their promises. Boyd used the same analysis to defeat surface-to-air missiles in Vietnam.*

The Air Force awarded Major Boyd the Air Force Systems Command Scientific Achievement Award for the best Engineering Analysis in 1965 and the next year awarded him the Air Force Research and Development Award for Outstanding Contribution to Aeronautical

*Some fighter pilots claim that briefings they received from Boyd were responsible for saving their lives. (Statements made by numerous pilots to the author.)

Engineering. He accomplished this as a newly promoted major.

In late 1966 the Air Force transferred Major Boyd to the Pentagon to unravel the F-15, then known as the FX. The FX began as a response to General McConnell's Air Superiority Doctrine. In spite of the need to develop a maneuvering dogfighter, it was evolving as another F-111, an aircraft designed from the keel up as a consummate nuclear bomber. Boyd's initial assignment was to evaluate the FX as it stood. His first response to his immediate superior was: "I could fuck up and do better than this!"

Boyd's contribution to the the F-15 (and U.S. Air Force) is heralded by a memorandum Riccioni wrote at the time. (The complete memorandum is reproduced in appendix A.)

> When he came to the Air Staff, he was asked to evaluate the accepted solution and Air Staff position on the FX aircraft. This concept had been given an "optimum" solution culminating in a 62,500 lb aircraft and a thrust-to-weight ratio at take-off (T/W) of 0.75, a wing loading (W/S) equal to 100 lbs/ft^2, with a turbofan engine of 2.2 bypass ratio. He correctly saw that this would lead to a disaster both before the Congress and before the enemy. He held forth the results of his analysis (trade-off study) and the first cut was to modify the solution to a 40,000 lb aircraft with T/W at takeoff equal to 0.97, a W/S of 110/ft^2. He became suspicious of the effects of high wing loading so he made an intensive investigation of aircraft drag polars. ["I noticed a remarkable phenomenon," Boyd said in a later interview. "As the wing loading on the 60,000-pound aircraft increased, the airplane was able to turn tighter. This meant that if you took off all the wing, you got the tightest turn."] The result of this analysis was to bring the wing loading down to 80 lbs/ft^2 and an engine by pass ratio of 0.9. Only with this progress did it become clear that at light wing loadings a fixed wing could become competitive with a variable sweep wing. Limited engine data provided by the contractors showed that the best value of engine bypass ratio was the least possible value, 0.6. He developed new task relevant rules for fuel budgeting. Now his tradeoff analyses in another iteration led to a 40,000 lb aircraft with T/W= 1.1, and a W/S of 80 lbs/ft^2 for a variable sweep wing. His computations then revealed that a fixed wing of 60-65 lbs/sq ft had definite combat advantages over the fashionable variable sweep wing. This led to the definition of the F-15 as it is today. No one else in the USAF could have achieved these results.*

*Quoted from a document Riccioni wrote in in 1971 to request that the U.S. Air Force encourage Boyd not to retire. The Air Force was rewarding Boyd like it rewarded Claire Chennault. Chennault was forced out of the U.S. Army Air Corps as a captain because he contested the conventional wisdom, stating that bombers might need fighter escort. Chennault later proved his theories with his successful leadership of the Flying Tigers in China. The Air Force leadership, humbled by Chennault's success, asked for forgiveness, by asking him to come back into active duty, and promoted him to major general. Boyd, like Chennault, has gone on to develop his theories on what works in conflict. The Air Force is slowly adopting them. The Army and Marines were quicker. They applied a significant portion of them in Desert Storm.

Many call John Boyd the father of the F-15, but Boyd shuns the title. His F-15 was an even smaller, lighter, less expensive, and more maneuverable version that weighed 33,000 to 35,000 pounds. Boyd's airplane never gained acceptance from the Air Force; furthermore, they ordered him to stop his investigations into these smaller designs. While Boyd gave the appearance of obeying orders, orders could not deter Boyd's strong ally, Pierre Sprey.

From 1965 to 1970 Pierre Sprey, formerly a Grumman analyst, was a special assistant to the Assistant Secretary of Defense for Systems Analysis. Shortly after Boyd arrived at the Pentagon he briefed Sprey on his analysis and the two joined forces like a pilot fish to a shark.

Sprey's background differed sharply from Boyd's. Sprey had been to college, earned a masters degree, and made a large dent into a Ph.D. program in statistics by the time he was nineteen. He was as relaxed discussing Goethe and Göring in German as he was in discussing the Maginot Line and Molière's *Le Medcin Malgré Lui* in French. He would discuss the Golden Section and its influence on the Gent Altarpiece with an art historian or the interquartile deviation and bias of the three point perspective in Van Eyk's work with a fellow statistician.

With his command of military history, Sprey fired facts at proponents of technological solutions to military problems in a fusillade of acerbic sarcasm. Whatever he lacked in diplomacy, he made up for with in accuracy. When Sprey answered a question with a question, one could be assured that he was being brought, through Socratic irony, into an argument from which agreement was the only exit.

Sprey continued Boyd's work, but with Boyd's help. Their work led to continued trade-off studies from which the Lightweight Fighter grew. During 1967 Boyd and Sprey briefed various elements of the Air Force on the benefits of more numerous, smaller, higher-performance aircraft. Sprey and Boyd applied Boyd's theories to the FX in late 1967. They found that by reducing the top speed requirement of Mach 2.5, the diameter of the radar antenna, and some unnecessary structural specifications, they could build a lower-cost aircraft with higher performance in all areas except top speed.

In the spring of 1968 Boyd and Sprey, sometimes in the company of Larry Welch, briefed the Air Staff and the Commander of the Air Force Systems Command with no results. Welch went away, and Boyd and Sprey remained silent for the rest of 1968. The Air Force and the Office of the Secretary of Defense (OSD) crystallized the FX concept in September 1968 and named it the F-15.

Boyd and Sprey were encouraged, nevertheless, by the results of their analysis. Using their same trade-off data, they pressed to the maximum limit their challenge of the FX requirements. They ended with a single-engine aircraft weighing under 25,000 pounds, which Sprey named the F-XX (pronounced "FX squared"). In light of Northrop's P-530 Cobra work and General Dynamics' smaller design submissions in the FX competition, Sprey validated their analysis with Northrop and General Dynamics. By late 1968 these two companies confirmed Boyd's and Sprey's work.

Sprey documented his analysis in a study he wrote in June 1969 entitled, "F-XX and VF-XX—Feasible High Performance Low Cost Fighter Alternatives."[5] Sprey's paper was as well received as Martin Luther's Ninety-Five Theses on the Castle Church at Wittenberg. Just as Luther's documents led to the Protestant Reformation, Boyd and Sprey's work led to the Lightweight Fighter competition, a competition as heretical to the Air Force as Martin Luther was to the Roman Catholic Church.

Sprey began with a historical basis for the need for a lighter-weight airplane, a more maneuverable version of the F-15. Taking on the TacAir canon that the missile would end the dogfight and the need for maneuverability, Sprey claimed that just the opposite was true. Pilots cannot evade missiles with straight acceleration or diving extensions, so the need for maneuverability was increased.*

Sprey maintained that historical and current (as of 1969) experience in North Vietnam and the 1967 Arab-Israeli Six-Day War showed that winning in air-to-air conflict was, in priority order, a function of pilot skill, maneuverability, detection and acquisition, and armaments.†

Throughout his F-XX paper Sprey continued to emphasize the importance of maneuverability.

> As long as weapons/missiles of restricted maneuverability or limited aspect launch envelopes[1] continue to be used on fighters (which we have sound technical reasons to expect), our aircraft must have sufficient

*The AIMVAL/ACEVAL test during 1977 proved that under some conditions, an airplane with radar warning devices can outrun a radar-guided Sparrow missile.

†The U.S. Navy substantiated Sprey's assertion that pilot skill is the most important factor in air-to-air combat. The Navy formed the Navy Fighter Weapons School (Topgun) after the 1968 pause in the Vietnamese air war. Prior to the formation of the school, the Navy's exchange ratio between it and the North Vietnamese was 2.5 to 1, the same as the U.S. Air Force's exchange ratio. When the war resumed in the air, however, the Navy's exchange ratio jumped to 12.5 to 1 while the Air Force's remained the same 2.5 to 1. The only difference between the two services was the Navy's increased emphasis on training. No aeronautical or electronic technology has had that kind of effect on an increase in exchange ratios.

maneuverability at cruise speed to defeat enemy "bounces" (based on the enemy's GCI positioning advantage) if we wish to operate over enemy territory. Since we now know from NVN [North Vietnam] experience that missiles can be defeated by a properly executed hard turn, the first performance requirement for a fighter is sufficient instantaneous turn capability to defeat any missile attack by means of a defensive "break."

'It is of more than just philosophical importance to note that if missiles which cannot be outmaneuvered or countered-measured and which have true all-aspect launch envelopes could be built, then the era of the fighter and the manned military aircraft would come to an end. Thus, if one believes that it is possible to develop missiles and identification procedures good enough to make the hypothetical concept of "stand-off" combat feasible, the[n] to be consistent one must conclude that there is no need for any new fighter. This follows from the fact that these same invincible missiles would be at least as effective launched from the ground or from a transport-type aircraft.*[6]

Sprey also discounted the need for high top speed. He observed that most combat starts with a "bounce," so the defending side will be at cruise speed. The attacker will be at a relatively high speed, but at a speed that is not too high to effectively employ his weapon. Too high a speed relative to the defending airplane offers the possibility of an overshoot, converting the offensive aircraft into a defensive one. The desirable speeds for a fighter is, then, the initial speed "plus the speeds that can be reached and sustained during the hard maneuvers and the short time span of normal jet combat (30-180 seconds.)"[7]

Sprey concluded that to attain high top speed was a waste of money because of the added expense for heat-resistant, lighter, more expensive metals, variable speed inlet ramps, and other technology.†

Sprey added that as 50 percent or more of the aerial victories were achieved against unaware pilots, the most important capability of a

*The concept of multiple missiles on a subsonic aircraft was given in a series of proposals for the F6D Missileer/Eagle missile competition. The idea was also proposed by Douglas that the A3D Skywarrior carry Eagle missiles. In the Carter administration, Russell Murray II, Assistant Secretary of Defense for Program Analysis and Evaluation (PA&E) advocated P-3 Orions bristling with Phoenix missiles.

†The F-15 again offers an example. The F-15 is advertised as a Mach 2.5 airplane. The handbook states that the speed between 2.3 and 2.5 is available for only a brief period. It also requires the use of the V_{MAX} switch, which gives an additional 75 degrees of turbine inlet temperature that results in 2,500 pounds more thrust per engine. The V_{MAX} switch is not to be used more than 5 minutes during a 2,000-hour period.

The Mach 2.3 and Mach 2.5 speeds are tactically useless because they cannot be obtained with the F-15's complement of four Sparrow and four Sidewinder mounted on the airplane. With these eight missiles on board, the F-15 has a top speed of Mach 1.78; below 10,000 feet the top speed difference between the F-15 and the F-5E is less than 80 knots. If the F-15 were to take off in maximum power, without missiles, in an attempt to reach its maximum speed, it could fly no further than 80 miles before having to return to base.

fighter was tail warning. This warning should come from good rearward visibility, passive warning receivers, and "possible future rearward sensors."[8] Our own research and development has been, Sprey admonished, on forward sensors. We could have taken advantage of offensive positioning of our own ground-based radar in Vietnam, but we did not. We could in a NATO or Korean scenario, he added.

Radar target acquisition was unsuccessful in Vietnam, according to Sprey. Less than 15 percent of air-to-air acquisition in radar-equipped airplanes has been accomplished by the radar. This trend will continue, Sprey predicted, because the enemy with its ground-based radar will carefully vector its fighters out of the plus or minus 40 to 60 degree radar coverage. Sprey's comments were made in 1969. By the end of the air war in 1972, only 2.8 percent of all target acquisition was made by the airplane's radar without assistance. (See C. E. Myers comments, page 36 above.)

Sprey claimed that single-seat fighter pilots would not stick their heads inside the cockpit and forgo the lookout doctrine. The look-down-shoot-down radar "has not been demonstrated and there are technical reasons for expecting this situation to prevail through another fighter generation." Fighter pilots are reluctant to turn on their radar because, with passive detection, others would be aware in advance of their arrival, in some cases by several hundred miles.*

The enemy rarely used airborne radar. When they did, the radar did not emit enough energy to give any indication on our electronic countermeasure receivers, a fact documented in the Comfy-Coat studies.

Sprey then attacked the value of airborne missiles. The U.S. tactical air forces introduced three families of air-to-air missiles in Vietnam. The missiles offered little of what they promised. Their lethality was low. The infrared Falcon missile, "despite almost $1.5 billion invested in program R & D, procurement and 'get well' " programs, and the Sparrow radar-guided missile (which traveled from the model A to the model E) struggled to obtain a 10 percent success rate. The AIM-9D Sidewinder infrared missile, which cost one-third as much as either the Falcon or Sparrow, had almost as acceptable kill rates. Sprey further contended that even though the launch envelopes were smaller, the F-86 achieved lethalities of 34 percent or a probability of kill (P_K) of 0.34 per burst in Korea, and the FW 190 achieved 0.50 lethalities per burst against the B-17 in World War II. The Israelis, he added, achieved 54 gun kills and zero infrared missile kills in the Six-Day War using an old technology gun.

*Sprey calls radar the "antistealth" device.

History and analysis have shown, according to Sprey, that missiles have limitations because of guidance and aerodynamic time lags, seeker dynamic limits, and *g* limits. These limitations are especially true with large, long-range missiles. The all-aspect promise of a radar-guided missile vanishes when the target maneuvers. High-target angular rates exist because of the Visual Identification (VID) requirement. The missile is not useful inside gun range and it does not appear that the VID requirement will be eliminated. Desert Storm did not change this. "Despite years of effort, IFF [Identification Friend or Foe] schemes of sufficient reliability, security, and un-countermeasurability to allow firing at non-responding blips on a radar scope have not materialized."[9]

The over-size airframes necessary to house large radar systems, coupled with their lack of success in the dynamics of air-to-air warfare, should not penalize the next fighter, Sprey concluded. All of the money tied up in the weapon system was subject to countermeasures, particularly if the radar was designed to pick up low-flying targets.

Maneuvers in the Sea of Japan demonstrated that A-7As using passive ECM and chaff could detect and defeat F-4 radar lock-on and then maneuver into attack position.[10]

After Sprey laid out the premise for the F-XX, he outlined the design philosophy for it. He said that as the maneuverability of the Soviet threat is unknown, and as they have the ability to create high thrust-to-weight ratio aircraft due to a need for less fuel and avionics, the F-XX must be a lighter, hotter design to anticipate future Soviet fighters.*

To achieve this, the Air Force should eliminate 7,000 to 10,000 pounds from the F-15. For every pound of deadweight in the F-15, the gross weight could be lowered five pounds, Sprey claimed. The areas that offer the greatest potential for weight savings are fuel, structure, avionics, speed, and number of engines.

Sprey maintained that the requirement for excessive internal fuel degraded the performance of aircraft. He cited the F-111 and the A-7 as examples. By using external fuel to size the requirement, the range requirement could be designed around the use of external

*Proponents of long-range radar and sophisticated fighters pointed out that after 12 years the Soviets showed that they were headed in the direction of sophisticated fighters, such as the MiG-23. Lightweight fighter advocates retorted at that time that the Russians were building a lightweight fighter known as the MiG-29. The current trend in Russian tactical aircraft is to emulate the production of increasingly sophisticated airplanes. It follows that they are developing a less sophisticated lightweight fighter, and thus merely emulating U.S. tactical fighter procurement.

tanks. This principle used on the multistaged rockets was successfully employed by the Germans in the Spanish Civil War and the Americans on their long-range bombing escort during World War II. On this basis, the F-XX could have a 33 percent increase in range over the 450 nautical mile range of the F-4, or the 850-900 nautical mile range then claimed for the F-15.

The military increased the structural requirements since the 1950s, Sprey maintained. As the lower structural requirements were once adequate, he advocated going back to them as an additional weight-saving measure.

The avionics necessary for visual air combat are all that are required, he stated. "[The] Sparrow is deleted due to its large size/complexity, severe installation weight penalties and poor performance despite several 'get well' modifications."[11]

The F-XX design would have a requirement of Mach 1.4 to 1.5 as its maximum speed, since higher speeds were seldom used. Paradoxically, this "will probably enable it to reach Mach 2.0 as a fallout."*

Sprey believed that the drag associated with twin engines was greater than an equal amount of thrust from a single engine, by at least 100 to 200 feet per second at one g P_s. This would equate during straight and level flight to a 6,000 to 12,000 feet per minute advantage in acceleration, or climb, for the single-engine aircraft. Sprey discounted the peacetime or wartime advantage attributed to twin engines.

Sprey and Boyd used two aircraft designs to substantiate their work: the General Dynamics FX-404 and the Northrop N-700. The N-700 was one of the P-530 Cobra designs, which led to the YF-17.

Once Sprey showed that he could make a smaller and lighter design, he wanted to change the acquisition process by employing a modified prototype system. He would select two contractors for the F-XX design and have them compete against each other. Two other contractors would build two models each of a navalized version that Sprey dubbed VF-XX. Each service would have four aircraft and two different designs. Sprey also wanted four engine contractors competing. The winner of each design would result from the outcome of aerial dogfights.†

*The F-16 top speed requirement was Mach 1.6 but it can reach Mach 2.0, which confirms Sprey's contention.

†This concept of building prototypes was partially implemented in the Advanced Tactical Fighter (ATF) program that led to the YF-22 and YF-23 flyoff. The ATF flyoff failed to test *in situ* some critical concepts, however. While the YF-22 demonstrated that it could cruise supersonically, it did not fly with production engines, avionics, nor the stealth technology that was destined for the production version. As a result,

SOURCE: Northrop Corporation

The Northrop YF-17 is visually similar to the F-18A. Note the smooth leading-edge of the wing. When McDonnell Douglas modified the Northrop design, they added a snag to the leading edge to generate a vortex for low speed control around the aircraft carrier. This snag generated side loads of up to 1 g at 5.6 HZ that required its removal in the final design. The snag has been reintroduced in the F-18E.

Along with this approach, Sprey wanted to copy the low paper work and manpower standards used by the Lockheed "Skunk Works" to reduce development and start-up cost for aircraft and engines approximately by one half that of the F-14 and F-15 development costs. The average flyaway cost Sprey used for the F-14B, F-15, and F-XX was $13 million, $11.1 million, and $3.3 million, respectively.

Sprey's F-XX proposal created a reaction throughout the U.S. Air Force and U.S. Navy. The Air Force resisted his concepts, claiming that it needed the F-15 to defeat the high-speed, high-altitude MiG-25 Foxbat. The Navy was even more vocal.

George Spangenberg, Director of the Evaluation Division of the Naval Air Systems Command, along with Fred Gloeckler of the Systems Analysis Division, replied inside the Navy unofficially, to Congress, and to the press.

> These basic concepts have been considered in detail by the Services during the formative stages of the F-14 and F-15, have been reviewed by DDR&E, and rejected in all decisions to date by OSD [Office of the Secretary of Defense]. The reconsideration of the concept (F-XX) as a

the production version has a recontoured canopy, no doubt to accommodate the increased drag (not demonstrated on the prototype). The redesigned canopy will reduce the pilot's rearward vision, the direction from which most kills occur.

> viable alternative should have been turned down before submission to the Services. . . .
>
> In common with past papers by the same author, this study contains many fallacious assumptions, half truths, distortions, and erroneous extrapolations. Unsubstantiated opinions are presented as facts. Any rebuttals give the appearance of arguments against the rudimentary virtues of simplicity, high performance and low cost.*

Sprey went public with his F-XX paper nine months after he published it internally. He gave his paper in March 1970 at a symposium sponsored by the American Institute for Aeronautics and Astronautics (AIAA) in St. Louis. Ironically, the conference was held at McDonnell Douglas, which had received the F-15 contract three months earlier.

Sprey's briefing was the last public F-XX activity. However, the momentum continued. As a result, others were adopting the F-XX concept. The U.S. Air Force's F-15 advocates thought that the F-XX had disappeared. On the contrary, the F-XX was in gestation. It would reappear as the Lightweight Fighter. The Navy, on the other hand, would be successful in suppressing Navy-originated versions of a lightweight fighter.

*One of the criticisms that Spangenberg has against the F-XX concept is that small aircraft do not have adequate range. As of 1980, he was still unaware that the F-16—the smallest U.S. tactical fighter—has the longest range. (Statement made by Spangenberg to the author.)

Chapter 5

The Aborted Navy Lightweight Fighter

[The ME 262] was very good, and very fast, but there were too many Allied fighters in the air at that late stage of the war for the number of ME 262s we had. . . . One day in 1944 I saw about 2,000 Allied aircraft over Germany. On that day I had fourteen ME 262s.

Erich Rudorffer, 222 victory ace
from E. H. Sims, *Fighter Tactics*

The halt in the Vietnam air war in the fall of 1968 gave many Navy pilots time to reflect on the promises and realities of their aircraft during air-to-air engagements with the North Vietnamese. Press reports notwithstanding, the United States' tactical forces fared poorly. At one point the United States was losing more airplanes than it was shooting down. While the overall exchange ratio was approximately two-to-one in favor of the United States, the trend was not favorable. Pierre Sprey summed it up this way:

> Our tactical air forces have never been less effective. In Korea, against an Oriental air force with little combat experience, our first line F-86 fighters achieved a 10-1 exchange ratio against the similar-performing MiG-15. In Vietnam, against a much smaller Oriental air force with no combat experience, our first line F-4 could achieve not better than 1:1 or 2:1 edge over the simpler but equal-performing MiG-21. Why did we do much worse in Vietnam? There are three principal reasons: inadequate pilot training; the ease with which MiG's could find and surprise the large, highly visible F-4; and the less than 10 percent kill rate of the Sparrow radar missile around which the F-4 had been designed.[1]

These lessons were not lost on most Navy pilots. Cdr. Ernie Waller, USN, had flown three combat tours and spent a fourth tour on an Admiral's staff in Vietnam. With the lessons of Vietnam fresh in his mind, Waller was assigned to the Naval Air Systems Command in January 1969. Waller's experience was that Navy fighter aircraft were too fragile and inappropriate to fight a Vietnamese-type air war. He believed that the Navy needed a new airplane.

When Waller arrived in Washington, D.C., the Navy was in the process of awarding the F-14 contract to Grumman. To Waller, the F-14 might be an adequate fleet air defense airplane, but for going over the beach and escorting the attack airplanes, the F-14 would exacerbate the problems already existing in Naval aviation.

Waller's new assignment made him the Navy's adviser on fighter aircraft to a civilian enclave known as the Advanced Concepts Group. He reviewed the long-range plans for the Navy fighter projected to follow the F-14. What he saw in the Navy Aviation Plan (a document that came out every spring) was a 1983 Initial Operating Capability (IOC) fighter that would fly Mach 4.5 with a dash speed of Mach 6. The weapons were to be long-range radar missiles with a large offset axis capability.

Waller believed that in a turning dogfight, the Mach 4.5 airplane's turning radius would be so large that it could not see the threatening airplane on the other side of the circle, with or without radar. He also cringed at the thought of the aircraft's complexity.

Waller went to his superior, Capt. Richard Hoffman, USN, and expressed his concerns. Together they went to the head of the Advanced Concepts Group, a civilian named Fred Locke, who listened to Waller's ideas for a simpler, less complex fighter for the air superiority escort mission. To Waller, the two basic Navy fighter missions were to defend the carrier or fleet, commonly called fleet air defense, and to escort the attack aircraft. Locke liked Waller's ideas and the two of them talked to industrial representatives who came into NAVAIR (the term the Navy and industry gave to the Naval Air Systems Command). Eventually Waller and Locke visited Northrop, General Dynamics Convair (San Diego), North American, and Grumman. When they returned, Locke informed Waller that their group had the funds to study this new airplane concept. He suggested that they pick one of the companies to study the fighter escort mission. They picked General Dynamics.

During the spring of 1969 Waller met Chuck Myers who in turn introduced Waller to Pierre Sprey. Sprey was several months from publishing his F-XX study but filled Waller with more ideas on the escort fighter concept. Sprey published the F-XX study in June and Waller crystallized his ideas on the F-XX concept, which had been influenced by conversations with several members of the Navy's lightweight fighter mafia, including Tooter Teague and Cal Swanson. Waller was not, however, the only one working on the lightweight fighter problem.

From 1969 until 1971, a small group at the David Taylor Naval Ship Research and Development Center (DTNSRDC) was also working on technological applications to a lightweight fighter, which they called the NSRDC Light Fighter. Bob Thompson ran the study, which was also funded by Fred Locke's Advanced Study Group. Thompson and his group were looking at an advanced, inexpensive Navy air superiority fighter with improved maneuverability. Their investigations focused on a close-coupled canard wing for higher lift coefficients. They also assumed limited avionics, good cockpit visibility, and simplicity. While Thompson continued to work on his NSRDC Light Fighter, Waller expanded his work on the nonfleet air defense role, which he called "the other fighter mission."

On December 10, 1969, General Dynamics submitted a proposal to study Waller's other fighter mission.[2] The study sought to correct the mismatch between theory and reality. The authors pointed out that the long range missile was designed to end the dogfight and hence end the need for maneuverability. The proposal maintained that the missile actually placed a premium on maneuverability because maneuverability was the only way to defeat it. To that extent, they were emulating Sprey's F-XX paper. They also said that the missile was easily out-maneuvered or jammed and that positive identification required a visual identification, which put the large interceptor fighter at a disadvantage.

The proposal advocated examining the philosophic design divergence indicated by recent history, that is, multimission fighter-interceptors versus a mix of fighter and interceptor types specialized and optimized around specific "point" mission objectives.[3]

Based on interviews and the Convair proposal, Locke awarded General Dynamics a $70,000 contract to study the alternative mission fighter.

By the spring of 1970 Waller had amassed more data to justify an attempt to generate a budget request for a less expensive, less complex fighter for the fighter escort role. Increasing public interest in the attributes of a lightweight fighter bolstered Waller's position. Pierre Sprey, who presented his F-XX paper at the March AIAA meeting was joined by Tooter Teague, then a lieutenant commander and part of the Navy lightweight fighter mafia. Teague's paper was entitled "Southeast Asian Aerial Combat Environment." Teague, skipper of the USS *Kitty Hawk* in the early 1980s, said his presentation was not well received by the F-14 proponents within the Navy.[4]

Teague was a qualified representative of the fighter community. He flew 172 missions in F-8 Crusaders between June 1966 and November 1967. He was hit several times from ground fire and on one occasion was shot down and wounded. His opinions about the role of a lightweight fighter were based on experience.

Teague began his talk at the AIAA conference by recalling that at the end of each war the long-range planners always said there would never be another dogfight. At the end of World War I they said there would never be another dogfight because airplanes would fly as fast as 200 miles per hour. At those speeds who could dogfight? He concluded his introductory anecdote with the pre-Vietnam prediction that missiles would eliminate the dogfight.

Teague's talk criticized the multimission training given to Navy fighter pilots and contended that fighter pilots were mission-saturated: "We continue today to train [a] fighter pilot to do every air combat job, and wonder why he isn't as proficient as we think he should be—at any of them."*[5]

Teague enumerated some of the other problems that existed in Vietnam and that would probably exist in future aerial combat. For one thing, he emphasized, the enemy had very good ground control intercept (GCI) radar, which gave him an advantage. The U.S. radar was not as effective.

Teague attacked fighter paucity, fighter sophistication, and pilot training in his concluding remarks.

> We now know the MiG-17 is no match for the F8 or F4. Yet the MiG-17 shot them down. We know the old, inexpensive F8 shot down

*Historically, the U.S. Navy had maintained separate communities for fighter and attack pilots. Fighter squadrons had separate designations for these squadrons such as VF-1, VF-211, etc. They also flew aircraft with "F" designations such as the F-4, F-14, etc.

Attack pilots flew "A" designated aircraft such as the A-4 and A-7 and were assigned to VA squadrons such as VA-96. These communities were also stationed separately. Naval Air Station (NAS) Miramar in San Diego was a fighter base; NAS Whidbey Island in Washington State was an attack base.

The Air Force, on the other hand, calls virtually all of its tactical aircraft *fighters*, reserving for internal consumption the distinction as to the primary function of the squadron. Thus, you could go to an Air Force "fighter" squadron and find airplanes that did not have the capability to fire any missiles or guns. In this example, the "fighter" squadron would have a Designated Operational Capability, or DOC, as an attack squadron. The Air Force in Desert Storm DOCed all of the F-16s (conceived as pure air-to-air fighters) as bombers to avoid competing with the F-15s. The DOD claimed that an F-16 shot down an Iraqi MIG on December 27, 1992, with an AIM-120 (AMRAAM) missile. If this is true, it verifies that the F-16 could have been used as an air-to-air platform from the beginning. Furthermore, since the MIG was shot down within visual range, it tends to indicate that the F-16 could have used its Sidewinder heat-seeking missile.

> over twice as many MIG's as did the more modern, sophisticated Navy F4. We were taught a lesson in simplicity that we continue to ignore. The F4 pilots had to do every air combat job except photo recon. Consequently the pilot's training effort was diluted in the one area where there is no second best, the dogfight. The F8 pilot was basically a "dogfight" trained pilot. . . .
>
> It [paid] off when the fight was on for real. The enemy air threat was always weak at best. They never had sufficient numbers of fighters to provide a serious challenge to U.S. air superiority. . . .
>
> There were never any large numbers of MIGS in the North. The American forces could have, on any given day, put a numerically superior force of fighters in the air. . . .
>
> A large force of MIG 21's and 17's, equal in number to the strike force and flown properly, could have wreaked havoc on the Navy attack aircraft.[6]

Waller was fortified by Teague's public assertions, and by his private talks with designers Cliff Adcock, Ken Hinman, and Dave Wheaton of General Dynamics Convair (San Diego), as well as Maurice King of North American. Waller approached the budget process with mixed feelings. He was convinced of the need for a lightweight fighter. However, he knew the establishment would consider it a threat to the F-14.

The first step was to draft a document called a Proposed Technical Approach, or PTA, which was required for all budget items. After PTAS were drafted, the creator would send them through the system to seek a supporter. When the Waller PTA, entitled "Advanced Air Superiority Aircraft System -VFX(AS)," first surfaced, the F-14 was seven months from its first flight.

Waller's major premise was that there was another role for fighters besides defending the fleet. As the F-8 Crusader was being phased out, carrier fighter composition shifted to airplanes designed specifically to provide fleet air defense. Fleet defense was overemphasized at the expense of other missions. It was not cost effective, according to Waller, to send the more expensive fleet defense aircraft on a bombing raid to protect relatively low-cost attack aircraft. In short, what the Navy needed was a mix.

To illustrate the value of a mix, Waller used the F-8 as an example of an obsolescent, less sophisticated airplane that had a higher exchange ratio in air-to-air combat than the more complex, more expensive F-4. (The overall air-to-air exchange ratio in Vietnam for F-4s was approximately 2.4 to 1, but the exchange ratio of the F-8s was 6.3 to 1.)

History confirms that numbers are critical, Waller wrote. Individual airplane capabilities are important, but tactics can take away any advantage. It is fundamental, he continued, that two can usually defeat one regardless of the degree of capability of the one.*

Waller contended that the VFX(AS) should be able to obtain a four-to-one exchange ratio over enemy aircraft while performing the fighter escort role. He believed that mathematical attrition models, as well as tests of threat aircraft captured by the Israelis during the 1967 Six-Day War, confirmed this. Waller added that current U.S. aircraft were four times as expensive as threat aircraft. The VFX(AS) would not have to be an expensive all-weather fighter. Experience in World War II, Korea, and Vietnam showed that for night and inclement weather attacks the fighter escort was not needed.

Waller foresaw problems with the fleet air defense F-14 in the 1975–1985 time period. He speculated that the enemy would try to overload the carrier. They would come in with false starts and feints that would use up the F-14's allotment of Phoenix missiles.†

The other concern Waller had was the ability of the more complex F-14 to maintain the sortie rate necessary if the enemy made around-the-clock attacks. He believed, based on his Vietnam experience, that an airplane as complex as the F-14 would lose the fleet air defense mission, not to combat losses but to maintenance attrition.

Contemporary and postulated Navy fighters all suffered from poor maneuverability, poor cockpit visibility, relatively large size, poor sortie rates, high maintenance, and no capability to create a four-to-one exchange ratio against the MiG-21. To correct this, Waller proposed an airplane that would have the primary mission of offensive air superiority. The secondary and tertiary missions could be fleet air defense and interdiction.

Waller's VFX(AS) differed from Bob Thompson's Light Fighter by including some high technology. Waller was a realist; he believed that his design would survive only if some high technology were associated with it.[7]

*This fact was impressively demonstrated in March 1977 when two F-5ES flown by Lt. Jim Harris and Lt. Mike Garland fought a single YF-17 flown by Lt. Cmdr. Monroe Smith, Commanding Officer of the Navy Fighter Weapons School (Topgun). In simulated air combat maneuvering (ACM), the two F-5ES took the offensive, took turns shooting down the YF-17, and never allowed the YF-17 to gain the offensive. It was, in the words of Bill Brinks (who would later become McDonnell Douglas's Chief Test Pilot and F-18 Deputy Program Manager) the finest example of two versus one he had ever seen. (Statement made by Bill Brinks to the author.)

†Waller's prediction remained a concern until the fall of the Iron Curtain. The total number of Phoenix missiles that most U.S. aircraft carriers carry is 96. This number allows two squadrons of 12 F-14s to carry a total of four Phoenix missiles against any incoming threat.

Waller used a super-critical airfoil to give his Air Superiority Lightweight Fighter a 60-knot higher cruise speed. Most fighter aircraft were cruising between Mach 0.8 and 0.85. (As a point of comparison, the F-8 Crusader routinely cruised at Mach 0.92; the yet-to-fly F-14 would end up cruising at approximately Mach 0.72.) Waller also wanted to explore the canard wing to see if it would increase the coefficient of lift to 1.9.

Waller wanted to increase the thrust-to-weight ratio by using composite materials to reduce weight. He was also intrigued by the fact that composite materials would not reflect radar. He introduced the idea of using radar-absorbing materials to reduce the radar cross-sectional area of his fighter to 2 square meters head-on and 5 square meters from any angle in the 500 to 12,000 MHZ range.

Waller proposed concept engines for his VFX(AS) fighter design. In view of the almost eight-to-one thrust-to-weight ratio of the arriving F100 engine for the F-15, he believed that the higher-ratio stoichiometric engines (engines that run hot enough to completely burn all of the ingested oxygen) were a possibility.* At these high temperatures the turbine would produce the maximum thrust without an afterburner. Eliminating the afterburner would save weight.

Engines for his VFX(AS) were theoretical, but cockpit visibility was not. Waller was a student of history, particularly air-to-air warfare. He did not need to reread history to know that the preponderance of lost fighter pilots were shot down by airplanes they never saw. He was another cantor of "first sight wins the fight."

In spite of his experience in the two-seat F-4 Phantom II community, Waller knew that side-by-side and tandem seating compromised pilot visibility. His VFX(AS) would have only a single seat.

To increase rearward visibility, he suggested that the seat should be inclined. (Boeing went on to suggest this concept in its proposal for the Lightweight Fighter Competition a year later.) This feature was also proposed and incorporated into the YF-16 and YF-17. The seat tilt was incorporated into the production F-16 but not the F-18.

Both Waller's and Bob Thompson's fighters had similar price tags. Their estimates differed on individual elements, but the concept was the same: keep it cheap so that the United States could have a superabundance of fighters. Contemporaneous experience demonstrated that the United States would need them. Although not all fighters, at the time Waller was writing the PTA, the United States had already lost more than 6,000 aircraft in Vietnam.

*The stoichiometric temperature is 3,700°. By comparison, the F100 engine has a turbine inlet temperature in the 2,500° range.

Lower cost implied less complexity and would contribute to the design goal of five maintenance man-hours per flight-hour. This was a big step from the F-4's 72 maintenance man-hours per flight-hour (MMH/FH). (It was also a long way from the 97 MMH/sortie that the F-14 experienced in fiscal year 1979.)

Commander Waller circulated his proposal just before he retired from the Navy in June 1970, but the lightweight VFX(AS) fighter never achieved support within the Navy. In fact, George Spangenberg said the PTA should be burned.[8]

The General Dynamics (Convair) report came out six months after Waller retired from the Navy.[9] It said that for the 500-mile escort mission, Convair could develop a 26,000-pound aircraft with a flyaway cost of $2.1 million. (This would equate to $7.1 million in FY 1990 dollars.) The report emphasized that the avionics and armament subsystem weight (radar and missiles) would be the inhibiting factor in the design size and cost. Incremental subsystem weight, the report said, had a four-to-one effect on the gross weight of the aircraft and affected the flyaway cost by $400 per pound in 1971 dollars. ($1,351 in 1990 dollars.) This seems consistent with Pierre Sprey's comments on page 81 above and World War II experience mentioned on page 65 above.

The Hinman-Wheaton-Adcock study concluded that a lightweight high-performance fighter could meet the 1980 time frame but would be dependent on such high technology as an engine with turbine inlet temperatures of 3,000 degrees, a compression ratio of 33, and a bypass ratio of 1.5 or lower. Within a little over a year, General Dynamics (Fort Worth division) would submit a design that would weigh almost 10,000 pounds less, use a less exotic engine (2,500 degrees of turbine inlet temperature), a lower overall pressure ratio of 26, and a bypass ratio of 0.72.

The airplane that Convair submitted to the Navy was remarkably similar to the YF-16 design that the Fort Worth division would submit a year later, except that Convair's design was a taildragger. However, the alternative Convair design used for performance comparisons was of the conventional tricycle design and had many of the design characteristics of the YF-16, which it visually resembled. At the time the Convair report came out, the Fort Worth division was looking at multiple configurations including twin-tailed models, visually different from the final YF-16.

General Dynamics took advantage of the separate fighter design teams at the two divisions and in 1971 sent a Convair team to Fort Worth. Cliff Adcock, Convair's Manager of Advanced Design, headed the group. His assistant was Ken Hinman, Convair's Project Engineer for Advanced Navy Fighters. Their assigned task was to challenge the Fort Worth YF-16 design configuration being developed by Harry Hillaker. This "red team" approach ensured that the Fort Worth designers had looked at all of the options, performed all of the trade-offs, and had prepared a winning Lightweight Fighter proposal. As a result of the challenges by Hinman and Adcock, the YF-16 went to a single tail.*

In spite of the quick death of the VFX(AS), Commander Waller's efforts were felt throughout the Air Force. At the end of June 1970, just before his retirement from the Navy, Waller met John Boyd and Everest Riccioni. Riccioni listened to Waller's discourse on the VFX(AS). He quickly went to his superiors and convinced them that the Navy—the internal threat—was working on a lightweight fighter. As a result, Waller's influence on the ultimate development of the Lightweight Fighter was significant. Since the Air Force suffered from the delusion that the Navy was developing a lightweight fighter, and since the Navy had imposed the last two aircraft on the Air Force—the F-4 and A-7—the Air Force allowed Riccioni greater latitude in developing an environment for the Lightweight Fighter. The Air Force was not responding with a lightweight fighter to any external threat, only to the possibility that the Navy might impose one on the Air Force. Waller deserves much of the credit for creating the lightweight fighter environment. He added to the internal dynamics that inspired the continued efforts by insurgent bureaucratic tacticians Boyd, Sprey, and Riccioni. Neither the efforts of Bob Thompson nor Ernie Waller were in vain. Their legacy would ultimately appear in the Lightweight Fighter competition, the results of which were ultimately imposed on the Navy.

*Any similarities between the Convair Model 23 and the designs at Fort Worth may be due to conversations between Ken Hinman and the father of the F-16 design, Harry Hillaker. Hinman and Hillaker discussed fighter design concepts when the two met on trips to Washington, D.C.

Chapter 6

The Air Force Lightweight Fighter

Insights come, but not on schedule
E. E. Riccioni

Boyd and Sprey continued to do their analysis on the benefits of lightweight fighters. Unfortunately, their efforts were not converted into action plans within the U.S. Air Force. In fact, quite the opposite. The Air Force perceived their continued efforts as a threat to the already sanctioned F-15 Eagle. The lightweight fighter concept might have died but for the willingness of the newest member of the Lightweight Fighter Mafia, Col. Everest E. Riccioni, USAF, to ignore the normal institutional mine field warning signs and create an environment that would allow continued lightweight fighter efforts.

When Riccioni arrived in Washington, D.C., in 1969, he was briefed by Boyd, Sprey, and Chuck Myers. Riccioni had a predisposition for small lightweight fighters because of his previous research on the value of smaller fighters. Their discussions, however, contradicted Riccioni's previous notion that lower cost meant lower performance. Once he was convinced, Riccioni began looking at designs even smaller than Sprey's.[1]

Riccioni reasoned that if the F-15's high-risk components failed to develop properly—such as the look-down radar, the 25-mm gun (which did fail to develop), the radar-guided missile, and the now-infamous infrared AIM-82 missile (which also failed to develop)—the U.S. Air Force would not be able to justify the F-15's escalating cost. Riccioni began developing a back-up.[2]

SOURCE: E. E. Riccioni
Col. Everest E. Riccioni, USAF, around the time of the Lightweight Fighter competition.

As 1970 approached, Riccioni learned of the AIAA meeting in St. Louis where Sprey was to give his F-XX paper. The combination of the community's increasing awareness (at least as Riccioni perceived it) and his own recognition of the work Boyd and Sprey had done, encouraged Riccioni to increase his tempo in the lightweight fighter area.

While Riccioni had more than enough incentive to develop an alternative to the F-15, he was further inspired by the possibility that the Navy was developing one.* Riccioni reasoned that if the Navy developed a lightweight fighter, and the F-14 was not funded by Congress, the Navy would adopt its emerging lightweight fighter design. If that happened, and the Air Force's F-15 failed to justify its

*Chuck Myers provided Riccioni with most of this information.

SOURCE: U.S. Air Force

Riccioni would become Commander of the Aeromechanics Division at the Air Force Flight Dynamics Laboratory, where he would push the conceptual limits of lightweight fighters. One of his projects involved an airborne aircraft carrier, a Boeing 747 transport stuffed with 10 microfighters each weighing less than 10,000 pounds.

increasing costs, Riccioni concluded that the Air Force would end up with another Navy aircraft.

Riccioni wrote a memorandum to his boss, Gen. Donovan Smith, but Smith was not available to act on the memo. Riccioni went to Smith's boss, Lt. Gen. Otto Glasser, Deputy Chief of Staff for Research and Development.* The memorandum, written March 29, 1970, contained the following message:

> MEMORANDUM FOR GENERAL SMITH
> SUBJECT: Air Superiority Aircraft
>
> 1. A long series of small incidental factors and rumors has led me to ask a critcial question - "Is the U.S. Navy studying or mounting an effort to develop a light weight air superiority aircraft?"
>
> 2. My initial research has revealed the following:
>
> a. The answer is YES! The U.S. Navy is studying the problem through funded studies with the San Diego Engineering Corporation, General Dynamics and possibly LTV.
>
> b. This (presently unknown) element of the Navy is working [on] the problem without the awareness or consonance of Admiral Connolly.
>
> c. The fighter weights under analysis range from 10,000# to 24,000#. A guess is that the 24,000# airframe would be wrapped around one engine destined for the F-14B providing a thrust to weight ratio at take-off comparable to our F-15—about 1.2:1.

*The Deputy Chief of Staff for Research and Development (DSCR&D) was the highest post for research and development at Headquarters Air Force. The position was normally held by a lieutenant general, with two subordinate divisions: one for tactical and the other for strategic systems. Maj. Gen. Donovan Smith was in charge of the tactical subdivision.

d. They are looking at clean ranges in the air superiority (dog fight) mission of 500 NMi but they will undoubtedly fall off this number.

3. This effort is fed by the desire of these elements of the Navy to have a hedge in case the Congress denies them their $13M stand-off weapon, the F-14A/B.

This is very good thinking, which analysis the Air Force was encouraged to do some year and a half ago.

4. This state of the Navy, and the results of the study could have a serious impact on the F-15 program. If the F-14 fails to get the production go-ahead from lack of funds in a cutback era, 1 $2M-$3M fighter proposal would seriously threaten the F-15's chances for survival. Even the International Freedom Fighter would see a perturbation.

5. Lt Col John R. Boyd and I are quietly pushing an informational probe deeper to get more information and more substantial, precise information.

[signed Everest E. Riccioni]

EVEREST E. RICCIONI

Col., USAF

AFRDQRT

When Otto Glasser saw the memo he scratched a note to Riccioni at the bottom: "Stay on this. I've long urged an a/c of this type—We could have scooped all—with it—Run with this."[3]

Riccioni's two immediate superiors, Cols. Jess Allen and Charles Watry, had ordered him not to talk to contractors about any fighter efforts that might compete with the F-15. But, with General Glasser's handwritten encouragement, Riccioni felt the restrictions lifted. Riccioni used the threat of the U.S. Navy—the internal threat—as an opportunity to steal more freedom.

Using the Navy, Riccioni created the master stroke for bringing life back to the lightweight fighter concept. From Riccioni's point of view it was as though Boyd and Sprey had wheeled in their last four years of work to a hospital emergency room. On the stretcher lay the lightweight fighter. Diagnosis: lightweight fighter cardiac arrest. Riccioni thought he was applying electroshock therapy with his first of a continuing series of memoranda.

At Boyd's suggestion, Riccioni nursed the lightweight fighter back to health through a study proposal that would validate many of the ideas all three of them were now advocating. The concept, if expressed openly, would have been disapproved because of the potential threat to the F-15, but they hid its true purpose behind the title, "Study to Validate the Integration of Advanced Energy-Maneuverability Theory with Trade-off Analysis." The title was a ruse. The study was nothing more than a continuation of Boyd's and Sprey's original work. Without Riccioni's making this study happen, Sprey and Boyd believe that the F-16 would not exist today.[4]

The study was actually an analysis of three lightweight fighter designs: a single-engine design based on the F100 engine; a single-engine design with the GE 1 engine; and a twin-engine design using two GE 1 engines. (The GE 1 engine went on to become the YJ101 and eventually the F404 that powers the F-18 today.)

Riccioni introduced an early version of his task-oriented mission requirements, which he developed with Boyd and Sprey's help. Riccioni looked for a design that would be lighter than 20,000 pounds and have minimum radar and avionics, no maneuvering requirement above Mach 1.6, a combat radius of 225 miles, and an acceleration time of 80 seconds from Mach 0.9 to 1.5 at 30,000 feet. To size the fuel and drag-lift trade-off, he demanded three 360-degree turns at Mach 0.8 and two turns at Mach 1.2.[5]

The nine months that Riccioni spent in the Pentagon had been eventful in other respects. During the second half of 1969 the U.S. Air Force had evaluated the three finalists in the F-15 competition. Richard Nixon's new Deputy Secretary of Defense, David Packard, instructed the U.S. Air Force, under a program called Project Focus, to look at every possible way to reduce the cost of the F-15. The range, maneuverability, and size of the F-15 were left intact, but the avionics and air-to-ground aspects were altered.[6]

The F-15 community interpreted the results as a reduction in capability. Concurrent with this perceived emasculation, Packard sent a letter requesting the Air Force to begin developing a "Free World Fighter." The request was a result of a Nixon foreign policy pronouncement made July 25, 1969, on Guam. "In cases involving other types of aggression we shall furnish military and economic assistance when requested and as appropriate. But we shall look to the nation directly threatened to assume the primary responsibility of providing the manpower for its defense."[7]

This message became known as the Nixon Doctrine and signaled a new emphasis on foreign arms sales. It provided an incentive for an increased tempo of fighter development. In October 1969 Secretary of Defense Laird wrote to the Chairman of the Senate Armed Services Committee asking for support of a new International Fighter Aircraft (IFA) program that would be inexpensive and simple so our foreign allies could operate it with minimum U.S. involvement.* [8]

*The U.S. Air Force designated the Military Assistance Program airplane the "Advanced International Fighter" in December 1969. Within a few months the name changed to "International Fighter Aircraft." No doubt the term "Advanced" worried some Air Force officers who feared that the term might imply a step beyond the F-15.

The Air Force issued eight Requests for Proposals (RFP) to eight companies on February 26, 1970. Four responded. The RFP stated that the IFA had to have a 100-mile radius of action for counter air, point intercept, and close-air-support capability. The IFA, which should be produced from existing hardware, would be selected by the end of 1970, with an initial operational capability (IOC) by 1974.* [9]

As the evaluation of the International Fighter Aircraft progressed, Nixon's regime again attacked the increasing cost of military weapon systems. In May, Secretary Packard issued a draft memorandum regarding his ideas on how the Department of Defense should acquire major weapon systems. In June, Dr. John Foster, the Director of Defense Research and Engineering (DDR&E), recommended sharing research and development costs with our allies. The following month, a Presidential Blue Ribbon Panel issued a report highly critical of the entire defense procurement procedures and, among other things, recommended more use of prototyping.

In July, perhaps as a reaction to this mounting criticism, the Air Force took another look at reducing costs on the F-15. It eliminated the TISEO, the backup radar-guided missile to the AIM-7F, and the heat-seeking AIM-82.† [10]

As the fall of 1970 approached, Riccioni received news, after a two-hour argument with General Chapman, that he would get the $149,000 he needed for his subrosa study. And there was other activity. The internal evaluations for the International Fighter Aircraft kept giving the same results. There were three Air Force evaluations and each time the Air Force selected the LTV V-1000. The V-1000 was an F-8 Crusader with some of the avionics taken out, and a more powerful General Electric J79 engine instead of the F-8's Pratt & Whitney J57.

Originally four entrants were in the IFA Competition: LTV's V-1000, McDonnell Douglas' F-4E(F), Northrop's F-5E, and Lockheed's CL-1200. Lockheed dropped out of the competition because it was unwilling to admit to an early miscalclation in an aeronautical equation that, if believed, would have required its airplane design to be chained to the runway to keep it from flying while the engine was off. Although the CL-1200 briefing for the final evaluation was

*Riccioni wrote the rules for the International Fighter Competition at the request of Maj. Robert Taylor, the PEM for the program.

†The AIM-82 system definition phase began with the Request for Proposal (RFP) release on February 9, 1970. Six companies responded on March 9, 1970. The Air Force designated a 90-day competitive design period.

given to the Air Force Chief of Staff General Ryan, he did not ask any questions. He knew of the Lockheed withdrawal.

Perhaps in an attempt to steer clear of the F-5, which more closely approximated the attributes that Sprey claimed for the F-XX in his March 1970 speech, the Air Force kept selecting the V-1000 design. In spite of the Air Force's selection, Secretary of the Air Force Seamans overruled the decision. Seamans acknowledged that the V-1000 design had the best performance and showed up better on the TAC Avenger computer model—the same computer model that developed the 955-1 exchange ratio for the F-15/MIG-21 simulation. Nevertheless, he chose the F-5E on other grounds. He felt that maintainability, cost, and the ability of foreign customers to cope with the aircraft were factors that he must consider.[11]

The F-5E was announced as the winner on November 20, 1970. Now the Air Force, or more precisely, the F-15 union within the Air Force, was more threatened than ever. Its V-1000 decision had been rebuffed for an aircraft more in keeping with the lightweight fighter mafia concept. It should have come as no surprise to the Lightweight Fighter Mafia that the momentum against them would increase.

Riccioni, a quixotic fighter pilot, was as naive about Pentagon politics as he was dedicated to increasing aircraft numbers and reducing their cost. Assured that his study was funded, he became braver in his discussions about his personal views on fighter aircraft procurement.

He became vocal at the highest levels. At a social function in December 1970, Gen. John C. Myer, then Vice Chief of Staff, approached Riccioni and asked him to explain his theories on fighter procurement. Riccioni expressed his concerns about the F-15: the expense, the possible failures of some of the collateral programs (the AIM-82, TISEO, etc.), and the need for increased numbers. Riccioni sensed Myer's disenchantment.

The following Monday Myer called in several generals, including Lt. Gen. Otto Glasser, Riccioni's ultimate superior. Myer told Glasser that he wanted Riccioni out of the Pentagon immediately.[12]

December 1970 was an eventful month for other reasons. The Grumman F-14 Tomcat made its first flight, but more important to the gestation of the F-18, the Presidential Blue Ribbon Panel recommended prototyping the AX—the Attack Experimental—the competition that led to a flyoff between the Northrop A-9 and the Fairchild A-10.* To anyone who could read the signs, prototyping was on its way back.

*Pierre Sprey is considered by many to be the father of the AX and the A-10.

SOURCE: Lockheed Aircraft Co.
Kelly Johnson stands next to a variation of the F-104 which was catalytic in beginning the competition that led to the Lightweight Fighters, the YF-16 and YF-17.

Kelly Johnson, the celebrated designer of Lockheed's F-80, F-104, U-2, and SR-71, read the tea leaves and saw this as the opportunity to get back into the fighter design business. He was still smarting from the sophomoric mistakes his staff had made during the International Fighter Aircraft Competition that caused Lockheed to withdraw from the competition.

Johnson left Lockheed (Burbank) on December 14, 1970, to visit Air Force Secretary Robert Seamans. The next day, Johnson had a 30-minute meeting with Seamans and Brig. Gen. Bill Smith. He briefly reviewed the CL-1200-2 and outlined his idea for a joint contribution plan. Lockheed would build the CL-1200-2 fighter in a year; the trainer would follow two months later. Johnson proposed borrowing two F-104GS from the Dutch, two TF30 engines from Pratt & Whitney, and getting commitments from additional vendors so that his proposal would cost the Air Force nothing. Lockheed, he told Seamans, would invest $10 million of its own money.

Seamans told Johnson that he was interested, favored prototypes, and saw a definite need for an aircraft between the International Fighter Aircraft and the F-15. However, Seamans said, he could not give Lockheed a blank check. Instead, he wanted Johnson to come back with a firm proposal after the first of the year.

Johnson told Seamans that the CL-1200 could fly within a year, which meant that it could fly chase on the F-15 during the F-15's

SOURCE: Lockheed Aircraft Co.
The Lockheed CL-1200-2 that Kelly Johnson proposed to Air Force Secretary Seamans.

first flight. Seamans emphasized that he did not want the CL-1200 to compete with the F-15. Thinking that the photograph Johnson showed them was real, Seamans and General Smith ran down the hall to ask Johnson if they could have a picture of the CL-1200. "When he saw this damn picture that we'd made, he thought we'd rolled out the airplane. It was a mock up. We just rolled it outside and took a picture."[13]

In an attempt to make the CL-1200 less threatening, Secretary Seamans suggested giving the design the designation X-27 to indicate its "experimental" status. Experimental could not have been further from the truth.*

Johnson opened 1971 with a proposal to build two CL-1200s for $30 million. Johnson's proposal began a process that has reserved for him the right to share the title "Father of the Lightweight Fighter." His proposal was catalytic in its effect because it started the process that resulted in the many unsolicited proposals that ultimately led to the Lightweight Fighter Program, without which the F-18 would not exist.

One might reasonably ask, why did Kelly Johnson believe that the Air Force would give him a sole source contract to develop a lightweight fighter under the then evolving prototype renaissance? One answer might be Johnson's experience. Both the U-2 and the SR-71 were sole source contracts developed by the celebrated "Skunk Works." When asked the question directly, Johnson said that Lock-

*Designation are often changed to alter perceptions. For example, the Northrop Tigershark began life as the F-5G, but because of the resistance in the marketplace to "another F-5," Northrop changed the airplane's name to the F-20, with the hope that it would appear to be more than a modern version of the F-5E.

The X-27 was, in essence, an F-104 with a large wing and more fuel. However, the Air Force thought that by giving it the "X" designation, (meaning that it was strictly an experimental aircraft) the F-104 would not evolve into another F-104 lightweight fighter.

The airplane that the Air Force repeatedly told Congress was an experimental aircraft, the YF-16 ("Y" stands for prototype), would end up in the inventory.

heed could build it "cheaper and faster than anybody. . . . They [the other aerospace companies] didn't have the Skunk Works."[14]

The Lockheed proposal generated an overflow of unsolicited fighter proposals.[15] Northrop followed Lockheed on January 31; Boeing submitted its design in February, and LTV in June. As these unsolicited prototype proposals began invading the Pentagon, the Director of Defense Research & Engineering, Dr. John Foster, wrote a memorandum to Secretary Packard suggesting that the Department of Defense take an interest in these various proposals. Packard responded within four days. On February 16 he approved Foster's idea with the following annotation:

> APPROVED: I think this could be a very useful approach. I am not sure we have to establish a specific requirement—there will always be a need for a better aircraft, especially if less costly. It is important that each program have these features.
>
> 1. Each should stand on its own feet—two, at least, aircraft should be obtained. Only the price shall be firm.
>
> 2. All specifications shall be open.
>
> 3. A plan for fly-off testing will be required.
>
> 4. It must be clear that there is no commitment to go ahead with a further program.
>
> 5. At the same time we will lose benefit of this approach if, after a fly-off, we go back to some other competition for full development and production. In other words, the fly-off testing is the source selection if we decide to go ahead.[16]

March roared in like a lion for Riccioni. The Air Force notified him that he was to give up his position as Chief of Development, Plans and Analysis (RDQL). The Air Force was assigning him instead to Korea. The reassignment was the result of General Myer's reaction to Riccioni's work. Prior to his leaving, however, the Air Force "stashed" him. Stashing is a military term applied to someone who is given no job or a job with no responsibility. The irony was that by being stashed Riccioni had nothing to do between March and his departure in September except concentrate on the lightweight fighter project. This is an example of the Riccioni Corollory to the Pentagon Paradox: The results are inversely proportional to the intent.*

The result of Riccioni's efforts, with the ongoing aid of Boyd and Sprey, was a presentation called "The Falcon Brief." There is some poetic justice in the name of Riccioni's brief. Not only is Riccioni the proximate cause for the F-16's existence, but the name he used in his briefing was later incorporated into the F-16's name, Fighting

*Glasser believes to this day that Riccioni left immediately after General Myer ordered him out of the Pentagon. (Statement made by General Glasser to the author.)

Falcon. The "Fighting" portion was added only to avoid trademark infringements with the Dassault Fan Jet Falcon.[17]

Shortly after Riccioni gained his new freedom, he and Boyd made a trip to several of the aerospace companies that had expressed an interest in the emerging new prototype program, an interest that had been piqued by Riccioni's work statement for his clandestine study contract. Boyd and Riccioni visited Boeing, Lockheed, Northrop, LTV, and General Dynamics.

One evening over a beer, Riccioni mildly challenged Boyd as to why they had bothered to make the trip. Riccioni was convinced that General Dynamics and Northrop had both substantiated the Mafia's theories, and could fulfill the requirements. "Boyd looked at me like a teacher at an eager student," Riccioni recalls, "and said, " 'Rich, the General's pointer can fall on any of the designs. If we want a good lightweight fighter, we need to be sure everyone submits a good design.' "[18]

The trip was worthwhile. Boyd and Riccioni were particularly impressed with the work that Bud Nelson, and Ray Utterstrom were doing at Boeing. Boyd and Riccioni were concerned that upper management at General Dynamics was not seriously supporting the efforts of Harry Hillaker, whom Boyd, Sprey, and Riccioni credit with the development and design of the F-16. General Dynamics's new chairman, David Lewis, had recently arrived from McDonnell Douglas. Lewis, they surmised, may still have believed that the F-15 was the proper solution. After their trip, Boyd and Riccioni felt that General Dynamics would take Harry Hillaker's efforts more seriously.

Back from his trip, unfettered by duties, reassured by more data from Northrop, General Dynamics, and Boeing, Riccioni became more vocal with his emerging Falcon briefing. He justified the Falcon for two reasons: the external threat and the internal threat. The external threat was the increasing numbers of Russian and Warsaw Pact aircraft. The internal threat was the Navy's lightweight fighter studies. To the Air Force, the internal threat was more imminent.

By March, Riccioni had determined that San Diego Engineering Corporation (SANDAIRE), LTV, Lockheed, North American Rockwell, and China Lake were working on lightweight fighter studies. The most threatening study was Cdr. Ernie Waller's VFX (AS) design done at General Dynamics-Convair (San Diego).

Riccioni was frustrated by the Air Force's lack of response to the increasing number of Soviet threat aircraft. But he knew what would strike fear in the heart of any high-ranking Air Force officer, so he included excerpts from some of his clandestinely acquired Navy lightweight fighter studies. He quoted from the David Taylor Model Basin fighter study in his "Falcon Brief":

> To apply the capabilities represented by the preliminary design to fill projected gaps in the Navy VF inventory in a manner which complements-does not compete with the acquisition and fleet introduction of the F-14.
>
> To obtain a preliminary definition on a prototype program which would lead to ultimate fleet acquisition of a light weight day fighter.
>
> With the current and expected trend in defense budgets, dollar limitations would seem to preclude the replacement of the (declining) F-8 and A-4 fleet with the F-14. The buy of a new, less sophisticated, less expensive fighter with attack capabilities would complement the F-14, and would provide sufficient numbers of advanced capability aircraft under the expected budget constraints.

To back up these comments, Riccioni quoted from the Navy's brief. The comments from this brief, lightweight fighter advocates maintain, have virtually all come true. Riccioni extracted the SLF brief in this order:

1. Maneuvering performance is the key to fighter aircraft effectiveness.
2. Twin place and twin engines have not enabled the F-4 to counter MIGs better than the F-8.
3. All aspect radar guided missiles may not be the answer.
4. Can an expensive fighter out fight an enemy which has a 3 or 4 to one numerical advantage?
5. Can we accept the inherent unreliability of the complex/expensive aircraft?
6. Simple planes will cost less so more can be purchased for the same amount of funds.
7. Simplicity makes it more maintainable so more sorties and flight hours can be flown.
8. Question- How will large fighters acquire visual on the enemy first?
9. Question- When will swing wing be used in any dogfight?
10. A. [with added capability], weight and size and complexity increase
    B. This requires:
       More maintenance men
       More maintenance equipment/space
       Bigger ground handling equipment
       Two-man crew
       Bigger engines
       More fuel
    C. Results in aircraft which costs more, flies less, and does the mission poorly.

At this point during his briefing, Riccioni knew he had his audience's attention. He then went into details on his "Falcon Brief," which had acquired the title, "Advanced Fighter Aircraft Study—Avenging Falcons (AVFFX)." The briefing, which Riccioni usually gave using an arrow as a pointer, was the result of the Lightweight Fighter Mafia's surreptitiously funded study, which looked at three aircraft: a single-engine aircraft with a large engine, a single-engine aircraft with a smaller engine, and a twin-engine aircraft with two of these same smaller engines. The large engine was the F100, and the small engines were the GE1 series, which evolved into the YF101 and ultimately the F404 in the F-18.

Riccioni advocated an aircraft that carried a subsystem that was the "minimum essential equipment [that] will provide the greatest achievements in performance, reliability, utilization rates, and least cost." He recommended a ranging radar with the capability for only a "snap shot."* All of these designs would carry two Sidewinder missiles, with provisions for four, as well as 500 pounds of 20mm ammunition. Riccioni also had provisions in the design for three hardpoints for external tanks, bombs, or two single-megaton bombs. His design had no engine blade containment—that presupposed that the engine was unreliable. Riccioni not only put in a requirement for engine reliability, he also demanded engine stability at 50,000 feet and at air speeds as slow as 100 knots. To save weight he eliminated nose wheel steering, powered canopy, tail hooks, drag chutes, foam and self-sealing fuel tanks, and automated navigation aids other than the horizontal situation indicator.

To substantiate his conclusions, Riccioni used two designs in his Avenging Falcon briefing: General Dynamics design, FW71-274-VG1369 (25 Feb. 1971) and Northrop design N314-2, a variant of the P-530 proposal that Northrop had displayed through Europe for the preceding half decade.

Riccioni showed that with equal investment and equal operating costs, the Air Force could own 72—an entire wing of Falcons—compared to a squadron of 24 of the more sophisticated aircraft, which in Riccioni's mind was either the F-4 or F-15. In addition, the Falcons could collectively carry one-third more ordnance. This was an example of putting the power into the Air Force as a collective unit rather than attempting to make each unit as powerful as possible.

To Riccioni, the ultimate issue was not how many more aircraft the Air Force could own, but how many more aircraft the Air Force could pit against the enemy on any given day. For this analysis,

*A ranging radar is used for measuring the distance from the aircraft with a gun or heat-seeking missile for the purpose of determining if the target is within the firing envelope. A ranging radar does not require a large frontal area and is not as complicated to design or maintain.

Riccioni used the maximum daily steady-state sortie rates. (He distinguished steady-state from sortie surge rates because of the lack of sustenance in the latter.)* He generated a chart (see table 6-1) that illustrates the relative number of aircraft the Air Force could buy and impose on the enemy for equal dollars.

Riccioni also predicted that the maintenance man-hours per flight hour for the more sophisticated aircraft would exceed the F100-powered version of the Falcon, the Øalkoh-2 in Table 6-2, which was almost identical to today's F-16.

Table 6-1
Aircraft Available for Equal Dollars

	Number for Equal Cost*	Steady-State Sortie Rate	Enemy Sees Per Day	Percent Increase over F-15
F–15	500	1.3†	650	N/A
F–4E	875	1.5	1,312	201%
Øalkoh‡	1625	2.74	387	675%

SOURCE: Falcon Brief

*Based on the F–15 costing $7 million for 500 in FY70 dollars.

†1977 testimony showed F–15s at Langley AFB averaging 0.75 steady state sortie rates, with predictions to 1.0

‡Russian for Falcon

Riccioni's Falcon briefing illustrated the issue that Boyd and Sprey before him, and others after him, would argue for: with simplicity the Air Force could achieve numbers. Riccioni admitted that the Falcon would have an inferior range-payload per aircraft.† He also admitted that the aircraft would not be an "all-weather" aircraft, not have the look-down, shoot-down capability that the AIM-7F-equipped F-15 was alleged to have. He even said that the Falcon would have inferior range, a quality that those in the F-15 union would later try to use to kill the Lightweight Fighter program. They would discover, with true Pentagon Paradox panache, what Riccioni already knew—that quite the opposite was true. The F-16 would turn out to be the longest-range fighter in the U. S. inventory.

"A contradiction to preparedness for war is to possess forces which one does not risk for fear of their loss," Riccioni commented (sounding much like Leroy Grumman in his memo discussing small carriers

Table 6-2
Projected and Actual Utilization Rate

	1971	1979 25 FH/Mo.	1979 40 FH/Mo.*
F–15	36.1 MMH/FH	34.4 MMH/FH	33.0 MMH/FH
Øalkoh-2	5.3 MMH/FH	14.1 MMH/FH	18.1 MMH/FH

SOURCE: Falcon Brief

*The 1979 data come from F. C. Spinney, "Defense Facts of Life," and Congressional Sources

*Riccioni would characterize the evolution in the Gulf War as a surge rate.

†Payload is the weight of the variables over which the pilot or mission planner has control, such as weight of fuel, ordnance, missiles, bullets, etc.

on page 68 above) as he briefed on the aircraft the United States had already lost in the Vietnam war: 2,215 fixed wing and 2,101 helicopters, for a total of 4,316.*[19] Riccioni increased his attacks on the conventional Air Force wisdom. He said that the maximum speed of a dogfight was less important than the maximum maneuverability; that small size, which he called stealth, was vital; and that the U.S. Air Force, contrary to institutional thinking, did not have a fixed force mandate. The only limitation to the number of aircraft was the budget.

Table 6-3
Example of Riccioni and Lightweight Fighter Mafia Analysis

	Aircraft for = $	x	OR Rate	=	Available Aircraft	x	Sorties For Equal $	=	Aircraft Enemy Sees	x	Missiles On Aircraft	=	Missiles Enemy Sees
F-14D	1.0		0.7		0.7		1		0.7		8		5.6
F-18	2.5		0.8		2.0		2		4.0		8		32.2
F-16	7.0		0.85		5.9		3		17.8		4		71.3

SOURCE: E. E. Riccioni

The ultimate purpose of a fighter aircraft is to be deployed against the enemy. Because money is always an issue for U.S. tactical aviation, Riccioni maintained that for equal dollars, an air wing commander could throw more lightweight fighters into the air because he could afford to buy more, initially, as well as afford to generate more sorties. The hidden benefit is the ability to train more.

Forces within the Office of the Secretary of Defense, somewhat adversarial to the U.S. Air Force, began to recognize the benefits of some of the Lightweight Fighter Mafia's concepts. Allan Simon, Assistant Director for Air Warfare, and a member of Dr. Foster's staff, began implementing Foster's procurement ideas. Simon drafted a plan entitled "Fighter/Attack Aircraft Prototype Study," which became known as the Simon Study. The study, which amounted to 20 briefing charts, proposed looking at the possible candidates for prototyping. It supplemented Packard's annotation.[20] Simon presented a simple analogy for the prototype concept. At the beginning of the study, he started growing a mustache. When asked why, Simon said that his mustache was like the prototype program: it did not cost much to do, he could do it in a short period of time, he could try it out on his wife to see if she liked it, and if it did not work out he could shave it off. "If there were a requirement for my mustache," said Simon, "it would have been staffed all over the Pentagon, gone through several committees, and might have taken several years before there was an agreement on the size and shape of it."[21]

*As early as 1967 the U.S. Air Force had lost 730 aircraft. They lost 270 F-4s and 326 F-105s. Using the cost of F-4s in 1970 dollars, that amounts to $1.08 billion. If the U.S. had had attrition rates like those with the F-15, the U.S. would have been able to replace only 154 F-15s with the $1.08 billion.

At one point during the study, General Furgerson heard about the Simon Study and suggested that John Boyd investigate to see if Boyd should become involved. Boyd approached Simon but Simon suggested that Boyd continue doing the good technical work on the Lightweight Fighters. Simon told Boyd that the Lightweight Fighter Mafia had spent years trying to get a new fighter by attacking the existing F-15. Now, said Simon, he was going to help get a new fighter by using positive comments on the benefits of prototyping, and take only six weeks to do it. From Simon's prospective, the Lightweight Fighter Mafia was the technical part; he and his associates were the marketing department.[22]

During the beginning of March 1971, the Air Force asked Kelly Johnson to modify his proposal so it would be less threatening to the F-15. The modified proposal was less menacing to the F-15, both in substance and in form: the Air Force officially applied the designation X-27. The price had increased to $35 million and the Air Force would have to purchase its own F-104 as it did not want to have any obligation to a foreign government.

On March 16 Northrop submitted a proposal that modified its January 31 proposal. Northrop proposed to build two Air Research Vehicles (P-530-4S), which now had a specified engine, the GE15/J1A5. Northrop eliminated its previous contingent requirement for a foreign commitment and said it would provide the two vehicles for $82 million including engines.[23] Northrop learned that no positive response could be given because of fiscal limitations, but the Air Force would continue to study the proposal.

Riccioni, meanwhile, continued to exert pressure on Air Force upper management. He played upon the apprehensions of senior Air Force officers—specifically Lt. Gen. Otto Glasser—that the Navy could impose another aircraft on the Air Force. On April 6, 1971, Riccioni sent Glasser a memorandum summarizing the naval activity that had taken place during the past year since his first memorandum of March 29, 1970. The memorandum is reproduced here in its entirety.

AIR FORCE EYES ONLY*

6 Apr 1971

MEMORANDUM FOR GENERAL GLASSER
SUBJECT: US Navy Progress with the Complementary Fighter Program
General Smith suggested that I write this memorandum to you. Its

*Riccioni's classification "Air Force Eyes Only" supports retired Air Force Maj. Gen. Bob Scurlock's position that the only purpose of the Pentagon is to serve as an arena for each service to fight for its market share of the military budget.

purpose is to review Navy actions, Navy gaming strategy, and to form some conclusions and recommendations.

The following is a review of the past USN efforts and known involvement with light weight fighters.

1. In March of 1970 I asked a key question, "Is the USN seriously working the Light Weight Fighter (LWF) concept?" The answer was a solid yes. In my memorandum to General Smith which was given you in his absence, the following information was presented:

a. A smooth draft of the USN Proposed Technical Approach (PTA) on the Advanced Air Superiority Aircraft System - VFX(AS) existed and a copy was "procured."

b. Knowledge of four contractors working the problem: San Diego Engineering Corp., Lockheed, North American Rockwell, and (possibly) LTV was obtained.

c. A China Lake effort was being made to prototype a 5,000 lb takeoff gross weight fighter using a 5,000 lb. thrust engine. The British Folland Gnat aircraft and the fabrication methods developed by Dr. Wyndecker (Dentist) were the inspiration for this.

2. By June 1970, sources had provided me copies of the NAR report and the final NAVAIR Report 72-133, their PTA. The NAR report has a complete definition of their fighter designs.

3. In July, I had received from Air Force and civilian contacts a rough draft copy of the formal Navy light weight fighter briefing, the formal Navy light weight fighter briefing, and a NASA (USN inspired) fighter analysis.

4. In December, information was provided that Convair was studying USN LWFS.

5. In January 1971, it was established that NASC had funded the David Taylor Model Basin to do a configuration search for small fighters and to cooperate with NASA, especially on close-coupled canards.

6. In February 1971, the Navy presented their Advanced Deck Launched Interceptor (ADLI) concepts and their Beach Head Air Defense (BHAD) fighter designs to an Air-to-Air tactics Workshop at W-P AFB. The BHAD designs are advanced, light weight, very high performance aircraft designed by McDonnell-Douglas and General Dynamics.

7. In March 1971, it was established that the China Lake team was studying a grown version of the 5,000 lb. aircraft. The team, recently augmented by two aircraft designers, is now studying an aircraft weighting 8,500 lbs at 60% fuel, with two missiles and guns. The uninstalled thrust to combat weight is 1.6; the combat wing-loading is 55 lbs per sq ft. The uninstalled thrust to takeoff weight is 1.5. More important was the evidence of Navy actions on the VFX(AS) concept. Both Convair and LTV are working the concept developed in the PTA. The aircraft using projected 1980 technology has the following performance parameters:

Gross /weight at take-off	26,000. lbs
Escort mission radius (no tanks)	500. NM
Uninstalled sea level static thrust	40,000. lbs
Thrust to weight at take-off	1.5
Wing area	368. sq ft
Wing-loading at take-off	70. lbs/sq ft

The USN seems to be meeting its schedule for the implementation of the plan for the VFX(AS).

The following is one view of the formal, overt USN plan or strategy for F-14 acquisition. First a few facts. The USN is willing to concede that the F-15 considerably exceeds the F-14's airbattle capability. This was expressed in their May 1970 PTA. However, they know of the AFSC/FTD threat analysis which indicates that the 1980 threat's maneuverability will exceed that of both the F-14B and the F-15. Their position will "prove" that only the stand-off capability (stand-off is a very ephemeral tactic for aircraft) of the Phoenix equipped F-14B will serve. Once the F-14B is solidly in the procurement process they will announce the VFX(AS) to the detriment of the F-15. Their intended result—an F-14B for both services and a Navy lightweight fighter for the Other Fighter Roles (OFR).

A much more subtle, confusing, and dangerous set of possibilities known to be in some USN minds is the following. The Navy is hiding a large cost increment of the F-14B in other line items; e.g., they may be hiding as much as $2.5M cost per aircraft on the F-14B avionics package. The Navy contract with Grumman is a bad one as has been known for some time. The cost increase combined with the low fighting potential and the bad stall and spin characteristics make the F-14B very unattractive to Admiral Zumwalt. The Admiral admitted the cost and stability problem to Congress. The seaborne Navy must ingest the overruns. Admiral Zumwalt may not be as concerned about Grumman's future as the airborne Navy. The USN having learned of the advanced 1980 threat analysis by AFSC/FTD is also generating their own advanced threat carefully tailored to be inferior to the VFX(AS) and superior to the F-15. The USN is aware of the existence of the AVFFX, KOH[*] aircraft, though they undoubtedly have seen none of the output data. They know of the CL-1200-2G and the P-530-4 aircraft designs. With these facts, it is not inconceivable that the USN will cancel or cut back the F-14B buy, limit its cost overrun, raise the F-15's engine cost, and convert to their VFX(AS). In no case does the USN plan to permit the F-15 to survive in a political environment dedicated to reduced budgets and commonal approaches.

The USN is well down the road planning their next aircraft. If the Air Force fails to do its planning for the future, the Navy is currently doing it for us. We are presently behind in this effort. Only your encouragement of back burner efforts on fighter aircraft has permitted the Air Force to be where it is today. With this encouragement, some studies are underway, and an absolutely dominant (winning) capability for fighter design has been created in the recent past months. Fighter contractors have embraced these methods because they understand the power and capability implicit in the approach. One cannot achieve or maintain dominance unless more effort is laid on to surpass the Navy lead. Failure to do so will mean the gradual leak of our winning methods to the USN. Today the *action* and *plan* lie in the Navy; the insight and "the method" lie in a very limited group in the Air Force. Given a little time to permit the contractors to employ the new design approach, some spectacular outputs will be achieved.

*Riccioni's Falcon aircraft

Thus I feel compelled to ask your permission to present a revised "Austere High Performance Fighter" briefing to the AF Vice Chief of Staff that he may be fully aware of the problems, and aware of Air Force efforts to define the complimentary fighter force. The briefing should be ready by 20 April.

EVEREST E. RICCIONI, Colonel, USAF
Special Assistant to the Director,
D/Operational Requirements and
Development Plan, DCS/R&D[24]

Riccioni's warnings were ratified by the upcoming testimony that Glasser would give to the House Survey and Investigation committee, which had previously implied that both services should use the F-14. The Air Force's basic premise was that the F-14 was a defensive aircraft for fleet air defense; the F-15 was an offensive aircraft that needed to be able to maneuver and did not possess the multi-shot Phoenix missile. To summarize in a manner that was certain to gain attention, Glasser reminded Congress that commonality had been tried before and had not worked.[25]

Within the Air Force interest in the X-27 had generated enough support to proceed with it. Lockheed was so sure it had won the sole source contract to produce the X-27 that some of the Lockheed marketeers had a celebration at 1789, a posh Washington, D.C., restaurant.[26] Lockheed's enthusiasm clouded its perception: it did not get the sole source contract because Packard felt it would be too political.[27] (Packard was correct. Toward the end of May, Senator Proxmire accused DOD of trying to bail out Lockheed with a sole source contract for the X-27.)[28]

In the beginning of May, Air Force Secretary Seamans sent David Packard a memorandum entitled "Aircraft Prototyping Plan." In it, Seamans outlined a plan to select prototyping candidates. The Air Force had been involved in the Simon Study and was no doubt keeping current on the status of any new prototype program. Knowing there would be a competition for funds if a prototype program was approved, the Air Force wanted to be prepared to justify why it should get its fair share. In his memorandum on May 7, Seamans outlined his concepts for selecting prototypes, with the commitment that the program would be ready by the end of July. The next day, Packard approved the idea and stated, "We ought to get one or two programs going in FY 72."[29]

The news of Packard's decision spread quickly. Any question of Packard's intent to prototype aircraft was eliminated with the release of his draft of the new DOD Directive 5000.1, "Acquisition of Major Defense Systems," which was the codification of his memo of May 1970. The new DOD directive stated in part: "Advanced technology effort includes prototyping, preferably using small, efficient design teams and a minimum amount of documentation. The objective is to obtain significant advances in technology at minimum cost."[30]

As if to give congressional consonance to the idea of a prototype program, a group called "Members of Congress for Peace Through Law" issued a report entitled "Report on the F-14 and F-15 Tactical Fighters." This group of almost 100 senators and congressmen was most critical of the F-15 and F-14. Their report (which critized the decreasing number of tactical aircraft) added momentum to the Packard prototype activity. The report said, in part:

As the following chart indicates, our total active fighter and attack forces will have dropped from about 5000 aircraft in 1970 to a projected 4020 by the close of FY 1972:

Active Fighter and Attack Aircraft (1970-72)

	Fiscal Year 1970	Fiscal Year 1971	Fiscal Year 1972
Total aircraft	5,000	4,600	4,020
Total wings	39	36	35
Navy wings	13	12	11
Air Force wings	23	21	21
Marine Corps wings	3	3	3

No detailed reason or rationale for this reduction has been provided by the Department of Defense in terms of expected military contingencies . . . .

The only apparent reason for the current reduction in total tactical air forces is the imminent modernization of these forces. This modernization is projected to be accomplished primarily by the planned introduction of the Navy's new F-14 fleet air defense general purpose fighter.

We recognize the need for modernization and improvement of our tactical air force to meet expanded capabilities on the part of potential enemies. However, both the F-14 and F-15 will cost several times more than the aircraft they are scheduled to replace (primarily the F-4 Phantom). As far was we are able to determine, no lower-cost options for tactical air force modernization are currently under active consideration.*

In our view, exclusive pursuit of high-cost options may require us in the future either to increase our expenditures on tactical air forces beyond desired or necessary budget restraints, or to purchase only an insufficient number of new aircraft in order to stay within such budgetary restraints. To avoid this dilemma, we favor keeping low cost options for tactical air force modernization open as long as possible. A number of our specific recommendations point to such low-cost options.[31]

*Sprey had thoroughly briefed Senator Proxmire's military legislative assistant on many of these issues.

Figure 6-1
TacAir Aircraft Inventory Declines Over Time

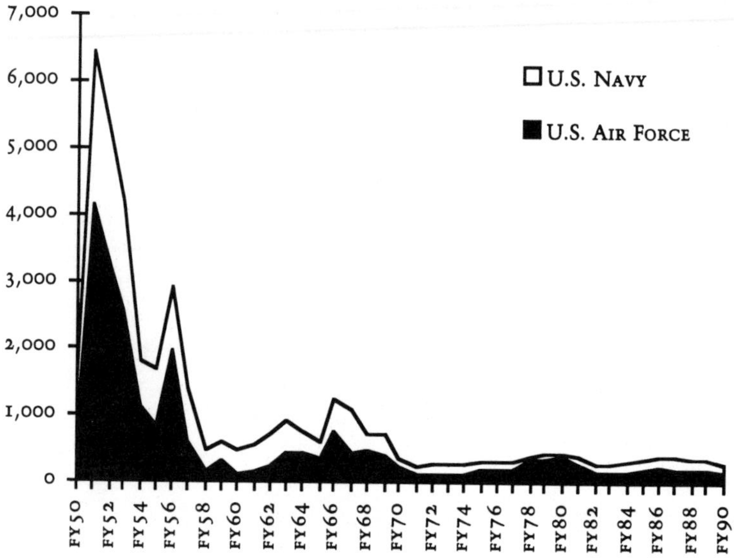

SOURCE: Department of Defense Data
The total TacAir inventory fell as the unit price for aircraft rose.

After this group presented its rationale and prophetic remarks, it made several recommendations. The group recommended killing the F-14A program as well as the Phoenix missile. It suggested, as a possible alternative, a flyoff between the F-14B, (an F-14A with the F401 engine) with the F-4M, a version of the Phantom the United States sold to England. The F-4M had a more powerful engine than the TF30 engine in the F-14A.

The report stated that there really was no justification for the Phoenix missile. If the threat was as great as the Navy stated, then even if the Phoenix missile performed exactly as advertised, there was no way to defend against massed raids by the air-to-surface missiles from the Russian bombers.*

In an approach-withdrawal manner, the report recommended continuing the funding of the F-15 but at the same time recommended

*This report was verified to some extent by an interview with Capt. F. S. "Tooter" Teague, USN, commanding officer, USS *Kitty Hawk*. In an interview with the author Teague admitted that if the Russians wanted to take out the carrier they could. When asked how the Navy could justify the F-14 on that basis, he stated that the F-14S were necessary for the fighter escort mission.

developing a smaller version of the F-15, or "an entirely new light fighter of the FX-X type."

The month of May found Lt. Gen. Otto Glasser in a congressional hearing defending the Air Force position against the House Survey & Investigation Committee. His testimony temporarily quelled the attack on the F-15. Near the end of the month, the Air Force started the prototype group initiated by Air Force Secretary Seamans and approved by Packard. The purpose of the prototype group was to recommend candidates to be prototyped, as well as to provide supporting justification. At the working level, the head of the group was Col. Lyle Cameron; his assistant was the ever-present Col. John Boyd.[32]

The justification for the prototype group's study was that it would pick candidates for development of anticipated military requirements, especially those projects that would require high technology. Out of this study came the streamlined process of the small system program office (SPO) as well as the reduced paperwork for all aspects of prototyping, starting with the request for proposal (RFP) and the response.

In June three separate proposals were submitted for lightweight prototypes: the V-1100 model by LTV, the P-610 by Northrop, and the Model 908-618 from Boeing.

Northrop submitted its P-610 proposal without the enthusiasm that had surrounded the P-530 designs. The P-610 design was a single-engine design based on the F-15's F100 engine. Although the airplane was approximately 7,000 pounds lighter with only a 3,000-pound reduction in thrust, Northrop felt the NATO countries wanted a twin-engine aircraft. But the DOD prototype aircraft program was favoring aircraft lighter than the P-530 series that Northrop had been working on for over six years and that now weighed in at 25,000 to 27,000 pounds. Northrop felt that to reduce the size of the P-530 down to a 20,000 pound aircraft from the design weight of 25,000 pounds would be a formidable job.

Furthermore, it was not a simple matter to substitute a single-engine design for a twin-engine one. Northrop had spent time developing the interface between the engine inlet on the twin-engine design, the P-530, and the General Electric GE-15 engine, the engine used in it. The two manufacturers had spent years working together in an attempt to make the combination of inlet-engine of their twin-engine design trouble free.[33] Northrop had not devoted a similar effort to interfacing the F100 engine to the P-610 single-engine design.

On 15 June, Boeing submitted its unsolicited proposal to Col.

John G. Paulisick, Deputy for Development Planning (ASD-XR) at the Aeronautical Systems Division at Wright-Patterson Air Force Base. A copy of the proposal went to Brig. Gen. Kenneth R. Chapman and Lt. Gen. Otto Glasser. The Boeing proposal was for a 16,000-pound single-engine airplane built around the Pratt & Whitney F100. The 240-foot wing area gave the design a 66.6 pound per square foot wing loading and a 1.5-to-1 thrust to weight ratio at takeoff. The internal fuel weight was 4,300 pounds and gave the Boeing model 908-618-2 a healthy fuel fraction of 0.268.

The Navy was aware of all the activity on prototyping. The Commander of the Naval Air Systems Command issued a notice, on June 22 referencing Packard's memorandum of May 28, 1970. The purpose of the notice was to establish an approach to the prototyping program that would eventually result from the "fly-before-buy" program instituted by Packard.[34]

Perhaps another reason for the interest in the prototyping program was the increasing interest by the Navy, personified by the Chief of Naval Operations Admiral Zumwalt, in the Sea Control Ship, a new name for an old concept: the Navy could buy greater numbers of smaller, simpler ships, which would make the Navy ubiquitous.

The Sea Control Ship (SCS) would be in the 10,000- to 12,000-ton displacement range with 12 to 15 airplanes. The SCS was not designed to compete with the attack carriers, but to complement them as the escort, or jeep, carriers (CVE) did during World War II. The proposed cost ratio of Sea Control Ships to the attack carrier was about seven to one. In World War II the number of escort carriers was approximately seven to five.

The basic mission of the Sea Control Ship was not power projection, but, as the name implied, control of the sea. It was for this mission that some Navy personnel were thinking of prototyping two types of aircraft: the antisubmarine and fighter-attack mission.[35]

As an answer to the Sea Control Ship requirement, the Navy issued a Specific Operational Requirement (SOR) on July 23, 1971, for a Vertical and Short Take-off and Landing (V/STOL) Multi-Missile on Aircraft referred to as the VX. The purpose of the VX was to provide intercept, surface strike, and surveillance capability for the Sea Control Ships.*

*The concept of the Sea Control Ship was not new. Many Navy officers believe that the distributed threat required greater dispersion of fighter/attack aircraft. The Sea Control Ship could be used against many countries that would not require the full force of an attack carrier task force. For example, in 1981, 35 countries had no air force of any significance and another 35 had an air force with two squadrons or less. (Statement made by Ernie Waller to the author.) The National Geographic Society

Figure 6-2
Fuel Fractions and the Breguet Range Equation

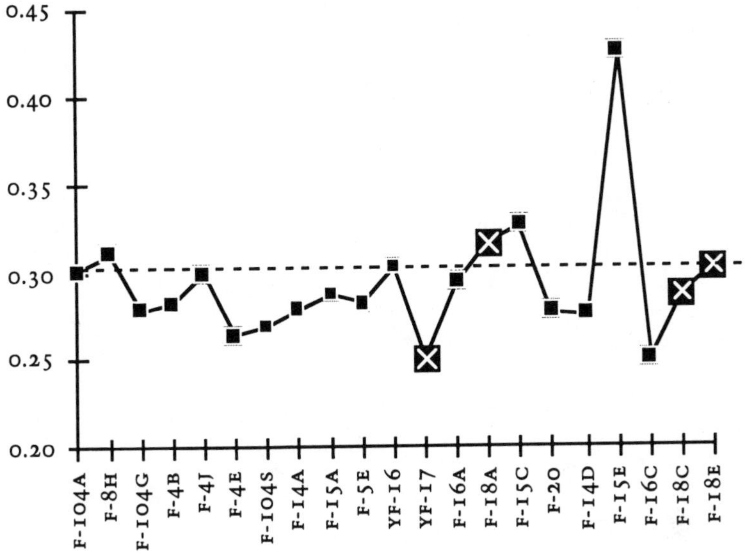

SOURCE: U.S. Air Force and U.S.Navy data via Northrop

The fuel fraction is a large factor in determining aircraft range. It is a ratio of the weight of the fuel to the gross weight of the aircraft. Specifically, range is computed by the Breguet range equation, which is (speed/specific fuel consumption [SFC]) multiplied by lift divided by drag (L/D) multiplied by some additional factors. The formula for determining an aircraft's range is in rough approximation, the fuel fraction times fuel consumption. (The larger the fuel fraction, the longer the range). As a point of comparison, the fuel fractions for current jet fighters are shown above (fig. 6-2). Note how the Navy increased the fuel fraction of the YF-17 when it created the F-18A. Then note also that the fule fraction went down with the F-18C. The reduction in fuel fraction is a direct result in the increased weight of the aircraft since the fuel load remained consistent. The F-18E was an attempt, among other things, to get the fuel fraction back to the original F-18A.

The third Lightweight Fighter proposal was submitted by LTV on June 28. Its model V-1100 was also built around the F100 engine; however, the gross takeoff weight was 19,000 pounds. The design was similar in appearance to both the Boeing entry and the General Dynamics design, but it had an extendible canard for reduced trim drag during supersonic maneuvering. The proposal, which included a three-month flight test, would cost the government over $29.5 million.[36]

The Lightweight Fighter Mafia was excited by the data flowing into the Air Force. The new designs and the refinements of existing

claims that 20 new countries have been added to their Atlas since 1990.

SOURCE: Boeing
Boeing's Mach 2.8 entry into the Sea Control Ship Fighter Competition.

studies confirmed the earlier work that Boyd and Sprey had begun. The initial work on a lower-weight FX, as well as Sprey's F-XX, appeared to be conservative.

In an attempt to help the Navy and Army prepare their requests for prototype funds, Packard invited members of these other two services to hear the Air Force Prototype Study Group briefing. Notable among those present was Robert Frosch, Assistant Secretary of the Navy for Research and Development. Frosch was a strong-willed individual, and to some of those who worked with him he *was* Research and Development in the Navy at that time. Frosch reigned as an Assistant Naval Secretary from 1966 until 1973: he was in a secure and entrenched position.

When the Air Force had finished its briefing, Packard turned to Frosch and asked him what prototype programs the Navy was working on. Frosch indicated that the Navy had some things in the works. Simon did not believe him and contradicted Frosch to his face; he told Packard that in fact the Navy had nothing in preparation. Frosch responded by storming out of the meeting. "Frosch was strong-willed and simply did not like being told what to do," said Simon.[37]

Frosch's perspective is somewhat different. He felt that the entire prototype business was some group's approach to a magical solution at procurement. He was also skeptical about getting the money. "I knew damn well we wouldn't get money to do anything. We'd get an Air Force plane shoved down our throat. I had been through the tail end of the F-111."

Frosch saw the entire approach as a threat to the F-14 and treated it accordingly. Any benefits that might accrue from increasing the numbers was illusory to Frosch because, he believed, it simply would not happen.

> The military frequently does not trust anybody. They get promised greater numbers of aircraft if they will accept a simpler design. However, they know from experience that two things happen: first the airplane doesn't stay simple; secondly they still do not get very many of them anyway.
>
> I had lived through a number of years of discussions of lightweight fighters. What I suddenly saw was another attempt at commonality. In effect, it ended up a mess: the Navy now has two airplanes at the same price—only one of them is more capable that the other.

Since the Navy's requirement for the Phoenix missile was the counter to the lightweight fighter argument, it raised the obvious question: Why did the Navy believe that the Phoenix missile would produce better results than the Sparrow? The Sparrow, Dr. Frosch was reminded, had promised P_Ks in the 0.7-0.8 range, but in actual combat delivered only 0.10. "For one thing, testing of the Phoenix was better, and 10 percent wasn't bad. . . I can think of some circumstances where 10 percent is pretty good."[38]

The Deputy Chief of Naval Operation for Air Warfare, V. Adm. Tom Connolly, had testified prior to the Packard meeting that the Navy had no interest in a lightweight day fighter.[39] The resolution of the Members of Congress for Peace Through Law had no doubt stiffened naval resistance to any system that threatened the school solution, as Dr. Frosch indicated the prototype group did.

The Air Force prototype selection group, which Dr. Frosch left, selected several possible candidates: an advanced STOL transport, a low radar cross-section vehicle, a large tanker aircraft, a remotely piloted vehicle (RPV), and a lightweight fighter. The Air Force's prototype presentation did not rank the programs in any order, but of the group, the Lightweight Fighter was clearly the most likely candidate. Packard was aware of the visibility of the Lightweight Fighter and, therefore, was partial to it. He understood that to develop interest in the Air Force, he needed a highly visible program.[40]

Some within the Navy, however, took action on the evolving prototype program. As a result of the June 22 letter from Naval Air Systems Command as well as the U.S. Air Force prototype briefing, the U.S. Navy was developing a posture to capture the opportunities as they became available. After the Air Force briefing, on August 6, the Navy sent a letter to DDR&E outlining their position on the prototyping programs. From the end of June through August the Navy had worked on the requirements and details to implement a new prototype program.[41]

The major input came on August 11, 1971, when David Packard was the featured speaker at a Joint Department of Defense and National Security Industrial Association Symposium on "Major Defense Systems Acquisition." Packard was joined by Dr. Foster, DDR&E, and other DOD officials. The following day Adm. Jackson D. Arnold, USN, Chief of Naval Materiel, and Gen. George S. Brown, USAF, Commander of the Air Force Systems Command, spoke on service implementation.[42]

Secretary Packard extolled the benefits of the prototype concept. He stated that there was a strong possibility that DOD would fund a new fighter program under the prototype program.[43]

Packard outlined the intent and purpose of prototyping with the following frame of reference:

- Experimental, not pre-production prototypes (will precede, not be part of, engineering development)
- Will normally contain technical uncertainty
- Not the basis for system procurement (because of prototype source selection)
- Will support a future military need
- Will reduce uncertainties in future development (technical, operational, cost, schedule)
- Will offer lower cost alternatives (relative to those programmed)
- Will possess reasonable chance of success
- Will be of low cost relative to the program cost[44]

These comments by Packard prompted Sen. Stuart Symington (the Senator from Missouri, where the F-15 was built) to ask about the status of the F-15 program, as well as the status of the prototype program. Packard responded in a letter that the F-15 program was running smoothly. It must have occurred to Symington to ask why, if the F-15 was running smoothly, was there a need for a new fighter. Packard replied:

> A lightweight fighter would not be competitive with the F-15 for many reasons: it would have *much less range*, it would not have the Sparrow missile capability, it would not have the radar surveillance capability or an intricate avionics system. If the light-weight fighter prototype achieves its objective, the Air Force will have the option of

complementing the F-15 *force with light-weight, inexpensive fighters.*[45] (Emphasis added.)

As the emphasized portions of the statement above indicate, Packard always intended to procure an aircraft that would increase the force size.[46] This was Riccioni's stated purpose too. But, actually, he wanted to replace the F-15.[47]

Packard released a Program Decision Memorandum (PDM) on August 25, 1971, in which he approved the Air Force plans and approved the funds for the lightweight fighter and the AMST. The money for the lightweight fighter was for "an *operationally* suitable, lightweight fighter." (Emphasis added.)

The "operationally suitable" language is significant because the Air Force would spend institutional energy claiming that the Lightweight Fighter was *not* intended to be an *operational* aircraft but only an *experimental* prototype. To the Air Force the Lightweight Fighter was an "X-designated" aircraft but to the fighter mafia, it was definitely a "YF." The Navy was directed "to monitor the program to encourage carrier compatibility," a strong indication that Packard intended from the beginning to procure another fighter for the Air Force as well as for the Navy.[48] Shortly afterward, on August 27, the Air Force Prototype office was created at Wright-Patterson AFB.

Secretary Packard went before the Senate Armed Services committee on September 9 to ask for $67.5 million for fiscal year 1972 for the prototyping program. The $67.5 million budget figure was allocated among the services, with $24 million intended for the Air Force, $20 million for the Navy, and $23.5 million for the Army.[49]

As a result of Packard's request for the new prototype programs, Senator McIntyre asked why the prototype system could not be imposed on current or ongoing programs. Packard responded that he wanted visibility on the program, not just for the public, but also for the Services. "To be perfectly frank with you, it takes a long time to get the people in the services who have been doing a job one way for a long time to change their ways."[50]

Packard was blunt with the Armed Services Committee: "Competition in brochuremanship is not part of the prototype program. The prototype program will provide for competition in real performance and actual hardware and it will require the competing teams to demonstrate the superiority of their product rather than the superiority of their salesmanship."[51]

Packard's sentiments were not new. Writing in the May 1970 issue of the *Naval Institute Proceedings*, Capt. C. O. Holmquist said: "One possible way to improve our aircraft industrial competence is through the construction of competitive prototypes for a new design and an "fly-off" competition to select the winner. . . With our present system, too much money is spent on paper studies that are largely worthless."[52]

At this same Senate Armed Services Committee hearing, the Navy testified on its approach to the prototype program. Basically, the Navy was looking at three areas: antisubmarine warfare sensors, weaponization of ships, and V/STOL for Sea Control Ships. The V/STOL would include both fixed-wing aircraft and the Pegasus 15 advanced Harrier. All of these concepts were to be used on the Sea Control Ships as extensions of the ships' weapons. It was through this application that the ships' expenses could be kept down.[53]

One advocate of lightweight fighters for both the Navy and the Air Force was Sen. William Proxmire. On September 23 Proxmire gave a lengthy analysis on the Senate floor of the requirements for an air superiority fighter. The logic of his comments was similar to Pierre Sprey's. Proxmire congratulated the Air Force for proceeding on the development of a supplemental fighter to the F-15. He saw this as a necessary element to increase the numbers of the force structure. Taking upon himself the role of Naval Aviation's lightweight fighter advocate, Proxmire also became its prophet:

> If the Navy failed to undertake a prototype program to meet its own requirements, the Air Force prototypes could prove eminently adaptable to Navy use. . . .
>
> Our single most important need is to start work now on a new light fighter development program for the Navy. . . .
>
> We could simply wait and hand the Navy an Air Force developed plane but it would be better if we did not. A Navy program could give special emphasis to such things as spotting factor constraints and the rigors of carrier landings.[54]

The Navy has been critical of Senator Proxmire because of his position on the F-14 Tomcat. However, had the Navy heeded Proxmire's warning, the Navy could have developed its own fighter instead of modifying an Air Force design.

Proxmire later took up the Navy cause again, this time indirectly. Secretary Packard's attempt to get supplemental money for the prototype programs was not proceeding smoothly. Critics felt that if DOD and the military services believed that the prototyping program was a good idea, why not impose it on existing programs, or use existing money and apply it to the prototype program. Packard's request for additional money for the prototype program was interpreted by some members of Congress as a lack of military enthusiasm. This was a valid interpretation because the prototype program represented to both the Navy and the Air Force the potential threat to their de rigueur fighters, the F-14 and F-15.

Between September 9 when Packard testified and November 23, the $67.5-million request was knocked down to $34 million by the Senate-House Conference Committee. It was eliminated all together by the Senate Appropriations Committee. These reductions took place during the congressional criticism of the services' lack of support for the prototype program. One voice again championing the prototype was Senator Proxmire.

> On balance, I agree with the critical appraisal these committees have made of the Packard prototype program. . . .
>
> But I must object to one unfortunate side effect of the Senate Committee's action on the Packard package—its deletion from the bill of all funds specifically earmarked for the new Air Force lightweight fighter prototype program. Unlike some of the projects in the Packard package, this lightweight fighter is not a low priority program; in fact, it would provide for one of the highest priority procurement needs we face at the present time.[55]

Fortunately for the Lightweight Fighter, Proxmire's oratory was persuasive and the funds for its development remained.

The Office of the Secretary of Defense and the Air Force finished the necessary paperwork to complete the cycle so that if the prototype program, particularly the Lightweight Fighter program, was approved, the Air Force would be ready to proceed.

In December 1971 the Senate Armed Services Committee held special hearings on Weapons Systems Acquisition Process. One of their witnesses was Pierre Sprey. Sprey had left the Department of Defense in 1970, but as a dedicated defense devotee, he had remained as active as ever.

The hearings were held to determine whether the prototype process was the proper method for developing new aircraft. Sprey's testimony, along with others', was important input for the congressional inquiry. This hearing is historically significant. It summarizes—through Sprey's testimony and the series of questions raised by Senator Cannon—both sides of the quantity-quality, simplicity-sophistication issue.

In Sprey's testimony and his written statement, he compared the cost of tanks and aircraft. In World War II the two were built for roughly the same cost. By 1970 the tank had increased by a factor of 10 in real dollars; the airplane had increased by a factor of 100. The United States was now using an aircraft that cost 10 times as much as the tank it would try to destroy.

The individual components of the aircraft had gone up at an even greater rate: avionics increased 1,000 times, propulsion 50 times, and airframe 40 times. Sprey stated that none of these increases were necessary from either a tactical or technological perspective.

The quantum increase in avionics was totally out of line with the experience of warfare. The cost could be drastically reduced, contended Sprey, by

> leaving out equipment not absolutely essential to the mission of shooting down enemy aircraft and by applying the impressively reliable low cost technology of commercial and private aircraft electronics. The first approach has been applied with considerable success by the Soviets themselves in the MIG-21 as well as the Mirage III which is, after all, today's most successful MIG killer. These aircraft do not carry the performance-decreasing and expense complement of radar missile fire control, computers, jammers, navigation systems, etc., which we have come to view as standard for fighters.[56]

While Sprey questioned the tactical need for the expensive avionics, he went on to compare the price of identical equipment used in military and commercial aircraft. He cited general aviation transponders that cost $500 compared to similar units in military aircraft that cost $10,000 to $12,000. "Commercial customers," he added, "will not accept a radar that fails more than once every 800 hours . . . [whereas] the military has to live with radars that fail between every 5 and 10 hours. Our most complex operational system today, operational fighter radar, has a mean time between failure in one unit of 47 minutes. . . ."[57]

The propulsion price increase was, Sprey said, a function of attempts at technological increases with no concern for price. Increases in the higher pressure, temperature, and thrust-to-weight ratios had a corresponding decrease in readiness and engine life. According to Sprey, a more austere engine would be capable of better performance.

The airframe's development was the third major area responsible for increased cost in the development of fighter design. Seventy-five percent of the increase in the airframe cost, according to Sprey, was due to the accommodation of avionics. The implication was that since avionics of the complex weapons system yielded no advantage, they in fact created a disadvantage. Increasing the size of the aircraft made it easier to see and decreased the performance by increasing the weight and drag.

Another wasted cost in fighter design was the price paid for increasing top speeds to Mach 2. Sprey said that there were jumps in the cost of flying over 400 knots, then again at Mach 1 and at Mach 2. Mach 2, he said, was not tactically relevant because of the fuel consumed at that speed.*

The defense budget, Sprey said, had increased only 15 percent in real dollars between the Korean War and 1970. The cost of fighters, however, had increased at a rate significantly greater than 15 percent, impacting the number of aircraft available. In as much as the largest cost increase in fighter components was in avionics, and the largest increase in avionics was to serve the more complex weapons, Sprey investigated the increasing cost of munitions and their effectiveness to see if the increase in munitions cost was commensurate with their effectiveness. What he found was the Sprey Corollory to the Pentagon Paradox: The effectiveness of a weapons systems is inversely proportional to its cost.

The cost of firing a .50-calibre gun in Korea was roughly $20; the 1970-cost of firing a Sidewinder was $7,000 and for firing a Sparrow $40,000. Sprey did not give the P_K of the various air-to-air munitions during his testimony but he stated elsewhere that they were approximately 0.4 to 0.5 in World War II, 0.3 in Korea, and 0.2 for the Sidewinder and .1 for the Sparrow in Vietnam.[58]

> I think this contrary to the general assumption that if you reduce the cost of the weapon [and] you increase the numbers you can afford to buy, you would lose quality in some sense; . . . the studies I performed at this time convinced me that this assumption is simply not warranted. There are ways through clever design, through emphasizing simplicity in single missions . . . of decreasing costs, increasing simplicity and, at the same time, increasing effectiveness.[59]

Sprey also discussed the problem of force levels and training. More complicated aircraft prevent sortie rates necessary for adequate training; the total number of aircraft that the budget will allow are not high enough to handle the threat. The reason for the limited numbers, Sprey stated, was a carryover from the fixed force concept that was instituted by McNamara. The organizational tendency is ingrained to gravitate toward more complex weapons.

> Organizations perceive, with considerable justification, that their budgets depend on "selling" new weapons programs and that more costly and complex weapons receive more funding from both the Administration and the Congress than programs based on large numbers of simpler weapons. This trend was considerably accelerated, though un-

*While working on the FX design to determine the relevancy of Mach 2, John Boyd questioned a roomful of pilots. He asked the group of high-time pilots how much flight time they had at Mach 2, twice the speed of sound. Very few had any. One pilot with several thousand hours of jet flight time had five minutes at Mach 2, but he qualified the statement by adding that he had been a test pilot whose duties required that he fly at Mach 2. Current experience on the F-15 substantiates Boyd's concerns.

intentionally, by Secretary McNamara's fixed force structure where military missions were programmed by numbers of carriers, wings and divisions rather than by dollars. Under this system, it was clearly in the self-interest of each Service to maximize the multi-mission capability, complexity and cost of each major force unit. Today's major development programs are the logical result of the motivations created during the 1960-1967 era. Unfortunately, I do not believe there has been any substantial change in these basic motivating factors since the change of Administration; the Services have yet to be shown a single example of one program being allowed to acquire the larger numbers of weapons as a result of decreased unit cost.[60]

Senator Cannon, the Chairman of the Senate Armed Services Subcommittee on Tactical Air, challenged Sprey's conclusions. He questioned Sprey's analysis, citing the Navy's criticism at the time Sprey first came out with the F-XX study. Cannon quoted from the Navy document: "In common with past papers by the same author, this study contains many fallacious assumptions, half truths, distortions, and erroneous extrapolations. Unsubstantiated opinions are presented as facts. Any rebuttals give the appearance of arguments against the rudimentary virtues of simplicity, high performance and low cost."[61]

After citing from the Navy's argumentum ad hominem, authored by George Spangenberg, Cannon went on to remind Sprey that the Navy claimed an airplane would have to weigh 50,000 pounds to have the performance that Sprey claimed was possible. Finally, in what he thought would be the coup de grace, Cannon cited the withdrawal of the F-104s from combat in Vietnam after two were shot down while on an escort mission. The F-104 was withdrawn, according to Cannon,

(1) because it has short legs; (2) because it cannot carry the long range, sophisticated weaponry associated with the intercept mission of the F-14 or F-15; and (3) because of the necessity to keep it lightweight, you can't have the sophisticated avionics that are necessary to permit it to exist in a hostile defense environment such as in Central Europe, where you have a very complicated SAM system and defenses of this sort, which the pilot of the aircraft can't even detect without electronic warning systems unless he happens to see it visually.[62]

Cannon reiterated that a fighter needs to be able to carry electronic counter measures (ECM) equipment such as active jammers and passive radar homing. He recited again the Navy claim that the F-XX aircraft would weigh at least 50,000 pounds and said that the currently proposed Lightweight Fighter, according to Air Force analysis, (but not Lightweight Fighter Mafia analysis), would be a short-range fighter of about 200 miles.* If it were to be used on an escort mission,

*The belief that the Lightweight Fighter was a short-legged aircraft was set in

according to Cannon, it would need a range of 400 to 500 miles.

Sprey interrupted to say that either the F-XX or the Lightweight Fighter could, under any combat circumstances in the air-to-air mission, go further than the F-4. He also added that all of his analysis of the F-XX included the sophisticated equipment that Senator Cannon said was necessary for a fighter.

Senator Cannon closed by inserting into the record some remarks he had made earlier on the Senate floor. They are included here because they represent the capstone argument against the concept of the Lightweight Fighter that is still heard today. In fact, McDonnell Douglas marketing representatives will cite Cannon's remarks as a source for understanding why no lightweight fighter is a valid concept.

LIGHTWEIGHT FIGHTERS NO PANACEA

Mr. President, there has been some discussion during our recent debates on the Authorization Bill of the supposed advantages of developing a "small, cheap, effective" lightweight fighter as a substitute for the F-14. Today, I would like to address some of the pros and cons of the lightweight fighter concept as a potential operational weapons system. I believe the facts will show that the lightweight fighter is no panacea and most certainly is not the total answer to our country's fighter needs of the future.

As a point of departure, I would like to describe what kind of an airplane currently is envisioned under the term "lightweight fighter," and then I will give some examples of the operational problem areas that such a fighter might have. In closing, I will give a specific example of operating experience with one of our own lightweight fighters.

Deputy Secretary of Defense Packard briefed the Senate Armed Services Committee earlier this month on his new approach to development through the use of prototyping. One of the particular programs that is being considered as a candidate for this prototyping by the Air Force is what they call a lightweight fighter. The tentative plans for this particular program would be for two aircraft companies to build two prototypes a piece, and the resulting test aircraft could be used to evaluate advanced technology of high performance airplanes.

Conceptually, the class of airplane currently envisioned has a takeoff weight of about 20,000 pounds. It will have a single engine, using the engine developed for the F-15. This will give it a thrust to weight ratio of better than one at takeoff (which means the plane will have outstanding acceleration and rate of climb). It also will have a relatively low wing loading (which means it will have good turning maneuverability for dogfighting). Proponents of building operational airplanes of this class point out, correctly, that they would have the kind of performance capability needed for good close-range dogfight airplane.

In many ways, this design concept for a lightweight fighter that I

motion by DepSecDef Packard when he said, in his letter to Senator Symington, that the lightweight fighter would have less range than the F-15.

have just described can be considered to be the Air Force F-15 cut in half. Let me expand on what I mean. The F-15 has a takeoff weight of about 40,000 pounds, double that of the lightweight fighter. The F-15 has two engines. The F-15 has a relatively low wing loading. Thus the thrust to weight ratio of the F-15 and also the wing loading are about the same as the proposed lightweight fighter. The performance of the two airplanes in dogfights should be the same.

If this is true, advocates of the smaller airplane argue, then why not buy the lightweight fighter since presumably it only will cost half as much? (Half the weight and one engine versus two certainly indicates half the cost.) The answer to that question lies in the comparative range and useful payload that the two classes of airplanes will have.

The armament that the smaller airplane can carry is limited to an internal gun plus two Sidewinder close-in dogfight missiles. This is a fact of life dictated by the very limited dimensional size of the airplane. The lightweight airplane cannot carry a search radar with any appreciable range coverage to warn it of approaching enemy aircraft. It certainly cannot carry an avionics system with a look-down and shoot-down capability against fighter targets masked by the clutter of the ground on conventional radar scopes. Also, the small-sized fighter does not have the payload capacity of ECM electronic jammers that experience in Southeast Asia has proven is mandatory for survival over enemy held airspace defended by SAM missiles. Finally, the small, lightweight fighter cannot carry the radar and electronics needed for radar-guided longer-range missiles such as our Sparrow or Phoenix. These missiles provide an all-weather launch capability and also have a much larger firing envelope than a Sidewinder, particularly from the rear during a tail chase.

It is the requirement for these operational capabilities mentioned above, long range search radar, look-down and shoot-down, longer range missiles, all-weather guidance, and effective electronic countermeasures, that gives an F-14 or an F-15 an overwhelming operational advantage over a "lightweight fighter."

Experience in Southeast Asia has confirmed the need for these requirements. I would like to cite one particular example of what happened over there when we did deploy a lightweight fighter, in this case the F-104. It should be noted first, that the F-104 almost perfectly matches the description of the proposed lightweight fighter. It is about the same weight, has very limited range, carries only two Sidewinders and a gun, no search or fire control radar, but has outstanding acceleration and rate of climb. In 1966, a squadron of F-104s was sent to Southeast Asia with the mission of escorting F-105s on their strikes into the hot areas of Route Package 6 in North Vietnam. The first problem encountered was their lack of range. The small F-104 was so range-limited that the Sidewinder missiles had to be removed and replaced with extra external fuel tanks, in addition to the two normally carried. The F-104 ventured over the North armed with a Gatling gun and a small and useless radar set. The results were neutral; the F-104s didn't shoot down any MiGs and the MiGs didn't get any 104s.

There was one deficiency of the F-104, however, in that it did not carry any radar warning or electronic countermeasures (ECM) gear. In one day, two of the F-104s were shot down by SAMs and the planes were immediately withdrawn from the North and never sent back again. The conclusion reached was that they just did not have the capabilities as compared with the F-4s that were needed to be an effective air superiority fighter in the conditions existing over North Vietnam. The F-4, with a superior load of offensive and defensive equipments and considerably longer range and endurance, was a far superior fighter weapons system.

I do not want to imply from these remarks that I am opposed to the lightweight fighter prototype program because I am not. There is a school of thought among fighter pilots and among force planners that we should examine the possibility of complementing the capabilities of our F-14 and F-15 forces with larger numbers of smaller, cheaper, dogfighters of this lightweight fighter class. These aircraft could be a specific counter to the swarms of MiG-21s that the Communist countries possess. While not being suitable for the longer range missions into the high threat defensive areas, these less capable aircraft could offset the disparity in numbers with which we are faced in the forward battle areas. Such a concept certainly is worthy of operational test and evaluation and the light fighter prototype program could be used to serve this purpose. I would feel that this would be a worthwhile objective for this prototype program.

But on the other hand, I do not believe that we should consider this lightweight fighter to be a panacea. There is no simple, cheap easy solution to our need for the world's best fighter force. The Navy F-14 and Air Force F-15, while expensive, are the best that we can produce to meet modern fighter requirements and to counter the sophisticated Russian threat exhibited by Foxbat and Flagon. The sophisticated threat requires a sophisticated defense. The Sparrow and Phoenix missile systems are the only possible counter to the Foxbat, for example. The Sidewinder and gun cannot even be brought within firing range of a Foxbat airplane flying at Mach 3 at 70,000 feet. Better capabilities definitely are needed.

The lightweight fighter concept, if it should prove viable, will be useful in a complementary role. I believe that we would be foolish to scrap our F-14 and F-15 aircraft with its limited capabilities.[63]

Senator Cannon's diatribe against the Lightweight Fighter concept was the last major attempt to kill it before the funding was released. His remarks were also inaccurate.

He criticized the F-104 for being short legged, yet the F-104 had the same range in the air-to-air role as the F-4 Phantom. He criticized the F-104 for not being able to carry the radar-guided Sparrow missile, which according to Cannon would increase the envelope, particularly during a tail chase. The Vietnam experience showed just the opposite. Airplanes equipped with the Sparrow had to close in to visually identify the enemy, then back off to fire the Sparrow. One could say that this was an increased envelope geographically, but it was a decreased envelope tactically. Nevertheless, as events in the 1977 AIMVAL/ACEVAL evolution were to show, the F-5E could, under some circumstances in the tail chase environment, outrun the Sparrow.

Cannon next criticized the F-104 because it could not carry radar of appreciable range to warn the pilot of approaching aircraft. Yet, as experience in Vietnam showed, almost all contacts were visual—less than 3 percent were with their on-board radar.

The biggest criticism that Cannon levied against the F-104 was that the Air Force took it out of service because it could not cope in the exotic electronic environment: it was too small to carry adequate ECM equipment and too short-legged to escort other aircraft. As a result of these limitations, Cannon said, the F-104 was taken out of service after two of them were shot down.

History tells a different story. Col. Don Madonna, a former F-104 pilot in Vietnam and former Commander of both the Air Force Test Pilot School and the Air Force Aggressor Squadron, describes the events that led to the shooting down of the two F-104s. Note that, contrary to Cannon's statement that the F-104s were shot down by surface-to-air missiles (SAMS), the F-104s were downed by guns.

> The F-104s were placed in an outrigger position, that is on the outside of the F-105s, at least while they could stay with them. On the particular mission in which the F-104 got shot down, the F-105s were on a strike mission with the 104s escorting. The 105s were flying below 1,000 feet going about 800 knots. The F-104s couldn't keep up with their speed. When the triple A started firing at the F-105s it missed because they were traveling so fast, but the F-104s flew right into it. Electronic countermeasures would have been irrelevant at this altitude.
>
> None of the aircraft we had in the inventory could keep up with the F-105s in speed or range. Certainly the F-4 couldn't. If we had invested just 10 percent of the improvements in the F-104 that were invested in the F-4, the F-104 would have been the superior aircraft. The CL-1200 would have been magnificent.[64]

More to the point, however, by November 1967 the U.S. Air Force alone had lost 730 airplanes on missions to North Vietnam.[65] This hardly precipitated the removal of the various types shot down.

Cannon's remarks about defeating a MiG-25 Foxbat raised one of the biggest questions of the 1971 debates: How can a lightweight fighter kill the MiG-25 Foxbat? This question was submitted for the record by Senator Symington, the Senator from Missouri, where the F-15 was manufactured. The twin-tails and Mach 2.5 requirement was put into the F-15 design as a direct result of the perceived MiG-25 Foxbat threat.

> *Question 7. On costs of air-to-air munitions, you compare a very short and limited day munition against a medium (or short range) day*

> *or night all-weather munition. Can the cheap munition kill a Foxbat? Can it be used in a non-visual encounter?*
>
> Answer. If we chose to build an aircraft optimized to the Foxbat's high speed, high altitude regime, then a variety of weapons would serve to shoot the Foxbat down. If such an aircraft had high speed maneuvering superiority adequate to gain firing position, it could use a gun effectively. Another interesting alternative would be a Sidewinder or other simple IR missile modified for high altitude and preferably with extended range (bigger rocket motor only); this would have head-on and shoot down capabilities simply because any aircraft going Mach 3 is hot enough to make a superb infrared target. Since there are no clouds or non-visual conditions to speak of at these high altitudes, a specialized Foxbat killer would only be incurring performance losses and vulnerability increases by using an all-weather radar missile.
>
> On the other hand, trying to kill a Foxbat from within the normal tactical flight envelope of an F-4, F-14, F-15 or an F-XX using an IR or radar missile under either visual or non-visual conditions is probably close to operationally impossible because of (a) the very limited head-on zone into which one must position the firing aircraft and (b) the very short time available to accomplish identification, lock-on and firing procedures at the high closing speeds involved.*[66]

Finally, Sprey tried to put to rest the issue of why the F-XX concept or the Lightweight Fighter did not have a radar-guided missile.

> *Question 5. Isn't there a realistic minimum of avionics required in a modern fighter; and if so, what is this minimum in terms of functions?*
>
> Answer. The realistic minimum of avionics required for a modern fighter depends on two things: the number of different missions one wishes to perform and the electronics equipment available that will actually work in combat. Assuming that (a) our country needs an air superiority fighter, and (b) that a single purpose air-to-air fighter is necessarily better in its design mission than a multi-purpose one, the minimum avionics for such a fighter can be easily defined based on recent U.S. and Israeli combat experience. These minimum functions are the following:
>
> a. Weapons.—the gun is still the single most effective air-to-air weapon in terms of kills per firing attempt; therefore, it is central to air-to-air combat. The only existing missile that comes within a factor of two of the gun's lethality is the simple passive IR Sidewinder. It adds the capability of defeating a straight high speed diving attempt to disengage from gun range although its capability against maneuvering targets is poor. These are the only two weapons essential to a modern fighter. It should be possible to build an equally simple new IR missile to improve on the Sidewinder in combat effectiveness. Despite continuous development programs to develop an effective all-weather missile since 1948, we have an unbroken record of failures in this area, culminating in the

*The U.S. Air Force had the YF-12, an aircraft whose operational design points were similar to those of the MIG-25. While both the YF-12 and the YF-16/YF-17 were designated as prototypes with the "Y" designations, the U.S. Air Force fought to procure the YF-12 and eliminate the YF-16. Both attempts failed.

disappointingly poor performance of the Sparrow D and E models in North Vietnam. There is reason to believe that these failures are inherent in the concept of an all-weather radar missile due to the unreliability, noise and clutter problems, and relatively heavy weight of radar missile sensors. Even if these problems are overcome at some time in the future, there remain two inseparable problems: (1) radar missiles require an active radar illuminator which immediately warns the enemy he is under attack and (2) the number of simple, feasible passive and active countermeasures to airborne radars is multiplying fast enough to not only counter the effectiveness of airborne radars but also to make their use in combat actually dangerous.

Since we have been unable to conduct an all-weather (non-visual) tactical air battle, even with our current all-weather fighters and since there are technical reasons why all-weather weapons will probably continue to be ineffective, there is no reason to include an all-weather weapon in the minimum functional requirements of a modern, single-purpose air superiority fighter. On the other hand, the very heavy performance, cost and sortie generation penalties associated with all-weather weapons and their fire control provide strong incentives to keep all-weather weapons off the single-purpose air-to-air fighter as long as pilot training, maneuvering performance and large numbers remain the key determinants of air battle victory.

b. Fire control.—the Sidewinder missile requires nothing but firing circuits and pilot earphones for fire control. The gun could be considerably enhanced in lethality with a better gunsight of improved accuracy and time response, relative to the sights we currently have. This can be accomplished with simple analog circuitry and a small ranging device such as a range-only radar or laser.

c. Navigation.—air-to-air fighters need only simple navigational aids since precise geographical positioning has no relevance to aerial combat; thus TACAN radio direction-finding, a compass and possibly a small inertial set are functionally adequate.

d. Communications.—a simple, reliable UHF radio plus an emergency backup radio are the only communications necessary for tactical air combat. Unfortunately, we have not yet been able to equip a fighter with a radio of adequate reliability, e.g., one equal to the reliability of any standard commercial light plane radio.

e. Electronic countermeasures.—the single-purpose air-to-air fighter needs one warning that he is under attack by ground or air-launched radar missiles plus the capability to carry podded jammers, when and if effective jammers are developed.

It has already been demonstrated by at least five major design teams that these functions (gun and Sidewinder with associated fire control, navigation, communications, and ECM) can be accomplished at a weight of less than 200 pounds and a cost of less than $200,000—considerably less than the 600 pounds and $500,000 I included in the estimates of the F-XX.

f. Expanding on the points I raised in my answer to questions 3, let me begin by saying that all we know about the weaponry of the Flagon, Foxbat and Flogger is that they have larger radar dishes than previous

Soviet fighters and that they carry already known Soviet missiles, some of which have radar seeker heads. We know nothing of the sophistication or performance of these radars and weapons, though in general the Soviets are at least five years behind us in micro-miniaturization and have shown little or no visible interest and progress in Pulse Doppler radars and lookdown techniques (they do produce excellent though simple ground radars for AA purposes). Performance in the maneuvering combat arena for each of the three Soviet aircraft is quite poor, as can be deduced from even unclassified evidence on thrust-to-weight and wing loading. Within the limitations of classification, I would give the following capsule summary of the performance of each:

(a) Flagon.—this aircraft has such small wing area that one must conclude that it is optimized for non-maneuvering, low altitude bomber defense. Its thrust-to-weight gives it accelerating performance slightly better than the F-4 but short of the F-15, F-XX or lightweight fighter class. Its low wing area and aspect ratio should give it turning performance slightly inferior to the relatively unmaneuverable F-14. Range cannot be estimated precisely without more detailed knowledge of the engine than we have, but it should be somewhere between the range of a MiG-21 and an F-4.

(b) Flogger.—this is a variable sweep aircraft with an even higher wing loading and lower thrust-to-weight than the Flagon, placing its maneuvering performance down in the F-105 class, though somewhat better than that of the F-111. Thus, this aircraft has no real air-to-air potential. It probably has better air-to-ground range and payload than the very limited MiG-21 or SU-7 though still not comparable to F-4 or A-7 bombloads.

(c) Foxbat.—this aircraft is clearly optimized for the very high altitude, high-speed regime of the F-12 and SR-71, though its size and range are markedly smaller (using Aviation Week published figures, the Foxbat typical missions are only 30 to 45 minutes). This optimization entails severe penalties in structural strength for maneuvering and severe maximum speed penalties at low altitude, making it unusable for maneuvering dogfights in the under 40,000 foot altitude and under M[ach] 1.5 air combat arena. It follows that this aircraft is unlikely to prove dangerous to any of our fighters or attack aircraft unless one attributes to it a remarkably flexible lookdown shoot-down capability for which we have no evidence and which we have been unable to achieve ourselves.

However, the fact that these three aircraft are not optimized for tactical air superiority should under no circumstances be taken as grounds for complacency in U.S. fighter development. There is sound reason to believe that the Soviets will build or are building a direct MiG-21 follow-on that will continue their tradition of small, simple, highly maneuverable fighters. Given their modest range and equipment requirements, such an aircraft could easily have performance superiority over our current developmental fighters.[67]

On December 14, 1971, six days after the hearings, the FY 1972 Appropriations Bill came out with $12 million allocated for two of the prototype programs: the Lightweight Fighter and the medium

STOL transport aircraft (AMST). None of the other services received any money for their prototype proposals. The Air Force launched the program with the request for proposals on New Year's Eve 1971.* [68]

The Navy was not funded for a Naval prototype program. This illustrates two things: (1) the Navy's ability to suppress what it does not want, (in this case a Lightweight Fighter) and (2) the Navy's loss of control over what was later imposed on it: an Air Force design, nourished by the belief that the Navy would impose a design on the Air Force.

The Air Force response to the Navy's previous lightweight fighter studies certainly was more immediate than any long-range threat of the Soviets. The possibility that the Navy could impose another aircraft on the Air Force was an imminent threat to career enhancement and institutional pride. The A-7 and F-4 were enough. Certainly Riccioni's memo to General Glasser reflected the concern toward the Navy threat. The Navy, conversely, had an institutional arrogance that prevented it from perceiving that the Air Force could ever impose a lightweight fighter on it. The Navy may have given it a second thought after Senator Proxmire's speech on the Senate floor, but by that time it was too late. The Air Force had done its homework; the Navy, with the exception of Ernie Waller, Bob Thompson, and a few others, had not.

Waller did not stay in the Navy long enough to have the persistence that was necessary, if indeed any persistence would have been enough within the Navy structure. When Riccioni came into the lightweight fighter scene as a latter-day disciple, he stood on the shoulders of Boyd and Sprey. Through their combined efforts, the Lightweight Fighter developed into a full-fledged program. First Boyd and Sprey tried to reduce the size of the FX into the 33,000- to 35,000-pound aircraft. Boyd was then ordered to stop all his efforts on the FX. A patriot undeterred, in the tradition of Claire Chennault, Boyd continued to support Sprey with large amounts of data. Although Sprey's F-XX paper was kept within the system, he publicized his work shortly after Riccioni joined the Lightweight Fighter Mafia.

It was Riccioni, the third member of the Lightweight Fighter Mafia insurgent triad, who drew fire as he pursued the lightweight fighter concept like a member of the Light Brigade. Riccioni's masterstroke touched Air Force vital tissues when he told General Glasser of the Navy's plans for a lightweight fighter. Only such input could

*The actual Request for Proposal (RFP), No. F33657-72-R-0235, was dated January 6, 1972. The proposal called for a return date 43 days later on February 18, 1972.

get an Air Force general to join a conspiracy to work against the canonized F-15, as the progress toward developing the Lightweight Fighter surely represented. It is safe to say that without the unending preparation by Sprey and Boyd, along with Riccioni's masterstroke of getting subrosa funding, and acting as the point man, the Lightweight Fighter would never have had the momentum to fly through the system.*

In spite of aborted attempts by Senator Cannon and others, the Lightweight Fighter appeared to be on firm ground at the end of 1971. But other battles would be waged against it by its foster parent, the U.S. Air Force. The Lightweight Fighter was like an unwanted pregnancy: it was fun in the making (because it countered Navy Lightweight Fighter efforts), but what did one do with the baby? The Air Force would try to put it up for adoption.

*Harry Hillaker, in a statement to the author, said, "I'm convinced that if it hadn't been for Ken Chapman, Lyle Cameron, and Jim Stewart, the F-16 would have never gone." Chapman was AFSC (XR), Development and Planning, and Cameron was the first F-16 SPO.

Chapter 7

The Lightweight Fighter Program

It seems to be easier to go to the moon than it is to get a good air-to-air missile.

V. Adm. Tom Connolly, USN
Deputy Chief of Naval Operations
1971 Senate Armed Services Committee

From January 1972 to January 1975, the U.S. Air Force worked on the Lightweight Fighter Prototype program, from which would evolve the U.S. Navy's next fighter. Since the F-111 affair—when the Navy had almost been forced to procure an Air Force airplane—the Navy had successfully evaded the imposition of an Air Force imprimatur on a Navy aircraft. In the process, the Navy had successfully imposed two of its designs on the Air Force: the LTV A-7 Corsair II and the McDonnell Douglas F-4 Phantom II. With the commencement of the Lightweight Fighter program, the Air Force began to think it might be able to reverse this trend and impose an Air Force airplane on the Navy, not the Lightweight Fighter, but the F-15.

The Air Force's new optimism was based on the Navy's increasing cost and contractual problems with the F-14. In July 1971 Deputy Secretary of Defense David Packard had requested that the Navy look at a navalized version of the F-15. Senator Proxmire made his speech on the Senate floor in the fall of 1971. He said the Navy should consider developing a lightweight fighter or end up taking the Air Force's lightweight fighter. The problems for the F-14 were just beginning, however, and as a result, the Navy received continuous pressure to adopt a complementary aircraft to supplement the F-14.

The Lightweight Fighter Prototype program progressed, with the institutionalized Air Force believing that the purpose of the program

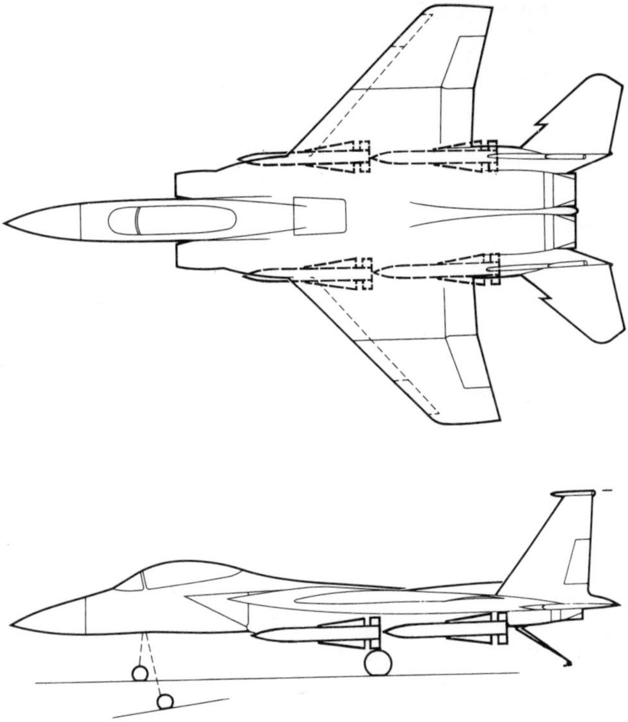

SOURCE: McDonnell Douglas
This is a line drawing of an F-15N proposal that McDonnell Douglas made during the congressional hearings for a suggested Phoenix version of the F-15.

was to test new technology. A small part of the Air Force knew the real purpose of the Lightweight Fighter.

The Lightweight Fighter Request for Proposals (RFP) was released to nine companies on January 6, 1972, with responses due by February 18, 1972. The RFP was 21 pages long and asked for a response 60 pages long—50 pages for technical, 10 for management. The RFP was unique. It was short and asked for the contractors to design to goals rather than specifications. The suggested parameters were a high thrust-to-weight ratio, good transonic maneuverability, simple avionics and fire control system, 6.5-g load factor, a suggested gross weight of 20,000 pounds, and a suggested $3 million flyaway cost in 1972 dollars based on 300 aircraft at the rate of 100 per year.[1] The Air Force held a bidders' briefing on January 20. McDonnell Douglas, Rockwell, Grumman, and Fairchild did not respond to the Lightweight Fighter RFP. Submissions came from the same companies that had submitted proposals in 1971: Boeing, General Dynamics, Northrop, LTV, and Lockheed.

Even before the proposals were received, the Air Force was testifying in front of the Senate Armed Services subcommittee on Research and Development on the USAF Advanced Prototype Development Program. This was the beginning of their propaganda campaign to render the significance of the Lightweight Fighter program *de minimus.* At this and subsequent hearings the Air Force would attempt to keep the Lightweight Fighter from competing with the F-15.

The Air Force claimed that the Lightweight Fighter prototypes would not possess the F-15's full spectrum of air combat capability nor equal its combat radius.[2] It focused on the perceived lack of range in the series of attacks that followed the announcement of the Lightweight Fighter program. Whenever Riccioni or Boyd briefed the program, the response they received was similar to this: "But the Lightweight Fighter is a short-legged airplane." Before Riccioni left for Korea in September 1971, Boyd cautioned him not to say otherwise. "Yes," Boyd would reply, "the Lightweight Fighter is a short-legged airplane." The F-15 union continued to focus on this perceived defect and build their objections to the Lightweight Fighter around it. The Lightweight Fighter Mafia obligingly fed this paradigm.

Brig. Gen. John J. Burns was one of the elite taken in by this ruse. During Senate hearings, he testified that the Lightweight Fighter would have a 150-mile radius of action; the F-15, for the identical mission, would have a longer radius. The radius goal for the F-15 was 260 nautical miles, and the threshold was 240 miles. (The F-15 would ultimately fail to meet either the radius goal or threshold.) General Burns characterized the Lightweight Fighter in the following way:

> [The Lightweight Fighter] will not have the radius of action [of the F-15], and our concept has always been to take the fight to the enemy. The lightweight fighter really is a step backward to something like the European approach where the enemy has to bring the fight to you and I think that is a very important concept . . . I think we want to be fighting over his country and not be fighting over ours. . . .
>
> I will tell you a story I heard, if I may. Some friends of mine were arguing in a pub in London in 1944. One of them was a Spitfire driver and the other fellow was a P-51 pilot. They were arguing the relative merits of their aircraft, and they decided they were going to meet the next day at 9 o'clock at 15,000 feet and they just had to resolve where they were going to have the encounter and the 51 pilot said "over Hiligoland." The Spitfire pilot said "I cannot get there." The 51 pilot said, "Tough, that is where the fight is." And I think that is a very important consideration.[3] *

*John J. Burns is considered by many within the U.S. Air Force to be the Father of the F-15—not as Boyd and Sprey had intended the F-15—but as it ultimately

While Burns had his facts correct when he said the P-51 had longer range than the Spitfire, he jumbled his analogy when applying it to the Lightweight Fighter. Burns clearly meant in his analogy for the P-51 to represent the F-15. But in fact, the analogy would only work if he substituted the F-15 for the Spitfire and the Lightweight Fighter for the P-51. Like most senior Air Force officers, he was totally in the dark about the Lightweight Fighter's superior range. Nor did anyone bother to educate him about such fundamentals as the Breguet range equations (see fig. 6-1).

The ignorance of the senior Air Force officers would work in favor of the Lightweight Fighter; they used its short range as a rallying point, a cause célèbre. The Lightweight Fighter's short range was the central focus of virtually all conversations by those who wanted it eliminated. When the truth surfaced, that the Lightweight Fighter had the longest range of any Air Force fighter, these same senior Air Force officers were furious with Boyd. Boyd's rebuttal was pithy: "Yes, I agreed with you when you told me the Lightweight Fighter was short legged, but so is the F-15. The Lightweight Fighter just happens to have longer legs!"[4] Several years later, the Air Force would ask for an additional $500,000 per F-15 to increase the range of the F-15. They admitted that even with the PEP-2000 range improvement program, the F-15 still could not equal the F-16's range.

In response to this misleading testimony by the Air Force, members of the various Senate committees asked why the Air Force was procuring the Lightweight Fighter. Senator McIntyre asked, "Why do we try to come up with a lightweight fighter that will be a victim of the bigger fighters, the MiG-21GS or 23S. What do we need this little fellow for?"

General Hansen replied that the Lightweight Fighter could be used to modernize our allies and the Air National Guard or used "in an auxiliary role to a properly equipped force."[5] Lt. Gen. Otto Glasser testified in a separate hearing that it would be difficult to get our allies interested in buying the F-15; letting them buy a lightweight fighter-type aircraft would be more likely and could complement the F-15 in a NATO environment.[6]

The questions from Congress persisted. Why did the Air Force want the Lightweight Fighter? The Air Force, as a corporate body, did not want the Lightweight Fighter. This made much of its testimony awkward. As a result, many congressmen found contradictions in the statements. Secretary Packard, on the one hand, said that the

became. Burns became a vice president of McDonnell Douglas, the manufacturer of the F-15.

advantage of the prototype program would give the Department of Defense the "opportunity to evaluate the utility of the design against requirements." On the other hand, the Air Force stated that the purpose of the prototype program was to "demonstrate hardware . . . in advance of stated operational requirements."[7] General Burns exacerbated the confusion by saying that the Air Force had not concluded that the F-15 needed a complement and "if it is determined that an operational requirement does exist for such a fighter, and force structure considerations permit, one of the prototypes, or a synthesis of the two prototypes, could be selected to proceed into a full-scale development in a missionized configuration. This is not presently planned, however."[8]

General Burns noted two other optional uses for the data gained from the Lightweight Fighter prototype program. The U.S. Allies could become customers for an aircraft modified to their needs—undoubtedly reflected in Northrop's marketing efforts—or the technology could be used in longer-term fighter developments.

As the Lightweight Fighter continued to threaten conventional wisdom, as well as the F-15's share of the tactical air budget, the Air Force ultimately focused on three areas to justify why the "little fellow" was not likely to become an addition in the force structure. Its limited range was the hub of the argument, but the Air Force made two additional arguments: there was no requirement for the Lightweight Fighter; the Lightweight Fighter was only a technology demonstrator. General Burns told Congress, "We want to prototype some lightweight fighters because we want to determine whether or not it is feasible to develop a small, lightweight, low-cost fighter; determine what such an aircraft can do; and establish its operational utility."*

The argument that the Lightweight Fighter was a technology demonstrator was a specious one in this respect: one could easily infer that the word technology in the term "technology demonstrator" implied new or high or advancing technology even when not expressed. But the word technology has the following definition:† "The science of the application of knowledge to practical purposes: Applied science (1): the application of scientific knowledge to practical purposes in a particular field (2): a technical method of achieving a practical purpose."[9]

*Because the Air Force's doctrine was based on the radar-guided Sparrow missile, an airplane designed without the Sparrow was outside of the doctrine.

†Boyd views technology as the application of engineering which he defines as a self-correcting process of observations, analysis/synthesis, design, and test.

To the extent that the Lightweight Fighter applied the known arts and sciences to a practical purpose, the Lightweight Fighter was a technology demonstrator. The alleged high technology items were absent from the Request for Proposal.[10]

The aircraft were expected to arrive at the competition ready to fire their guns and Sidewinder missiles. Whatever technology the contractor might include would have to function. The contractors knew what was at stake. At the very least this would be a demonstration of why the Europeans should buy their airplane; at the most it would remedy the declining force structure of the U.S. Air Force. The cutting edge of technology was not found in the Lightweight Fighter.

Despite the plain language of the Request for Proposal, the Air Force fostered the notion that the Lightweight Fighter would demonstrate technological breakthroughs. At the early hearings, the automatic variable camber, gunsight system, flight control system, and aerodynamic refinements in drag and lift were offered as reasons why the Lightweight Fighter was demonstrating new technology.[11] Later in the Lightweight Fighter program, the underneath inlet location on the YF-16 and the use of composite materials would be added to the list of high technology items. The Air Force added that the Lightweight Fighter could not be procured because of the risk involved in the program.

The cost for the Lightweight Fighter program was estimated, during these early 1972 hearings, to be $106 million between FY1972 and FY1975. Each contractor was allocated $45 million, with $8 million held in reserve. The remaining $16 million would pay for government-furnished equipment (GFE).[12]

As the hearings progressed, Senator Goldwater expressed concern that the United States was placing all of its confidence on radars with questionable reliability. He interrogated General Burns on the radar reliability of the F-4. Burns bragged that the mean time between failure (MTBF) of the F-4 radar was between 13 and 14 hours.

"While I was there," Burns said, referring to Vietnam, "I do not remember ever flying an airplane without an operative radar. . . ." He added that the last two MIG kills were the result of Sparrow missiles. However, Burns's argument stands the issue on its head: Air Force doctrine was not likely to let him fly an F-4 with inoperative radar.

Goldwater countered by citing the 47 minute mean time between failure of the Navy's F-4J radar. However, General Glasser retorted that while the Navy was not having good experience, there was no reason to be concerned because the F-15 radar had new technology. (The F-15 was several months from its July 1972 first flight.) Paradoxically, Glasser had stated moments before that the reason that the F-4E APG-120 radar was having problems was due to the miniaturization, that is, because of new technology. Glasser summarized the Air Force radar position precisely when he added, "The problem is cost. They are costly and that is what you are talking about here. Do you want that capability and with this high cost or do you want to back away from that and have simply a ranging radar [used in gun ranging] which you can do quite inexpensively. But you must recognize the vast difference in capability in the two aircraft to fight."[13]

Glasser's comment did not answer this question: Does the military have a more capable radar if it seldom works—regardless of the cost? It was this question that Boyd, Sprey, and Riccioni answered by eliminating the requirement for anything but a ranging radar in the RFP for the Lightweight Fighter competition.

The designs were delivered to the Air Force on February 18, 1972. Boeing submitted model 908-909. (Boeing used 908 for all fighter aircraft design numbers.) Model 908-618-2 had been used in much of the backup material used in Riccioni's "Falcon Brief." Model -618 had a leading edge extension that, according to Bud Nelson, could not be converged into a workable design. For its final proposal, Boeing arbitrarily skipped some numbers to come up with model 908-909.[14]

General Dynamics submitted its model 401, which ultimately became the YF-16, and Northrop submitted its model P-600, which was selected as the YF-17. LTV's design was the V-1100, the same design used in its unsolicited proposal back in June 1971. Lockheed submitted the CL-1200 as the fifth entry. The preliminary analysis was completed and delivered to the source selection authority on March 18, 1972.[15]

According to Lyle Cameron, head of the evaluation group, the designs were not ranked. Other members of the evaluation group, which included John Boyd, stated that the ranking was fairly clear. The Boeing design was ranked first, with the General Dynamics design a very close second. Northrop's twin-engine design was a distant third; the LTV was fourth; the Lockheed design was a distant fifth. In fact, the CL-1200 was not considered responsive to the Request for Proposal, which Kelly Johnson admitted. Johnson felt that the RFP was not valid and wanted to give the Air Force the fighter that the country needed.[16]

Lockheed's failure to effectively respond to the RFP was not because of a lack of information. "I was receiving information on a regular basis from at least 15 different Air Force officers," said one Lockheed marketeer.[17] "Several of them went on to the higest positions with the Air Force." Asked if these Air Force officers were feeding Lockheed because they felt it had the best chance of winning, he said "No, they were just enamored with Kelly Johnson." The hero worship went further. "Kelly would never meet with a customer in public. but I said, 'Kelly, these guys really want to meet you.' So I set up a meeting in Kelly's room at the Hilton in Washington, D.C. They came just to touch his hemline." Sprey added that these Air Force officers were not singling out Lockheed. "They were sharing the same information with other contractors," Sprey said.

According to Kelly Johnson, one of the sources of information was Col. Larry Welch.

> I talked to Ray Crandall [a Lockheed marketing representative] prior to the RFP being released and he suggested I talk to Colonel Larry Welch, now going to War college, but who was one of General Kent's most excellent officers. Larry said that it was his advice that we go all out for performance. There will be no credit for producibility or use of the airplane for NATO or other export purposes. It would certainly be necessary to win the basic competition before there would be any talk of producing the aircraft in quantity. The number one requirement was to have extremely good maneuverability, acceleration, and climb. I asked him about the creditability of various co-contractors entered in the competition and he said all were creditable. I questioned whether Boeing, who has never built a modern fighter, lit an afterburner or had a supersonic airplane could be considered creditable, and he said that would be based on their transport reputation. (I did not make any snide remarks about the supersonic transport fiasco.) Larry said the Air Force is split up the middle on the desirability of the lightweight fighter because it definitely was a threat to the F-15. The RDT&E cost of the F-15 will exceed $1.7 billion and the obvious implication is that if a smaller, cheaper airplane would do the air superiority mission, the Air Force would be in a very untenable position.
>
> I have the feeling that a group of young officers like Larry Welch, John Boyd and Mike Loh are struggling to get an aircraft that we definitely need, but they are being kept under wraps because of the F-15 political problems.*

The Source Selection Authority (SSA) for the Lightweight Fighter was Lt. Gen. James Stewart, Commander of the Aeronautical Systems Division. The final authority of the selection of the Lightweight Fighter finalists rested with Stewart. (Normally the authority was maintained by the Air Force Secretary.)

*From Kelly Johnson's personal log dated January 6, 1972.

General Stewart recalls the ranking of the designs differently from some of the other members of the evaluation group. Stewart made the final decision in front of a group that consisted of Lt. Gen. Otto Glasser; Deputy Secretary of the Air Force for Research & Development, Grant Hansen; Air Force Secretary, Robert Seamans; Air Force Chief of Staff, John D. Ryan; and George Brown, Commander of the Air Force Systems Command.

Stewart recalls saying to the group, "Unless you have some input," deferring particularly to Air Force Secretary Seamans, "I'd pick the General Dynamics and Northrop designs." Stewart remembers the Boeing design as a close third.[18]

Air Force Secretary Robert Seamans recalls that when he asked Stewart which two designs Stewart would pick, Stewart told Seamans he could be happy with any two of the three designs, referring to Boeing, General Dynamics, and Northrop. Since that was the case, Seamans said, he could take other considerations into account. Seamans was concerned with what the Air Force would do with the General Dynamics plant, which was winding down its F-111 operation. He was also aware of the money invested in the YJ101 engine that powered the twin-engine Northrop design. There was also the consideration of having a single engine and a twin-engine design as opposed to two single-engine designs.* Finally, Seamans took into consideration the fact that Boeing had not ever fired an afterburner in anger.[†19]

The evaluation group, which provided the technical data to Stewart, was critical of the Northrop design because of Northrop's excessive underestimation of weight. Walt Fellers, a Northrop designer, admitted that Northrop was overly optimistic, but justified their inaccurate weight statement on the basis that they "knew" that General Dynamics's would be submitting false weight statements too. Northrop's concern was unfounded, according to General Stewart. He was surprised at how close General Dynamics's weight statements, proposal data, and wind tunnel data were to the actual flight vehicle once it was built. While the evaluation group added some weight when they evaluated Harry Hillaker's design model 401, it was not very much. On the other hand, the evaluation group added a significant amount of weight to the Northrop design. "Had I known that the Northrop airplane would grow in weight as much as it

*Seamans's telephone log of incoming calls indicates numerous calls from Northrop's chairman, Tom Jones, immediately preceding the decision to select the Lightweight Fighter finalists, but little or no activity from other companies.

†The rhetoric is great, but the logic is bad," Riccioni said in response to Seamans's comment.

did—some 4,000 pounds—I might have chosen a different design," said Stewart.[20]

Northrop also submitted a single-engine design, the P-610, which, according to General Stewart, was not as refined a design as Northrop's twin-engine P-600. Nevertheless, Stewart said that the single-engine P-610 design looked as good or better than the twin-engine P-600 design, an opinion shared by Sprey. The Northrop single-engine design was submitted at the insistence of Sprey and Boyd. Northrop no doubt submitted it to take advantage of the inherent benefits of a design incorporating the engine used in the F-15, the Pratt & Whitney F100. Bill Roth, a Northrop engineer, designed the P-610. Other Northrop engineers felt that the P-610 threatened the sanctioned twin-engine P-600 design, which had been the raison d'être at Northrop for many years. Roth died of a heart attack before finishing his design.

The Northrop twin-engine P-600 gained support from Europe before the final Lightweight Fighter decision. On March 29, 1972—two weeks before the final decision—the U.S. ambassador to Holland, William Middendorf II, wrote to Secretary of Defense Melvin Laird. Referring to the Dutch, Middendorf said: "I am quite optimistic that they will go American, especially since the interview that was conducted by the press here. In this interview [Defense Minister] De Koster commented favorably on the Northrop P-530 as a possible replacement for the F-104G."

The Lightweight Fighter prototype contract was awarded to General Dynamics and Northrop on April 13, 1972. General Dynamics was awarded a contract for $37,943,000 for its model 401, and Northrop received $39,878,715 for its twin-engine model P-600.

The proposal weight for the General Dynamics model 401 was 16,062 pounds based on a 6.5-g airplane at 60 percent internal fuel. The RFP did not specify a radius of action. It stated that the Lightweight Fighter should be able to perform four supersonic 360-degree turns at Mach 1.2 at 30,000 feet, perform two subsonic turns at 0.9 Mach, and fly home 500 miles. Internal fuel was not specified.

When the companies submitted their designs, they presented no new technology. If they had, they would not have been responsive to the RFP. The purpose of the prototype competition was to prove that a less expensive fighter could successfully compete with the F-15, without cutting-edge technology.

The technology of which General Dynamics was perhaps most proud was the variable camber wing. Variable camber was another solution to getting the maximum lift throughout the flight envelope.

It was a less expensive, lighter, and more effective approach than the swing wing, which General Dynamics used in the F-111. Variable camber on the YF-16 was not new, but General Dynamics made the camber vary infinitely. The F-5E, built by Northrop, had variable camber in its wing. The leading edge flaps and trailing edge flaps could be positioned, in combination, in five different positions for cruising, maneuvering, or takeoff and landing. As the F-5E first flew almost two years before the F-16, variable camber could hardly be considered a new technology.

The variable camber technology was actually much older than the F-5E. One of the first aircraft to fly with a variable camber wing was designed by Melvin E. Dare. He built and tested the first prototype in 1921 using the same concept later applied to the YF-16.[21]

The F-16's use of variable camber is not new, but it is a practical use of technology. To the credit of General Dynamics, it perfected the application of variable camber: the entire leading edge and trailing edge are connected to the flight computer and the leading and trailing edge flaps move as a function of *g*.

Another new technology, according to the Air Force and General Dynamics, was the totally fly-by-wire flight control system in the YF-16. A fly-by-wire system is different from a hydraulic system in that the signals are sent to a computer, which in turn sends signals to the control actuator. Most aircraft flight control systems are composed of push rods that use hydraulic fluid under pressure to exert adequate force to more of the various controls such as ailerons, flaps, etc.

Fly-by-wire systems had been in research and development for several years before the YF-16 flew. Abbreviated systems had been used in a Load Alleviation Mode Stabilization (LAMS) B-52 and a Tactical Weapons Delivery (TWEAD) F-4. More serious fly-by-wire systems appeared before the YF-16 in a YF-4E, a NASA F-8, a C-141, and VAK-191B.

The Air Force might have claimed that the YF-16 was the first production aircraft to fly with a fly-by-wire system. But to do so would have put the Air Force in a bind, because it claimed that the YF-16 was merely a technology demonstrator. If the Air Force held that position, then the YF-16 was a continuation of a long line of platforms used to investigate a fly-by-wire flight control system. If the Air Force admitted that the YF-16 had always been intended to be procured, then the F-16A would not have new technology because the technology was thoroughly tested in the YF-16 prototype.

The Air Force arguments that the blended body shape of the YF-16 was new technology suffer the same fate as the assertions concerning variable camber. Blended body technology also goes back to the 1920s. In 1923 the Westland Aircraft Company built an aircraft named the Dreadnought to test the continuous airfoil theories of Woyevodsky, a Russian designer. The airplane went into a deep stall on takeoff and crashed. Other examples of blended body designs are the Miles C 9, Douglas F4D, McDonnell XP-67, and the Douglas F5D.*[22]

One of the more interesting claims of new technology was the underneath inlet. The first underneath inlet for a jet aircraft was the inlet found on a French design, the Arsenal VG-70, built shortly after World War II. Another French design, the Nord Griffon II, was also the proud owner of an underneath inlet. In the United States the F-86D, F-86K, F8U, F8U-3, and a large series of Ryan drones were designed with underneath inlets of various degrees. In fact, aeronautical data from Ryan drones convinced General Dynamics engineers that an underneath inlet would be beneficial at high angles of attack. Sprey had also investigated the Ryan data and continually insisted that the inlet should be underneath. Hillaker gives Sprey credit for insisting on it.[23]

The advantage of the underneath inlet is that at high angles of attack the local angle of attack of the air is reduced. For example, at 25 degrees angle of attack, the local angle of attack of the incoming air is 35 degrees in the F-15, but only 10 degrees in the F-16.

One of the latter-day designs for a fixed underneath inlet came from the N-102 Fang designed by Northrop, General Dynamics's arch competitor in the Lightweight Fighter competition. In the middle 1950s Ed Schmued, designer of the P-51, designed the Fang to be the smallest, lightest, least expensive aircraft possible. Schmued was guided by the same principle that inspired his design of the P-51.† Although the Fang never got past the mock-up stage, it did emulate many of the features found on the F-16. It was small and simple, with a bubble canopy and a delta wing, a wing design for which General Dynamics had long been known. The design of the Fang

*Hillaker was actually inspired by some blended shapes on boats done at Convair (San Diego). He also admired the F4D Skyray.

†The Chief of Staff of the Army Air Force, General H. H. ("Hap") Arnold (an advocate of lightweight fighter concepts), asked Ed Schmued to make the P-51 even lighter, which led to the P-51F. Other factions in the Army Air Force insisted on increasing the structural *g*-limit and adding more weight, which diminished the advantages that the lower weight gave the P-51F. Nevertheless, the P-51F, according to Schmued, did reach 499 miles per hour. It seems appropriate that Colonel Riccioni was nominated for the Arnold Trophy for his work on lightweight fighters.

SOURCE: Northrop Corporation
The Northrop Fang has more of the characteristics of the General Dynamics YF-16 than Northrop's YF-17 which would fly two decades later.

was the transition for Northrop from heavy, complex, sophisticated designs that had earned them a negative reputation. For General Dynamics the F-16 represened the same transition from the F-111.

The Fang would lead to the T-38 and F-5 series of aircraft from which the P-530 and ultimately YF-17 would evolve. Many design features of the YF-17's progenitor, the N-102 Fang, would be found in the YF-17's competitor, but not in the YF-17 itself.

During the same period that the Lightweight Fighter program developed—1972 through 1974—the Department of Defense and Congress increased their attacks on the Navy for allowing the F-14's cost to increase and for allowing the fighter force to decrease. The attacks on the F-14 began to escalate in 1971. The F-14 escaped the budget hatchet that year, but activity increased for a complementary fighter. In the fall of 1971 the Navy issued a letter of interest in the *Commerce Business Daily* for an airplane to fulfill the emerging Sea Control Ship program. The new aircraft was called the VFA V/STOL Prototype Candidate. Industry submitted 11 designs.

The letter of interest was only 2-1/2 pages long and lacked the usual detailed specifications. As a result, the designs varied. The Naval Air Systems Command evaluated these 11 designs. Its first choice was the General Dynamics (Convair) San Diego Model 200; second was the Fairchild Republic Model FR-150; the LTV V-517 was third. It isolated the North American Rockwell NR-356 and put it in

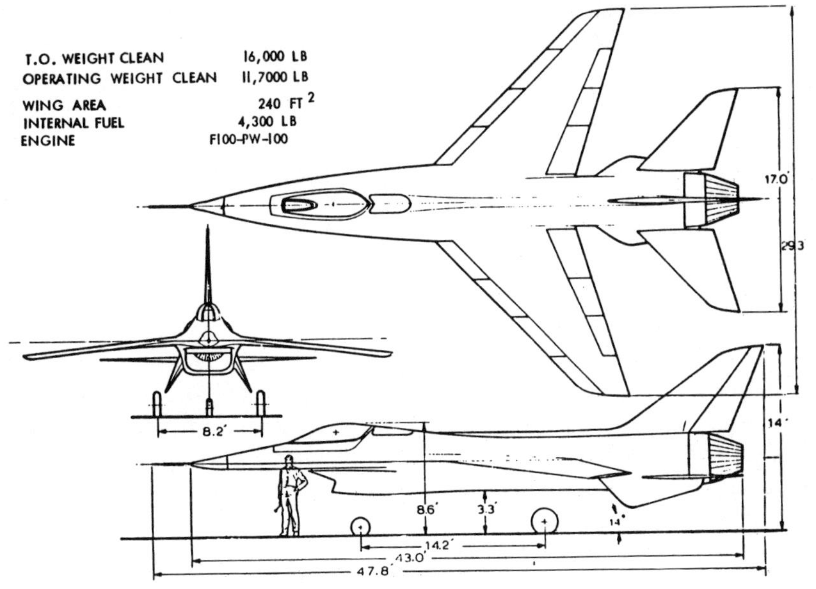

SOURCE: Boeing Corporation
This is a three-view drawing of the Boeing 908-618-2 used in Riccioni's Falcon Brief and precursor to the 908-909 entry into the Lightweight Fighter Competition.

a category of "not recommended." However, it commented that the NR-356 merited further research.

All the designs claimed supersonic capabilities, and two designs claimed the ability to cruise supersonically at Mach 2 without after burner. Boeing's vertical attitude takeoff and vertical landing (VATOL) design claimed a top speed of Mach 2.8. North American claimed Mach 2.7 for its NR-356 design. The Stinger from San Diego Aircraft Engineering (Sandaire) was the lightest; it weighed 17,377 pounds. LTV's V-517 weighed 19,950 pounds. The Grumman heavyweight weighed in at a hefty 37,353 pounds and lacked vertical takeoff ability. As most of the designs were significantly below the gross weights of contemporary aircraft, they could easily be defined as lightweight fighters.

The technical arm of the Navy, the Naval Air Systems Command, made its evaluation for the Sea Control Ship fighter, but the operational branch of the Navy, the Office of the Chief of Naval Operations (known as OPNAV) wanted its own evaluation. OPNAV handed the job to the Navy Fighter Study III group.

The Navy Fighter Study III group was created in the middle of 1971 during the height of debates surrounding the increased cost of the F-14. In theory the group was formed to look at alternatives to the F-14; in reality, it massed to defend the Tomcat. The Navy Fighter Study III group advocated the experimental nature of prototyping for two reasons. A faction within the group actually believed in the emerging V/STOL aircraft concept. They believed it was consistent with Secretary Packard's language on the prototype concept and the Navy's interpretation of Packard's language. Furthermore, the more experimental the aircraft design, the less it would threaten the F-14. And reducing the threat to the F-14 was the group's mission. Consequently, the group advocated the Rockwell design for a thrust-augmented wing.

In spite of the recommendation by the Naval Air Systems Command, Chief of Naval Operations Elmo Zumwalt announced on March 29, 1972, that he would use separate research and development money to fund what would become known as the XFV-12A. Zumwalt announced that the Navy would also fund the Convair Model 200, but at a slower pace.[24]

During the investigation of the VFA V/STOL aircraft, Capt. Jerry O'Rourke investigated a conventional lightweight fighter. Out of necessity the proposals submitted for the VFA V/STOL Sea Control Ship were lightweight in nature. O'Rourke asked Sandaire, a San Diego firm, to look at an airplane designed from the beginning as a lightweight fighter. He picked Sandaire because it had submitted the lightest VFA design.

O'Rourke gave Sandaire some desired characteristics. He asked if the company could meet his design with an airplane using the YJ101 engine. It could not. Sandaire took the basic design of its V/STOL submission and used a single engine in it, without the lift engines that were in its Stinger design. (For a comparison of O'Rourke's and Sandaire's characteristics see table 7-1.)

Whereas Vietnam showed that the top speeds above Mach 2 were useless, the air war showed that a supersonic cruise was a desirable trait. O'Rourke's desire for the ability to cruise in intermediate power (without afterburner) at Mach 1.6 reflects this experience.

One can only speculate what the Navy Fighter Study III group would have done if the Sandaire report had shown that it could meet the desired characteristics. Most likely the report would have been suppressed. After all, the purpose of the group was to defend the F-14, not create competition for it. The Sandaire design was not elevated to the level of the project created by the Naval Air Systems Command. Ernie Waller and Bob Thompson came closer to pushing their lightweight fighters into the Navy system.

Table 7–1
Summary U.S. Navy Fighter Study Group
Mini-Fighter Characteristics

	Realistic	Desired
Engine	Single J101	Single J101
Missile	(2) Agile	(2) Agile
Cannon	(1) or (2) LPG 20-MM	(1) LPG 20-MM
FLIR	FLIR	FLIR
Takeoff Gross Weight (lbs)	14,174	14,800
Trust -to-Weight at Takeoff	0.94:1	1:1
Thrust-to-Weight at Combat	1:1	1.3:1
Wing Loading at Takeoff-lbs/sq. ft.	60	60
V_{Max} Afterburner	2.16M	2.4M
V_{Max} Military Power	1.02	1.6
Specific Energy 0.9 M at 10,000 ft./sec.	727	1,200
Percent Composite	20	20
Spotting Factor (A-4=1.0)	.0975	0.90

SOURCE: "Investigation of Advanced Mini-Fighter System," SAI 72–005 February 29, 1972, San Diego Aircraft Engineering, San Diego, CA

None of the VFA V/STOL evaluations nor the lightweight fighter investigations reduced the controversy over the escalating costs of the F-14. The Navy wanted F-14s, many of them. Escalating costs threatened the number they could have.

Yet even the number of F-14s the Navy believed necessary varied. The original estimate in February 1969 was for 469. By September of that year the number had dropped to 293. In December it bounced up to 722. In 1970 the F-14 total dipped to 437, then went back up to 722. In 1971 the total fluctuated between 437 and 313. By 1972 the total F-14s needed was back to 722.[25]

The Department of Defense did not agree with the Navy numbers. The Navy maintained it needed 722 F-14s; the Department of Defense fixed the total F-14 requirement at 313. The Marine Corps was assigned 68 of them, which it took—reluctantly.[26] The controversy over the number of F-14s the Navy would ultimately receive appeared academic in 1972 because Grumman threatened not to produce them.

On February 3, 1969, Grumman had signed a fixed price incentive contract with the Navy to build F-14 Tomcats. The contract specified that Grumman would be paid for research and development and a fixed price option for production over eight years. Each lot could be increased or decreased by 50 percent. On December 8, 1972, the Navy exercised its option to purchase the lot V aircraft. Grumman rejected the option on December 11, 1972. It issued a stop work order, claiming that it had lost too much money. Grumman asserted that the original terms of the contract would force it into bankruptcy.

Figure 7-2

Projected Total of F-14s Over Time

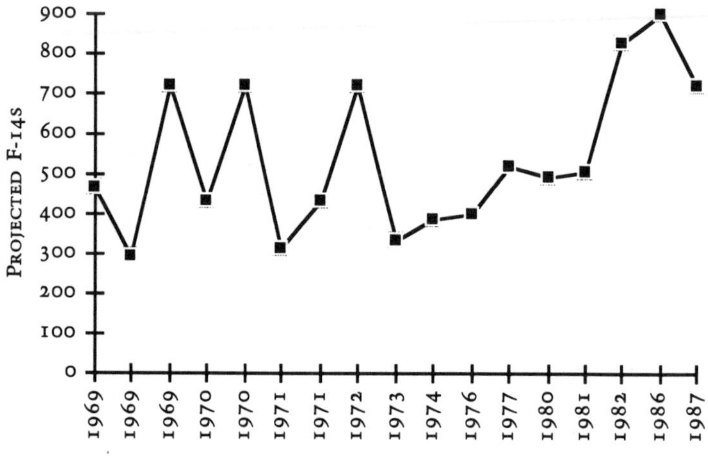

SOURCE: Congressional Research Service and Congressional hearings

An observer outside the system might believe that there is stability in the projected number of tactical aircraft. This chart would tend to indicate otherwise. (Note variations in time.)

Grumman also claimed losses of $65 million in 1971 and $140 million in 1972 on production of the F-14.

The Navy and Grumman reached an agreement on March 8, 1973. The agreement required Grumman to produce 48 lot V aircraft under the original terms of the 1969 contract, but for fiscal year 1974 aircraft, and thereafter, the Navy and Grumman would negotiate on a year-by-year basis.

Deputy Secretary of Defense Clements, who was sworn in approximately one month before this contract settlement, suggested a prototype flyoff three months later. On June 19, 1973, Clements proposed a flyoff between a navalized version of the F-15, which he designated the F-15N, and a lighter-weight version of the F-14 (one without 1,000 to 1,300 pounds of Phoenix missile avionics), which he called the F-14D. Clements proposed building two copies of each airplane at a cost of $250 million. Even though he proposed taking the funds from other Navy programs, the Navy supported this prototype program—officially.

Within a month the Senate Tactical Air subcommittee recommended against the prototype program. Testimony from George Spangenberg, former director of the Evaluation Division of the Naval Air Systems Command, claimed that the cost would not be $250 million, as Clements said, but $367.8 million for the four aircraft. If the F-15N were the winner, there would be an additional $214 million and if the F-14D won, an additional $51.8 million. According to Spangenberg's testimony, Secretary Clements knew this on June 13, six days before his testimony. A month later, based on Spangenberg's testimony, the Senate Tactical Air subcommittee rejected Clements's idea as too expensive.

Nevertheless, momentum increased for a larger force structure. Various senators and congressmen began openly advocating larger numbers of aircraft. Proxmire had been a champion; Goldwater was becoming an advocate. And after the Tactical Air Subcommittee rejected the F-14/F-15 prototype flyoff proposal, Senator Cannon made the following remarks in the subcommittee's written report to the full Senate Armed Service Committee:

> The Navy should request proposals from the aircraft industry and evaluate these proposals to determine if a smaller and presumably cheaper aircraft can be designed to serve as an air-superiority fighter and to complement the F-14. If such a fighter is found to have the operational potential to serve the Navy and Marines in the fighter roles other than fleet air defense, I would urge the Committee to encourage the Navy to begin a competitive prototype program once this determination has been made and after all costs of such an alternative had been thoroughly evaluated.[27]

Although these congressmen, and Deputy Secretary Packard before them, had been the Lightweight Fighter Mafia's champions, what the Mafia needed was a godfather. On July 2, 1973, the godfather-to-be, James Schlesinger, was sworn in as the new Secretary of Defense. Even before Schlesinger was sworn in, he received a letter from Senator Proxmire, dated June 29, asking about the possibility of using the YF-16 or YF-17 as a complement to the 134 authorized F-14s.

Proxmire asked Schlesinger what plans were under consideration for a Naval Lightweight Fighter; what would prevent the Air Force's Lightweight Fighter from becoming carrier capable; what the Navy's force level requirement for fighters would be in the 1980s; and what the relative capabilities were of the F-14 compared with the YF-16 and YF-17.

Malcolm Currie, the Director of Defense Research & Engineering, answered Proxmire's letter. Currie was vague on whether the Navy had any lightweight fighters under consideration. The Navy had examined the lightweight fighter but "efforts to date have not identified a suitable system meeting cost objectives," wrote Currie. What impinged upon the Navy using either the YF-16 or YF-17, Currie wrote, was the possible need for a radar-guided missile, increased structural strength for the arrested landings on aircraft carriers, sufficient range for the navy mission, flying qualities for carrier approaches, and efficient use of aircraft carrier deck space. The cost objective for a lightweight fighter was not more than for an F-4 (which at that time was slightly over $6 million), and the launch and recovery cycle time better.

Currie told Proxmire that the Navy expected to have 12 aircraft carriers in 1980, with two fighter squadrons per carrier. It planned to have one squadron of F-14s per aircraft carrier, and a total of four F-14 squadrons in the U.S. Marine Corps. The Lightweight Fighter, Currie told Proxmire, was considered superior to the F-14 in the following categories: acceleration, turning radius (except at very low speeds), rate of climb, maintainability, effectiveness in close combat, an equal radius of action, reliability, and cost. The F-14 would be superior in ordnance capability, long range combat, Combat Air Patrol (CAP) loiter time, and in effectiveness against air-to-surface and surface-to-surface missiles.

By the fall of 1973 the Navy and Grumman still had not signed the replacement contract for the original 1969 versions. On September 25 the Senate debated whether to continue funding the F-14. The number of F-14s ordered to date totaled 134. The total money appropriated was $3.5 billion—$1.063 billion for F-14 research & development, ($4.09 billion in FY1990 dollars), $370.5 million for F-14B research and development and $2.070 billion in procurement funds. The Senate debate focused on the issues that had pursued the F-15 during the Lightweight Fighter discussions: cost, force levels, capability, and mission.

The defenders of the F-14 argued that it was needed to protect the fleet. Senator Tower, for example, reiterated a Navy study that said that the F-14 was equivalent to three F-4Js. Another senator remarked that the United States had already spent $3.5 billion on the F-14; to stop now would give the United States handsful of fighters at a very high cost per aircraft. The unit price would be $26 million ($76 million in FY1990) if the procurement stopped at 134 aircraft.

Other senators argued for the capability of the Phoenix weapon system. Nothing else, the F-14 advocates said, could defeat the various surface-to-surface and air-to-surface threats that plagued the carrier task force as well as the Phoenix missile. They extolled the virtues of the F-14's weapon system, the Airborne Weapons Group 9 (AWG-9).

The AWG-9 had an advertised capability to track 24 targets and fire 6 separate Phoenix missiles at any of the 24 targets. A distinguishing feature of the AWG-9 was its ability to track multiple targets without individually illuminating each specific target. This feature, called track-while-scan (TWS), worked only with the Phoenix missile. The F-4 and F-15, by contrast, have to scan an area with their radar, determine which individual aircraft they wish to attack, and then track (continuously illuminate) that target as long as their Sparrow missile is in the air. Tracking has two disadvantages: it alerts the target aircraft that it is the intended victim, and it takes more of the pilot's time. An added feature of the Phoenix missile was its ability to transition to active mode. When Phoenix missiles got within 10 to 12 miles, the missile was no longer dependent on the F-14 for radar ilumination.

At the time of this debate, the AWG-9 system cost almost $2 million dollars per aircraft. The program unit price of the Phoenix missile was $.913 million for 37 research & development missiles and 555 production missiles. The AWG-9 as well as the Phoenix missile, of which 2,420 were programmed for procurement, added significantly to the cost to the F-14 program.*

Some senators extolled virtues that the F-14 had not successfully demonstrated. Sen. Barry Goldwater, for example, claimed that the F-14 could be used as an attack aircraft, a role in which it had never demonstrated competency.†

> The Navy's F-14 fighter plane is designed to accomplish several missions. It will be very effective in escorting our attack planes to their targets and protecting them against attack by enemy fighters. After it has established air supremacy, it can be converted to an attack role itself, but its main job will be to defend the fleet—the carrier and other fighting ships plus the more vulnerable tankers and freighters which we have to support our allies and our own forces overseas.‡[28]

Not all of the senators favored continued procurement of the F-14. Senator Symington asked the Navy if any of the F-14 performance specifications were reduced for that fiscal year procurement. The Navy replied that while the F-14 was not paradoxically (its use of the word) meeting originally specified contractual requirements, it was exceeding the Navy's original operational requirement. As an example, the Navy cited the Grumman contractual guarantee that the F-14 would fly 500 miles on an internal load of fuel weighing

*The FY1991 unit price of each Phoenix missile was $1.2 million.

†The U.S. Navy demonstrated the air-to-ground capability of the F-14 in an operational squadron for the first time in the spring of 1991.

‡Ernie Waller's justification for the lightweight fighter was based in part on the Navy's inability to absorb higher losses if the F-14 were used in an escort role, much less as an attack aircraft. Sprey maintains that the F-14 will never be used in a role other than escort.

14,300 pounds. The Navy calculated that the F-14 would be able to fly only a 456-mile radius on this fuel load. However, with the tanks full, the F-14 could fly a 508-mile radius, which exceeded the Navy's operational requirement. The airplane met the requirement "because Grumman built more fuel capability in the plane than was required, but fails to meet the . . . contract specification. . . ." *

Senator Proxmire felt that the Navy's argument for the F-14 requirement employed circular logic. The Tomcat had been justified on its ability to track and fire on multiple targets simultaneously at long ranges. Proxmire quoted Chief of Naval Operations Admiral Zumwalt: "Two primary fighter requirements have repeatedly emerged (from studies); the requirement for large radar search volume and a long range track-while-scan multiple shoot-while-scan capability.

"These requirement must be achieved if the Navy is to survive and operate forces in the face of enemy air and missile concentrations."

But after arguing that the Phoenix missile was the F-14's primary asset, the Navy was willing to drop the Phoenix missile based on the "F-14D versus F-15N" prototype competition. Proxmire became perplexed. "Suddenly the primary positive characteristics of the F-14 turned out to be its dogfighter capability."

Proxmire doubted the ability of the carrier, even with the Phoenix capability, to defend itself against a massive raid of land-based Soviet aircraft. The Soviets would come in numbers that would saturate the carrier defense, Proxmire stated. If the need for these defenses did exist, he speculated, they existed only in certain high-threat areas, such as the eastern Mediterranean and the North Sea. From his perspective, the 134 F-14s already procured could be employed only on those carriers that would be in these high-threat regions and not in the vicinity of countries that did not pose a threat to the carrier.

*Convair (San Diego) claimed that an airplane's structural weight increases four pounds for every pound of added weight. If this ratio is correct, the F-14 grew 8,000 pounds to accommodate the increase in fuel. The Navy added 3,100 pounds of fuel to the YF-17 to accommodate the Navy mission. According to the Convair prediction, the F/A-18A should weigh 12,000 pounds more than the 25,500-pound YF-17. Testimony in the summer of 1981 claimed a 36,000-pound specification weight for the F-18, which misses the Convair prediction by only a percent.

For a comprehensive list of F-14 deficiencies from the contractual requirements, *see*, U.S. Congress. Senate. Committee on Appropriations. *F-18 Navy Air Combat Fighter* Hearings on H.R. 9861, 31. These hearings also list the Naval Air Combat Fighter range specification. It contradicts the range cited above for the F-14. The F-14's actual radius of action, according to Captain Halleland's Naval Air Combat Fighter briefing, is 468 miles.

In his departing retirement comments, Adm. Hyman Rickover had told Congress that in a confrontation with the Soviets an aircraft carrier would last only two days. This is not difficult to calculate. An aircraft carrier carries a maximum of 96 Phoenix missiles. If one assumes that all 24 F-14s are operationally ready, then each F-14 can carry four missiles. If each F-14 fires all four at an incoming raid of Russian bombers, and we allow a P_K (probability of kill) of 0.7, then each aircraft will shoot down 2.8 airplanes, or a total of (2.8 x 24) 67.2 bombers. Reality tells us, however, that the practical P_K, based on real-world experience is more likely to be 0.1, in which case the total bombers shot down would be fewer than 10. In either event, the aircraft carrier would be out of missiles after firing 96 missiles and unlikely to rearm against the next raid. All of this discussion assumes an unlikely F-14 operational readiness rate of 100 percent. The rate would more likely be 80 percent in a high-threat environment.

In his speech Senator Proxmire emphasized the declining force levels and then pressed his central theme. The increasing price of the F-14 meant that either Russia or China could produce 10 MiG-21's for every F-14 procured, "and the F-14 has not been made that can handle 10 MiG-21's by itself even with its heralded six-shot Phoenix capability and 100 percent reliability."[29]

Proxmire was incensed that the North Korean Air Force could muster more fighters than the U.S. Navy could from its carriers. The continuous reduction in firepower in the Navy, Proxmire continued, was due to the increasing price of fighters. Not only was the Navy getting fewer fighters because of rising costs, but the F-14 lacked the multirole capability of the F-4, which could double as an attack aircraft. The justification of an aircraft carrier was offensive fire power. But the cost of protecting the carrier with F-14s threatened the budgets of additional carriers and the offensive attack aircraft to go on them. One-for-one replacements were not possible. In fact, Proxmire pointed out, the Navy was buying half the number of aircraft in 1973 that it had four years earlier.

Proxmire made three recommendations. (1) He proposed stopping the purchase of the F-14 at 134. This would allow six carriers to have one squadron of F-14s, and three carriers—those in high-threat areas—to have two squadrons of F-14s. (2) The Navy should substitute the Lightweight Fighter, either a YF-16, YF-17—one pure Navy design—for the F-4J, whose technological value had been assured by Malcolm Currie through 1985. (3) Until that time, the F-4J should be procured.

Proxmire's argument did not prevail. He lost by a vote of 66 to 26. But unknown to Proxmire, three forces were at work making Secretary of Defense Schlesinger aware of the value of the Lightweight Fighter. The forces were Pierre Sprey, Chuck Myers, and Richard Hallock.

Hallock, a serious student of war, defense organizations, and acquisition, was a personal adviser to Schlesinger, having first met him when they both worked in the Bureau of the Budget. Hallock understood the need for simplicity, reliability, and maintainability in war equipment. He introduced Schlesinger to these concepts. In the case of the Lightweight Fighter, Hallock educated himself on the issue largely through discussions with Pierre Sprey. Hallock went to Schlesinger and said in essence: "You can take up space and pass time as the Secretary of Defense or you can leave something behind that you'll be remembered for and which will be a significant contribution." Hallock recommended to Schlesinger that the Lightweight Fighter be fostered and procured as an offset to and as more effective and affordable than either the F-14 or F-15 to which the Navy and Air Force were wedded.[30]

Schlesinger had a predisposition to favor numbers, and Hallock found a sympathetic ear in the new Defense Secretary. As early as 1969, while in the Bureau of the Budget, Schlesinger had publicly advocated increasing the force structure.[31]

Chuck Myers became the Director of Air Warfare in the office of Defense, Research & Engineering in the summer of 1973. His marching orders from the Director, Malcolm Currie, were clear: the Secretary of Defense wants a Lightweight Fighter.

While Maj. Gen. William J. Evans—known as "Hollywood Bill" because of his youthful appearance—was testifying on June 27, 1973, that "these prototypes are not missionized aircraft—rather they are demonstrators of promising new technology which could not be incorporated in production aircraft because of the risk involved," Secretary of Defense James Schlesinger was developing plans to procure the very planes that Evans said could not be procure (Once the decision to procure the F-16A was made, Evans, quick to adapt, testified that the Air Force would prefer them to the F-15s. This was generalized patriotic genuflection at its finest.) At the same time Evans was testifying that the Air Force could not develop the Lightweight Fighter, the Air Force requested a fighter force increase from the OSD authorized 22 wings, which amounted to 1,584 aircraft.[32] The Air Force wanted a larger force structure, but it rejected the only program that would make this possible: the Lightweight Fighter.

In August 1973 the Air Force was telling Congress that the Lightweight Fighter would not become part of its inventory, and Congress was telling the Navy that the Lightweight Fighter should become part of its inventory. Deputy Secretary of Defense Clements directed the Navy to pursue a study of lower-cost alternatives to the F-14, which became known as Navy Fighter Study Group IV.[33] The group was supplemented by two other groups already in existence. The first group was PMA 241, which had been assigned to look at lower-cost versions of the F-14. The other group, PMA 265, also from Naval Air Systems Command, had been formed under Capt. Hank Halleland to run the prototype flyoff between the F-15N, F-14D, and the F-4J. Halleland's group continued to give information to the Navy Fighter Study Group on the F-15.

Pressure to reduce costs came from within the Navy as well. In the fall of 1972, shortly before Grumman's announcement that it would not honor the original 1969 contract, the Vice Chief of Naval Operations, Admiral Weisner, issued a memorandum outlining the conclusions of a CNO Executive Board (CEB). His memorandum sounded more like a lightweight fighter philosopher than the number-two man in the U.S. Navy.

> I consider soaring weapons system costs to be our principal management problem. We are pricing ourselves out of business. . . . *Emphasize Numbers Vice Individual Capability.* The trend toward fewer numbers of weapons systems with high individual capability must be reversed. We need a balance—a few "super-systems" to meet maximum threats, and large numbers of less expensive systems to meet world-wide responsibilities. . . .
>
> *Develop Systems/Programs We Can Afford.* In the past, we have developed systems too expensive to procure in adequate numbers. Additionally, our initial inventory objectives have been generally too high, and last-minute reductions, to conform to fiscal constraints, have contributed to even higher unit costs. We have had both, an over emphasis on meeting a ten-foot tall threat single-handedly and an undue accent on technological achievability (e.g. TYPHON, SHORTSTOP). We have developed inadequate attention to affordability, and to the related issue of how best to spend limited funds.[34]

In essence Admiral Weisner echoed Boyd, Sprey, Riccioni, and Myers. Nor were Weinser's comments much different from Senator Proxmire's in previous senatorial debates.

Reflecting some of Weisner's comments, the Senate Armed Services Committee on September 6, 1973, instructed the Navy to "obtain proposals from industry and evaluate these proposals to determine if a smaller and presumably cheaper aircraft can be designed to serve as an air superiority fighter to complement the F-14."

The Navy Fighter Study Group IV anticipated this direction. On November 15, 1973, the group issued an interim report. The report summarized the activity then in progress. The Fighter Study Group was looking at nine designs to supplement the F-14A. The PMA 265 group looked at the F-15N; PMA 241 looked at four versions of the F-14, called variously the AF-14X with four Phoenix missiles; AF-14X with four Phoenix missiles and A-6 type air-to-ground radar; F-14X with an F-15 APG-64 radar with Sparrow missiles; and F-14X with Sparrow missiles and a Westinghouse WX-250G radar that would ultimately go into the F-16A.

The Fighter Study Group responded in proper institutional fashion. It saw the need for "at least 16 USN/USMC F-14A/Phoenix squadrons." This would put one squadron of F-14AS on each carrier and allow four squadrons for the Marine Corps. The lower-cost fighter must have "high performance, high radius of action, gun, short and *medium* range missiles" (emphasis added). The medium range missile requirement mandated the Sparrow missile. The new fighter, according to the group, "should augment attack forces with smart weapons and A-7E type delivery system." The basic mission for the augmented fighter would be fighter escort. The other missions would be interdiction, combat air patrol, close air support, deck launch interception, and ferry.

The Fighter Study Group asked industry to submit design ideas. General Dynamics submitted a navalized version of its YF-16, called the F-16N.* The F-16N design was significant because it claimed to meet the performance demanded of the VFX, the designation the Navy Fighter Study Group gave to a generic, low-cost fighter complement. While the Navy Fighter Study Group predicted a $5.3-million price for the average unit flyaway cost on a VFX, General Dynamics offered its F-16N at a cost of $3.9 million, ($11.4 million FY1990) based on a total of 400 aircraft procured at the rate of six per month. General Dynamics's figure was significantly below the Navy estimate. Furthermore, it had the Sparrow missile and claimed to accomplish the Navy mission.

The Fighter Study Group said that the VFX design should be a strike fighter with an all-weather capability that would eventually replace the A-7.† The design-to-cost target was $5 to $5.5 million

*Ironically, the U.S. Navy would ultimately buy an F-16N. The designation would be applied to the F-16A used at the Navy's Fighter Weapons School as aircraft simulating the Russian threat.

†The *Air Force Dictionary* defines strike as "an attack upon a surface target." The term "strike" crept into the Navy's lexicon with increased frequency. Calling an aircraft a "strike fighter" put the emphasis on its air-to-ground capability.

in FY1973 dollars. Ironically, the F-14X costs were not available. The group recommended continuing the feasibility study on the VFX.

Within a month from the release of the interim report, the Air Force and General Dynamics rolled out the first YF-16. During the months preceding the roll out on December 13, 1973, the Air Force and the Office of the Secretary of Defense (OSD) had escalated their opposing interest: the Air Force wanted to increase its force structure, but not with the Lightweight Fighter; OSD wanted to increase the force structure with the Lightweight Fighter and was ready to proceed with full-scale development. As a result, the Air Force tried to make the Lightweight Fighter disappear by underfunding the program. The Lightweight Fighter management in both the Air Force and General Dynamics believed that the program was dead.[35]

Unknown to the Air Force and General Dynamics, however, Schlesinger had already decided, through the efforts of Hallock, Sprey, Myers, and his own predisposition, to procure the Lightweight Fighter. The Presidential Budget Request for 1975, which was submitted to Congress in January 1974, included a $36-million line item for a missionized version of the Lightweight Fighter. (In the Budget Request the Lightweight Fighter had been renamed the Air Combat Fighter.)* The money had been inserted into the budget by the office of the director of Defense Research & Engineering—the office in which Chuck Myers worked.[36]

The following month, on February 2, 1974, the YF-16 made its first flight. (The YF-17 would not make its first flight until June 9.) Schlesinger announced his decision to develop the Lightweight Fighter two weeks after the first flight of the YF-16.[37] This decision was made without any indication that the Air Force would be willing to include the Lightweight Fighter in its force structure. Schlesinger thus fulfilled the original goal set by Deputy Secretary Packard in the Fall of 1971. Schlesinger argued for the Lightweight Fighter in this way:

> On the basis of the work already accomplished in the experimental prototype lightweight fighter program, we believe that the development of a new low-cost, high-performance fighter which can perform tactical air missions *under visual flight conditions* is entirely practical and should be vigorously pursued.
>
> Accordingly, we have included in the FY 1975 Budget $23 million ($13 million for the aircraft and $10 million for the engine) to proceed

*The term "lightweight" connotes to the institutional Air Force lack of capability. That was, no doubt, at least one reason for the change. The name would change again to Multirole Fighter after the Air Force chose the F-16 to replace the F-4 phantom II which had both an air-to-air and air-to-ground mission.

> with the experimental prototype lightweight fighter program on an accelerated basis, and $36 million to start the development of a new Air Combat Fighter. (Emphasis added.)[38]

In describing the arena in which the new fighter would operate, the operative word was "visual." This eliminated any need for a Sparrow missile. The word was intentionally chosen to prevent the Sparrow from becoming the dream of any Navy add-on committee.

The Navy received more specific direction. The DDR&E Review Guidance, which responded to the interim report's requirement for Sparrows on the generic VFX design, said, "The Navy should reexamine the basic operational requirement for a lightweight, low cost fighter aircraft with the intent of determining whether a lower cost, less sophisticated system than that characterized by the VFX . . . can be used to complement the F-14A aboard carriers."[39]

The instructions were clear: less sophisticated systems meant a VFX with guns and Sidewinders only. Myers claims that his original directive was much stronger. It went something like this: "Get those goddamn Sparrows off the VFX."[40]

In April 1974, as a result of the Navy Fighter Study Grop IV investigation, the Navy finally made a recommendation. True to form, it recommended a lower-cost F-14X without Phoenix missiles. Deputy Secretary Clements disapproved this recommendation.

Senator Cannon, chairman of the Senate Tactical Air Power subcommittee, asked Clements to attend the May 2 hearings to discuss the Navy's request for FY 1975 funds amounting to $34 million "to start R&D on a VFX type airplane" to supplement the 334 F-14A's that were then programmed through FY 1977.[41] Cannon was not aware that Clements had rejected the recommendation of the Navy Fighter Study Group.

Shortly after the Study Group recommendation, Secretary Schlesinger received from the Secretary of the Navy a memorandum on "Navy and Marine Corps Fighter Modernization." The memorandum summarized the Navy analysis of the investigation into the appropriate alternatives, or complementary fighter, that is, the results of the Fighter Study Group. The results came as no surprise.

The Navy had looked, according to the memorandum sent by Acting Secretary Middendorf to Schlesinger, at the F-14A minus the Phoenix, the F-15N, the two lightweight fighters, the YF-16, and the YF-17. It had also looked at a mediumweight fighter, "which, for purposes of the study, we designated the VFX." In parallel, the Navy looked at reducing the varieties of different types of aircraft on the aircraft carrier to minimize support costs.

The VFX would require, according to Navy estimates, $900 million to $1.1 billion (escalated in nonrecurring R&D costs). The VFX would be a good dogfighter but "mission performance" is "substantially less than the F-14X with the AWG-9 fire control system." The VFX would have low maintenance but high unit cost and the "initial operating capability would not be until 1982."

The YF-16 and YF-17 were unacceptable in their present configuration because the additional weight needed to make the aircraft carrier suitable, would degrade the "finely tuned" design. Scaled-up versions, Middendorf claimed, would be competitive with other VFX candidates.

The Navy considered the F-15N a good performing aircraft, and it would offer a lower flyaway cost than the F-14A. The drawback would be the half billion escalated dollars of nonrecurring research cost to make the F-15 carrier-suitable. This would increase the program unit price. Not surprisingly, the F-15 aircraft carrier suitability was worse than any of the other choices.

The Navy studied, Middendorf continued, five lower-cost F-14s. These differed principally in the fire control system. The design of choice was called F-14X, which Middendorf told the Secretary, was an F-14A without the Phoenix missile. In an apparent attempt to lower costs, the Navy's F-14X concept would have a "more reliable, lower cost computer in the AWG-9 fire control system, and an improved weapons system display as well as other cost reducing hardware items."

The F-14X compared with the other designs would have "a lower program unit cost, better performance, lower near-term non-recurring costs and flexibility for future upgrading, but with higher maintenance costs." The Navy estimated the nonrecurring costs on the F-14X to be $64 million (escalated) with the breakeven point 72 aircraft past the 334 planned F-14A buy, or at aircraft 406. The Navy estimated that the average procurement unit cost would be $12 million compared to $13.9 million for FY 1974 F-14s. The unit savings would amount to $500,000 per aircraft.

The Navy concluded that the F-14X, in spite of a savings of only $0.5 million per aircraft, was "the most cost effective alternative candidate." The Navy also justified the F-14X on the grounds that it reduced the number of aircraft types on board the carrier, as well as the different types between the Navy and Marine Corps.

Middendorf recommend the F-14X to the Secretary, but added that another aircraft might follow: "It appears very possible that a lighter weight, less expensive, combination fighter and attack aircraft, which we might call 'VFAX,' could be developed which would complement the F-14 in the fighter role for the Navy and Marine Corps and also could provide an eventual replacement for the A-7."

Based on its analysis, the Navy made the following recommendations to Secretary Schlesinger: The Navy should initiate F-14X design changes for 12 squadrons and start studies on a new multirole concept fighter which they called the VFAX concept. The study would take six months.

Middendorf's memorandum to Schlesinger is significant because it explains the Navy mindset. In spite of the pressure to develop an alternative fighter to the expensive F-14, the Navy's solution was to shave 3.73 percent off the price of the Tomcat by adding a new computer and avionics displays. These efforts would reduce the cost of the F-14 by $500,000 so that the FY 1974 procurement unit price was $13.4 million. In essence, the Navy's F-14X solution was merely a tonsured F-14A.

The new avionics was probably the avionics originally scheduled for the F-14C. Furthermore, adding new equipment with the promise of reducing costs had been tried on the F-111. It failed.*[42] The Navy's approach to the decreasing numbers of tactical aircraft was a wink and a nod at the problem. Myers, whose marching orders were to help the Secretary get the Lightweight Fighter, prepared an alternative program to the one Secretary Middendorf suggested. In late April 1974 Myers suggested that instead of the F-14X, the Department of Defense should allow the Navy to procure 50 to 80 additional F-14A's, which had the Phoenix missile. DOD should also transfer the Marine Corps F-14s back to the Navy.

In the same spirit of the Navy's VFAX proposal, Myers suggested that the Navy define a fighter-light attack aircraft that he called VFLAX. It should use the F401 engine, weigh less than 28,000 pounds, and forget the Sparrow. Such a plane could be used, Myers said, for air combat and shallow interdiction (day/marginal weather) and close air support in visual weather. For the fleet air defense mission, the VFLAX could take directions from GCI and E-2CS: "It would provide a long term, lower cost alternative than the F-14X plan which must

*Air Force Secretary Harold Brown advocated adding Mark II avionics to the F-111. He claimed that the reduction in maintenance man-hours per flight hours and the increase in mean time between failure would more than offset the increased cost of the new avionics. Brown erred. In 1980 the maintenance man-hours per sortie (MMH/S) was not the promised 1.42 but 33.6; the mean time between failure was not 60 hours but 3. The Mark II avionics cost four times their original estimate and took two years longer to develop.

eventually and surely be followed by an AF-14, ad infinitum, in order to modernize the force."† [43]

On April 30, Chuck Myers along with Dr. Malcolm Currie, DDR&E, and David Heebner, Deputy Director of Tactical Warfare Plans, met in Deputy Secretary Clements's office. Myers explained the alternatives. If the Navy procured a Sparrow version of either the F-14X or the VFX, the Department of Defense and the Navy would lose the objective of a lower-cost fighter. On the other hand, if the Navy limited the alternative fighter to guns and Sidewinders, it could meet the objectives of increasing the force structure.

The Navy, Myers told Clements, wanted F-14A's and Phoenix missiles for the carriers's protection. Myers outlined his plan for increasing the total F-14A buy from 334 to 390 in exchange for the Navy's agreement to build a lower-cost alternative without the Sparrow missile. Clements authorized Myers to proceed with this concept. As Currie, Heebner, and Myers were leaving his office, Clements said, "Y'all better get in the saddle, ya hear."

Myers drafted the statement Clements would read at the Tactical Air Subcommittee hearing on May 2. Myers and Clements met with several Navy representatives at a breakfast meeting right before the hearing.[44] Everyone approved of the statement Myers had prepared for Clements.[45]

Although the Navy Lightweight Fighter advocates did not realize it, the May 2 hearing was the beginning of their Waterloo. At the time, they thought victory was theirs.

For Chuck Myers and the Lightweight Fighter advocates who contributed to the event, Secretary Clements's May 2 congressional testimony represented the political culmination of years of effort. Clements would confirm that the F-14X was not a viable option. Furthermore, he would publicly announce that the complementary fighter would not have the Sparrow missile. Myers listened intently as the Secretary spoke.

> The Navy at my direction, has been investigating the feasibility of lower cost alternatives to the F-14A/Phoenix weapons which could permit us to reverse the trend of a declining tactical force structure and provide for a good combat capability across the broad spectrum of Navy and Marine Corps mission responsibilities. . . .
>
> The high attrition of the early days of [the Arab-Israeli War] has led the Navy and Marine Corps to place more emphasis on the value of increased numbers of aircraft. . . . The display of Soviet naval action

†As later events would show, this was a realistic assessment. The F-18 was dependent on so many additional platforms (tankers, E-2C, AWACS, etc.) in Desert Storm, as were fighters in Vietnam, that this was more a prediction than a proposal.

did little to comfort us regarding the need for a strong defense capability for our aircraft carries. . . . Although how many fleet air defense interceptors such as the F-14A are needed is highly judgmental, there is a strong case for the full Phoenix capability for defense of the carrier at sea.

It is for this reason that I have rejected one alternative of the Navy study, that being the procurement of a non-Phoenix version of the Tomcat, referred to as the F-14X. . . .

I received this week from Acting Secretary Middendorf [a memorandum] on this subject [which] states that:

It appears very possible that a lighter weight, less expensive combination fighter and attack aircraft, which we might call "VFAX," could be developed which would complement the F-14 in the fighter role for the Navy and Marine Corps and also provide an eventual replacement for the A-7. . . .

It is the development of this type of airplane that I am directing the Navy and Marine Corps to pursue subject to your approval of the VFX line item in the fiscal year 1975 budget. . . .

Part of the $34 million in the VFX line item will be used to support the aircraft definition, a brief industry design exercise, issuance of the RFP and the selection of VFAX design. The balance of the money will be directed toward the continued development of the F-401 engine which could be the primary candidate powerplant for this new attack airplane. . . .

The VFAX program is to be responsive to the Marine Corps requirement for a fighter aircraft beyond the F-14A four-squadron force that retains commonalty with the Navy force yet favors a "low mix" aircraft design. . . .

Our goal would be an airplane which would have a spot factor close to 1,* weigh less than 30,000 pounds at takeoff, be equipped with *a cannon and IR missiles*, have a crew of one and provisions to utilize such air-to-ground weapons as laser-guided and optical homing missiles. . . .

We have found no magic formula which would provide for a "cheap" fighter. However, we are going to exploit one major item of leverage to yield an airplane at an endurable cost; that leverage is numbers. We have focused on a mission combination that will permit us to replace much of the fleet of naval and Marine fighter-attack aircraft inventory composed of A-7's and F-4's. . . .

I trust you will support our request for the fiscal year 1975 line item referred to as VFX, so that we may proceed expeditiously toward our goal. (Emphasis added.)[46]

The number-two man in the Department of Defense had spoken. That should have ended the discussion on what the Navy was going

*Spotting factor is the space that an aircraft takes on an aircraft carrier relative to a constant, usually the smallest aircraft on the carrier, but not always. It can be an aircraft resident somewhere in the fleet. The spotting factor is relative to the period. At the time of this hearing, the A-7 had a spotting factor of one and was the aircraft against which the other spotting factors were determined.

to have. Chuck Myers's words were on the record. The rest should have been easy.

One could properly infer from Secretary Clements's statement that the VFAX aircraft would be a scaled-up version of the Air Force's Lightweight Fighter. There was no mention of the Sparrow missile. It was left out. The Navy agreed to the Sparrow's omission. During the questioning, however, the committee asked if the Navy and Marine Corps wanted the Sparrow missile. Maj. Gen. Edward Fris, Assistant Chief of Staff for Marine Corps Air, answered: "We feel we need a night and all-weather capability. Sparrow is the only system around now that is available and we just don't feel that we can give up the night and all-weather to the enemy."[47]

Admiral Lee, Commander of the Naval Air Systems Command, added, "We think it would not be a large penalty to pay in a technical sense to put the Sparrow missile capability [on] such an airplane."[48]

The point of departure for the VFAX as a Sparrowless aircraft came during the questioning by a committee staff member, Charles Cromwell, a former member of the Naval Air Systems Command. Cromwell asked Clements about his omission of the Sparrow.

> Mr. Secretary, in your statement, I believe you mentioned having a gun and infrared missile in the new VFAX but I didn't see anything about a Sparrow missile in there. Is there a position on that taken at this time?
>
> MR. CLEMENTS. In my statement it says it will doubtlessly be equipped with a short range acquisition radar, a computer and fire control system to maximize its potential for low visibility intercept and air fighting problem. The final configuration and weapon suite will evolve from trade-off analysis.
>
> I want to emphasize that. One of the purposes that we would want to go to industry for would be to establish these very criteria that you are talking about. In my judgment, it would be a terrible mistake for us to so constrain industry that they would be working within tight limitations and would come back with something that would preempt their initiatives. So I certainly do not want to leave the committee with the thought that we are going to tightly specify this airplane and design it before we hear from industry as to what, in their opinion, the state-of-the-air is today and what they can do in these out-years to give us this airplane in the 1980's. I don't want to be specifying everything about this airplane in a tight configuration at this point. That is one of the reasons we want to make the study.[49]

Secretary Clements's response to Cromwell's question effectively destroyed all of Chuck Myers's previous efforts to get an agreement between the Office of the Secretary of Defense and the Navy. Clements recanted the Sparrowless position and left the decision up to the military-industrial complex, the very combination Myers was attempting to constrain. Clements did not say that the VFAX would have the Sparrow. Instead, he left up to industry the responsibility of determining something that would not be in their best interest—a cheaper airplane. "It was a case," said Chuck Myers, "of a civilian getting dazzled by military brass and caving in at the last minute."[50]

In what appeared to be an attempt to get both sides of the issue on record, Charlie Cromwell asked Chuck Myers questions.* For example, he asked Myers why he thought the Navy recommended that the VFX should have the Sparrow. Myers replied that the Navy originally looked at the VFX as a supplement to the fleet air defense problem.

> MR. CROMWELL. Doesn't Sparrow give you advantages at night, doesn't it allow you to shoot an enemy airplane that flies into the clouds?
>
> MR. MYERS. Now, we are talking fleet air defense again. Absolutely. Not only does it give you night, but the primary benefit to be derived from a Sparrow is the head-on capability. You recall that the weapons system, in fact, the entire F-4 and Sparrow weapon system was developed in the late 1950's when we were all engaged in the development of weapon systems for a probable nuclear confrontation. Whether you were land-based or sea-based your problem was an incoming raid of air-breathing bombers that were probably going to launch either nuclear bombs or nuclear standoff missiles. The consequence of letting them accomplish that was so high that you were quite justified, operationally, in launching an interceptor and trying to cut them off in a head-on attack, and that is what the Sparrow is extra good at. . . .
>
> Not carrying a Sparrow does not mean you cannot make an intercept or a kill at night. It is very simple to make an intercept: GCI can bring you into the rear hemisphere and if you want to kill whatever is there without ever seeing it, even though it is dark, you can do that with a Sidewinder missile providing you are not firing through clouds. . . .
>
> MR. CROMWELL. . . . The Air Force got one-third of their kills [in Vietnam] with the Sparrow, even in dog fight situations. In fact, the Air Force Ace, Major Steven Ritchie, was up here and he got all five of his kills with Sparrows. He is a strong proponent of a total mix, of having the Sparrow, Sidewinders, and the gun.[51]

Myers replied that most of the Sparrow kills could have been made with other weapons, such as the Sidewinder or gun. Since the rules of engagement required closing to within visual range, in many cases the Sparrow missile was useless. The military imposed the visual identification on pilots after some Americans shot down other U.S. aircraft.†

*Cromwell was later hired by Northrop to work in its Washington, D.C., office.

†While it is true that Ritchie got five kills with Sparrow missiles, the more important point is that he got them all within visual range. Furthermore, Richie fired at least two Sparrows for every attempt. An even bigger question is the unresolved issue of the beyond–visual–range radar kills that some of Richie's fellow pilots made

Myers emphasized that the Israeli pilots exacted high exchange ratios from the Egyptian pilots in the 1973 war without the Sparrow missile.* While the actual exchange ratio is unclear, it was far in excess of any American exchange ratio in any war.

Capt. Gerry O'Rourke, Head of the Navy Fighter Study Group IV, disagreed with Myers:

> The weather in the Middle East is not exactly the kind of warfare that the Navy or Marines would probably be mixed up in the future. Not the most probable. We might get into it but we might not. The quality of the Israeli pilots as opposed to the Arabs was noticeably different. This was not the case even in North Vietnam. The Sparrow missile is complicated, it is troublesome, it does add complications to the airplanes. We think now though that these complications that it does add, cost, weight, and so on, are not serious penalties considering what else you are going to put in the airplane. Once you have already put the radar, the computer, the display and so on in, it doesn't take much more to put a Sparrow in, and having the Sparrow may give you that little advantage in a dogfight, largely as Chuck says, because of the all-aspect capability as well as the all-weather capability. The all-weather capability for the Navy is terribly important because when you need fleet air defense you need every bit of it that you can possibly muster, and you may only need it for a short time, you may need it for a long time, but you need it around the clock and you need it in all kinds of weather. You don't have good weather to fire in all the time. You don't have a nice clear desert and desert air and so on, when everybody goes home at night and forgets about it.†[52]

These comments represented the Navy's position then and now. Protecting the aircraft carrier comes first; it is the raison d'être of all carrier aircraft except the attack airplanes.

Captain O'Rourke's comments on the penalties associated with the addition of Sparrow missiles are the result, according to the Lightweight Fighter Mafia, of circular logic. According to O'Rourke,

that turned out to be American aircraft.

In Vietnam, 34 percent of the kills were with guns and more than 56 percent were made by combining short range, heat-seeking missiles or guns.

*The original reports on the 1973 Arab–Israeli War claimed a P_K (Probability of kill) of 0.45 for the Sparrow. However, Major General Mordechi Hod of the Israeli Air Force refuted that claim. Hod said there were no beyond-visual-range Sparrow kills in the 1973 war. Statement made by General Hod to the author.

Closer to home, the U.S. Air Force asked various commands what they wanted to see in a new IR (within visual range) missile. Their responses are listed in Appendix E and are instructive.

†O'Rourke's comment on the difference in pilots makes another point. Either he believes that the Israeli pilots are far superior to American pilots—which many American pilots admit—or he believes that Arab pilots are far inferior to the North Vietnamese pilots, which is not likely. Both the Arabs and North Vietnamese flew the same aircraft and were trained by the same instructors. The only other conclusion one could draw is that there is some genetic inferiority in the North Vietnamese.

once all the elements necessary to control Sparrow missiles are in place, adding the Sparrows affects cost and performance only slightly. The objects that Captain O'Rourke refers to are in place, however, only because of the Sparrow missile. But for the Sparrow, the cost and weight associated with Sparrow missiles, as well as the associated computers and radar, would not exist. At 500 pounds each, four Sparrows add one ton of weight to a fighter. However, carrying around Sparrow missiles is not the only consideration. An airplane without a Sparrow missile would not require the longer-range radar. Accordingly, the diameter of the radar would be smaller. The smaller radar would result in a smaller frontal cross-sectional area, which would reduce the entire size of the fighter. The reduced frontal area would result in less drag supersonically, and the smaller fighter would reduce the drag subsonically. The fighter would, therefore, require less thrust, or, at the very least, could have the same performance with an engine running at a cooler and more reliable temperature.

Eliminating the Sparrow affects every aspect of the fighter, but the net effect is that the military can buy more airplanes for the same budget. If the Navy believed it had adequate fleet air defense protection with 390 F-14A's, the Lightweight Fighter advocates contend, then the reasoning for adding the Sparrow to the VFAX is specious. If it did not believe it had adequate defense, it should have raised the issue within the Navy before the May 2 hearing. After all, the Navy was willing to go with the Phoenixless F-14X until Myers gave it an opportunity to increase its numbers by accepting a Sparrowless VFAX. Myers summarized his fears.

> It is the associated burdens that bother us more than just the physical penalty on the airplane, the total support cost, and we use the number five times procurement cost as the burden for the care and feeding of a missile, the manpower burden and the additional missiles that you have to buy for war requirements. . . .
>
> There is no doubt about it, it is a nice thing to have, but if you have to take it out of your hide, maybe you are going to think twice about it. What we have begun to do is think in terms of operating under a fixed budget for tactical air. When you tell me you want to buy X, Y, Z, missile or this or that system, the questions I ask is how many fighter airplanes are you ready to trade for that system.[53]

Myers contrasted the cost of the missile and the cost of the associated system and its maintenance. The Navy did not want to address this issue. In questions submitted for the record, the Senate asked: "How much cost does the Phoenix missile add to the F-14?" The Navy answered, "Approximately $165,000 per aircraft is attributed to the F-14 carriage of the Phoenix missile."[54] Yet the cost of the

AWG-9 weapons system, without which the Phoenix missile is merely extra weight and drag, cost $2 million each. The missiles themselves cost close to $1 million each in 1974. The $165,000 figure was undoubtedly the cost of the pallets to attach the missiles to the F-14. In any event, the answer was not responsive. The cost of the AWG-9 and six missiles was closer to $8 million. Even this figure, under the logic outlined above for the Sparrow, is incomplete. It does not take into account the trickle-down costs caused by the larger radar antenna.

The House Armed Services Committee was the first to respond to the Navy's request for $34 million to start the VFAX, née VFX. On May 10 it deleted the request and suggested that the Navy adopt the YF-16 or YF-17.

The Air Force's Lightweight Fighter momentum did not stop during the hearings on the Navy's supplemental fighter. The Air Force began formal overtures to enlarge its force structure. On May 17th, it issued a Program Objective Memorandum requesting a 26 wing Air Force with 72 aircraft per wing.* The Department of Defense authorized the request because the four extra wings would come from the Lightweight Fighter program, recently renamed Air Combat Fighter.[55] (The Air Force does not like to admit that it bartered for the additional aircraft.)

The Navy issued its Program Objective Memorandum for 1976. It had 24 USN and 4 USMC F-14A's listed for a total 574 plus 80 for Iran. The VFAX Initial Operational Capability (IOC) date was targeted for 1983. Within a few days, on May 29, the Senate funded the entire $34 million for VFAX based on the Navy Fighter Study IV report.

The Senate Armed Services Committee support, as well as Secretary Clements's waffling on the Sparrow issue, bolstered the Navy's position. On June 5 the Navy and the Deputy Director of Defense Research & Engineering for Tactical Warfare Programs, David Heebner, met to discuss the Navy's Program Objective Memorandum: Heebner reasserted the OSD position—no Sparrows.

In spite of the OSD directive, the Navy was prepared to release a VFAX Presolicitation Notice (PSN) to industry the following morning (June 6), with the Sparrow missile as a requirement. Myers received a contraband copy of the PSN before the Navy released it. When he discovered that the Sparrow requirement was in the PSN, he prepared a memo for the director, Malcolm Currie. Myers's memorandum reminded the Navy that the PSN was inconsistent with Secretary

*A Program Objective Memorandum, or POM, is the functional equivalent of a wish list.

Clements's opening statement at the May 2 hearings. Furthermore, it was a breach of the Navy's agreement at the breakfast meeting held before the hearing, as well as subsequent meetings with his staff.

Myers's memorandum was meant to exert the constitutionally prescribed civilian control over the military, but as Myers pointed out:

> Normally, the procedure to release a Presolicitation Notice would result in a notification in the *Commerce Daily* that would have said in two weeks we're going to send these things out. They never did that. While I was writing the memo for Currie, I figured we had a few days to stop them. The Navy spy in my office passed the word on what I was doing upstairs to Admiral Houser and company in OP-05, and that afternoon the Navy called contractors on the phone and told them to come in the next morning and pick up their copies of the PSN.[56]

When Currie found this out he was upset, but he did nothing. "The Navy really backed down OSD management when they did that," Myers said. "They did it right in front of the whole world. Industry knew who was running things after that."[57]

Currie's failure to exert civilian control over the Navy unleashed the naval bureaucracy. The final maneuver at Waterloo was over. The Presolicitation Notice was issued; the Lightweight Fighter advocates had lost.

The Presolicitation Notice for the VFAX summarized what would ultimately become the F-18. It merits study because the Navy would judge the F-18 against its requirements. One can contrast the latitude the Navy allowed the F-18 in meeting requirements against the carrier requirements mandated for a navalized version of the Air Force YF-16. Furthermore, one can compare later performance characteristics to see how much the Navy allowed the F-18 to fall short of the its own original desires. (Compare, for example, the range and cycle time of the F-4 Phantom II on page 54 above with the threshold for the VFAX, which the F-18 would be unable to meet.) Table 7-2 lists the PSN criteria. Note the two columns, threshold and goal, which are the mandatory and desired requirements respectively. Note also the degree of importance indicated.

The VFAX Presolicitation Notice, which the Navy wanted returned by July 15, 1974, asked for V/STOL derivative possibilities that were originally mentioned in the Secretary of the Navy's memorandum to the Secretary of Defense. The V/STOL option was influenced by the Navy Fighter Study IV Group, which had a continuing desire to procure the V/STOL concept for the Navy.[58]

Although the major objective of the VFAX was to reduce the cost of fighter aircraft acquisition, the Presolicitation Notice also emphasized the reduction of operating costs through reliability and maintainability. It reiterated some remarks by the Chief of Naval Material.

> Specifically, we are fooling no one but ourselves when we accept without challenge remarkable performance by new weapons systems —which are performing well in the hands of technicians (civilian and military) whose experience and competence far exceed the average to be expected aboard ship far from a support base without a completely adequate spare parts storeroom no closer than several thousand miles.
>
> We have now in hand a splendid reliability and maintainability nucleus which, coupled with new standards in our contract office, can pay immeasurable dividends for the Navy in hand and for the Navy in the future. No contract will be cleared which does not provide hard demands written in unmistakable simple English where infinite minimums for MTBF (mean time between failure) are prescribed. Every commodity which we invent, contract for and produce must be able to perform without failure at least 75% of the time during a 60 consecutive day period of time wherein deployed ships and aircraft might be expected to be without unlimited logistic support.[59]

Although saying that no contract will be cleared unless certain language is included in the contract sounds good, the directive is useless if the agreement is not enforced. It seldom is. The Navy and other services usually state that if they cancel a program they will have nothing to replace it with. Consequently, the military tends to accept what it receives.

The Presolicitation Notice stated, as a threshold, an aircraft that would not exceed $6 million in 1975 dollars for a total of 400 aircraft produced at the rate of 6 aircraft per month. During this same time, the Air Force was asking for a production version of the Air Combat Fighter to cost no more than $4.5 million. Thus one could argue that carrier suitability and radar-guided missile capability added 30 percent to the cost of the aircraft. Due to the pressure from Chuck Myers's office, the Navy sent an addendum to the original PSN asking industry to look at a $4.5-million airplane.[60]

The PSN asked contractors to look at twin-engine versus single-engine, dual cockpit versus single, and "All-Weather Fighter (SPIII) vs. Non-All-Weather Fighter." Within a week after the PSN release, Myers had reviewed the document in detail. He issued a memorandum entitled "VFAX Guidance" to the Air Warfare staff. His concern was that the PSN was "at variance with the VFAX concept approved by the DepSecDef." He was afraid that the PSN guidance would lead to another fleet air defense interceptor, which would duplicate the mission of the F-14A and thus obviate the need for more F-14A attrition aircraft.

Two months before the Presolicitation Notice went to industry, Gen. George Brown, Chief of Staff of the U.S. Air Force, assembled a group at Wright-Patterson Air Force Base to see if the Lightweight Fighter could be a useful fighter in the Air Force inventory. In June

Table 7-2
VFAX Requirements (edited)

Parameter	Threshold	Goal
Fighter Escort Radius (Internal fuel, 2 Sparrows, 2 Sidewinders, gun & 400rds ammo. retained)	400 NM	550 NM
Self-Escorted Interdiction (2 Sparrows, 2 Sidewinders, gun & ammo 4,000 LBS ordnance drag=4MK 83LD)	550 NM	600 NM
Close Air Support (2 Sparrows, 2 Sidewinders, gun & ammo), internal fuel, 8 MK-82HD, 12MK-82LD		1.5 hr time on station.
Acceleration 0.8M to 1.6M 35,000 ft. at max thrust	120 sec	80 sec
Carrier Approach Speed	130 Kts	120 Kts
2-Seat Version Range Reduction		75 NM
Takeoff Gross Weight		28,000-30,000 lbs. or less
Ordnance		
MK-82 LD	8	12
MK 83 LD	4	6
MK 83 LGB	4	4
MK 84 LGB	2	2
Bulldog/Maverick	4	4
Walleye	2	2
HARM	2	2
CBU (ROCKEYE/APAM)	8	12
FAE II (500/100 lb)	8-Mar	12-Jun
Rockets	4	6
Fire Bombs	6	8
Radar (Coherent Pulse Doppler & Pulse)		
Scan Volume	±60AZ,EL	±90AZ
Detection Range, Lookdown (Rgo, 5M², ±60º, 2 Bar)	30 NM	45 NM
Utilization Rate		45 ft/ac/month
Operational Readiness Rate	0.75	0.85
Main. Man Hours/Ft. Hour	11	6
Cost (at 6/mo.; 400 Total)		$6,000,000 FY75

SOURCE: VFAX Presolicitation Notice

1974, before the Air Force could complete its analysis, the Office of the Secretary of Defense formally announced that a full-scale engineering development would proceed. The Air Force plan called for 400 Air Combat Fighters and a design-to-cost goal of $4.5 million flyaway unit cost for 300 aircraft. The 23-month flight testing program

SOURCE: McDonnell Douglas
This is the design that McDonnell Douglas was offering at the time of the VFAX hearings prior to the requirement to navalize the Air Combat Fighter.

was compressed so that the data could be analyzed to meet the NATO consortium's desire to choose a new plane, a decision it wanted to make by January 1975.[61]

The NATO consortium took the Pentagon almost by surprise. In June 1974, a group of 54 individuals representing four NATO countries (Norway, Denmark, Belgium, and Holland) visited the United States and began talking with the U.S. Air Force. During the early 1970s many European countries were close to deciding on the Northrop P-530 or one of the European designs. In 1972 Harry Hillaker and Otto Glasser, Riccioni's former boss—who was now Vice President for International Sales for General Dynamics—went to Europe and suggested that the Europeans need not make any decision because the U.S. government was about to conduct a test program for them. During this same time period, Dassault was trying to sell the Mirage FIE, which was only a design study. As a result of the Lightweight Fighter prototype flyoff in the United States, Dassault was forced to prototype the Mirage FIE as well.

By the middle of 1974, the NATO consortium had waited long enough. Its approach to the U.S. Air Force went something like this: we want 350 airplanes and participation.

The U.S. Air Force took the group to see Deputy Secretary of Defense Clements. As a result, Clements made the formal announcement that the United States would procure the Lightweight Fighter.

Clements sent a formal memorandum to the Chairman of the Multinational Fighter Committee on July 11, 1974, confirming the

United States commitments and emphasizing three U.S. decisions: the United States would develop the Lightweight Fighter; it would introduce the Lightweight Fighter into the U.S. Air Force inventory; and it would deploy the Lightweight Fighter in Europe. More important to the NATO group, the United States gave full backing to the program, which had been a limiting factor in the sale of U.S. aircraft to these NATO countries.[62]

Slightly over two weeks later, on July 29, 1974, Secretary of Defense Schlesinger issued the Program Decision Memorandum (PDM) to the Secretary of the Air Force. It verified that the Air Force had agreed to accept the Air Combat Fighter (ACF) as a result of its request for four additional wings. Schlesinger said, "Tactical Air Force Mix: POM [Program Objective Memorandum] force structure is approved contingent on ACF entering force on approved accelerated schedule. POM force structure increases above the 22 wing level are approved specifically for the purpose of accommodating ACF deliveries."[63]

The Navy was in great need of additional aircraft, but what it wanted was more of its sophisticated F-14s. When the House Appropriations Committee deleted all the funds for the VFX* line item on August 1, there were mixed feelings in the Navy. Some thought that this would require Congress to increase the number of F-14A's. Others believed that it signalled a permanent state of decreasing numbers of tactical naval aircraft. Because the House Appropriations Committee apparently deleted the funds because of a lack of commonality with the Air Force Air Combat Fighter, some observers predicted a common aircraft with the U.S. Air Force.

Five days later, (August 6) Malcolm Currie sent a memorandum to the Assistant Secretary of the Navy for Research and Development discussing the VFAX Development Concept Paper.[64] Currie reiterated the purpose of the VFAX concept, which was to arrest the decline of the tactical aircraft inventory. Currie told the Navy to assume that the F-14A solved the all-weather fleet air defense mission. The remaining issues, Currie told the Navy, were the air-to-air combat over a given area; battlefield interdiction in support of ground action; parametric analysis on cost versus performance based on $5 million in fiscal year 1975 dollars; spotting factor of one; and a comparison between the VFAX and the Air Force's Lightweight Fighter or Air Combat Fighter. Currie's memorandum also raised the question of reliability, maintainability, and V/STOL options.

*The original name of the VFAX

Currie's memorandum reflected the message from Congress: bring the VFAX and Air Combat Fighter closer together. Congress, it seemed, was attempting to do what Robert McNamara had tried to do 13 years earlier. It wanted a common Air Force-Navy aircraft.

In August it appeared that the Navy was going to receive the necessary money to fund its VFAX. Although the House Armed Services Committee had recommended in May that the Navy procure either the YF-16 or YF-17, in August the Senate Appropriations Committee put money back into the budget for the VFAX aircraft. But it lowered the amount to $20 million and added the provision that by January 1, 1975, the Deputy Secretary of Defense justify to the committee the separate development of these two aircraft.

August was also significant for the Air Combat Fighter. The Air Force awarded $4-million contracts to Northrop and General Dynamics to convert the YF model prototypes into aircraft capable of performing the evolving mission.[65]

The activity on the Air Combat Fighter was competing for the same budget dollars that McDonnell Aircraft Company wanted for its F-15. Consequently, McDonnell offered the Air Force 300 additional F-15's (beyond the original planned buy of 729) at a flyaway unit cost of $5.8 million.

By September 7, 1974, the U.S. Air Force released formal proposal instructions for the full-scale development versions of the two lightweight Fighters into Air Combat Fighters. The proposals were due by December so that the NATO consortium could incorporate the Air Combat Fighter into its decision.[66]

The performance requirements for the Air Combat production proposal for the air-to-air role was similar to the original criteria for the Lightweight Fighter. The winner should be abe to fly 500 miles with external tanks and two Sidewinders, full internal fuel, and ammunition, drop tanks, and execute four maximum sustained turns at Mach 0.9 and three turns at Mach 1.2 at 30,000 feet. The requirement then called for an acceleration from 0.9 to 1.6 Mach in 80 seconds and a return home 500 miles with 20 minutes of reserve fuel.[67]

The full-scale development instructions also called for the Air Combat Fighter to have air-to-ground capabilities. There were suggestions that the F-15 be used air-to-ground as well as suggestions to develop two separate versions of the Air Combat Fighter, one for air-to-air and the other for air-to-ground.[68] The Air Force resisted these suggestions. It had decided that the Air Combat Fighter would replace the F-4 Phantom II, which the Air Force used in both roles.

Gen. David C. Jones, Air Force Chief of Staff, decided in the fall of 1974—once the Air Force knew it was getting the F-16 or F-17—to employ the F-15 only in the air-to-air role. Simultaneously, the Air Force establish a Configuration Steering Group whose purpose was to decide what items would be added to the F-16 for the dual role of air-to-air and air-to-ground missions.

The F-15 had originally been scheduled for both the air-to-air and air-to-ground missions.* Jones's decision to change the mission of the F-15 from a multirole fighter to a pure air-to-air fighter was made to reduce the threat the YF-16 created for the F-15. The YF-16 was not allowed to fly against the F-15 in mock dogfights because if it defeated the F-15, (which it later often did) future F-15 procurement would be jeopardized.

On September 12, 1974, Secretary of Defense Schlesinger announced that the Air Force would increase the number of Air Combat Fighters from 400 to 650.[69] The announcement may or may not have had any influence on the September 18, 1974, Joint Committee on Appropriations Report. The language of the committee is important for two reasons: Congress told the Navy what the Navy should do with the VFAX funds; the Navy ignored it. Congress told the Navy the *name* to use for the new fighter and the Navy would ignore that too.

> The Managers are in agreement on the appropriation of $20,000,000 as proposed by the Senate instead of no funding as proposed by the House for the VFAX aircraft. The conferees support the need for a lower cost alternative fighter to complement the F-14A and replace F-4 and A-7 aircraft; however, the conferees direct that the development of this aircraft make maximum use of the Air Force Lightweight Fighter and Air Combat Fighter technology and hardware. The $20,000,000 provided is to be placed in a new program element titled "Navy Air Combat Fighter" rather than VFAX. Adaptation of the selected Air Force Combat Fighter to be capable of carrier operations is the prerequisite for use of the funds provided. Funds may be released to a contractor for the purpose of designing the modifications required for Navy use. Future funding is to be contingent upon the capability of the Navy to produce a derivative of the selected Air Force Air Combat Fighter design.[70]

The message was clear: whoever won the Air Force's Air Combat Fighter competition won both the Air Force and Navy Air Combat Fighter competition. It was certainly clear to Northrop and General Dynamics. Both companies had started making overtures in July

*This isolation of the F-16s from the air-to-air Designated Operation Capability (DOC) would continue to the point that F-16's were never procured with Sparrow missile capability and were used in the same capacity in Desert Storm as B-17s were in World War II.

1974 to other aerospace companies with experience in building aircraft carrier capable airplanes. At that time both Northrop and General Dynamics had submitted versions of their YF-17 and YF-16 designs to the Navy in response to the Presolicitation Notice for the VFAX.

General Dynamics considered teaming with LTV Aerospace, McDonnell Aircraft, and Grumman. According to its chairman, David Lewis, General Dynamics felt that LTV would be the strongest ally because Grumman was busy with the F-14 and McDonnell was beginning delivery of production versions of the F-15.[71] Lewis called W. Paul Thayer, president and chairman of the board of LTV, in July and suggested the possibility of teaming on the VFAX aircraft. Thayer told Lewis that LTV, had received overtures from Thomas V. Jones at Northrop and felt that LTV should study both aircraft designs before making a commitment. Lewis then told Thayer that General Dynamics would continue discussions with other aerospace companies.

Lewis held several discussions with McDonnell Aircraft Company over the next several months. LTV continued its discussions and evaluations with both Northrop and General Dynamics. When the Joint Appropriations Committee issued its September 18 report, LTV became convinced it should choose whichever design would likely win the Air Combat Fighter competition. After all, the language of the report mandated that the winner become the VFAX aircraft, now named Navy Air Combat Fighter.[72]

Northrop proposed a teaming agreement to LTV on September 26, 1974. However, LTV decided against teaming with Northrop because LTV was convinced that General Dynamics would win the Air Combat Fighter competition. That would automatically make LTV the prime contractor on the Navy version. Thayer notified Lewis on September 28 that LTV would join forces with General Dynamics. Lewis told Thayer that he was obligated to keep a September 30 appointment with McDonnell Douglas. Thayer than called Thomas Jones and told him that LTV would not be teaming with Northrop. LTV would either team with General Dynamics or not get involved in the competition.

At the meeting between David Lewis and Sanford McDonnell, president of McDonnell Douglas, McDonnell did not make any commitments, but David Lewis recalls that Sandy McDonnell said that a "better carrier-based aircraft could be developed from the F-17 ACF than from the F-16 ACF." It is not clear whether McDonnell Douglas believed that the F-17 ACF proposal would win the Air Combat Fighter competition, or whether it believed that only the twin-engine design would fulfill the Navy's propensity for twin-engine fighters. (McDonnell Aircraft is alleged to have a corporate policy never to design a single engine fighter after the single-engine F3H Demon disaster.) In any case, Sandy McDonnell called David Lewis on October 2, 1974, and told him that McDonnell Douglas decided to team with Northrop. Lewis wasted no time. He called Thayer and told him that General Dynamics would team with LTV.

Now that General Dynamics and Northrop had picked their teams, it was only a matter of time before the Joint Committee's language imposing an Air Force fighter on the Navy would take effect. The Joint Committee had just imposed a new name on the Navy—an Air Force name at that. The only thing left to do, or so it seemed, was to wait.

Like everything in Washington, the congressional language in the Joint Committee report was subject to interpretation. For example, Malcolm Currie believed that the "congressional language should not be interpreted too literally."[73] Most observers took the language to mean that the aircraft would be common. The veterans of joint procurement programs knew better.

They smiled on October 12 when the U.S. Air Force issued, on behalf of the Navy, a Request for Quotation (No. N00019-75-Q-00289) based on Navy Type Specification 169 to the joint teams of LTV/General Dynamics and McDonnell Douglas/Northrop.[74] The RFQ notified the contractors that the Conference Report directed the Navy to make maximum use of "technology and hardware." The design should make maximum use of commonalty with the operational requirements that were enclosed with the RFQ. The operational requirements are not available, but reasonable investigation indicates that they were similar, if not identical, to the requirements listed in the Presolicitation Notice of June 1974. As a throwback to previous attempts at a Sparrowless fighter, the RFQ included this sentence: "In addition the contractors are also requested to provide a variant which has only provisions in place of the full all weather air-to-air missile capability and identify the gains and penalties associated therewith."

The RFQ emphasized commonalty with the Air Force's Air Combat Fighter. It required that the design include the engine used in the Air Combat Fighter.

The Criteria for Evaluation and Source Selection stated that cost and performance would be weighed equally. The two primary missions were Fighter Escort and Interdiction.* The Navy rated per-

*Currie's August 6 "Outline for Navy VFAX Aircraft Development Concept Paper" formance, production, reliability and maintainability as the order of importance for evaluation. The production criteria were based on 800 aircraft produced at a rate of nine aircraft per month.

The first of November was the deadline for the proposals for the production versions of the U.S. Air Force Air Combat Fighter. It was also on this date that the Deputy Secretary of Defense sent a letter to the Chairman of the House and Senate Appropriations Committee informing the committee that the Defense Department intended to use part of the $20 million for financing studies of derivatives of the two Air Combat Fighter designs for Navy use. Clements was relying on the Joint Committee's language, which said: "Adaptation of the selected Air Force Air Combat Fighter to be capable of carrier operation is the prerequisite for use of the funds provided. Funds may be released to a contractor for the purpose of designing the modifications required for Navy use."

These two sentences appear to be in conflict. The first sentence implies that the Air Force must have already made its selection of the winning Air Combat Fighter design before any of the $20 million can be used; the second sentence by itself implies that the money could be used for the purposes listed in Clements's letter. Both committee chairmen authorized use of the money but encouraged Clements to maintain maximum commonalty.

Within a few days after the November 1 deadline, some of the initial data on the Navy designs were established. One of the striking differences between the avionics requirements of the Air Force's Air Combat Fighter and the Navy Air Combat Fighter was the beyond-visual-range requirement of the Navy radar. The Air Force had a requirement for detecting a 5 square-meter target with pulse doppler radar in the look-down mode at a range of at least 19 miles. The Navy's requirement for the same size target was 30 nautical miles. In addition, the Navy VFAX requirement asked for two radar-guided Sparrow AIM-7F missiles.

The other major difference between the Air Combat Fighter and the Navy Air Combat Fighter was the carrier suitability requirements for the Navy aircraft. These carrier requirements were important for two reasons. They would, of course, permit carrier operations. But more importantly to the U.S. Navy, the carrier suitability re-

called for the strike mission to be "battlefield interdiction in support of ground action." Interdiction per se normally implies "deep strike interdiction," which is the modern equivalent of World War II strategic bombing,that is, the bombing of factories, towns, etc. Battlefield interdiction in support of ground action comes closer in definition to close air support. (See Figure 1-7.) The importance of this distinction lies in the fundamental assumptions needed to design the aircraft. However, in the this case, the constraints were already mandated by the YF-16 and YF-17.

quirements would be the fulcrum upon which it would reject the aircraft—as it had done with the Air Force's F-111.

THE AIR COMBAT FIGHTER DIFFERENCES

The Navy had an approach speed requirement of 115 to 124 knots, a sink rate requirement of 23 to 25 feet per second (or the ability to withstand slamming into the carrier deck at 1,380 to 1,500 feet per minute), and a catapult shot requirement off the carrier with only 10 knots of wind. The Navy also demanded a spotting factor, relative to the A-7, of 1.0 to 1.1.

The Navy made its first overt move toward a two-engine aircraft by discriminating between the F-16 and F-17 fuel tank designs: imposing bladder fuel tanks on the F-16 but not on the F-17. The disadvantage of bladder fuel cells is that they restrict the fuel load. But bladder fuel tanks are made from collapsible linings, which provide insurance against fuel leakage. As late as 1981, the F-17's derivative, the F-18, continued to suffer from fuel tank leakage problems. The weight increases associated solely with carrier suitability for the two designs were 1,253 pounds for the F-16 and 1,625 for the F-17. The F-17 would have weighed 100 pounds more if bladder fuel cells had been required.

General Dynamics submitted several designs as the competition progressed. The wing area on the initial General Dynamics submission, the F-16, was 280 square feet, the same area that the YF-16 had and not the 300 square feet that was ultimately used. The F-16-1 was 39.6 inches longer than the F-16 and 8.4 inches longer than the 46-foot, 6-inch, YF-16. General Dynamics wanted to make the F-16 approximately 30 inches longer than the YF-16 to accommodate the two-seat version, which also would allow the F-16-1 to carry 2,018 pounds more fuel.

Chuck Myers was in the battle to eliminate the second seat altogether. The Air Force would ultimately compromise on a 10 inch plug for the F-16A; John Boyd would argue for an additional 20 square feet of wing area to accommodate the weight growth that he knew would come.

The beginning of December 1974 was the beginning of the end. The technical responses to the Request for Quotations were due to the Navy by December 2; the source selection began on the Air Force's Air Combat Fighter. Many observers saw the selection of the Air Force Air Combat Fighter as the determinant to the selection of the Navy Air Combat Fighter. The congressional language appeared straight forward and clear. There would not be separate designs, only a Navy airplane beefed up to work off the carrier with Sparrow missiles hanging on it. The only thing to do was await the Air Force source selection of the Air Combat Fighter. The bonus to the winning contractor would be a navalized version.

Chapter 8

Winner Take All

> *We don't use our brains and our pencils enough. We don't think about going back to simplicity to save lives. Many simpler, earlier solutions are not only more reliable but even more effective than solutions which use the very latest technology.*
>
> *It should be a principle in the development and engineering of weapons systems never to use a more advanced technology than you have to in the light of battlefield needs. The moment you try you introduce high risk and you get increased cost and low reliability. I am interested in systems that will work.*
>
> Robert S. McNamara
> Secretary of Defense, 1961–1968

To the uninitiated, the announcement on January 13, 1975, that the YF-16 was the winner of the Lightweight Fighter competition meant that the YF-16 was the Navy's Air Combat Fighter. After all, the previous September the Joint Appropriations Committee had directed that whichever fighter the Air Force selected would also become the Navy's Air Combat Fighter. But the Navy had a successful track record of avoiding the imposition of Air Force initiated designs. The Navy would not accept the F-16 without a fight, and the Navy had help.

As the end of 1974 approached, Lieutenant General Stewart was finishing his analysis on the cost of a common Air Combat Fighter for the Air Force and Navy. The Office of the Secretary of Defense had been assigned the same task. Senator McClellan, chairman of the powerful Defense Appropriations Subcommittee, had asked in August for a report on commonality of the two aircraft—even before the Joint Conference Committee Report of September 18, 1974—when it appeared that the Navy and the Air Force were going in two separate directions with their respective VFAX and ACF aircraft. McClellan's committee said:

> The Committee recommends that the Secretary of Defense provide the committee with a report by January 1, 1975, that (1) justifies the need for duplicative development of a lo-mix fighter aircraft by both the Air Force and Navy, (2) cites both the cost and operational advantages and disadvantages of the use of the same basic design aircraft (e.g. F-4, A-7) by Air Force, Navy and Marine Corps, (3) lists the life cycle cost

implications of different basic design Air Force and Navy lo-mix fighter aircraft for the future force.[1]

The task of creating the report requested by Senator McClellan went to an office within the Secretary of Defense's structure known as the Office of Program, Analysis & Evaluation, (PA&E) which formerly operated under the name of Systems Analysis. Systems Analysis flourished under McNamara where every question seemed to have a mathematical or statistically derivable answer. The military fought against Systems Analysis constantly, and within the military someone branded as an *analyst* was only one step above traitor. When the Republicans came to power under President Nixon, Secretary of Defense Laird changed the name Systems Analysis to Program Analysis & Evaluation (PA&E), because the mere mention of System Analysis was offensive to the military and many members of Congress. Systems Analysis originally confined its functions to budget issues, but it evolved as the devil's advocate to the office of the UnderSecretary of Defense for Research & Engineering (USDR&E) formerly DDR&E. Classically USDR&E supported high technology solutions, and PA&E challenged these solutions.* But over the last 20 years the rolls of PA&E and the military have reversed. PA&E offers military analysis and solutions to problems, and the military argues technology and budgets. Many military officers conceded to the author that PA&E had a better grasp than the military on military history and tactics, but they rationalized that any future war was not likely to be based on the past.

Toward the end of December 1974 PA&E realized it could not complete the McClellan Report by January 1. All of the material needed to create the report was designated as source selection sensitive. This restricted it from analysis until after the announcement of the ACF winner. Tom Christie, who had co-developed the Energy-Maneuverability studies that Col. John Boyd used to develop the Lightweight Fighters, was working in PA&E and was charged with writing the McClellan Report. Christie went to his boss, John Ahern, then the Deputy Assistant Secretary of Defense for Program, Analysis & Evaluation for General Purpose Forces, and suggested that they ask to delay the report. Christie explained to Ahern that although PA&E's cost analysts were cleared for monitoring the source selection sensitive material, the rest of PA&E did not have access to those data.

*Secretary of Defense Aspin worked in PA&E prior to running for the House of Representatives. The job he held prior to becoming the Secretary of Defense was Chairman of the House Armed Services Committee.

Ahern agreed. He discussed the possibility of a postponement with one of McClellan's staff assistants, Tom Gunn. Gunn, who went on to become the president of a McDonnell Douglas division, agreed to the delay but forgot to notify McClellan. One might logically ask why McClellan would want the report since language of the subsequent and prevailing Joint Committee Report directed a common airplane. PA&E speculated that McClellan was against the idea of a common airplane and wanted to get the Secretary of Defense on record.

The original date for the announcement of the Air Force selection of the Air Combat Fighter winner was scheduled for Friday, January 10, 1975. Three days before this, the LTV/General Dynamics team with their navalized F-16, and the McDonnell Douglas/Northrop team with their navalized F-17, were told that their designs were deficient and unacceptable. On Thursday, January 9, DDR&E told the Air Force it was going to postpone the announcement because of concerns about commonality.

DDR&E and PA&E were often on opposite sides on an issue. DDR&E was established as a reaction to the Soviet launch of *Sputnik*. The directors of DDR&E have traditionally been PH.D.'s in physics with a background in missile technology. Their charter and mind set have been to seek high technology solutions. PA&E has opted for simpler, practical solutions.

DDR&E knew the Air Force had made a decision that would not be satisfactory to the Navy. The number-two position within DDR&E was held by Robert Parker. Parker asked his boss, Malcolm Currie, to postpone the decision for a couple of weeks.* Parker and Currie were successful in getting a delay through Deputy Secretary of Defense Clements.

PA&E looked at the decision the Air Force had made to see if the decision made fiscal sense. Its tentative conclusion was that a common F-16 would be the least expensive, while a common YF-17 would be the most expensive. Between these two extremes was an F-16 for the Air Force and an F-17 for the Navy. PA&E even believed that the common F-17 was more expensive than an F-16 for the Air Force and a totally new VFAX for the Navy. The costs at the time

*Parker takes credit for the insertion of a gas turbine engine in the Abrams M-1 tank, as opposed to the simpler, more reliable, but less sophisticated diesel engine. Parker preferred the gas turbine in spite of the fact that the heat source made the tank a much larger infrared source, burned forests, was extremely susceptible to dust, and was too hot for foot soldiers to walk behind. The turbine was such a fuel hog that, during Desert Storm, the Army had to place fuel in front of its advance to supply the M-1 which averaged 7 gallons per mile. (See Burton, *Pentagon Wars*.)

were approximately \$4.5 to \$5.0 million for the F-16 and \$6.8 million for the F-17. The cost of development on the J101 engine was unknown. (The cost that PA&E derived was different from the costs developed by General Stewart's cost group but the conclusions were identical.)

When Secretary of the Air Force John L. McLucas heard that DDR&E was going to postpone the announcement, he called Leonard Sullivan, the Assistant Secretary of Defense for PA&E and ordered Sullivan to his office. The Air Force Secretary had the data from Lieutenant General Stewart that supported the Air Force decision to select the F-16. McLucas believed that PA&E would be called upon to support the decision inspired by Parker and blessed by Clements. McLucas was going to ask Secretary of Defense Schlesinger to intervene. McLucas issued a warning to Sullivan: if Sullivan was going to support Clements's approval to postpone, Sullivan had better have supporting data.

When Sullivan left McLucas's office, he explained the Air Force position to Christie and Milt Margolis, who was in charge of the cost analysis group. Both Christie and Margolis reconfirmed the position that a common F-17 would be more expensive than a separate F-16 for the Air Force and an F-17 for the Navy. Sullivan then called Malcolm Currie and told him that at the meeting with Schlesinger, in which McLucas would ask Schlesinger to overturn the Clements decision, PA&E would be supporting the Air Force.

The next morning, the Friday originally scheduled for the announcement, McLucas had his meeting with Schlesinger. Currie and Parker were there from DDR&E, Sullivan and Margolis from PA&E. Lieutenant General Stewart was there to present the Air Force rationale. When Stewart was finished, Schlesinger turned to Currie and Parker and said in essence, "You want to tell the Air Force to go back to the drawing boards, change their minds so that they can build the same airplane that the Navy is going to select, when you and I both know that the Navy has no intention of ever supporting this airplane.

"I don't know," Schlesinger continued, "why I should force the one service that is supporting the program to change their mind. They have gone out and made up their mind and now you, DDR&E, are telling me I should make them change it."[2] Schlesinger authorized the Air Force to announce the following Monday the F-16 as the winning design.

Northrop began to regroup from this temporary setback. The next day, Saturday, Tom Christie got a call at home from Bill Bailey, a

Northrop employee. Christie knew from the noise in the background that a meeting was in progress. Bailey wanted to know if the commonality report that Senator McClellan had requested the previous August had ever been submitted to the McClellan committee. Christie told him no because PA&E got the date postponed.

Congress was not in session but Northrop tracked down Senator McClellan and reminded him that he had asked for the commonality report to be delivered to him on January 1, that the report had not been delivered, that the Pentagon was off on another game just like the TFX days; and that General Dynamics, the same contractor, was involved. Senator McClellan was familiar with the TFX conflict because he chaired the hearings. McClellan was not aware that his staff assistant had postponed the January 1 deadline.

McClellan did his own tracking, found Secretary Schlesinger at home, and informed him that he was supposed to send McClellan a report on the first of January, which had not been delivered. McClellan added that until he received the report, no announcement had better be made by the Air Force.

Schlesinger was not aware of any of the discussions on the McClellan report. He called John Ahern to find out what McClellan was talking about. Ahern told Schlesinger that PA&E had been relieved of the deadline. Schlesinger was unmoved; he told Ahern that he had to have the report on Schlesinger's desk Monday morning.

Ahern was left with no option. He called the Navy and McLucas to tell them that he needed their people to write the appropriate parts of the report. He also called Christie but he was not home. When Christie arrived home at two o'clock Sunday morning, Ahern was waiting on his front porch. Christie called his organization together to produce their part of the report.

At seven A.M. Sunday, January 12, a dozen civilian and military employees from the Navy, Air Force, and the Office of the Secretary of Defense forfeited their inalienable right to watch the Superbowl by working through the day until one A.M. Monday. The Navy group was led by the Commander of the Naval Air Systems Command, Vice Admiral Lee. The Air Force was there too, but unlike the Navy, was not very cooperative. Their attitude was, "you write it and we'll look it over." In essence, the report was written by PA&E and the Navy.

The report supported the Air Force conclusion that the F-16 was the proper aircraft and that a common F-17 was the most expensive answer. PA&E's position was that a common F-17 not only cost more, but would give the Air Force an inferior aircraft. During the process of writing the McClellan report, the group found the written agreement from McClellan's assistant that postponed the original January 1 deadline.

The next morning, January 13, PA&E delivered the commonality report to Schlesinger. The Secretary then gave the report to his General Counsel, Marty Hoffman. Hoffman was also armed with the agreement to postpone the report. Schlesinger permitted the Air Force to proceed with the announcement that the General Dynamics F-16 was the winner. This announcement was preceded by a telegram from Senator Chiles who questioned Schlesinger's wisdom in letting the Air Force make a decision before the Navy. Chile's position was that both decisions should be announced together because of the commonality issue. "If the Navy review runs counter to your decision it is my understanding we stand to pay nearly $1 billion extra because of reduced commonality in the U.S. Forces."[3]

Chiles had no way of knowing that both the Air Force and PA&E had concluded that it would be cheaper to let both services develop their own aircraft than to impose the F-17 on both. Yet while PA&E knew what the Navy meant when it said *navalize* the Lightweight Fighter, it may be that Chiles also knew, and that the $1 billion dollars was in reference to the research and development costs over and above the cost of the development of the F-16.

The day after the F-16 announcement, Secretary Schlesinger disregarded the Joint Committee language of September 18, 1974. He said the Navy could continue to evaluate both aircraft. " 'The Navy will be continuing an evaluation of that air combat fighter that is most appropriate from the Navy's standpoint in terms of resources that must be expanded, as well as in terms of the effectiveness of the various aircraft. . . . The only impact of the Air Force decision would be to make a variant of the F-16 cheaper for the Navy. Nonetheless, the Navy must pursue the questions of whether such an aircraft would appropriately serve the Navy mission.' "[4]

One can speculate why Schlesinger allowed the Navy to continue looking at both designs. It was clear from both the Air Force and PA&E that commonality as an end in itself did not serve the public interest, at least, not if the common airplane were the F-17. Perhaps Schlesinger felt that the Navy would never support the prospects of a Lightweight Fighter and, therefore, the country's interests were best served by increasing the Air Force structure and letting the Navy come along as a by-product of the decision. Undoubtedly the January deadline set by the NATO consortium set the pace for the Air Force announcement. When asked directly why he allowed the

Navy to continue the evaluation when Congress had directed a common aircraft, Schlesinger replied, "I just considered it one more obstacle to overcome."[5]

LTV Aerospace, which had teamed with General Dynamics, must have had mixed emotions with the announcement of the F-16 as the ACF winner. Clearly the language of the Joint Committee Report had directed that the Navy airplane be a derivative of the Air Force selection. This should have meant that LTV would be developing a new Navy fighter. On the other hand, six days prior to the selection, the Navy had told LTV that its design was not acceptable.

Why did LTV not protest the delay immediately after Schlesinger's announcement, or raise the issue and at least obscure the Navy's decision-making process? Some speculation is that LTV felt it was certain to win. However, senior vice president of LTV (later Vought Corporation), Jack Welsh, in response to the question said, "We weren't smart enough."[6] LTV could have raised the issue during the next two days, January 15 and 16, when, along with McDonnell Douglas, it had technical discussions with the Navy on the design deficiencies.

Whether LTV was complacent is arguable, but Northrop was definitely not. Northrop retained the services of an influential Washington, D.C., lawyer, Tommy Corcoran, who had a close relationship with Senator McIntyre, Chairman of the Senate Armed Services subcommittee on Research and Development. Corcoran and a Northrop representative asked for McIntyre's help. Northrop's position was that the Navy should be able, as Schlesinger stated, to evaluate the F-17 fairly without unnecessary influence from the Texas delegation in whose jurisdiction both General Dynamics and LTV resided.

Northrop was equally concerned about whether the Navy was obligated to choose the F-16 because of the commonality language in the Joint Committee Report. At that time the Navy was analyzing that legal issue.

McIntyre agreed to help. He called the Assistant Secretary of the Navy for Research & Development and encouraged him to disregard the outside influences. He wrote two letters on January 23 urging Schlesinger and the Comptroller General of the United States to disregard external pressure, though arguably not his. McIntyre also suggested to Schlesinger that the market was large enough for two different fighters, that the selection of the F-17 by the Navy would encourage competition, and that the work force would be distributed more broadly.

Within the next 11 days, the Navy received new designs from LTV and McDonnell Douglas. LTV submitted its design on January 27 and McDonnell Douglas submitted its revised design on February 3.

February 3 was also the day that President Ford sent his 1976 Budget to Congress. The Office of Management and Budget (OMB), the makers of the budget, included a narrative on the Lightweight Fighter. As testimony that the Executive Department does not work as a cohesive whole, the description of the Lightweight Fighter reflected the sentiment of Congress, not the Department of Defense, by referring to a common fighter for both the U.S. Air Force and the U.S. Navy.[7]

After the Air Force announced the winner of the Air Combat Fighter competition on January 13, Robert Parker of DDR&E continued to press his perspective. He "began what one official called 'an almost hourly dialogue with Northrop to get the Air Force source selection reversed and get the YF-17 adopted by the Air Force.' "[8] In spite of an eight-hour source selection briefing at the end of January, Parker continued to bring up new data and new reasons why the F-17 would be the better aircraft for both services. When asked why he kept insisting on the F-17, Parker said, "I just didn't think it made any sense to procure an airplane for the Air Force that would be unacceptable for the Navy; and I knew that the F-16 would be unacceptable."[9]

Once the Air Force made its selection, PA&E hoped engineering and development would begin right away based on the prototype, with very few modifications to the aircraft. However, the Air Force had a dilemma: the F-15 had originally been conceived as a replacement for the F-4, but the F-16 was being imposed on the Air Force because the F-15 was too expensive. The Air Force's original plans called for the procurement of 772 F-15s, which with the attrition, training, and replacement aircraft, would give the Air Force 432 F-15s—enough for six wings. However, the Air Force had more than 1,000 F-4s to replace. The long-range goal had been to replace all of the F-4s with F-15s. Now the F-16 threatened to replace the F-15. So the Air Force rewrote history, claiming that the F-15 had always been intended as a pure air-to-air fighter. "Not a pound for air-to-ground," became the institutional chant. Thus, the Air Force gave the F-15 a new niche and gave the role of replacing the F-4 to the F-16. Once the F-16 became the replacement for the F-4, it had to become worthy of the air-to-ground mission.*

*One must appreciate the U.S. Air Force's predilection for dropping bombs. Regardless of the original intent of an aircraft's design or requirement, the Air Force

Once the decision was made to make the F-16 an F-4 replacement, the Air Force began *missionizing* the F-16. The decision as to what should go into the F-16 was delegated to a committee called the Configuration Steering Group, led by Lt. Gen. Alton Slay. As the group proceeded through their analysis, they decided that the F-16 had to have more range than the YF-16, which required a plug in the fuselage (and allowed for more avionics); they decided that the Air Force needed a two-seat version for training, in spite of the many pilot transitions made in the YF-16 without such benefit; and they increased the avionics requirement. All of these additions prompted Pierre Sprey to dub the Slay group the "Configuration Add-on Committee."

This phenomenon of adding equipment is endemic to the Air Force in general and specifically to the Tactical Air Command. During the TFX hearings in the early 1960s, one Air Force general confessed to this phenomenon of unbridled growth.

> General MOORE. Senator Jackson, I have been in the fighter business and in Tactical Air Command almost my entire career and can say one thing for sure that I have learned, and that is if the airplane can carry it, it will be put on it.
>
> Senator JACKSON. Say that again.
>
> General MOORE. If the fighter aircraft can carry it into combat, it is going to be put on it.[10]

The increasing weight of the F-16 was not without opposition, as Tom Christie recalls:

> It was Chuck Myers and I versus the Air Force. We assumed all along we had Schlesinger on our side; that he would stop the trend of sophistication of the aircraft, because the cost was going to go up to the point that we weren't going to be able to buy as many as we indicated. The Air Force also used the NATO connection. The Air Force talked NATO into wanting all this crap on the airplane so that they could use that as an argument for justifying the increased sophistication in order to sell it. We got word up to Schlesinger through his guy Bing West, who was his exec so to speak, that if Schlesinger didn't personally intervene, the Air Force was going to get away with screwing up this airplane. We knew that Currie and Parker were supporting the Air Force in their so-called missionization. I assumed that in particular Parker's intent

will convert it to an air-to-ground aircraft. When the Air Force wanted to continue building F-105s, an airplane designed from the ground up as a nuclear bomber, Secretary of Defense McNamara imposed the F-4 on the Air Force instead. Yet the F-4 was originally designed by the Navy as a single-purpose air defense interceptor. Nevertheless, the Air Force made maximum use of the F-4 as an air-to-ground fighter; the designated operational capability (DOC) of many F-4 squadrons was air-to-ground. As such, these airplane squadrons would have been designated attack squadrons in the U.S. Navy. In mid-1993 the Air Force added to its supersonic cruise F-22 the additional mission of an attack aircraft.

> was to run up the cost to where the previous cost calculations done in the McClellan report would permit the Air Force's selection to become invalid, because the cost would come in as high as the F-17.
>
> To me, that was a good part of the motivation on the part of the Air Force who thought, "O.K. you guys, [the Lightweight Fighter Mafia] you thought you were so smart . . . well by the time we're finished with this, the F-16 will cost as much as the F-15."*[11]

Chuck Myers was also making his own arrangements to get material to Secretary Schlesinger. Those who work within the Pentagon know how difficult it is to make sure that the Secretary of Defense is aware of the events that take place under his command. He is surrounded by military assistants who read everything before the Secretary receives it. Anything that is not consistent with the policy of a particular assistant's military service, may not survive for the Secretary of Defense to read. The assistants act as a kind of thought police. In order to avoid the possibility that Myers's comments might not find their way to the Secretary's desk, Myers sought out Marty Hoffman, Schlesinger's general counsel, to give him material to take to Schlesinger.

Myers drafted a note on February 21, 1975, to attach to a memorandum that he felt Schlesinger should read in order to understand the degree to which the Air Force was increasing the cost of the F-16.

> Marty—
>
> The continuous dialogue with the USAF including Jones and Dixon coupled with the executive session (pre DSARC) debates with LaBerge have pretty well established the AF position, fears and intentions. Our pleadings and "incentives" cannot hope to alter their position on the "missionization" for the F-16. It is destined to be a sophisticated all-purpose tactical airplane to replace the F-4 fleet. . . . We know how to control it but it will require arbitrary action as suggested in my attached paper. . . . I am convinced that only the Secretary can cause such a stand to be taken by OSD. Also, I feel that once such a position is taken, the USAF will go along with it—they have bigger fish in the fire which need Sec Def support. We need assistance within the next couple of days.

This note was attached to a paper Myers wrote entitled, "F-16 (LWF/ACF) Program Restoration," and was a review of the design-to-cost goals of the Air Combat Fighter, the effect of the increase in cost due to the Air Force actions, and a suggestion on how to remedy the increasing costs. Myers reminded Secretary Schlesinger that in his Presidential Decision Memorandum (PDM) of July 29, 1974, he

*As to the fulfillment of the prophecy, one need only to examine the cost of the F-16C and F-16D developed under the aegis of the Multinational Staged Improvement Program.

stressed simplicity and low life cycle cost with "a minimum of sophistication in fire control and weapons delivery systems," in the transition from Lightweight Fighter to Air Combat Fighter.

The original design-to-cost goal of the Lightweight Fighter had been $3 million in 1972 dollars, yet, Myers pointed out to Schlesinger, the Air Force was estimating $300,000 increase in the original $450,000 goal for avionics. The increase was more likely to be, Myers speculated, $1 million. The program needed rigid guidance to be restored to its original intent. Myers suggested that an avionics ceiling cost of $510,000 in fiscal year 1975 dollars *installed* be imposed on the Air Force. In addition, he suggested that the two-place model be eliminated as well as a relaxation of the strength and fatigue criteria.

Myers fought the idea of a two-place airplane, which the Air Force originally said would require a 30-inch plug in the YF-16 design. Two-place airplanes, Myers argued, were a recent concept, which the Air Force said was needed for check-out rides. Myers argued that no one has an accident in the transition to a new plane; it's always some time later. The longer airplane, which would have been the design of both the single- and two-place F-16, was merely an excuse to stuff in fuel and avionics. "The Air Force was using the European requirement to break down the resistance against the sophisticated aircraft. If the Europeans had not been interested in more sophisticated aircraft, the Air Force would have said, 'To hell with the Europeans—we need it.' "

Myers and Christie tried to establish a weight limit on the F-16 as a way to control the increasing costs. "Len Sullivan [Assistant Secretary of Defense for Program Analysis & Evaluation] fought us on that idea. 'If you knew anything about aircraft design, you'd never make that statement,' " Myers recalled Sullivan saying in one of the pre-DSARC II meetings with Currie and Parker. "Sullivan was in favor of constraining the F-16 but did not believe that putting a weight limit on it was the proper approach."[12]

Also attached to Myers's plea to Schlesinger to stop the escalation of cost in the F-16 was a copy of a paper Myers had written the previous March (1974) to justify the Lightweight Fighter concept and, specifically, why the Navy could operate without a Sparrow missile.[13] The paper's first paragraph opened with a revelation seldom addressed: "The total DOD [Department of Defense] investment since 1955, in air-to-air radar weapons system for 'F' designated aircraft now exceeds $10 billion."*[14]

*To put into perspective the $10 billion spent on radar-guided missiles for "F"

Such an investment, Myers continued, would cause anyone, but particularly Congress, to wonder why, after all the money spent, the Department of Defense would recommend a fighter without a radar-guided missile. To explain it, Myers's paper tried to show where the radar missile was supposed to work and, more importantly, *where it did not*.

Myers divided air warfare into three zones: the blue zone, home of the friendly forces; the red zone, home of the enemy forces; and the purple zone, in which the two forces would interact. The asset under the blue airspace were airfields in NATO or the U.S. Navy's task force at sea. On land the purple zone would be the area on which the ground war was fought. The red zone would be similar to the blue zone, but with more radars for control of the airborne fighters.

It was the blue zone, whether over land or at sea, that the radar-guided missile was designed to defend and in which it was most likely to succeed, Myers wrote. The exchange ratios of 50- to 70-to-1 of the 1967 and 1973 Arab-Israeli wars were illustrative of the power of fighters without radar-guided missiles, Myers added.

Armed with this surreptitiously supplied information from Myers, Schlesinger announced, in an unheard of maneuver, that he would attend the DSARC meeting scheduled for March 11.* "We showed up at the DSARC and a very interesting thing happened. Malcolm Currie began what had the elements of a filibuster. He began to ask detailed questions of the Air Force on the detailed cost of various items. He asked detailed questions about the avionics, and went on and on. The meeting started at 2 P.M. and Schlesinger made it clear that he had to leave by 4 P.M. to meet the German Foreign minister. As a result of all of Currie's questions, we never got to the issues."[15]

Several additional executive sessions of DSARC II were held after the formal DSARC II meeting on March 11, 1975. However, Schlesinger

designated aircraft, recall that only 10 percent of the Sparrow radar-guided missiles fired resulted in kills in Vietnam. With that same $10 billion, the United States could have had an additional 10 to 12 aircraft carriers, or approximately 2,000 additional F-4 Phantoms. This is not to suggest that research should not have been done on radar-guided missiles, but only to point out the relative costs of using them. In light of this expense, poor results in Vietnam, and the need for a visual identification before firing radar-guided missiles (upon which need the AWACS was once justified) it raises the questions whether the money would have been more judiciously spent on the anti-radar air-to-air Brazo missile, which had 100 percent rates in tests. More to the point, if one used only the $10 billion figure, between 1958 and 1982 each of the beyond-visual-range radar-guided missile kills cost $2.5 billion each.

*DSARC stands for Defense Systems Acquisition Review Council. Large programs must gain the approval of the DSARC process before they can advance to the next step. DSARCs approve most programs.

eventually decided in favor of the Air Force. The cost of the F-16 was increased substantially, but not enough to make the F-17 the less costly option for both services. In time, the Navy would eventually teach the Air Force the art of conducting a Configuration Add-on Committee.

The U.S. Air Force fattened the only airplane that offered the possibility to increase its fighter force. The deep strike bombing mentality exploded as the Lightweight Fighter grew into a reality. As a result of the DSARC II meeting, the Air Force made some compromises over what it had originally wanted for the F-16. The mission of the F-16 was definite; the F-16 would replace the F-4. To achieve the dual role that the F-4s were then assigned, the F-16 changed from the air superiority YF-16 to the multirole F-16, and in the process gained weight and complexity under the guise of capability.*

The DSARC II results called for an alternative to the proposed avionics concepts and a plan to ensure that the F-16 would be able to meet the reliability goals. The DSARC II called for a firm design-to-cost goal of $4.5 million average flyaway cost in fiscal year 1975 dollars.[16] There was also a plan to reduce the cost of the F100 engine.

Two significant decisions were made at the DSARC II meeting. One was the elimination of the 30-inch plug that the Air Force wanted to add. The two-seat version, the F-16B, was going to have the identical fuel as the single seat version, the F-16A. Some concern was expressed, other than by Christie and Myers, that aircraft with two different lengths might have different flying characteristics and present too large a risk. The compromise was to increase the YF-16 design by 10 inches for both the A and B versions and reduce the fuel load of the F-16B by approximately 900 pounds.[17] In addition, the wing of the YF-16 was increased 20 square feet. Harry Hillaker gives Boyd credit for this. Hillaker claims that Boyd commented that engine thrust was usually increased during the life of an airplane, but the wing was not. Boyd suggested that the wing on the F-16 should be given a head start. The second major decision was to reduce the number of full-scale development (FSD) aircraft from 15 to 8.[18]

*The U.S. Air Force uses the word *capability* so often that it numbs the senses. The *Random House* dictionary defines capability as "The capacity to be used, treated, or developed for a specific purpose," while the *Oxford English Dictionary* gives one definition as "the quality of having room for anything; ability to receive or contain." The U.S. Air Force would undoubtedly use the former definition in describing their F-16 efforts, while the Lightweight Fighter Mafia would use the latter.

Boyd also wanted to give the F-16 a larger horizontal tail. The F-16 horizontal tail was increased 15 percent, but Boyd wanted a larger increase. He looked at what a larger horizontal tail would do to acceleration and top speed. He saw that the degradation was slight, but the benefits in maneuverability were significant. Although Boyd was not persuasive in his arguments at the time, in 1981 the F-16 would finally get the Boydian tail.* Table 8-1 lists the design equipment changes to convert the YF-16 into the F-16.

Table 8-1

Design Changes

Recontoured nose
Ten inch fuselage extension
420 additional pounds of fuel
Two additional wing stations
Horizontal tail area increased 15 percent
Increased wing area from 280 to 300 sq. ft. sq. ft.
Improved access provisions
Deleted blow-in doors
Emergency power unit modified and relocated
Increased landing gear capacity
Added tail hook
Additional graphite composites
Improved engine removal
Changed engine from F100 PW-100(2) to -100(3) for 360 additional pounds of thrust†

Equipment Changes

Multimode radar
Missionized avionics
New ejection seat

SOURCE: House Committee on Appropriations, *Department of Defense Appropriations for 1976.* Part 9, "Lightweight Fighter Aircraft Program," June 10, 1975, p. 327.

One can only speculate whether the changes to the YF-16 would have been looked upon favorably by the Navy. Certainly the multirole aspects of the F-16A were more consistent with the Navy's VFAX. However, the F-16A still did not have a Sparrow missile. Having one would have meant it could compete with the F-15.

The Navy continued the selection process of the NACF through March. The Air Force continued its configuration discussions. The Navy originally expected to make its decision in March. Later it tried to put the March decision off until August, but congressional pressure forced a decision by May.[19] On April 4, Naval Air Systems Command told the joint teams of McDonnell Douglas/Northrop

*Boyd wanted the larger tail for maneuverability but also to avoid the deep stall propensity.

†One senior official at General Dynamics said they were fortunate that the YF-16 flew without the *improved* engine. The -100(3) version developed growing pains later in the F-15. "We might have lost the Lightweight Fighter competition with the improvements."

and LTV/General Dynamics to submit their best and final offers. They did so on April 15, 1975. The two companies made final presentations on April 24, 1975.[20]

As the May decision approached, LTV and General Dynamics must have been feeling confident. General Dynamics won the Air Combat Fighter competition easily. LTV had an established reputation for building Navy fighters. Its aircraft flew on the Navy's first carrier, and the F4U Corsair as well as the F-8 Crusader and A-7 Corsair II had been workhorses as Naval fighter and attack aircraft. All that stood in the way of LTV and General Dynamics was the Navy's history of refusing to accept an Air Force airplane.

Chapter 9

The Air Combat Fighter Evaluation

In war nothing is so light that it may not carry great weight in the end.
Livy, *Ab Urbe Condita, Praefatio*, xxv, 28

On January 13, 1975, Air Force Secretary John L. McLucas announced that the General Dynamics YF-16 design had won the Air Combat Fighter Competition. Some Northrop officials, upon hearing of their loss to build a follow-on aircraft to the F-5, scrutinized the comments made by Secretary McLucas with the fervor that a losing counsel would read a Supreme Court opinion.

> The flight test program that was conducted on the two lightweight fighters went extremely well. Both of the aircraft performed very well. Both of the contractors did an excellent job of supporting the prototype test program. Both of the engine companies did a good job of supporting the aircraft companies.
>
> On the other hand, there were significant differences in the performance of these prototypes. The YF-16 had many advantages in performance over the YF-17. It had advantages in agility, in acceleration, in turn rate and endurance over the YF-17.
>
> These factors applied principally in the transonic and the supersonic regimes. There were other advantages to the YF-16 over the YF-17. These factors included better tolerance of high G because of the tilt back seat, better visibility and better acceleration. In any case, the YF-16 met all the performance goals that we had established for it. The YF-17, while performing very well, did fall short on some of these goals. In the sub-sonic mission areas, the YF-16 and YF-17 were not as far apart as they were in the supersonic. This is indicative of the fact that the YF-16 had lower drag and was a cleaner design.[1]

Northrop, naturally, disagreed with the Air Force decision. Northrop's argument against the Air Force selection process was based on the contention that the evaluation between the two companies should have been based on the proposals for the production versions of the two prototypes, that is, the F-16 proposal and the

F-17 proposal, not the actual performance of the prototypes. Northrop's position was, and still is, that the U.S. Air Force relied too much on the prototypes for the evaluation and not enough on the proposals. In doing so, many Northrop officials contend, Northrop was penalized because their prototype was flying with a prototype engine, while the YF-16 was flying with a production engine developing full thrust throughout its flight envelope. Northrop also started out with a disadvantage because it flew six months later than the YF-16.

The General Dynamics aircraft made its first flight on January 20, 1974, for what was supposed to be the beginning of a 12-month flight test program. Shortly after the first flight Lt. Gen. James Stewart, Commander of the Aeronautical Systems Division, went to Washington, D.C., to brief Secretary of Defense James Schlesinger. At this meeting—attended by Col. Bill Thurman, Lightweight Fighter SPO, and Gen. George Brown, Air Force Chief of Staff, Stewart briefed Schlesinger on performance (with diagrams and other back-up material), showing all of the aspects of the YF-16 and YF-17. According to Stewart, Schlesinger was impressed with the performance for the price paid. Contrary to the opinions voiced by the F-15 union within the Air Force, the YF-16 was clearly a fighter with greater range and endurance than the F-15. Stewart made Schlesinger aware of this.

The Northrop YF-17 did not fly until June 9, 1974, almost six months later. The delay was caused by Northrop's use of the General Electric YJ101 engine, which had not completed its preliminary flight rating test (PFRT) until the preceding September. As a result, General Electric's schedule for delivery was delayed until early 1974. While this relative time difference in first fights was not an issue when both companies were told they could fly independent 12-month tests, it became an issue—at least to Northrop—when the tests were accelerated to meet the impending decision of the NATO consortium. Because the decision for the NATO consortium was to be made sometime in January 1975, the final test data from the two prototypes were due in December. This acceleration would give Northrop only six months to complete its test program, which it did by flying three shifts per day, seven days a week. It compressed the 12-month flight schedule into the 6-month period, but in so doing it gave up opportunities to make modifications. One of the most severe criticisms of the YF-17, its inability to transition from one maneuver to another as quickly as the YF-16, could have been fixed within three weeks, Northrop contended, if had been given the original 12 months in which to fly.

The selection between the two aircraft was based on performance and cost. On both issues Northrop felt that the Air Force made incorrect evaluations. It was Northrop's belief that because the YF-17 was heavier, it was characterized as more expensive. And because Northrop was not given full credit for the increase in thrust, its production version of the F-17 was unfairly credited with lower performance.

From the beginning of the Cobra Program Northrop's objective was to sell the Cobra (N-300 or P-530) aircraft to both the Air Force and the Navy. In fact, the 54-degree turn-over angle on the gear for carrier suitability was in the design from the beginning.

In its original analysis in the mid-1960s Northrop looked at both turbofan and turbojet engines to determine which engine cycle would offer the best engine for the N-300. As a result of this analysis, Northrop believed that for the same thrust turbofan engines were 10 percent lighter, yet cost 20 percent more. As a result, an airplane equipped with a turbofan engine, according to Northrop's analysis, would be 10 percent lighter but cost five percent more than one equipped with a turbojet engine.

Northrop's analysis showed that as the technology increased, the cost and weight went down, but only to a point. Beyond that point, the weight would continue to go down, but the technological advances to continue the weight reduction would begin to increase the cost. In other words, the Northrop contention was that minimum weight was not necessarily at the minimum cost.

One Northrop designer, Walt Fellers, believed that few people understand or accept that minimum weight is not minimum cost. Many of the Northrop employees who worked on the YF-17 believed that the Air Force used the Rand costing system, which does not take into account the fact that minimum weight is not the minimum cost. They believed that the Rand cost model was used on the evaluation in cost between the YF-16 and YF-17.

Northrop was critical of the Air Force's analysis of the costing methods, but was quick to give credit to the Air Force for its ability to estimate the correct weight of the YF-17 during the original Lightweight Fighter competition. Weight, which is important in both costing and performance, becomes a pivotal issue during the evaluation of a design. As one Northrop official stated, the Air Force told all the contractors that their weights would be scrutinized.

> [The Air Force] did their own weight estimate. We will use [the Air Force told us] our own weight estimate instead of the contractors because these contractors lie and brag. In this particular case it was true. We did it on purpose and G.D. did it on purpose. The guys told us they

were going to evaluate [our weight statements] correctly and they were going to put in their own weight estimates so its all right for you to put in your own real weight estimate because if the other guy lies we'll fix him.

Well, we didn't believe the Air Force. So we guessed how much G. D. was going to lie and brag and we guessed within 200 pounds. And we lied and bragged the same amount. It didn't make any difference because they picked us both.

They did an excellent job of evaluating the real weights of both airplanes. They did a fine job, excellent job. They were right on our real weight of the airplane.[2]

This admission of falsifying weight data on the one hand, while on the other complimenting the Air Force for its ability to see through inaccurate data, tends to discredit Northrop's complaints about the Air Force's inability to properly evaluate the cost of the YF-17 as a function of weight. It also clouds the issue on the second major contention, performance.

A literal interpretation of Secretary McLucas's announcement would indicate that the performance of the YF-16 was compared to the performance of the YF-17. Northrop readily admited that the YF-16 was superior in performance to the YF-17. The difference, Northrop claimed, was due to the prototype engine. The issue, according to Northrop, was whether the F-16 proposal production version was superior to the production version of the F-17. Northrop contended that its production proposal for the F-17 was not given proper credit for the difference in thrust between the prototype YJ101 engine and the production version of the J101.

The sea level static thrust of the prototype YF101 was 14,300 pounds, whereas the thrust of the J101, which General Electric and Northrop proposed for the F-17 production version, was 15,000 pounds. Northrop claimed that if it had been given full credit for its increased thrust, then the performances of the two aircraft would have been essentially equal.

To complicate the issue, the Air Force felt that the installed thrust of the YJ101 was not as high as the sea level static thrust. Since the design of the aircraft was held constant, the increased thrust of the proposed J101 was not going to be as great, according to the Air Force, as Northrop claimed. As Gen. James Stewart recalled, "We had a great technical argument with Northrop. We argued over installed thrust. Was it short on installed thrust or was it high in base drag?"[3]

The specific areas of disagreement were acceleration through Mach 1.0 and supersonic turns at Mach 1.2. The Air Force also thought the YF-17 had higher drag rise than Northrop did through the transonic region of .9 to 1.4 Mach. Northrop felt that it was hurt in accelerating through the higher Mach area because of the scheduling of the prototype engine. In the subsonic region it was already 5 percent below the production engine in thrust. In the transonic region of Mach 0.9 to 1.4 the YF101 scheduling produced even less thrust in the region of 10 percent. Lee Begin, a patent holder on the YF-17, said, "General Electric was conservative with the YF101 engine. They had it downturned so much that it wasn't putting out the power that we had predicted. We didn't find out until November or December."[4]

Walt Fellers had a different opinion from the Air Force evaluation team.

> From the YF101 engine to the projected production engine, when they went through the evaluation, the propulsion labs were not allowed to project that . . . and they never gave us credit for the production engine doing what it was supposed to do.
>
> On paper they went through their exercise but because we had to go from the prototype to the production it opened up room for judgment and they put their own judgment on it. And people who wanted the answer to come out the other way, put their judgment and said, "Well, we're not going to get hardly any improvement on the engine." Again, the propulsion labs didn't agree with that. They thought the engine would do what it was supposed to do, and it's been verified in principle since then by the F404 doing what it's intended to do. It's been verified when the Navy later went through and looked at flight test data and the engine data for performance purposes.[5]

In addition to the issue of reduced installed thrust was the issue of base drag. Base drag is that drag associated with the separation of airflow from the blunt trailing edge of the aft end of body, in this case the aft end of the YF-17. Many aeronautical designers believe that an increase in drag associated with a twin-engine design would not be there if a single-engine of equal thrust were used. The measurement of drag is a weak art at best; even the best engineers admit that its isolated measurement is difficult. However, in interpolating the increase in performance of the production version of the YF-17, the actual drag of the prototype became a significant issue.

To compare the drag of the two aircraft, the test pilots flew to a certain speed, then chopped the throttles. The relative deceleration would be an approximation of the difference in drag between the two aircraft. Accordingly, one could infer that if one airplane reduced speed more quickly than another, the faster deceleration meant greater drag. The YF-17 did decelerate faster than the YF-16, but Fellers claimed the reason was not due to drag.

> During supersonic flight, after the pilots would chop the throttles, the YF-16 would keep going while the pilot of the YF-17 was practically thrown through the instruments. Thus, everyone said that the YF-17 had more drag. What we found out much later after the decision was over was that the YF-16 kept going after the throttle chop because the F100 engine does not shut down. It decels at its own sweet time, short of shutting off the engine. Northrop was told that the YF-17 had to have a lot of drag to decelerate like that.
>
> There was a myth of afterbody drag interacting. This was supposed to be a supersonic shock wave intersecting between the vertical tails. This was merely an explanation for the increased drag.
>
> We did the most complete afterbody drag studies. Actually, with the low bypass ratio of the YJ101, and the difference in the nozzle angle variations, these made a difference in the drag in our favor. With the studies we did I can say that the drag associated with two engines is not greater than with a single engine of the same thrust of the two.[6]

However, Lee Begin, program manager of the YF-17 program, disputed Fellers' statement:

> Northrop did have a problem with the supersonic drag of the airplane. Subsonic drag was approximately what it was supposed to be. The performance wasn't quite what it was supposed to be. It is connected with some of the same things that have shown up with the F-18 which are connected with some of the slots, and we didn't work with the bleed doors.
>
> It is very, very difficult to properly evaluate the seriousness of the drag when we were overwhelmed . . . when it was covered up by the prototype engine missing production thrust. If you are missing on thrust, then your acceleration will be terrible.[7]

The performance of the proposed F-17 was a function of the credit the Air Force gave Northrop for YJ101 thrust and the diminution of drag. Northrop believed that the Navy's Air Combat Fighter substantiated its assertion. "The Navy gave us full credit for the drag we had estimated and for the engine performance we had estimated. The Navy asked the question, 'How did you guys let the Air Force screw you like they did?' And we said, 'Well, we didn't have much choice.' "[8]

The bigger issue on performance between the two prototypes was their ability to defeat other aircraft. The YF-16 and YF-17 did not fly against each other, as Sprey had advocated in his July 1969 F-XX paper. If they had, according to Lieutenant General Stewart, "the only place the YF-17 would have done well would have been at 0.6 Mach. It didn't have the range, acceleration, etc."[9]

There was an even larger reason, according to John Boyd. If the aircraft had been flown against each other, it would have been only a matter of time before the logical next step would have been to fly them against the F-15. That would have shown that either Lightweight Fighter was superior and threatened the F-15 program. Lieutenant General Stewart saw the rationale differently. "It would have been unfair to the prototypes to fly them against the F-15," he said, implying that the F-15 would have prevailed in the air-to-air confrontation. "There was a squib in the Lightweight Fighter Request for Proposal to fly against the threat if available, and they were, and we did."[10]

In flying against the threat aircraft, the YF-16 was able to defeat the threat more quickly than the YF-17. Quicker kills were a function of the YF-16's ability to transition from one maneuver to another, according to Colonel Boyd. Recalling Boyd's definition on maneuverability on page 21 above, it follows, then, that the ability to maneuver more quickly than the opponent—or in this case the competing prototype—is what allowed the pilots to transition through the observation-orientation-decision-action (OODA) loop more quickly than the pilot flying the threat aircraft. Lee Begin does not dispute the quicker transient maneuvers of the YF-16.

> Boyd and Sprey are right when they say that we lacked the transient maneuverability in roll. It's true, mainly with roll rate. We had a weak horizontal stabilator. At high q we used a combination of tail and aileron for roll rate. We did not have enough stiffeners in the fuselage. We needed to put a bigger diameter piston in. It would have taken 3 to 4 weeks. There were 345 frigging flying hours in seven months. Just not enough time. As a result, we did not have a good roll rate at 0.9 Mach. We would have fixed it in production.[11]

There is little argument that the three months between the September 1, 1974, request for proposal from the Air Force to General Dynamics and Northrop and the December 1 deadline left little time for either company to make changes. General Dynamics had the inherent advantage of flying with a production engine. One Northrop official claimed this meant General Dynamics was automatically the winner because of its engine commonality with the F-15.

Northrop's arguments abaout not being evaluated correctly did not convince the U.S. Air Force. Lieutenant General Stewart refutes Northrop's position that the Air Force used the Rand formula, which states that if the aircraft is heavier it must be more expensive. "Northrop doesn't know what they are talking about. We had four different cost formulas and the Rand formula was only one of them."[12]

In early January 1975, Lieutenant General Stewart briefed a group of senior defense officials, including Secretary Schlesinger, Dr. Currie of DDR&E, and his principal deputy, Robert Parker, on the methodology for selecting winning design.

The primary contributor was the need for 20 to 35 percent less fuel. The catalyst that forced the cost analysis was a campaign that Northrop was pursuing around the Pentagon in which the company maintained that a common F-17 for both the Air Force and the Navy would cost a billion dollars less. Lieutenant General Stewart, who was as perplexed as most, began his briefing with, "a billion dollars less than what?"

The purpose of the briefing was to explain the cost of procuring a common aircraft for both the Air Force and the Navy. Stewart showed that the cost of acquiring a Navy and Air Force version of the F-16 would be the least expensive, but that procuring a joint version of the F-17 would be the most expensive. In short, if the Air Force bought the F-16 and the Navy bought the F-17, this combination would be cheaper than imposing the F-17 on both services.

Contrary to Northrop's belief, the company was given credit for the ability to produce two J101's more cheaply than one F100. In January 1975 dollars, the cost was $1.2 million for the F100. The higher engine-related accident rate, due to a single engine over a 10-year period, was also factored in. In spite of these factors, the F-16/F-17 combination for the two services was less expensive.

The YF-16 life cycle cost in the production version was $1.1 billion less, not counting the possible development problems in the YJ101. The lower fuel consumption under normal operating conditions equated to 1 million barrels of oil per day.

Lieutenant General Stewart denied that Northrop did not get full credit for the performance increases in its F-17 production proposal. "The YF-17 performance was increased in our evaluation considerably and the YF-16 performance was degraded, due to their changes. Northrop flat wanted the contract and thought they had a better airplane."[13]

The basic guideline for picking an Air Combat Fighter winner was the air superiority mission. The YF-16 was "clearly superior in the transonic and supersonic portions of the air combat flight regime due to better maneuverability and greater excess thrust, as well as possessing a significantly larger radius of action."[14]

According to John Boyd and others on the evaluation committee, every pilot who flew both airplanes considered the YF-16 the superior aircraft. Northrop accepted that the YF-16 had the better performance, but claimed projections onto the production aircraft gave the advantage to the F-16 proposal. On the air-to-ground portion, the YF-16 had slightly greater radius of action with equal loads, but the YF-17 had a 25 percent greater combat payload.

Cdr. "Mugs" McKeown evaluated the YF-16 and YF-17 in January 1975 to assess the fighter capability. He flew the YF-16 against the YF-16 and the YF-17 against the YF-17. When asked by Senator Goldwater how these two aircraft compared with the F-4, specifically the F-4E, KcKeown replied:

> Sir, I have flown against virtually every kind of fighter in the world. My observation was that these airplanes . . . represented a very dramatic increase in fighter capability . . . I felt I could beat MIG 21s in basic engine in either aircraft.
>
> Senator GOLDWATER: In either aircraft did you experience any of the old fighter-type problems such as inadvertent stalls, snaps, anything like that?
>
> Commander MCKEOWN: The YF-16 had an angle of attack limiter, sir, at 20 units angle of attack; and it did exhibit adverse post-stall gyrations, and this type of characteristic, that was one of the reasons for the stall limiter. As I understand, Air Force test pilots in the joint task force did on three occasions that I know of spin the YF-16. The YF-17, conversely, exhibited none of these trends whatsoever. . . .
>
> [The YF-17] was probably the simplest jet airplane I had ever flown. On the very first flight I flew it to 45 degree angle of attack, 90 knots at 40,000 feet, put in full rudder, and the airplane just turned around 90 degrees.
>
> Oddly enough, when you get into a situation called the scissors, you go slow flight and try to fight them, you wind up the F-16 with really an odd-sight picture because both airplanes look more or less like cobras, going around cocked up at 45 degree to 50 degree angles. It is really a new dimension in dogfighting.[15]

Commander McKeown's comment was made after the Navy selected the Northrop aircraft as the basis for the F-18 derivative. In Navy parlance, he was "emphasizing the positive." However a few days after flying both aircraft, Commander McKeown told the author and others at the Navy Fighter Weapons School that the YF-16 was the far superior aircraft. He made these extemporaneous remarks several months prior to this congressional testimony. When asked why he didn't testify that the YF-16 was a better fighter, McKeown said, "The Navy had already decided. It wouldn't have made any difference."[16] But in all fairness, McKeown's preference was for the YF-16—the prototype—which Northrop admits was the better performing fighter.

The answer to which airplane—the F-16 or the F-17—would be the better airplane lies perhaps in the difference between what Northrop proposed in the original Lightweight Fighter competition and what they delivered. As one senior Air Force officer who worked on the program stated:

> Northrop didn't lie. Contractors don't lie. Contractors are overly optimistic. They ask their weight people if there is anything that can be done to eliminate weight and the weight people come back and say, well, if we can get some of this and if this can be substituted with that then I believe we can do it.
>
> In Northrop's original proposal for the Lightweight Fighter they were fourth in performance after Boeing, General Dynamics, and Vought. They promised us a lighter aircraft with more fuel. They gave us a heavier aircraft with less fuel.
>
> None of this had any effect on our evaluation of the proposal by Northrop for a production version of the F-17. All it did was affect their credibility as a contractor.[17]

Chapter 10

The Navy Buys Another Air Force Airplane

Before arranging to purchase aircraft, each service will *ascertain whether aircraft of the type desired can be obtained from the other service.*

Curtis D. Wilbur
Secretary of the Navy
General Order No. 132
July 7, 1924

The U.S. Navy announced that it would develop the loser in the Air Combat Fighter competition, a decision that appeared to be in direct contradiction to the congressional will. At the May 2, 1975, news conference, announcing the decision, Dr. David Potter said, "It is perfectly clear that this does not meet the language of the Congressional Report, and there is nothing further to be said on that score. We're aware of the fact that the proper selection for the Navy had this unfortunate property."

Dr. Potter had testified the previous year that neither the YF-16 nor the YF-17 could be made into a successful carrier-capable Navy fighter. Yet it was the FY-17 that the U.S. Navy was announcing on May 2 as the winner—well, not quite. It publicly redesignated the F-17 as the F-18 at the time of the announcement. This redesignation implied a new and different airplane. By changing the designation, the Navy violated the substance and form of the directive. The Joint Committee language said that the Naval Air Combat Fighter should be a common airplane with the Air Force Air Combat Fighter. Furthermore, the Navy should make maximum use of "technology and hardware."

The decision to redesignate the YF-17 as the F-18 had to be one of the worst public relations blunders of the decade. The Navy was saying to Congress, not only do we reject your directions for a common airplane, but we are going to take the uncommon airplane and make it *appear* even less common.

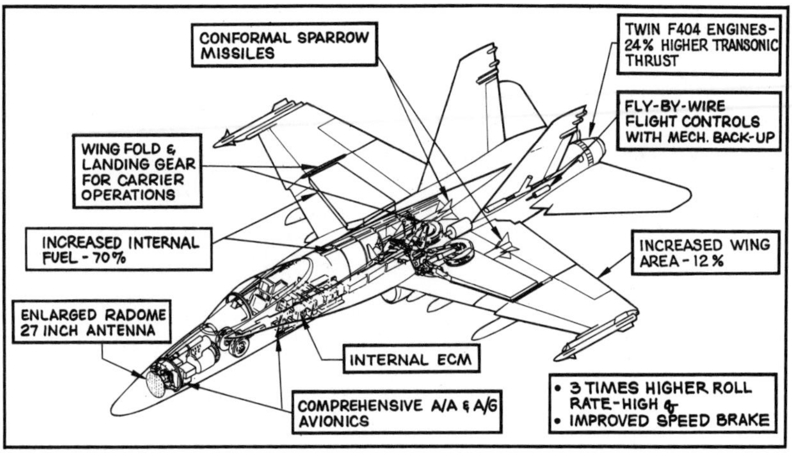

SOURCE: Northrop
The changes to the YF-17 to convert it to the F-18A.

The Navy knew better. The Navy is a master at using redesignations to slide difficult programs through Congress as former Chief of Naval Operations Adm. Arleigh Burke demonstrated when he called a cruiser a "frigate" (see page 32 above).[1]

Regardless of any comments to the contrary, the Air Force had successfully imposed one of its designs on the Navy. The interservice rivalry is so illogical that many fail to accept its existence. The intensity of the rivalry may explain the Navy's attempt to show that it had not acquired the YF-17—an Air Force airplane—but instead the F-18, a totally new aircraft. Indeed, R. W. McDonald, Chief Technology engineer for McDonnell Douglas, said the only thing that McDonnell Douglas did not change on the YF-17 was the position of the vertical tails.[2] The Navy redesignated the YF-17 to perpetuate the charade that it had not acquired an Air Force aircraft and in the process irritated Congress. Congress had, after all, required the Navy to change the designation of its VFAX to Naval Air Combat Fighter, so this may have been its chance to change the designation back.

It is not clear that the Navy was actually responsible for the redesignation. Deputy Secretary of Defense Clements said that he and Dr. Potter changed the number from YF-17 to F-18 one evening for bookkeeping purposes.[3] Dr. Malcolm Currie, then Director of Defense Research & Engineering (DDR&E), also takes credit for the redesignation: "I will have to take responsibility for injecting confusion. [General Electric] renamed their engine and I allowed the name of the 17 to go from F-17 to F-18 thinking it would clarify the issue rather than confuse it, which was a mistake."[4]

The redesignation of the YJ101-GE-100 to the F404-GE-400, like the change from YF-17 to F-18, is an example of the Designation Corollary to The Pentagon Paradox: "the clarity of a designation is inversely proportional to its political motivation." Military designations are designed to add clarity. In this case they added confusion. Congress wanted the two airplanes to be the same in *substance* and in *form*, otherwise the Joint Committee would not have instructed the Navy to remove the VFAX designation and replace it with *Naval* Air Combat Fighter. The Navy rebuffed Congress not only in substance, by not choosing the F-16, but in form with the change in designation. The confusion over the redesignation created an abundance of congressional testimony over the commonality, or lack of it, between the YF-17 and the F-18, when the real issue was the lack of commonality between the F-18 and the F-16. Perhaps that was the Navy's intent.

Commonality became the theme during the second half of 1975. In addition to the usual hearings, the Navy's decision to procure a separate design initiated five separate hearings on the Lightweight Fighter, four in the Senate and one in the House in spite of Dr. Potter's disclaimer, "there is nothing more to say. . . ."[5] Predictably, Congress discussed cost and performance, but the main thrust was commonality.

CARRIER CAPABILITY

The sine qua non for making the F-16 acceptable to the Navy was its ability to land safely on the aircraft carrier. The Navy hid behind the sanctuary of carrier incompatibility as the primary reason to reject the F-16. As the hearings began, the Navy knew it had the benefit of the TFX/F-111B hearings upon which to justify not procuring a common aircraft. Lack of carrier compatibility had scuttled it and the Navy was about to resurrect the maneuver. The specter of that failure still lingered in the minds of many of the powerful senators and congressmen.

During one of the hearings, Representative Mahon got right to the issue. He asked Dr. Currie what commonality there was between the F-16 and the F-18. Currie replied that there was none.[6] Currie admitted that the outcome had not been "in strict literal accordance" with the report, but felt that the Navy had kept to the spirit of the conference report by making maximum use of the Air Combat Fighter technology and hardware.[7]

In the first hearing on the F-18, Chairman McClellan asked Dr. Currie in what way the Navy had not complied with the conference report. Currie replied: "In the final line, it says, 'Future funding is contingent upon the capability of the Navy to produce a derivative of the selected Air Force Combat Fighter design.' We have found that we are not capable of producing a derivative of the selected Air Force Combat fighter design, that is, the F-16."[8]

The Navy, through the testimony of Vice Admiral Lee, Commander of the Naval Air Systems Command, relied on the alleged aircraft carrier incompatibility of the F-16 to reject it.*[9] For a group of congressmen to challenge the Navy in the delicate area of aircraft carrier suitability would be like challenging Dr. DeBakey on heart transplant operations. Both areas are sacrosanct, open only to an elite group, and shrouded with an aura of respect for those who participate in the process. Nevertheless, the Navy failed to make arguments for rejecting the F-16 that would stand up under the perspective of history.

The major factors that contribute to carrier suitability are tail clearance angle, precise and positive low-speed flying qualities, quick thrust responses, structural strength, salt spray corrosion resistance, and the ability to maintain the aircraft on board ship.[10] Of all these factors, however, tail clearance appears to be the most important, followed by the angle of attack, speed, and tire and strut compression.† [11]

The Navy rejected the LTV/General Dynamics navalized F-16 design because it believed the airplane would hit the carrier deck one out of six times. The Navy believed this in spite of the LTV angle of attack limiter, which limited the angle of attack to 20 degrees. The Navy claimed LTV's model 1600, the first of three designs submitted, approaching the carrier at 125 knots with a normal landing weight of 27,879 pounds, would drive the tail into the deck 14 inches. Furthermore, it could only fly at the lower speed of 125 knots by overriding the angle of attack limiter and approaching the carrier at 28 degrees.[12]

LTV revised its model 1600 and a later model 1602 so that according to its predictions, the tail bump would occur in "one in every one million landings." However, the Navy challenged LTV's data. The Navy said that the tolerances necessary to acquire that low a number of tail bumps was too exacting to meet LTV's predictions.[13]

LTV submitted its revised 1600A with a tail clearance angle of 7.1 degrees, which was increased from the previous 3.8 degrees. LTV

*The Department of Defense attempted to delete substantial portions of Admiral Lee's testimony.

†In response to Senator Chiles, the Navy, through adoptive admission, affirmed that tail clearance is the most important criterion.

argued that the 7.1 degrees was better than most contemporary aircraft. The Navy responded by saying that LTV's argument, "misses the point. Its tail bump characteristics are better than only a few of the older Navy aircraft whose problems generated the very tail-clearance specifications the F-16 derivatives do not meet. The NACF specifications are intended to advance Naval aviation, not to perpetuate old problems."[14]

According to the Navy, LTV's designs had an additional weakness. The designs needed a higher approach speed to perform the "pop-up" maneuver, which allows a pilot to make a 50-foot upward glide slope correction with a maximum of 50 percent load factor. The minimum speed at which the LTV designs would have to fly in order to successfully make the pop-up maneuver would be 135 knots, 10 knots faster than the threshold speed.

The Navy agreed that the full span leading edge Krueger flaps and drooped ailerons with boundary layer control proposed on LTV's best and final offer would be successful at high angles of attack. But, the Navy said, the alpha limiter would inhibit the full capability of the high lift devices since the aircraft could never get to those high angles of attack. In order to attain the lower carrier approach

SOURCE: LTV

The Model 1600 is the first of three iterations of the final joint project between LTV and GD which they submitted to the U.S. Navy in the Naval Air Combat Fighter competition.

speeds, the LTV design would have to fly at high angles of attack. However, the Navy did not say that at the 20-degree limit the high lift designs would not provide the carrier approach speed of 125 knots.[15]

There is a certain logic in the Navy's arguments for rejecting the LTV designs. But one might assume that the Navy has a predisposition to reject a common aircraft with the Air Force and would use whatever data necessary to justify its rejection. The following argument substantiates that assumption.

The Navy stated that the LTV design was unsuitable for carrier work because of the 7.1-degree tail bump angle. However, the tail clearance angle for the F-18 claimed at that time was only 8 degrees—a mere 0.9 degrees difference. Furthermore, Grumman told the Navy when it was developing the Tomcat that the F-14A would have a 9-degree tail clearance angle. Its actual tail clearance angle was 4.4

Figure 10-1

The Evolution of the LTV/GD F-16 Derivative to the NACF

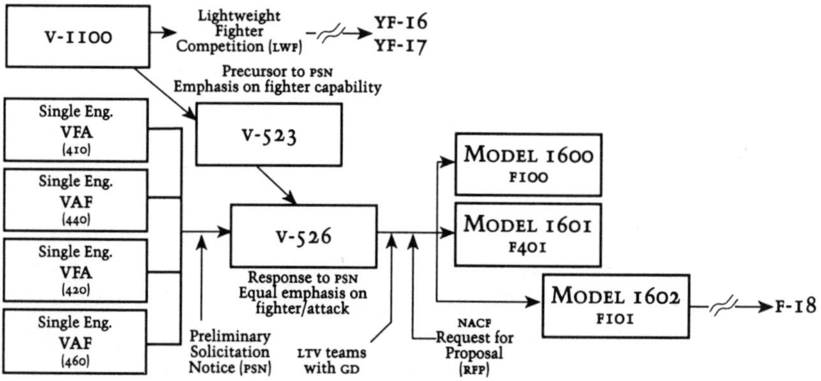

SOURCE: LTV
LTV's attempt to win the Lightweight Fighter and NACF competition

degrees. Yet, the Navy claimed that the F-14A was a very suitable aircraft around the carrier.[16] Although the Navy demanded that Grumman fix it or adjust the price for not meeting the specification, the Navy did not relegate the F-14 to shore duty, as it did the F4U Corsair in World War II, for not being carrier suitable. The Navy admitted that at nearly equal weights—28,370 for the F-16/401 and 28,981 pounds for the F-18—the carrier approach speeds were nearly identical. The F-16 with a speed of 135.5 knots was actually estimated to be almost 2 knots slower.[17]

The Navy also testified that the fly-by-wire system on the F-16 designs was not acceptable without a mechanical back-up system.

This argument implied that in a serious situation, like coming aboard the aircraft carrier at night or in bad weather, the pilot could switch over to the mechanical system that the Navy had relied on for years. In other words, while new technology can be used the majority of the time, the tried-and-true mechanical systems are mandatory in the aircraft carrier environment. In congressional testimony, the Navy gave the impression that the F-18 had a mechanical back-up system that would allow the pilot to land on the carrier if everything else failed.

These arguments are specious. The mechanical back-up system cannot be used to land aboard a 15,000-foot runway, much less an aircraft carrier. The pilot can use it to decide where to eject, and nothing more. While one might argue that selecting an ejection spot is an important survivability feature, the argument misses the point. Single versus twin engines, armor plating versus none, self-sealing tanks versus no sealant, all appeal to the same interests of survivability. The Navy used the lack of a mechanical back-up system to attack the carrier suitability of the F-16, when the mechanical back-up system had nothing to do with the carrier suitability. It was a survivability issue.

To further the distortion, when the LTV finally met the tail clearance angle, the Navy criticized the design for having a landing speed 10 knots over the threshold. Yet the Navy testified that the Northrop/McDonnell Douglas design was 13 knots over the threshold landing speed.[18]

Some of the senators and congressmen were convinced that the Navy was giving evidence to justify their predisposed position against the common aircraft. As Senator Chiles stated, ". . . the Navy made up their mind they didn't want any part of the F-16. They were going to have something else."[19]

The radar-guided missile requirement was another major factor driving the two aircraft in different directions. Imposing the same Sparrowless requirements on the Navy that the Department of Defense imposed on the Air Force would have made the two fighters more common. Sen. John Glenn reminded Dr. Currie that the "rationale, character, and combat mission" for the VFAX airplane had been established by Deputy Secretary of Defense Clements at the May 2, 1974, Tactical Air Power subcommittee hearings. Yet, Glenn went on, the Presolicitation Notice (sent without OSD approval) and the RFQ were describing different airplanes. It was Glenn's contention that by sticking to the common mission, and starting with the

Navy's requirements first, the Navy could have achieved commonality.

Currie responded that the VFAX Presolicitation Notice of June 1974 had been based on the VFX Presolicitation Notice issued by the Navy Fighter Study IV Group. Currie said that he and Admiral Houser wrote the VFX PSN and that it asked for trade-off designs with and without Sparrow. Currie's answer was misleading. He may have written the 1973 VFX PSN, and it may have asked for trade-offs with the Sparrow and without it, the June 1974 VFAX PSN listed the Sparrow as a requirement. As Currie saw it, the issue was simply a matter of putting a continuous wave illuminator in the radar for the radar-guided missile. As long as the radar was already in the airplane, according to Currie's logic, the only difference between an airplane equipped *with* Sparrows was the CW illuminator and the missiles on the airplane.

"I think that in the end we definitely decided that the illuminator should go in there, that we should have that kind of flexibility. But as far as I am concerned the jury is still out, frankly on this final requirement, how many of the airplanes in operation will actually have the missile on them as part of the armament."[20]

The logical inference from Currie's testimony is that there is no penalty in putting Sparrows on an otherwise all-weather airplane, other than the weight of the missiles and CW illuminator. But by

Table 10-1

Air Combat Fighter (ACF) and NACF Candidates

	F-16	F-16-1	F-16-3	F-17-1	VFAX
Weight (lbs)					
Empty	15,200	15,679	17,757	18,000	19,000
Int. Fuel	6,079	9,920	9,280	9,600	10,000
TOGW	21,297	25,599	27,037	27,600	29,000
Payload (A/A)	1864	620	1,864	620	1,864
Dimensions (ft.)					
Span	30	33	33	N/A	N/A
Length	47.2	52	52	N/A	N/A
Wing Area	280	331	331	N/A	N/A
Engines	(1) F100	(1) F401	(1) F401	(2) J101	(2) J101
Int. Thrust	14,380	16,120	16,120	(2) 9,675	(19,350)
AB Thrust	23,440	26,777	26,777	(2)14,400	(28,800)
SFC	.706/2.19	.693/2.19	.693/2.19	.851/1.89	.851/1.89
Weight	3,036	3,649	3,649	(2) 1,805	(3,610)
Weapons					
Gun	M61	M61	M61	M61	M61
Missiles	(2) AIM-9 2) AIM-7	(2) AIM-9	(2) AIM-9 (2) AIM-7	(2) AIM-9	(2) AIM-9 (2) AIM-7
Max. Speed (M)	1.6-1.8	1.6-1.8	1.6-1.8	1.6-1.8	1.6-1.8
Std. Load Factor (G)	8	8	8	7	7

Currie's own admission, if LTV had submitted an F-16 design without the Sparrow, then, "a superficial review of preliminary design data indicates that such an airplane, call it an F-16N, might be carrier suitable without resorting to Krueger LE [leading edge] flap, BLC [boundary layer control] and Alpha [angle of attack] Limiter. The F-16N could weigh at least 1,500 pounds less than the model 1600, exhibit better air-combat maneuvering performance and cost substantially less."*[21]

In other words, there *is* a penalty paid for having the Sparrow missile. The argument thus becomes whether the Sparrow delivers more than it costs. An F-16N, that is, a navalized F-16, but *without* Sparrows, would have somewhat degraded performance over the land-based version. The time to climb to 45,000 feet would be reduced 19 percent. The time to accelerate from 0.9 to 1.6 Mach would increase 11 percent and the fuel flow would increase 6.5 percent.[22]

In spite of these penalties, however, a navalized F-16 would outperform the current F/A-18. The Navy would argue that the F-18 has the Sparrow missile, which justified the degradation in performance. The point-counterpoint is unending. For every degradation in performance, the military offers an electronic marvel as the contervailing justification. Unfortunately, the electronic wizards increase the cost, at the same time, the Lightweight Fighter advocates would say, that they reduce the fighter's capability.

Regardless of the fighter's ability, the conventional wisdom in the U.S. Navy is that carrier-designated aircraft can be used on land, but land-based aircraft cannot be successfully modified to operate on aircraft carriers. History disagrees. The May announcement of the F-18 decision also marked the 24th anniversary of the FJ-2 Fury, which began life as an F-86F Sabre, an Air Force airplane. The success of converting the F-86 Sabre jet into a carrier capable fighter wrote volumes about the reality of what it takes to make an aircraft carrier capable. The FJ-2 Fury differed little from the F-86F.† [23]

There are many examples of common aircraft between the Air Force and Navy, some of which were originally designed as land-based

*Compare Currie's testimony with Chief of Naval Operations Admiral Holloway: "I don't care if [the F-16] cost $1 million apiece; it does not do any good to get something that has to be taken on and off a carrier with a crane."

†The contract for the XFJ-2 Fury was approved on May 29, 1951. The Fury was an F-86E equipped with a V-frame tail hook, a longer nose wheel and catapult points, nothing more. The FJ-2 differed less from its F-86F counterpart than the F-16 did from the YF-16. The production FJ-2 was an Air Force F-86F with the following differences: folding wings, four 20mm guns, modified gear, and landing hook. The take-off weight increased only 994 pounds and the mission time was reduced from 2.16 hours to 1.9, or 15 minutes.

aircraft. There have been over 50 examples in the various military categories.* [24] Some are listed in appendix B.

The appeal of a biservice aircraft is the potential for reduced costs. However, the services seldom cooperate to that end. The Navy resisted the TFX/F-111 commonality program and the Air Force ordered the Air Defense Command not to consider the F-14 in its evaluations—even after the Air Defense Command had selected the F-14 as the best solution. The Air Force made significant changes to the A-7 and F-4—both U.S. Navy-originated aircraft—after the Department of Defense imposed both aircraft on the Air Force. Today little commonality exists between them. Yet they have the same mission.

Coulam points out in his book *The Illusions of Choice* that the services destroy commonality programs by imposing regulations on the newly evolving program.[25] For example, the U.S. Army took the AR-15, a flawlessly functioning rifle that sold on the black market in Vietnam for $600, and subjected it to Army regulations. Once the AR-15 was brought up to specifications as the M-16, it seldom worked and was the only item that the Vietcong would not take from dead American soldiers.[26]

The Navy is guilty of similar maneuvers. It accepted the F-14 in spite of the airplane's failure to meet specifications in the same areas where the F-111B performed better. This is not to suggest the resurrection of the F-111B or to castigate the F-14. It merely illustrates the syndrome that services will support projects they initiate and actively destroy programs they did not. On their own projects, the services will look the other way if the projects fail to live up to specifications. In fact, they will change the specifications to conform to the aircraft's performance. The Navy did this with the F-14 and eventually with the F-18. If the Navy had sponsored the F-16 design, the Fighting Falcon would be flying off aircraft carriers today.

*Former Chief of Naval Operations ADM. E. J. King admitted to the natural superiority of land-based aircraft. After the Battle of Midway, King wanted Army Air Force fighters placed around the Pacific, particularly for Marine Corps fighter squadrons. The Army Air Force rejected the idea because it believed there would never be enough aircraft to support the Army Air Force's needs, much less the Navy's. During war, the military was preoccupied with numbers. As the F-18 came under attack in the spring of 1981, one suggestion advanced was to give the F-16 to the Marine Corps.

Chapter 11

Costs, Mission, and the Promised Performance

One man, one bomb—one hour

A common epigram made by the U.S. Navy's tactical pilot community about the F-18

If Congress and the Pentagon are about anything, they are about the acquisition of money—money for military projects to transform colonels into generals and money to ensure the reelection of senators and congresssmen who funded various military programs. During the ongoing F-18 debates, two of the most powerful men in Congress, Senator Ted Kennedy and Speaker of the House Tip O'Neill, knew that the F-18's engine would be built in their state of Massachusetts. They were mighty proponents of the F-18, and pivotal to its acceptance by Congress. Consequently, not only did the Navy have the carrier compatibility issue helping to prevent the F-16 from being pushed on it, the Navy also had some powerful congressmen pulling for the F-18.

Despite the inevitability of power politics, Congress investigated the cost, mission, and performance of the F-18. Lightweight Fighters promised to be less expensive than their stable mates equipped with radar-guided missiles. Blending both airplanes into a biservice aircraft promised to lower the cost even more. The Navy's announcement to *navalize* the YF-17 eliminated that promise.

All sides agreed that fighter aircraft were increasing in cost over time. The Lightweight Fighter advocates refused to accept the inevitability of this increasing cost, however. The military claimed that the cost increases were due primarily to inflation. Lightweight Fighter advocates claimed that the cost increase was due partly to inflation, but also to added requirements. These added requirements tended to translate into expensive black boxes.

With respect to the cost of the F-18, the confusion as to its actual cost is exacerbated by not knowing whether the speaker is discussing the cost of the airframe only, the airframe plus support, both of these plus the cost of research and development, or additional contributors to cost. Each of these categories has its own term.

Figure 11-1

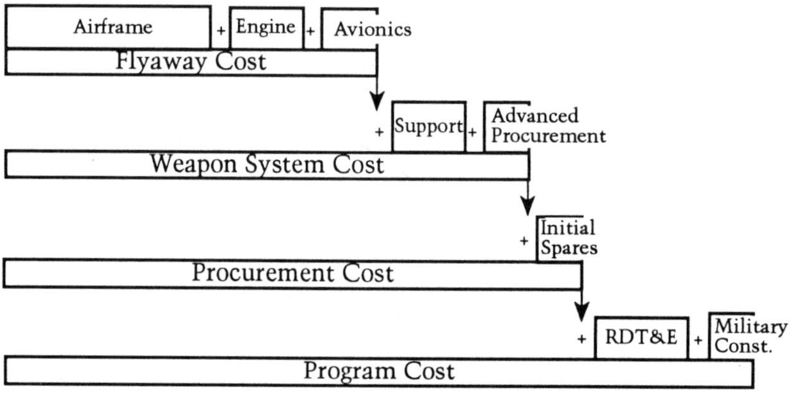

SOURCE: "Comparing the Cost of F-14s and F-18s," McDonnell Douglas

Fig. 11-1 illustrates the components of aircraft costs. The flyaway cost lacks fuel and support costs. None of the money spent on research and development is included. Many aerospace marketeers use flyaway costs (for comparison purposes, they claim) but it is of little value in determining what the airplane will cost the purchaser. The flyaway cost of an airplane will not allow the service to fly it—flyaway costs do not include fuel.

Comparing Costs over Time Spans

The cost of aircraft programs is stated in two types of dollars: "constant year" and "then-year" (TY) dollars. Constant year dollar costs are used to eliminate the effect of inflation; then-year dollars project increases due to inflation and program cost increases.

Table 11-1

F-18 Unit Costs—Constant FY1975 Dollars (in millions)

Flyaway Cost	$6.8M
Weapons System Cost	$8.0M
Procurement Cost	$8.5M
Program Cost	$9.7M

SOURCE: 31 March 1980 System Acquisition Report

These were the various unit costs of the F-18 three months before the F-18 was scheduled for its final approval at the DSARC III meeting in June 1981.

The unit costs are derived by dividing the types of costs—flyaway, weapon, procurement, or program—by the number of aircraft procured or expected to be procured. Thus, program unit costs are determined by dividing the total aircraft scheduled for procurement by the total program costs. For example, if 1,000 airplanes have a total cost of $1 billion during a period of no inflation, the program unit cost would be $1 million per aircraft in either constant year or then-year dollars. But if the 1,000 aircraft were procured during a period of inflation, it would be important to state whether dollars were constant year or then-year.

Figure 11-2

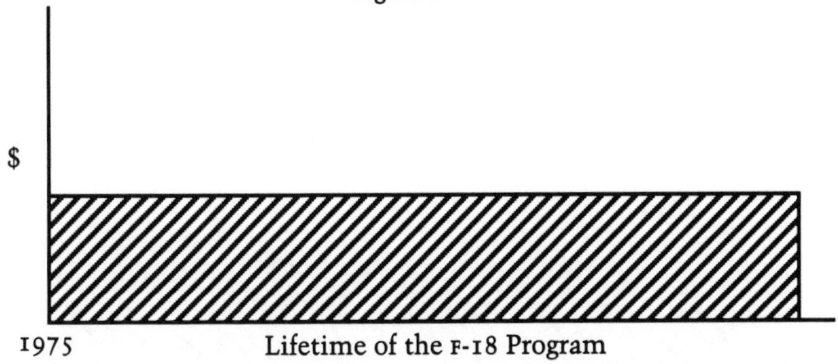

If there is no inflation, and the military service does not add costs through design, inadvertances, or mismanagement, the cost of the program will be the same at year one as it is at the end of the program.

Assume, for example, that these same 1,000 airplanes were procured from 1975 to 1985, that there were no additions to the airplanes, and that inflation increased the total program cost of all 1,000 airplanes from $1 billion to $1.5 billion. The program unit cost of each airplane would be $1.5 million in then-year dollars, but remain $1 million in 1975 dollars. If the cost in 1975 constant year dollars showed an increase, that would indicate that even after removing inflation, the aircraft cost increased. The Navy and critics of the F-18 program constantly debated how much cost increase was due to the additional requirements that the Navy imposed on the program.

The cost of aircraft procured during different time periods is another difficult area of cost comparison. Using constant year dollars for these two periods is deceptive. Aircraft procured in the past are measured by inflated dollars while an ongoing program has its cost lowered by eliminating future inflation effects. Some people argue that costs in the past are sunk costs that cannot be retrieved and are therefore moot.

Dr. Currie argued that for the F-18 to compete with the F-14, the F-18 procurement, operation, and maintenance had to be low because the F-14's research and development costs had been paid.[1] During these hearings, the Navy testified that the total cost for research and development for the F-18 would be $1.430 billion in constant 1975 year dollars.[2]

Figure 11-3

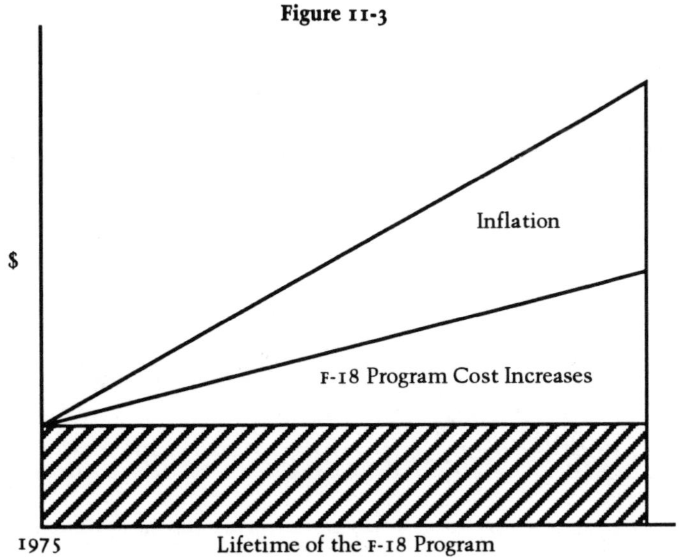

What happens in virtually every military program is that the cost of the weapon system, in this case the F-18, grows over time. These increases are due to two factors: (1) inflation and (2) program costs such as creeping elegance and mismanagement.

Figure 11-4

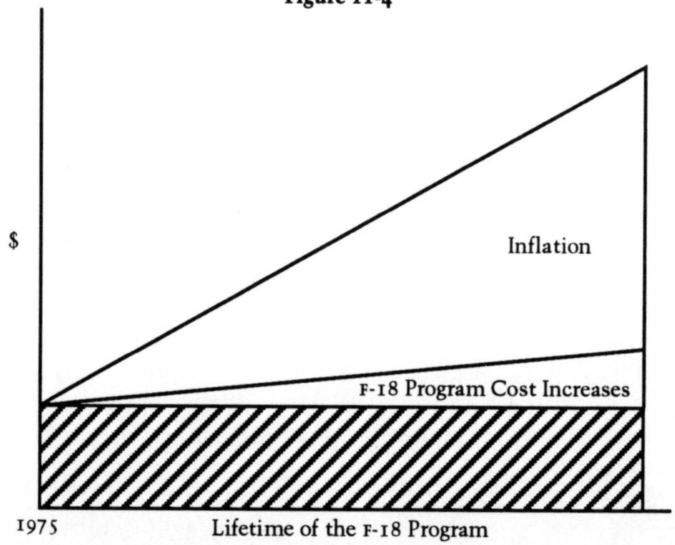

The military wants Congress to believe that the cost increases are due to inflation, as indicated by fig. 11-4 above; military reformers claim that the cost increase is due to add-ons as indicated by the fig. 11-5 below.

Figure 11-5

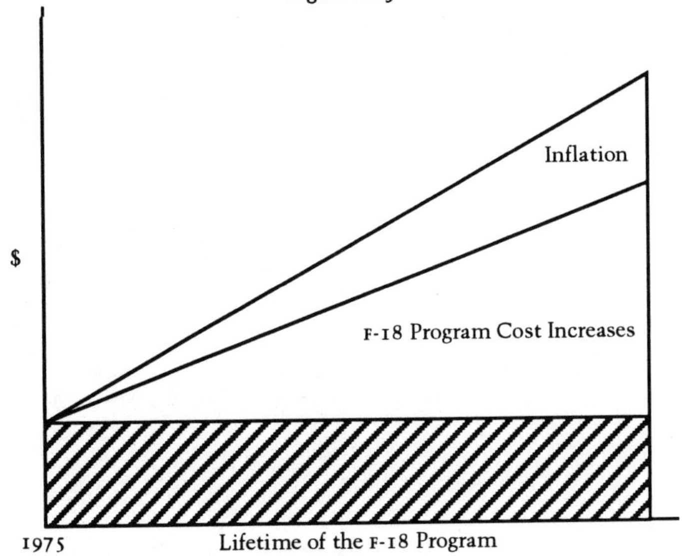

The research and development costs of the F-18 included 11 research and development aircraft, support, and spares.[3] There was conflicting testimony about whether the $1.43 billion included engines and some other government-furnished equipment and support items.[4] The $1.43 billion did not include an additional nine aircraft called "pilot production aircraft," which were for research and development testing. As a point of comparison, the research and development costs for the F-16 were estimated to be $495.5 million, or approximately one-third that of the F-18.[5]

Table 11-2
F-18 Research and Development Costs (in millions)

F404 engine development	$300
Airframe & avionics	$765
Government furnished equipment (GFE)	7
Test, evaluation, management, and support	358
Total	**$1,430**

SOURCE: Lightweight Fighter Hearings Summer 1975

The Navy's original estimate for procurement was 800 aircraft plus the additional 11 for the test and evaluation program. The total cost, the Navy estimated, would be $12.445 billion for 800 aircraft in then-year dollars and $7.837 billion in constant 1975 dollars. The corresponding unit program cost for these two amounts is $15.556 million and $9.796 million, respectively.[6]

By December 1980, the F-18 program had increased to 1,366 aircraft, but without a decrease in unit cost.

The percentage cost growth of the F-18 between 1975 and 1990 in unit program cost was 243 percent in constant dollars. But the tone of cost growth was set at the beginning of the program. The cost growth between program approval and the production approval is listed in Table 11-3.

Table 11-3
Unit Price Growth ofThe F-18 In Constant FY1975 (In Millions)

	Summer 1975	March 1976	Dec. 1980	Summer 1981
Flyaway	$8.0	$5.8	$6.14	$6.8
Procurement	$8.5	$7.9	$8.19	$10.3
Program	$9.6	$9.89	$11.4	$15.8

SOURCE: *Lightweight Fighter Aircraft Program*, p. 60 FY1977 Authorization for Military Dev. Part. 10, p. 5449; Dec. SAR; House Appropriations Committee FY1982 budget, part 6, p. 532; 31 March 1980 System Acquisition Report.

Because the F-14's research and development had been paid, the relative costs of the F-14 and the F-18 were similar in the beginning of the F-18 program. In the beginning years, the majority of the costs are paid to research and development. Because so few aircraft are acquired in the initial stages of procurement, the unit costs of the first aircraft are high. The unit cost decreases as more aircraft are purchased, assuming no inflation and no additions to the aircraft. The cost of additional F-14s in 1975 did not include the research and development costs.

Consequently, when 400 F-14s and 400 F-18s were compared, the unit cost of the F-14 was only $750,000 more. When 800 of the two airplanes were compared, the F-14 cost $1.625 million more.[7] When Senator Symington remarked on the small difference, Admiral Houser replied, "Yes, sir, that is . . . up to a certain point. The operating cost of the F-18 is substantially less, on the order of between 60 and 65 percent; that is where the savings accrue. But it's also in the second 400 planes that we plan to buy, where we really achieve the savings."[8]

The Navy claimed lower operating and support cost savings based on the expectation for greater reliability and easier maintenance in the F-18 than in the F-14. In 1975 the Navy expected a savings of $4 billion over a 15-year period. By 1979 it claimed a 20-year savings of $12 billion over an equivalent number of F-14s.[9]

Critics of the F-18 program claimed that the Navy sold Congress on the new aircraft based on reliability data that the Navy was in no position to successfully predict. Furthermore, these same critics claimed that the prediction of maintainability and reliability was compounded by the uncertain cost estimates. Various F-18 program managers, they said, were unreliable sources for predicting the future. As an example, F-18 critics cited the cost growth in then-year and constant year dollars. Neither type of "year" dollars, they asserted, accounted properly for either the actual inflation or the actual aircraft cost growth.

As shown in Table 11-4, the average growth of the F-18 program unit cost in then-year dollars from 1975 to 1980 is 12.1 percent; the program unit cost increase in constant year 1975 dollars is 3.5 percent. According to the Navy, the difference between these two figures, 8.6 percent, is inflation. Critics point out that Department of Defense deflators show that the average inflation rate over the 1975-80 period was only 7.3 percent. This leaves an unaccounted for 1.3 percent, which is 37 percent of the 3.5 percent growth of the F-18.

Table 11-4
Unit Price Percentage Price Growth of the F-18 in Constant and Then-Year Dollars

	1975	1980	% Increase
Program Unit $TY	$15.56	$27.5	12.1%
Program Unit $1975	$9.62	$11.44	3.5%

SOURCE: December 1980 Selected Acquisition Report

Predicting costs is an art for which there are many models and examples. Yet, the Navy has done a poor job. The 37-percent discrepancy suggests something more. How, critics asked, did the Navy expect to justify the F-18 over the F-14 with 15- and 20- year life cycles when it missed the cost increase by almost 40 percent within five years?

Mission

Not only did Congress question the Navy about the *un*commonality between the U.S. Navy's YF-17 and U.S. Air Force's YF-16, it also questioned the Navy on the wisdom of making common aircraft for both the fighter and attack mission. Admiral Holloway told Congress that there was an established precedent for a combination attack/fighter aircraft. "In World War II and the years immediately following World War II, for example, our fighter squadrons had Corsairs, F4US; so did the attack squadrons. We had aircraft that went in both directions. As you know the Air Force has employed the F-4 as an attack plane very successfully."

Senator Tower challenged Holloway. In his memory, he said, the Navy had a good assortment of aircraft in World War II. To this Admiral Holloway responded:

> Yes, sir; and also in the days immediately following World War II, 1946, for example, a year in which we probably reached the pinnacle of

> our capability in carrier aviation. Because of our experience and production in World War II, the air groups were made up of usually two types of aircraft, Corsairs, and SB2C's. That's all we had aboard ship, and as a result we had a phenomenal availability because we were able to stock the supply support for a minimal number of airplanes.
>
> This is the long-range objective toward which we keep trying to move today, to get away from the variety of different planes aboard ship that are so taxing both in training pilots and in maintaining the aircraft.[10]

There is a certain irony in Admiral Holloway's argument: he uses the same logic for combining a fighter and attack mission into one airplane that Congress used for a common Navy-Air Force fighter. Not only is Admiral Holloway selective in his precedents, his statement is misleading. While it is true that the F4U Corsair and the SB2C were the majority of the air wing composition in 1946, he omits 1945, the final year of the war. Contrary to his comment, 1945 represents the real "pinnacle" of the Navy's capability. In 1945 the F8F Bearcat was on its way to Japan when the Japanese surrendered. The antithesis of the multirole Corsair, the Bearcat was the quintessential lightweight fighter.

Furthermore, during the war, the F6F Hellcat, not the F4U Corsair, was the predominant carrier-borne fighter in the Pacific. The F6F Hellcat acquired an exchange ratio of 19-to-1 against the Japanese compared to the F4U Corsair's 11-to-1 kill-loss ratio. The Navy removed the F6F from the aircraft carrier after World War II, not because it had an unacceptable readiness rate; it had a readiness rate of 90 to 95 percent.[11] The Navy removed it to make way for the F4U Corsair, which made its first flight in May 1940—a year and seven months before Pearl Harbor—but did not qualify for aircraft carrier operations until January 1945, nine months before the end of the war.

The composition of the aircraft carrier in 1946 was more a reflection of determination to get the F4U Corsair on it than an attempt to increase aircraft availability through the reduction in types of aircraft on the carrier. The F6F Hellcat had already demonstrated magnificent readiness. In other words, by eliminating the F6F for an aircraft with a lower kill-loss ratio and lower readiness rate, the Navy kept the Pentagon Paradox in magnificent working order.

The Navy's decision to replace the F6F Hellcat with the F4U, a more expensive and demonstrably less effective fighter, indicates the Navy's determination to make the Corsair part of the carrier air wing. The Navy's tenacity reached its apogee with the decision to add the Curtiss SB2C Helldiver.

Figure 11-6
Development Time, Selected U.S. Navy Fighters, World War II

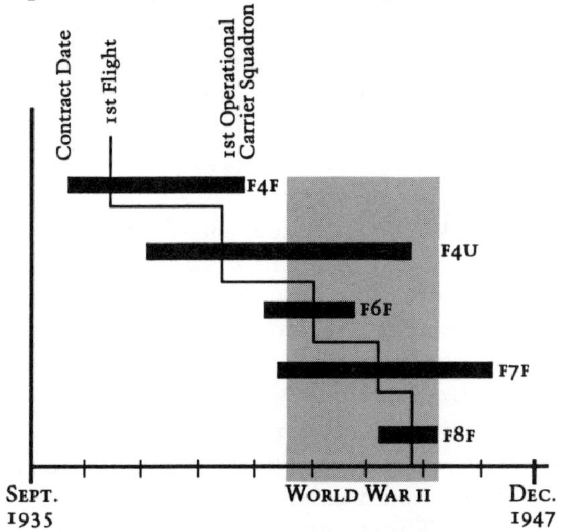

The F4U was conceived as the follow-on fighter to the F4F Wildcat. Because of numerous difficulties, of which carrier suitability was the most dominant, the U.S. Navy was forced to proceed with a backup plan. This generated the F6F Hellcat. Note that the contract date for the F6F was after the first flight of the F4U. The F8F was developed in rapid time, due no doubt to the pressure of war.

Admiral Holloway was correct when he said that the SB2C was one of the two aircraft in the Naval carrier structure in 1946. But he failed to give the reason. Although the Helldiver was conceived two and a half years before Pearl Harbor and first flew a year before its bombing, the Helldiver did not see action until late 1943. By that time the Douglas SBD Dauntless had ravaged the majority of the Japanese threat.

The Navy added the SB2C because it was totally committed to making the Helldiver work. A new factory was built for the sole purpose of constructing the Helldiver. But 889 changes were made before the SB2C was ready to enter service. The Navy crews that flew it and worked on it called it "the Beast." The Navy built 5,516 of them, in spite of the carrier skipper's recommendation during the initial carrier trials to cancel the SB2C program. Considering the political support for the Helldiver program, the airplane must have been a disaster for the skipper to make such a recommendation.[12] Had the Navy made this same commitment to the F-16N, it could have overcome any carrier incompatibility.[13]

Admiral Holloway's remarks on aircraft carrier composition after the war missed the point. The composition during the war was more important. In that respect, World War II supported the wartime contention that "an airplane cannot be used to fulfill many functions if any one of them is to be done well."[14]

Singleness-of-purpose was not a luxury available to the first carrier aircraft. The carriers were small, there were few carrier aircraft, and they had to perform multimissions such as "fighting, dive bombing, scouting, and torpedo missions."[15] The increase in the number of carriers in the 1930s allowed the Navy to increase its number of specialized aircraft.[16] After the war, as Admiral Holloway stated, the types of aircraft were reduced. However, Holloway gave the impression that the Navy went in that direction on purpose, and that if given the opportunity, it would not have numerous types of aircraft. However, in 1957, 11 years after 1946, a period Admiral Holloway described as "the pinnacle" of carrier capability, the Navy was operating 17 different types of aircraft.

Clearly the Navy was not attempting to reduce the types of aircraft. Furthermore, 1946 was hardly the pinnacle of carrier aviation. The year prior, the Navy had a carrier armada 300 percent larger with almost 100 carriers. The Navy's total carriers in 1946 dropped to 25. However, by 1956, even though the number of carriers remained at 25, the Navy added two attack carriers to the total, and substituted 8 antisubmarine carriers for the 10 escort carriers of 1946.[17]

Creating the multirole aircraft gives the appearance of solving one problem, space on the carrier deck, but it intensifies another problem—adequate training in the attack and fighter role. The Navy has traditionally trained pilots for one mission or the other. However, combining both missions in one airplane requires that the Navy train pilots in both missions. The F/A-18 threatened the separation of these two communities, which had honed their skills through each community's singleness-of-purpose in the separate fighter and attack mission.

Proponents of multirole training believe that the skills are transferable; thus, pilots of the F-18 can become competent in both air-to-ground and air-to-air environments. Pilots disagree. U.S. Air Force F-16 pilots believe they do not acquire enough training in the air-to-air role because of the demands on the air-to-ground training. As of 1981 the Navy had projected the same number of hours per month for F-18 pilots as the Air Force projected for F-16 pilots. Only time will tell if Navy pilots can accomplish what Air Force pilots claim they cannot.[18]

At the time of the 1975 congressional hearings, the Navy's long-range plan was to have 12 aircraft carriers, with two 12-airplane fighter squadrons on each carrier. The previous August, the Secretary of Defense had approved an 18-squadron F-14 force based on a total of 390 F-14s. The 390 total came from the discussions between the Navy and Chuck Myers. Of the 18 F-14 squadrons, 4 were allocated to the Marine Corps. Because 12 carriers require 24 fighter squadrons, the remaining 6 squadrons would be composed of F-4BS and F-4JS that would go through a Service Life Extension Program (SLEP). (They would be redesignated F-4N's and F-4S's, respectively.) The remainder of the Naval and Marine Corps force structure scheduled was composed of 12 Marine Corps fighter squadrons shared among three Marine Corps Air Wings, four Navy reserve squadrons, and two Marine Corps reserve squadrons. Based on this forecast, the Navy projected a deficit of 45 fighters in 1980 and 75 fighters in 1981. The Navy planned to introduce the F-18 in 1981.[19]

The Navy's plan in 1975 required 400 F-18s and 400 A-18s. The two versions would have 95 percent commonality. The fighter version would not have a horizontal situation display planned for the attack version. The attack version would have two additional ordnance stations on the wing and could carry Forward Looking Infrared (FLIR) pods where the fighter carried Sparrow missiles. The Marine Corps attack version would have electro-optical and laser designator capability and would operate Maverick and HARM.[20] The Navy planned six carriers to carry two squadrons of F-14s and two squadrons of A-18s. The remaining six carriers would have one squadron of F-14s, one squadron of F-18s, and two squadrons of A-18s.[21]

By the latter part of 1975, the Marine Corps had rejected the F-14, complaining that the F-14 squadrons would require one-third more critical manpower than either the F-4 or F-18. The F-14 had no planned attack capability and the Marine Corps had 42 percent of its fixed wing tactical aircraft dedicated to the fighter-attack role. Reducing these multimission squadrons to a fighter-only role was an unaffordable luxury.*[22] In 1975 the Navy designated the Marine Corps to receive the first six F-18 squadrons for 1982. The Navy scheduled the attack version of the Naval Air Combat Fighter for introduction in 1983.[23]

Promised Performance

During the 1975 hearings, many congressmen expressed concern over the relative capabilities of the F-18 and F-14, as well as the

*Marine Corps pilots, unlike the Navy pilot, have historically been trained for both air-to-air and air-to-ground roles. Consequently their squadrons are designated VMFA unlike the Navy squadrons which are designated VF or VA. (The M is for Marines.) The first F/A-18 squadron changed the designation to VFA to represent the dual-role.

Figure 11-7

The Evolution of the Merging of the A-18 and the F-18

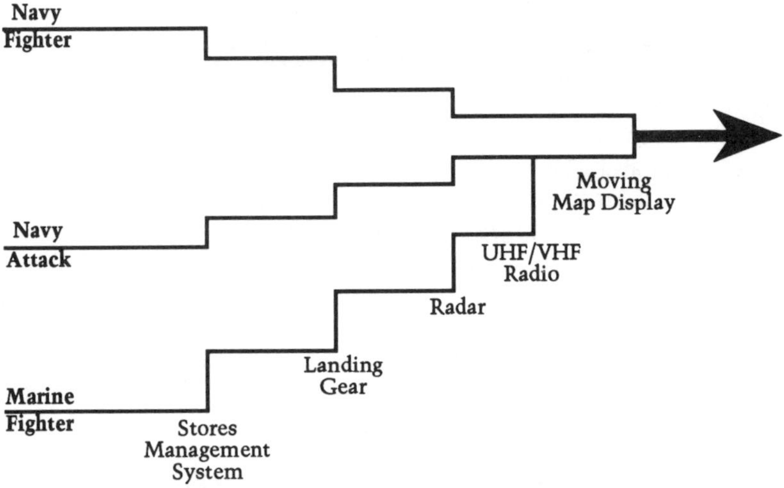

SOURCE: McDonnell Douglas

There were three distinct configurations of the Hornet at the DSARC meeting in December 1975. For the benefits of commonality, the Navy decided to converge all three designs into one aircraft at the cost of increased weight and drag as well as an increase in flyaway cost.

A-18 compared with the A-7. The F-18 was intended as a complement to the F-14; the A-18 was a replacement for the A-7. The majority of Naval testimony stated that the F-18 was less capable than the F-14 in all areas except maneuvering combat, the area that Chuck Myers called close-air combat and that was the mission of a Fighter-Fighter. The Navy said that the A-18 was more survivable, more accurate, but had less endurance or range than the A-7. The Navy reminded Congress that the F-18 was being procured to flesh out the declining inventory. The Navy walked a delicate balance because it knew it had to increase the force structure, and it wanted to do so it with all F-14s. It did not want to give the impression that F-18s could possibly do the job of the F-14, lest it have more F-18s than were already imposed on it.

Nevertheless, the Navy considered the F-18 superior to the F-14 for some missions. Vice Admiral Houser testified that the F-18 was more cost effective for escorting strike missions. He said that the best combination for fleet air defense was two F-14 squadrons and two F-18 squadrons, "due to the superiority of the F-14 against the high threat and the excellence of the F/A-18 as both a fighter and an attack aircraft. Cost effectiveness of the mix is heavily depended upon the quality and quantity of the threat and the engagement scenario. As the severity of the threat decreases, the cost effectiveness of the F/A-18 increases."[24]

This was the first reference to the F-18 and the A-18 as an F/A-18, a designation that the Navy would formally adopt in January 1979.*

Vice Admiral Houser also said that because of the improved radar of the F-18 and the AIM-7F Sparrow, the doctrine of "shoot-look-shoot" would make the F-18 carrying two Sparrows as effective as the F-4 Phantom carrying four Sparrows. The Navy's belief in the F-18's increased capability was based in part on a promised increase in missile and radar reliability. The F-18, Houser added, had a "useful" but limited capability against incoming air-to-surface missiles.[25]

Many senators and congressmen, aware of the greater load-carrying capability of the A-7, questioned the relative ability of the A-18. Vice Admiral Houser testified that under certain conditions the A-18 could carry more ordnance than the A-7E. However, when asked specifically by the counsel to the Tactical Air Subcommittee, Mr. Old, "if both aircraft were loaded up with the same amount of ordnance which would have the greater range," Houser said that the A-7 had slightly better range.

Admiral Holloway interjected that the trend was going away from gross tonnage of bombs, but rather toward so called smart bombs. He implied that the large load capability was not the premium design point nor the point of comparison. Senator Tower responded, logically enough, that if one smart bomb was good, weren't a "whole bunch" even better?

Admiral Holloway retorted that the problem with a lot of bombs was that they required too much time over the target. Senator Tower asked if the A-18 would have greater bombing accuracy than the A-7E, to which Vice Admiral Houser replied "slightly better."[26] The Navy did not justify the A-18 on the "ton-mile" basis it had used for former attack aircraft, but on the A-18's improved bombing system, greater agility, better self-protection, and greater reliability.[27]

In an apparent contradiction, Vice Admiral Houser admitted that the attack version of the F-18 had 5 to 15 percent less range than the A-7E. However, he quickly pointed out that the F-18 met the VFAX requirement. Furthermore, the F-18, he said, had excess range over the McDonnell Douglas A-4M Skyhawk. As events would later reveal, neither statement was true: The F-18 failed to meet the VFAX range requirement, and the F-18 and A-4 Skyhawk have approximately the same range.

*As mentioned in the preface, the official designation for the F/A-18 is F-18, which is the way it is referred to throughout this work.

The VFAX specifications (listed in part on page 174 above) called for the capability to deliver four MK-83 1,000-pound bombs 550 miles from the ship. The Navy testified that the F-18 could deliver that bomb load 650 miles. The A-4M Skyhawk has a radius with two Mk-83s of 345 miles.[28] As the Initial Operational Test and Evaluation would later reveal, the F-18's attack radius was similar to the A-4.

Congress criticized the A-18's inability to carry as many bombs as the A-7, regardless of the distance. The A-18 described in the 1975 hearings had a maximum stores capacity that was 40 percent of the A-7E. The Navy stated that at 650 miles both aircraft had the same bomb load capacity.[29] One Navy captain said that the larger load capacity of the A-7 was insignificant because the pilot had to download bombs to increase the A-7's survivability.[30]

In spite of some Navy F-18 advocates' attempts to cast the F-18 in a favorable light, George Spangenberg did not. He was the former head of the evaluation division at the Naval Air Systems Command, and, as such, was very influential in determining what went into Naval Air. Spangenberg had a reputation around the Naval community as an outstanding aircraft designer. He began working for the Navy before World War II, and eventually became the head of the evaluation division in the early 1950s. Many people within the aerospace industry credit Spangenberg with being the father of the F-14 Tomcat.

Spangenberg's testimony reflected the Navy's conventional wisdom. Listening to Spangenberg was like listening to the Navy's sanctum sanctorum. Spangenberg represented the sum total of the Naval bureaucracy's position on Naval aviation. Spangenberg said what Navy admirals would not, for fear of ending their careers. And he was direct.

> I think that the airplane, as a fighter, is inferior by a wide margin to the F-14 in virtually all the roles that we ever contemplated using them for. I personally think that it's even worse than an F-4 in the total sense, although it is certainly better in close-in dogfighting than the F-4.
>
> I think our analysts over the years would rate it, if we were doing an honest competition, and doing an honest operational evaluation, it would end up being a lesser airplane than the F-4, solely because it has lesser radar; has one man instead of two men; it has fewer missiles than are carried by the F-4.

Spangenberg added that as an attack aircraft, based on the data he had seen, the F-18 was completely inadequate, "unless the Navy wants to restrict its operation down to about the level of the A-4."[31]

Spangenberg's basic premise was that the United States fights its wars over someone else's territory. Because of that, the enemy has the advantage of ground-controlled radar as well as a shorter range requirement. Given these two facts, its designs do not require large fuel load or large radar antennas. As a result, the enemy can always design a better dogfighter. The United States should, according to Spangenberg, invest in better fire control systems and better missiles.[32]

Congress asked Spangenberg to explain the conflict between his testimony and that of Commander McKeown's three years previously. McKeown had testified that although the Navy had trained, prior to Vietnam, to shoot down other aircraft with radar-guided missiles, when they arrived in Vietnam, they were forced to dogfight. There was a dichotomy between Commander McKeown's experience, which was a testimony to the visual identification requirement, and Spangenberg's view, which was, and is, the current Navy position. Spangenberg explained the paradox this way:

> There has been debate since time immemorial on this particular issue. The Navy made the decision in 1954-55 to go to an all-missile fighter with the F-4, and I don't think that was a bum decision.
>
> The fact that we ended up dogfighting in Vietnam doesn't mean it was because of some physical law; it was a directive to the forces saying you had to see the whites of their eyes before you could shoot. If you wait until they go past you, you are obviously in a dogfight situation. But there were a heck of a lot of cases out there when Navy pilots had the ability to shoot down the enemy and didn't do it because they had a directive saying they couldn't.*
>
> Admiral Monroe testified at one of these hearings to the effect that if he had his druthers without direction from OSD on the way we would go on this thing, that he would have been willing to use a Phoenix system, or even the longer ranged Eagle type of system.[33]

*Which was fortunate. For example, Lt. Judd Halenza, USN, with his RIO Dennis Faherty, from VF-114, was flying in late April 1972 as wingman to his Commanding Officer, Cmdr. Pete Kellaway, on a northern BARCAP (barrier combat air patrol) for the USS *Kitty Hawk*. "We got a vector from Red Crown [the ship-based radar controller]," Halenza recalls, "that two bogies [unidentified targets] were coming south. We turned north, and intercepted them. We got a lockon at 25 to 30 miles. It was a classic intercept.

"We got a cleared-to-fire from Red Crown. The CO fired at 8 to 9 miles. When we saw the smoke trails, a tell-tale sight that these aircraft were F-4 Phantoms, the missiles were on their way. The Phantoms were still beyond visual range. The skipper shut off the CW [continuous wave illuminator], which made the Sparrows go stupid. If the J79 engine didn't act like a pointer in the sky, the skipper would have had the dubious distinction of shooting down our own guys. Of course, that presupposes that the missiles would have worked, which wasn't likely." Statement made to the author by Judd Halenza.

Not everyone agrees with Spangenberg's response. Lightweight Fighter advocates agree that the enemy can fight over his own territory and can have assistance from ground control intercept radar. However, far from seeing the "white of their eyes," Lightweight Fighter advocates claim that enemy pilots will be seeing the backs of our pilots helmets. The ground radar controllers will vector enemy pilots, as they did in Vietnam, to attack from the rear or blind side. Any response necessary by an American pilot will require the maximum maneuverability that is not inherent in large multi-role airplanes. The analysis that Spangenberg and others employ, according to some Lightweight Fighter advocates, is tantamount to predicting the outcome of a medieval battle by studying the relative merits of two knights in a joust.

Spangenberg continued saying that, to the uniformed, the attack radius of the F-18 seemed reasonable, except that it was designed around the least demanding of the attack radius problems. "Its true range characteristics can better be gauged by noting that it is inferior on internal fuel and without combat power usage to what was initially estimated for the A-4 in 1952."[34]

Although Vice Admiral Houser had testified that the most cost-effective force would be a carrier with F-14s and F-18s, Spangenberg said he had "never seen an analysis that came close to giving that result." Senator Goldwater asked him what an "effective force ratio" would be between the F-14 and F-18. Spangenberg replied that he would hate to say that the F-14 was twice as good only to have Congress give half as many F-14s. "You remember, we went through this during the McNamara days, also; the F-111 was twice as good, therefore we only had to buy half as many." He also recalled testimony wherein the F-14 was rated as worth three F-4s against "moderate performance bomber raid attacking the force." Since the F-18 was less capable than the F-4 in that role, the F-14 was superior to two F-18s.[35]

The F-14 concept, Spangenberg continued, evolved from the Douglas F6D Missileer/Eagle concept, which OSD killed, not the Navy.

> I put the weapons system above acceleration, turning performance, and so on. I think the Phoenix and its track-while-scan system can overcome the disadvantages that go with slightly lower turning rate. You will recall that back in 1958-59, the Navy was touting the Eagle Missileer which had a heck of a lot less aircraft performance. And yet, that kind of system, a long-range missile system operating out of a subsonic airplane, wins cost effectiveness games. As long as the enemy comes to you; it will still win in cost effectiveness.
>
> Unfortunately it won't handle some of the other cases. It's a poor escort, which is why many people thought the Missileer concept was

Figure 11-8
The Modern Equivalent of the Joust

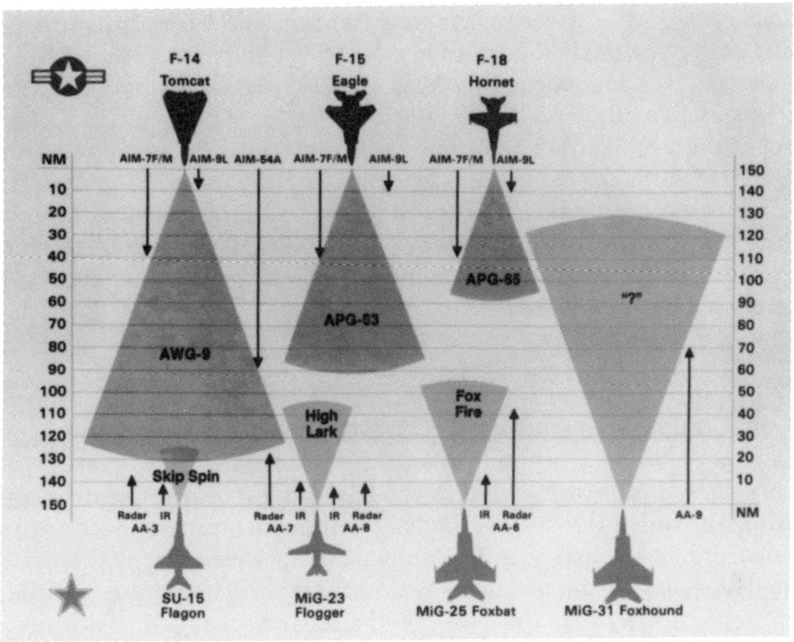

SOURCE: McDonnell Douglas

Most military analyses look at air-to-air encounters as though they were medieval jousts. A longer-range radar would serve the same purpose as looking at the results of a joust to predict the outcome of a medieval battle.

> not a good one; it did give us a mix on the carriers that we wanted to avoid. And we went to the concept of a high performance airplane that is still carrying a long-range missile. Something that would do the job beyond that which we know the enemy has. It's the only way we can win, by outranging.

Spangenberg believed that the Navy should drop the F-18, develop a new track-while-scan weapons system, and develop a multishot terminally homing missile. For the attack mission, the Navy needed a twin-engine aircraft with two crew because of the high work load.[36]

Spangenberg also attacked F-18 cost analysis. He cited previous testimony that the first 400 F-18s would cost $5.3 billion in 1975 dollars. This would give the F-18 an average program unit cost of $13 million. By contrast, an additional 400 F-14 Tomcats over the planned number would cost under $11 million. Since no one disputed that the F-14 was a better aircraft, Spangenberg said, "normal evaluation would end at this point with the showing of greater effectiveness at a lower acquisition cost for the F-14."[37] However, because of the $0.5 million savings per year for each F-18 in operating costs, he added, "we start delivering the new fighters in 6 years, finish in 11, and break even in total cost about the end of the next decade."[38]

No one ever rose through a bureaucracy by advocating a position inconsistent with the bureaucracy's self image; Spangenberg was no exception. Spangenberg made it apparent that the Navy was not enamored with the F-18. Spangenberg's arguments for the F-14, like all arguments for radar-guided concepts, require that one believe that the technology exists to accurately distinguish friend from foe, or that one disregard the consequences. Neither idea has been validated in aerial warfare.

The LTV Protest

When the Navy chose the loser in the Air Combat Fighter competition, Congress was incensed and responded by convening multiple hearings. The LTV Corporation was even more decisive: It sued the Navy.[39] LTV's protest lingered in the background during the hearings. Although it filed the protest on May 9, the Government Accounting Office did not release its decision until October 1, 1975. Consequently, many of the discussions during the hearings were qualified by the possibility that the GAO could alter the speaker's position.

LTV raised many issues in its protest, but the crux was that the Navy violated the law by not picking the Air Force Air Combat Fighter winner. At the very least, the Navy violated public policy.[40] LTV contended that the Request for Quotation (later redesignated Request for Proposal) supported the Conference Report direction on commonality. LTV asserted that the Navy's decision did not follow its own RFP since it used an engine in the F-18 other than the four specified in the RFP.

The Navy's position was that the language of the September 18, 1974, Joint Conference Report was not legally binding. The language gave legislative intent. But as it was not written into the law, it did not have legal effect. Furthermore, the Navy contended that even if the Joint Conference Report language did have that effect, the language made two separate points. The first directed the Navy to "make maximum use of the Air Force Lightweight Fighter and Air Combat Fighter technology and hardware," which the Navy said it did by restricting its solicitations to only General Dynamics/LTV and Northrop/McDonnell Douglas. The second point, that the "adaptation of the selected Air Force Air Combat Fighter . . .be capable of carrier operations is the prerequisite for use of the funds provided," was done with the express approval of the two appropriating committees involved in the original Joint Conference Report. The Navy's position was that since the LTV design could not be made carrier suitable, the spirit of the Conference Report was carried out.

The Government Accounting Office decision concluded that the Navy was correct. The Report was not legislation and did not have the effect of law. It stated further that the Navy's RFP listed commonality as the third criterion out of a list of four, with performance within cost limitations as the most important.

Other Legislative Activity

LTV's solution to the conflict set up by the Navy was to continue funding on the F401 and F404 engines and open the competition to industry. Naturally, the Grumman proposal was to continue procuring the F-14.

Proposals from various senators and congressmen were presented during the hearings. Senator Goldwater wanted to stop the F-18, continue development of the two engines, continue procurement of the F-14 and A-7, and eventually replace the A-7 with a new attack aircraft. Senator Chiles wanted to continue prototype competition by developing a navalized version of the F-16 and an Air Force version of the F-18. Senator Inouye favored stopping the F-18, continuing engine development, and reexamining the VFAX/NACF requirements.

Many of the arguments were well thought out. All were defeated. The F-18 was approved in the December 1975 DSARC II meeting, which authorized full-scale development—the testing phase. It would now be up to McDonnell Douglas, Northrop, and the United States Navy to deliver what they had promised.

Chapter 12

The Promise and the Reality

Vires acquirit eundo.
(It gains strength by continuing.)

In the three years between the December 1975 DSARC II meeting and the F-18's first flight in November 1978, the Navy expressed optimism over the F-18. The Hornet's promised performance declined slightly between the DSARC II meeting and the congressional hearings in 1977. Nevertheless, the Navy claimed that the F-18's performance was better than the thresholds established in Decision Coordinating Paper (DCP) 141. Captain Corky Lenox, the eternally optimistic Project Manager of the F-18, stretched the point by claiming that the performance of the F-18 was "nearly identical" with the performance of the YF-17.

These claims, based on Navy data during 1977, are difficult to believe; but what is more difficult to believe is that the Navy believed them. For example, the F-18 weighed approximately 8,500 pounds more than the YF-17. Even though the Navy increased the thrust of the YJ101 engine, the thrust-to-weight ratio on the F-18 was less. Secondly, the Navy F-18 had more drag than the land-based YF-17. The drag, combined with the F-18's greater weight, reduced the performance more than the Navy admitted. And the weight increased even more.

By 1978, the Navy admitted that the F-18 had grown 1,600 pounds, or 8 percent. The Navy justified the increase with reliability and maintainability improvements. As a result, according to Captain

Lenox, the combat radius would be reduced approximately 5 percent, the acceleration "over the spec acceleration range is impacted by about 4 seconds, and our carrier landing speed is increased by 4 or 5 knots."

The Navy believed that reliability and maintainability were important and had based long-term cost benefits of the F-18 on the promise that the Hornet would have much lower maintenance costs than the F-14. Vice Admiral Houser's 1975 testimony claimed that the F-18 was cheaper than additional F-14s because of the lower operational and maintenance costs. Since the F-14s research and development costs were sunk, and since the actual cost of the F-14 was similar, the only justification for the F-18 was its lower operating cost. Because operating and maintenance composed 60 percent of the cost of aircraft ownership, reliability and maintainability were significant factors in making the F-18 a lower cost complement to the F-14.

To persuade the Navy that the F-18 would be a much easier aircraft to maintain, McDonnell Douglas, known in the industry as McAir, promised very low maintenance and high reliability. McAir's promises were reminiscent of its promises to the Air Force with the F-15. Table 12-1 lists the Navy's requirement based on the McDonnell Douglas assertions.

Table 12-1
Required Maintainability for F-18

	Requirements
Direct Main, Man Hours/Flt. Hr.	11.02 MMH/FH
Operational Availablity	80.0 percent
Turn Around Time (max. 3 men)	15.0 minutes
Mean Time to Repair	1.0 Hr. 46 min.
Fault isolate time	5.0 min. (95 percent)
	10.0 min (5 percent)
Engine change	21.0 min. (4 men)
Radar Remove and Replace	21.0 min. (2 men)

SOURCE: Maintainable by Design (St. Louis, MO.: McDonnell Aircraft Co., 1978)(P.S. 1018) p. 4

McDonnell Douglas's assertions give a feeling of déja vu. For example, the F-15 Eagle had a maintenance man-hour per flight hour requirement of 11.3 hours—0.28 hours more than the F-18. (Table 12-2 lists the components that contribute to the 11.3 hours and shows the F-4E data for comparison.)

The reliability and maintainability claims made by McDonnell Douglas about the F-15 are important in the study of the F-18. If McDonnell Douglas was able to meet its claims for the Eagle, there would be little reason to believe it would fail on the Hornet. If the

Air Force claim that the F-15 would be less expensive to maintain than the F-4E was correct, then the Navy claim that the F-18 would be cheaper than the F-14 should hold.

The initial experience of the F-15 looked good. The maintenance man-hours per flight hour requirement was 19.83 after three and a half years from the first flight in July 1972. The Air Force required McDonnell Douglas to demonstrate 11.3 MMH/FH after four and a half years. After only slightly more than two years, the F-15 community claimed 19.83 MMH/FH. Furthermore, a demonstration tour near the end of the F-15's second year, involving 92 flights and 100.2 flight hours, required only 4.25 MMH/FH.[1] Two years later another F-15 tour of 50 flights with 87.1 flight hours required only 1.23 MMH/FH of organizational maintenance.*[2]

Table 12-2
Unscheduled Maintenance July-January 1974

	F-15	F-4E
ORGANIZATIONAL LEVEL		
Avionics	1.087	3.79
Airframe (less engine)	1.185	7.06
Engines	0.396	1.31
Armament	0.14	1.23
Organizational SubTotal	**4.158**	**13.39**
INTERMEDIATE LEVEL		
Avionics	1.73	3.16
Airframe (less engine)	0.738	1.41
Engines	0.783	0.29
Armament	0.073	0.73
Fault Isolate Time	3.32	5.59
Scheduled Maintenance	3.78	7.13
Intermediate SubTotal	**10.424**	**18.31**
Total	**14.582**	**31.7**

SOURCE: "F-15 Eagle: 'maximum availability . . . minimum maintenance' " McDonnell Douglas Corporation, P.S. 838, (1 Oct. 1974) p. 4

These promised lower maintenance man-hours per flight hour implied that the Air Force would need fewer mechanics and fewer spare parts to support the F-15, the same claim that the Navy made for the F-18. According to McDonnell Douglas brochures, a "utilization rate of 30 flight hours per month, [on] a 72 aircraft wing of F-15s will require 128 less maintenance personnel than the F-4E."[3] McDonnell Douglas also claimed that the high reliability of the F-15 contributed to its low maintenance man hours per flight hour. The reliability, usually discussed in terms of the average time between

*Maintenance was scheduled and unscheduled, no general support included: towing, servicing, and reconsideration.

failures, was high according to McDonnell Douglas. The F-15 mean time between failure (MTBF) was 3.5 hours compared to the 1.2 hours on the F-4.[4]

Table 12-3
F-15 Maintenance Promise and Reality

	Promise	Reality	Percentage Over
Mean Time Between Failure (MTBF)	3.5	0.5	700%
Main, Man-Hours/Flight Hour (MMH/FH)	1.3	24.0	1,846%
MMH/FH (with 20 Flt. hours/Mo.)	6.3	23.5	373%

SOURCE:"F-15 Eagle: 'Maximum availability . . . minimum maintenance.' " McDonnell Aircraft Co. P.S. 838 (1 Oct. 1976); Franklin C. Spinney, "Defense Facts of Life," U.S. Department of Defense (December 5, 1980) slide 34; Acquisition Management Aircraft Historical reliability and Maintainability Data, Vol. II Directorate of Engineering Services, Air Force Acquisition Logistic Division, Jan. 1981, AFALD Pamphlet 88-4.

If McDonnell Douglas had produced results that met the F-15 specification, there would have been no reason to believe it could not meet them on the F-18. However, history tells a different story. Table 12-3 above shows the difference between F-15 maintenance promises and F-15 reality.

The Navy might argue that McDonnell Douglas's failure to meet the F-15 requirements was unrelated to the F-18. The Navy might also argue that missing the requirements for maintainability is a natural course of conduct. However, airplanes are able to meet their specifications, provided those specifications are realistic. One can compare the MMH/FH of several airplanes to see if the Navy's optimistic F-18 goal of 11.02 MMH/FH was realistic. Table 12-4 lists simple, intermediate, and complex aircraft and compares their contractual requirements with their achievement. Note that both services promise low maintenance man-hours per flight hour on complex and simple aircraft. However, only the simple aircraft are able to deliver the promises.

Note that airplanes with simple avionics systems have been able to meet the MMH/FH goal and sustain it. Furthermore, both the T-38 and F-5E are simple in aspects other than their avionics. The A-7 is somewhat more complex. It missed its goal by over 400 percent. The F-15 missed its MMH/FH goal by 300 percent, and the F-14 by 400 percent.

The real issue in maintenance man-hours per flight hour is not the number of hours, but the cost. What difference would it make to the military services if it took 5,000 people working one hour each for every hour an airplane flew if it cost them five cents per hour to pay, house, clothe, and feed them? One could argue that beyond a certain point the number of maintenance personnel would become so cumbersome that its aggregate size would impose physical limits on working and housing conditions. This happened to the U.S. Navy when it introduced the F-4 to the fleet. Each aircraft carrier was suppose to have one squadron of day-fighter F-8 Crusaders

Table 12-4
Maintenance Man-Hours per Flying Hour of U.S. Air Force and Navy Aircraft

	Achieved Specification Demonstration	1981 MMH/FH	1986 MMH/FH
T-38	11.5	N/A	11
F-5E	16.0	15.0	15
A-7	11.5	10	28
F-14	20	20	97.*
F-15	11.3	19	33.*
F-18	11.02		

SOURCE: "F-15 Eagle: 'Maximum availability. . .minimum maintenance.' " McDonnell Aircraft Co. P.S. 838 (1 Oct. 1976); Franklin C. Spinney, "Defense Facts of Life," U.S. Department of Defense (December 5, 1980) slide 34; Acquisition Management Aircraft Historical reliability and Maintainability Data, Vol. II Directorate of Engineering Services, Air Force Acquisition Logistic Division [AFALD], Jan. 1981, AFALD Pamphlet 88-4.

*Maintenance man-hours per sortie

and one squadron of night-fighter F-4 Phantoms. The smaller carriers presented a problem. Since the F-4 required 50 percent more manpower to support it, the smaller carriers could not physically accommodate the F-4's support. People were not a direct factor, space was. Cost was an indirect factor because with more money the Navy could have built more carriers. However, the 50-percent increase in support costs for the F-4 inhibited the possibility of additional carriers, just as the F-15 maintenance expense inhibited additional wings of Eagles.

The F-15 illustrates a further maintenance dilemma that F-18 critics predicted for the Hornet. McDonnell Douglas anticipated a 150-percent reduction in MMH/FH for the F-15 over the F-4E. Yet the cost of operating the F-15 is 40 percent more than the cost of operating the F-4 (see Table 12-5). In fact, the F-15 costs more to operate than the B-52 even when the cost of fuel is removed. How can the F-15 cost more to operate and still have lower MMH/FH than the F-4?

Table 12-5
Direct Operating and Maintenance Cost per Flight Hour (1980 Dollars)

	F-5E	F-5G	F-16A	F-15	F-4E
Material/ Replenishment Spares	$163	$201	$503	$1,104	$513
Depot Material	87	99	361	549	214
Fuel ($1.18 per gallon)	690	627	870	1,742	2,006
Total $/Flight Hr.	**$940**	**$927**	**$1,734**	**$3,305**	**$2,733**

SOURCE: USAF AFP 173-13 August 1980 via Northrop.

The explanation lies in the data collection method. Of the three levels of maintenance—organization (or squadron), intermediate, and depot—only the first two collect MMH data. By design, the F-15, as well as the F-18, requires minimal time at the organizational level, slightly more at the intermediate level, and shifts to the depot level the burden of sorting out the problems of its highly complex weapons system. Since the MMH/FH are not tracked at the depot level, the F-15's MMH data are buried there. The Navy and McDonnell Douglas offered the same promise with the F-18 that they offered with the F-15: 5 to 10 times fewer MMH/FH than its predecessor.

The fact that the F-18 demonstrated a MMH/FH number below the specification did not guarantee that the F-18 would be able to sustain the low rate. One of the logical results of the high MMH/FH in the F-14, F-15, and the potential high rates in the F-18, was a predictable low readiness rate. In fiscal year 1979 the F-15 was not mission capable 44 percent of the time. Yet, in spite of these data, the Air Force continued to claim that the F-15 was a reliable airplane. Maj Gen. Carl H. Cathey, Jr., Deputy Chief of Staff for Requirements for the Tactical Air Command, reflected this view at the 1981 AIAA Annual Meeting and Technical Display.

> We must overcome . . . Soviet advantages with rapidly deployable, hard-hitting, quality forces that get the most out of every single combat element. This not only suggests, but demands, high sortie rates. Our tactical fighter aircraft, the A-10, A-7, F-16, F-15 and F-111 are capable of high sortie rates—they have the reliability and maintainability—but those rates are dependent, or course, on trained manpower and spares at required levels. Some would contend that the increase in sophistication of our system has, in fact, decreased readiness, and that we need to opt for a swarm of simple aircraft. . . .
>
> These critics often point to the peacetime statistics of modern tactical fighters—the F-15 is a case in point. But those peacetime rates reflect a severe shortage over the past five years of parts funding and supply, not of aircraft reliability. So we have put the matter to the test on several occasions. For example, this past October, TAC took an F-15 squadron to Bremgarten, Germany. We took the squadron's authorized maintenance people, avionics repair stations, load crews, etc. They operated for a month at this German base—flying less than two-thirds of each day due to local peacetime operating rules—and still averaged three sorties per day per aircraft for the entire time while maintaining an around the clock average rate of 80 percent of the aircraft fully mission capable, which means: All systems on board the F-15 operating perfectly. What made the difference? Simply this: this squadron was given the numbers and kinds of spares each operational F-15 squadron would have if our spares accounts were adequately funded.[5]

General Cathey makes a persuasive argument. However, his premise begs the question. Furthermore, to reach his conclusion requires circular reasoning. Under Cathey's definition, any system can be defined as reliable if it is supported with enough spare parts and maintenance personnel. The real issue is how many are reasonable. Based on Cathey's argument, the squadron would be under funded if the F-15 required one million maintenance people and the squadron had only 500,000. Regardless of the cost of an additional 500,000 workers, Cathey would hold the F-15 harmless, claiming that the shortfall of personnel prevented adequate maintenance. Naturally, the argument extends to spare parts.

Cathey implied in his statement that spare parts were not adequately funded. Although he did not admit the Air Force was at fault, many Air Force officers will. What contributes to this inadequate projection? For one thing, the optimistic Mean Time Between Failure (MTBF). An airplane that flies for months before it has a failure would obviously need fewer spare parts to support it than one that broke down every 30 minutes. When the Air Force predicted a MTBF of 3.5 hours, it purchased spare parts on that basis. But it missed that prediction by 700 percent, and the spare parts requirement is not adequate for the F-15, which does average a break down every 30 minutes.*

The first F-15 System Program Office (SPO) director, Gen. Benjamin Bellis, admitted that the Air Force did not purchase enough spare parts. "We don't have enough weapons today. We don't have enough spare parts today. We don't have enough fuel for flying today. We don't have enough money to do anything and here we are on the front lines."[6]

Bellis made these remarks as the Vice Commander in Chief of the United States Air Forces in Europe. His experience showed the dichotomy between the McDonnell Douglas promise and the reality he experienced with America's front line F-15 wing in Bitburg, Germany. McAir's brochures claimed that with little more than 400 maintenance personnel the Air Force should average 20 flight hours per month. The 36th Tactical Fighter Wing, with 1,480 maintenance officers and enlisted men, had trouble giving pilots more than 11 flights per month.† [7]

*As a point of comparison, Jeff Ethell said that the Yugoslavs he flew with preferred the MIG-29's simplicity over the complexity of the Mirage. They claimed that all they had to do was replenish the fluids ever 50 hours and the MIG-29 was ready to fly.

†A later brochure claimed that 400 maintenance personnel could support 22 flight hours per month and 850 personnel should support 50 flight hours per month, see "Free World Superiority F-15 Eagle," A4116 (St. Louis, MO: McDonnell Douglas Corp., April 1, 1976) p. 0-6.

If the U.S. Air Force is able to generate high sortie surge rates during certain periods, why does it have a lower steady state sortie rate? The answer lies in the cost of keeping the steady state sortie rate at the higher level. Observers of the F-15 sortie surge exercises that General Cathey referred to claimed that the U.S. Air Force devoured the spare parts of all the other U.S. F-15 bases to support the F-15 surge rates. The resident F-15 base in Germany complained that it was not flying because it had to support the demonstration at a nearby air base.

Just as the depot level maintenance intensity obscured the cost of operating the F-15 if the Air Force looked only at organizational and intermediate level maintenance, the depot level costs for the F-18 obscured the cost of Hornet maintenance. The F-18, like the F-15, bases its maintenance concept "on organizational-level replacement of WRAS (weapons replaceable assemblies) for subsequent intermediate or depot level repair."[8] Consequently, even though the F-18 may have shown initial impressive demonstrations, and may continue to show them, the Hornet had the potential to suffer the F-15's fate during the period the Navy was predicting substantial savings on operating costs.

The F-18 demonstrated impressive reliability during its 100-hour demonstration, just as other aircraft have. In fact, the F-18's demonstration was more impressive than the F-15's. The F-18 demonstrated a Mean Time Between Failure (MTBF) of 8.4 hours, and a Mean Time Between Repair (MTBR) of 1.8 hours. A company-demonstrated engine removal and reinstallation took only 16.3 minutes. (The same company demonstrated an F-15 engine removal in 18 minutes 55 seconds.) The radar demonstration was more realistic. The specification required the Hughes APG-65 radar to work 106 hours, on the average, between failures. During the 100-hour demonstration, the radar failed twice. Thus, the promised 106 MTBF was in reality only 34.

The F-18 Hornet promised less expense for flight operations due to better reliability and lower maintenance man hours per flight hours. However, McDonnell Douglas made that promise on the F-15 and did not deliver. During the decision-analysis period McDonnell Douglas maintained it could deliver in the Hornet an airplane less expensive to maintain than the F-15. To procure the F-18 required a leap of faith because the Air Force experience did not confirm the McDonnell Douglas perdictions. Indeed, the Air Force experience with the F-15 in Europe, a location more benign than any aircraft carrier, caused the Supreme Allied Commander to claim that with the F-15 "the U.S. is flat on its ass."[9]

It was questionable during the procurement phase whether the reliability and maintainability improvements would work. The reduced performance associated with their added weight was not. Furthermore, neither was the added weight associated with the combination of the attack and fighter version into one aircraft. At the December 1975 DSARC II meeting, the Navy had five different versions of the F-18: a Navy F-18, a Navy A-18, a Marine Corps F-18, and two versions of the TF-18, one for the Navy and one for the Marine Corps. The A-18 for the Navy had no Sparrow; the F-18 for the Marine Corps had Sparrow capability as well as increased attack capability.

By 1977 the Navy eliminated one of the TF-18s and increased commonality of the other versions of the F-18 and A-18. The Navy fighter and attack version differed little. The fighter had a black and white horizontal situation display, whereas the attack version had a color moving map display. The radars were identical, but the attack version was scheduled to have Doppler Beam Sharpening (DBS). The Marine fighter, scheduled to use Forward Looking Infrared (FLIR) and Laser Spot Tracking (LST) in lieu of the Sparrow missiles, had one of its UHF radios replaced with a VHF radio. With the incorporation of the Horizontal Situation Display and the ARC-182 UHF/VHF radio in all aircraft, the F-18s and A-18s became completely common by the beginning of 1979.

The Navy announced in early 1979 an increase in the total order of F-18s from 400 F-18s and 400 A-18s to a combined total of 1,366 F-18s, plus the 11 full-scale development aircraft. The Navy redesignated the Hornet as the F/A-18 to emphasize the dual role and its 100 percent commonality.

In the spring of 1979, the Navy allocated the 1,366 F-18s to the following communities: 153 TF-18s, for 30 Marine Corps Tactical Air Controller Airborne (TACA); 322 for eight squadrons of 20 UE plus pipeline, attrition, and training; 98 RF-18s and 146 for total force attrition. By the summer of 1981, the Navy had changed its allocation. The Marine Corps would replace its 322 F-18s for the light attack mission with AV-8Bs. To keep the program at 1,366, the 1983 Program Objective Memorandum (POM) dedicated 453 fighters between four Navy fighter squadrons and 12 Marine Corps fighter-attack squadrons; 672 attack aircraft for 24 Navy light attack squadrons; 112 reconnaissance versions, and 129 TF-18s from which the 30 TACA aircraft would come.

Congress criticized the insignificant cost savings that occurred when the Navy increased the F-18 buy from 800 to 1,366. Senator Hart questioned the small reduction in then-year program unit costs. When the Navy increased the buy, the 800 F-18s cost $17.7 million per airplane. An increase of 566 lowered the cost to only $17.4 million. Admiral Turner said that the reduction was minimal in then-year dollars because of the stretch out by two years of the program, but in constant year 1975 dollars the reduction had gone from $10.2 million to $9.1 million for the program unit cost.

In spite of the weight increases and in spite of the *slight program* unit cost reduction in then-year dollars, the Navy and OSD officials reflected optimism during the 1979 hearings. Although the weight increase of 1,600 pounds remained, there was, according to Admiral Turner, "no significant degradation in any performance capability." The greatest effect of weight, Turner said, was on carrier landing speed, acceleration from 0.8 to 1.6 Mach, and single-engine climb performance. "None of these parameters," he added, "is degraded beyond threshold by even the highest predicted weight increases."

Turner qualified the 1,600-pound weight increase. The actual empty weight increase was 1,503 pounds, with a 1,745-pound increase for the gross weight. As a result, there had been an 18 to 25 mile radius reduction. Most of the acceleration degradation occurred in the supersonic region. Vice Admiral Turner announced prophetically that "in the area of principal interest and normal utility of the aircraft (Mach 0.8 to 1.2), there has been virtually no loss in acceleration capability." This was the Navy's way of softening the later revelation that they would have to change the specification because the F-18 could not meet the acceleration requirement to Mach 1.6.

Despite Vice Admiral Turner's optimistic declaration that the Hornet's performance would not fall below the threshold, it did. Because of the F-18's inability to meet the NACF specification of 110 seconds, or the original VFAX Presolicitation Notice threshold of 120 seconds to accelerate between 0.8 and 1.6 Mach, the Navy changed the specification in November 1980. That specification required acceleration between 0.8 and 1.2 Mach and came from the repeated attempts to reduce the drag during the flight test program, attempts that were a limited success.

The flight test program exposed the early promises for what they were. Even the original first flight date was changed to accommodate a delay in the development of the digital fly-by-wire system. The original date was July 1978, which slipped to September and ultimately November 18, 1978.

The Navy experienced high and low points during the flight test program. Canada purchased 137 F-18A Hornets and Australia announced that it would buy 75 of them. However, the Navy lost two F-18s during the process. The first Hornet crashed on September 8, 1980, the day after its last appearance at the Farnborough Air Show in England. It went out of control after an engine exploded and damaged the flight control system. In November 1980, a VX-4 Operational Test and Evaluation pilot went into an uncontrollable spin during air combat maneuvering. In spite of the Navy's claims that the digital flight control system software would never allow a spin, the VX-4 pilot had to eject. The Pentagon Paradox continued to function.

The Navy and McDonnell Douglas claimed at the beginning of the F-18 program that the digital flight control system would eliminate the need to physically change the airplane, which typically happens during flight test programs. The Navy and the contractor insisted they could make any aerodynamic changes necessary by simply changing the software. McAir and the Navy made more physical changes to the F-18 than to any fighter aircraft in the last 20 years. They changed the leading edge of the wing, the nose, the leading edge extension, the horizontal tail twice, the ailerons, the wing structure, and the environmental control system exhaust. By comparison, McDonnell Douglas changed the F-15 visually in only three places; the wing tip, the speed brake, and the horizontal tail.

The Government Accounting Office (GAO) issued a report in February, 1980, questioning the effectiveness of the F-18.[10] One year later the GAO issued a progress report indicating that the Hornet had improved, but there was still room for improvement.[11]

The Navy commissioned the first F-18 squadron, VFA-125 on November 13, 1980, at Lemoore Naval Air Station, California, shortly after the Operational Test & Evaluation squadron (VX-4) pilots began their initial evaluation of the F-18 on October 27, 1980. At that time the Hornet had completed 100 percent of the speed and altitude envelope and 95 percent of the maneuvering envelope. Here is a brief summary of the F-18's performance during the flight test.

Acceleration

The F-18 contract specification required the Hornet to accelerate from 0.8 to 1.6 at 35,000 feet in the fighter configuration of two Sparrows, two Sidewinders, gun, and full ammunition in 110 seconds. The Navy demonstrated at the first Navy Preliminary Evaluation (NPE I) in March 1979 a time of 156 seconds. As a comparison, the YF-16's time was 56 seconds between 0.9 and 1.6 Mach. The production version of the YF-16, the F-16A, was slower. Its time was 70 seconds between these two Mach points. The F-18A Hornet's predecessor the YF-17, flew from 0.9 to 1.6 Mach in 103 seconds.

By the end of the first quarter of 1980, the Navy and McDonnell Douglas claimed that the F-18 could fly the Mach 0.8-1.6 range in 134 seconds. As of May 16, 1980, McDonnell Douglas's chief test pilot, Bill Brinks, said the acceleration time had been reduced by 25 percent from the NPE I time. This would bring the time to 116 seconds, six seconds from the threshold. Brinks said that the F-18 was fast enough to out-accelerate the F-15. "Between five and twenty thousand feet, from 150 to 535 knots, we routinely pull out ahead of the F-15s. We even let the F-15 get all five zones of their burner lit and let them retract their speed brake, and we walk away from them. It doesn't seem to make any difference what our weight is. And the F-15 is clean and we have two Sparrows and two Sidewinders and gun ballast."[12]

Another McDonnell test pilot, as well as a Navy test pilot, confirmed the Hornet's superior subsonic acceleration over both the F-14 and F-15.

On June 5, 1980, an F-18 flown by a McDonnell Douglas test pilot and an F-14 chase plane had an acceleration contest. Both aircraft had been topped off with fuel by an airborne tanker. The F-14 had two Sparrows, two Sidewinders, and gun ballast. The airplanes started at 0.8 Mach. As the F-18A reached 1.45 Mach, the F-14 call out was 1.25 Mach. When the F-18 hit 1.54 Mach, the F-14 pilot called out that he had fallen behind and lost sight of the Hornet. The F-18A reached 1.6 Mach and could fly no further because of a maximum speed restriction during flight tests. The F-14 passed the Hornet 50 miles later going 1.8 Mach.

Official data from the Navy, however, tell a different story. The Navy acknowledges that the F-18 has faster acceleration from .8 to 1.2 Mach—52 seconds versus 56 for the F-14—the F-14 out accelerates the F-18 from .8 to 1.6. The F-14 takes 114 seconds; the F-18 takes 134 seconds. Yet in spite of this, the Navy testified in July 1981 that the F-18 could out accelerate the F-4 and F-14. The Hornet's initial acceleration, said the Navy, was faster than any fighter, friend or foe. In drag races, the Hornet was one mile ahead of the F-14 at Mach 1.3 and one mile ahead of the F-4 at Mach 1.5. The Navy testified that the Hornet was 12 percent below the 0.8 to 1.6 Mach acceleration threshold. The Navy claimed it would have to add variable ramp inlets to make the F-18 accelerate beyond 1.4 to meet the specification. Such a fix would not have been worth the cost.

Besides, the Navy said, the F-18 would spend less than 0.5 percent of its time above 1.2.

But if the Hornet would spend so little time above Mach 1.2, why did the Navy design the airplane to fly there? Why did it make Mach 1.6 part of the original VFAX acceleration specification and repeat the specification for every subsequent requirement? This is another case where the Navy changed the specification to fit the result rather than requiring the contractor to make the airplane fit the specification.

Range

The threshold specification required a fighter escort mission radius of 400 miles on internal fuel. The strike mission specification required 550 nautical miles but with external fuel. One might assume that determining range in flight tests would be simple: fill up the tanks, fly out 400 or 550 miles, and see if you can get back. However, flight test works differently. The Navy and McDonnell simulated missions. Then they argued over how to interpret the data.

For the fighter mission, the Navy claimed in the first quarter of 1980 that the Hornet could fly a 384 nautical mile radius. McDonnell Douglas claimed that its data showed the F-18 could fly 422 nautical miles. McDonnell Douglas said the attack configuration could fly 610 nautical miles; the Navy claimed 570 nautical miles. Several months after all the analyses, the Navy and McDonnell settled their fighter escort arguments. The Navy claimed 396; McDonnell Douglas said 404 nautical miles.

By the summer of 1981 Deputy Chief of Naval Operations for Air Warfare, Vice Adm. Wesley McDonald, said that even though the F-18's fighter escort radius was short by 5 percent of the specification, its radius of action exceeded the F-4 *Phantom's* by 150 nautical miles and the F-14 by 50 miles.[13]

The significance of this statement is difficult to interpret. Perhaps the F-18 mission profile was different from the profile of the F-14 or F-4. On the other hand, the statement may not be true. In either event, Vice Admiral McDonald's statement is academic insofar as its tactical utility. The VX-4 pilots were more niggardly with their optimism than the admirals at the congressional hearings. They reduced the expected range of the F-18 by almost half.

Operational considerations, including retaining rather than jettisoning empty external fuel tanks, rendezvous, marshall, and fuel reserves for multiple looks at the deck before mandatory tanking, or bingo, were added to the F-18 specification combat profiles. With these additions, combat radius was 200 nautical miles for the fighter escort profile, and 340 nautical miles for the interdiction profile.*[14]

Weight

The 1980 GAO report stated that the F-18 was, as of October 1, 1979, 1,962 pounds over its specification empty weight of 20,146. According to the GAO report, the 1,962-pound increase was due to three factors: 166-pound increase due to reliability and maintainability fixes; 490 pounds due to under estimates by engineers; and 1,306 pounds due to the addition of survivability and design-to-life cycle cost items. The Navy had a weight reduction program of 341 pounds that it planned to introduce into the 123rd aircraft.

The original specification required a gross combat takeoff weight of 33,652 pounds in the fighter escort role. However, the performance weight of the aircraft during the first Navy Preliminary Evaluation (NPE 1) was 35,363. By the fall of 1980, the Navy changed the weight specification because the F-18 had grown to 36,000 pounds.

Drag

The drag associated with the F-18 was higher than either McDonnell or the Navy anticipated. The drag affects many of the other performance characteristics. The major contributors to the unanticipated drag were the slots in the leading edge extension (LEX), the leading edge of the wing, the environmental control system exhaust, and the computer controlled leading and training edge flap schedule.

Two of the three slots in the leading edge extension of the No. 2 and No. 6 full-scale development (FSD) aircraft were filled in an attempt to reduce drag. Because this program was successful, all test aircraft had the forward two slots filled in.

The Navy increased the radius of the leading edge of No. 1 and 4 full-scale development aircraft from a radius of 0.04 inches to 0.02 inches. Along with this radius change, McDonnell Douglas eliminated the snag on these two aircraft by removing two inches of the leading edge. This decreased the chord slightly as well as the wetted wing area. The reduction in the wetted area reduced the subsonic drag. The snag had not been on the Northrop YF-17, so in that respect the McDonnell wing reverted to its ancestral shape. McDonnell made two more changes to reduce drag.

The exhaust of the environmental control system previously directed upward on the dorsal side of the aircraft was vented rearward. The schedule of the leading and trailing edge flaps on all aircraft

*The VX-4 pilots seem to confirm George Spangenberg's premise that the F/A-18's radius of action was no better than the A-4's.

was reprogrammed so that the wing would produce its maximum lift over drag (L/D) at all airspeeds.

Lift-off Speed

The nose wheel lift-off speed was originally 150 knots. McDonnell Douglas toed in the rudders and changed the horizontal stabilator from a notched version back to a solid design. These two changes reduced the lift-off speed to 130 knots. McDonnell modified one of the flight control programs to reduce the leading edge flaps from 30 degrees to 12 degrees for takeoff. This further reduced the lift-off speed to 120 knots.

F404 Engine

The General Electric engine was, relatively speaking, a positive element in the flight test program. According to McDonnell Douglas's chief test pilot, the F404's reliability allowed the F-18 flight test program to progress at a much faster rate than that of the F-15. The lack of reliability of the F100, he said, slowed the F-15 test program. On acceptance flights, one engine had to be shut down at least 15 percent of the time.

The F404 specification required a sea level static thrust of 16,090 pounds and a specific fuel consumption of 1.85. However, the F404 demonstrated 16,650 pounds of thrust with a specific fuel consumption of 1.65. The only flaw in the F404 engine was the low-pressure turbine failure, which caused the crash of the second two-seat F-18 in September 1980.

The F404 required the same time for a burner light as the J79. However, from idle to military (intermediate) power, the F404 was more responsive. These afterburner lights are significantly quicker to respond than engines currently in the F-14, F-15, and F-16. The F404 has experienced, according to some Department of Defense officials, slow, and in some cases no, after burner lights due to blowouts at high altitudes.

Roll Rate

The roll rate specification for the F-18 is based on one-g flight conditions. Critics of the F-18 program claim that one-g roll rates are good only for air shows and will never be used tactically in war. Pilots need to reverse direction under high-g conditions, they claim, and only a test under high-g conditions is a valid testimony of the Hornet's ability to maneuver.

Nevertheless, the F-18 had difficulty rolling under one-g flight conditions while at high speeds at low altitudes, a condition pilots call "high q." The Navy and McDonnell Douglas maintain that the poor roll rate was a function of four items: stick torquing, uncommanded *g* excursions during rolls, higher than predicted roll damping, and outer wing panel twisting—the phenomenon that has caused aileron reversal at high dynamic pressures (high q) and well understood since the late 1940s.

The roll rate specification in the F-18 is 180 degrees/second between 10,000 and 20,000 feet. Military specification 8785B entitled *Military Specification of Flying Qualities of Piloted Airplanes* requires *all* military fighter aircraft to roll to 90 degrees in one second in the fighter configuration at all altitudes and all airspeeds. The roll rate in the F-18 as of the last week of May 1980 was degraded so that at speeds greater than 500 knots and at altitudes below 10,000 feet, some test pilots were afraid to roll it.

"I'm talking about roll rates on the order of five degrees per second," said one Naval officer close to the program. Bill Brinks contradicted the comment. He said that as of May 1980, the F-18A was rolling 40 degrees per second in one direction and 60 degrees per second in another. The difference was due primarily to the free play in the leading edge flaps.

Pilots experienced stick torquing when they gave full commands to the stick. For example, when giving a command for a full left roll, the pilot needed to apply nine pounds of pressure to the stick against the stop. Typically pilots would apply more than nine pounds. The transducer, which the stick was attached to in the floor of the cockpit, was interpreting any excess over nine pounds as a command in the opposite direction. If a pilot applied 14 pounds of pressure to the left, instead of getting 9 pounds of input, the flight control computer would come off the maximum by the difference between the 14 and 9 pounds, or command approximately 5 pounds to the right. Pilots were able to roll to the right by twisting the stick to the left. Although it has not been demonstrated, one could surmise that the roll rate could be increased to the left by putting the stick to the left, and twisting it to the right.

At the time the VX-4 pilots flew the TF-18, the stick torquing problem still existed. Moving the control stick against the control stop caused problems. In some cases the control stick never got to the stop; it reached a knee first. "The TF/A-18 FCS [flight control system] mechanization allowed reduced or no rolling motion in response to full lateral commands when the control stick in the other cockpit was obstructed by the pilot's leg, which could lead crews to suspect an FCS malfunction when none existed."[15]

The boron-epoxy composite wing of the F-18 twisted under high-*g* loads. The stiffness of the outer wing panel was not sufficient to counter the aerodynamic forces during high-*g* maneuvers.

"The load on the outboard leading edge flap was great enough," according to Bill Brinks, "that the hydraulic drive unit could not move the leading edge flaps until the speed was reduced or altitude increased. The least impact—and probably of beneficial effect in weight reduction—would occur if the snag was removed from the outboard wing and that's what was done. So far these tests have proved successful—we haven't had any recurrence of loads that would stop the flap from being programmed normally."[16]

Brinks went on to add that the roll rate had been improved a small amount due to the elimination of the snag. The wing twisting displayed at high-*g*s was exacerbated during aileron deflection. When the pilot commanded a right turn, for example, the aileron on the left wing was deflected down, which overcame the strength of the composite wing, and caused the trailing edge to balloon up and the leading edge to dig into the oncoming air. This action dumped lift.

Test pilots experienced uncommanded *g* excursions. For example, during a one-*g* roll, by the time pilots had rolled to the 140-degree position, they started to experience less than one *g*. By the time the roll reached the 280-degree position, the pilots had gone through zero-*g* and started to experience positive *g*'s again.

As of the summer of 1980, there was a placard limitation on rolling the F-18 with more than one *g* on the airplane. At that time, some test pilots speculated that at higher *g* the aircraft would transition from zero *g* into the negative *g* arena. Although the one *g* limitation no longer existed, the VX-4 pilots complained of related problems. "Precise tracking was degraded in the 15-20° AOA [angle of attack] region (routinely entered during ACM) by an objectionable Dutch roll evident in pilot production flight control laws."

The original McDonnell Douglas recommendation for the slow roll rate contained five fixes: three hardware and two software changes that were included in aircraft number 8 and all pilot production and production aircraft. The aileron was extended distally to within two inches of the sidewinder rail. This increased the aileron area 36 percent. An additional four plys of graphite-epoxy composite material was added to the outer wing panel, beginning at the aileron outer wing panel interface and forward one third of the distance to the outer wing panel-leading edge flap interface. The third hardware increased the webb along the aft spar.

Through software changes, the trailing edge flaps were programmed for eight degrees of movement and the differential stabilators had an additional four degrees of movement. These fixes added an additional 136 pounds to the F-18. In spite of these fixes, the roll rate was below the specification during the VX-4 initial operational test and evaluation.

The Navy tried to treat the roll rate problem as insignificant because it was located in only one part of the flight envelope, at high speed close to the ground. At the same time, it was in this arena that the Navy claimed it needed the F-18's excess speed and maneuverability in the first place. The A-7, the Navy said, could not fly fast enough or maneuver hard enough at low altitudes to dodge the surface-to-air missiles. Paradoxically, the Navy justified the Hornet on the grounds that it had higher speed close to the deck and greater maneuverability than the A-7. Then it dismissed criticism of the Hornet when tests showed that the airplane could not maneuver close to the flight deck.

Lateral Sluggishness and Roll Oscillation

A critic of the F-18A program in the Office of the Secretary of Defense (OSD) in the fall of 1980 stated, "The problem with the tracking of targets in the F-18 is that it has a roll oscillation which is caused by a delay in the input to the aileron after the pilot makes the command to the stick." As a result, one Navy test pilot said that while tracking an A-4 with fixed pipper and feet on the floor in a two-g turn (60 degree bank), the pipper oscillated plus or minus 10 mils from the nose to the tail of the A-4.

When asked about this, a Navy program office spokesman stated that this was not due to the longitudinal discrepancy that had shown up earlier in NPE 1. "A fix was made which has been verified in NPE3." The problem was rather one of radar glint, the Navy representative said. "Radar glint causes the radar to jump around because of the inherent problem with radar's inability to tell the centroid of a large target. We are fixing this with 'short range track' which will be incorporated this fall in all of the IOT&E aircraft."

Nevertheless, VX-4 pilots were not able to get consistent radar results either. The radar was slow to lock under g. Furthermore, the radar would not consistently resolve multiple targets or detect formation changes.

A Navy spokesman went on to add that the problem might not have been simply the time delay.

> The flight control system is so complex that if you totally eliminate the time delay, the problem may still be there because of something else.
>
> He [the OSD critic] is saying that the fact that we have a digital flight control system that you're always going to have time delays, and I can't argue—that's just the nature of the beast you've got to live with.
>
> Perhaps he is making a prediction. They are not really oscillations. They are imprecisions in the lateral channel. We can't precisely hold the pipper within plus or minus 5 laterally when we disturb it either purposely or when we get a wind gust.

Nevertheless, by the time of the Initial Operation & Test Evaluation, the problem remained. "Performance in the gunnery pattern was degraded by lateral and longitudinal flight control sensitivity, which hampered aggressive tracking, and low roll rate under *g*."

The Navy's acceptance of the F-18 regardless of its failure to meet the roll rate specification is another case of the futility of imposing the specifications in the first place. One might argue that the specification is only a point to approach, an idealized position to which the contractor should not be tightly held. However, goals serve this function. Thresholds are the "do not fall below" point. Thresholds are supposed to be the least acceptable performance. In the Hornet's case, the roll rate at the high speed-low altitude area is not a nice-to-have feature but an indispensable performance factor, especially if one accepts the Navy's justification of the F-18 over the A-7. The Navy argued that it would fix the roll rate, but in any event, the F-18's performance was good enough. If it was good enough, then why fix it? Alternatively, why approve the F-18 for production until it was fixed? Approving airplanes that will be fixed subsequent to the test and evaluation flights—upon which the DSARC decision process is based—makes a mockery of the testing process. Why not wait until the fix is finished and then approve the aircraft?

As the VX-4 test results trickled into the Navy, it stiffened. Many of the criticisms made earlier in the program did not disappear, and furthermore, the Navy's own pilots were saying so. The DSARC III decision to approve production had been scheduled originally for the fall of 1980, but DSARC postponed its meeting so it could get the input from the Initial Operational Test & Evaluation report. The meeting was rescheduled for March 1981, the month the VX-4 IOT&E would be finished. VX-4's report was crucial because DSARC's charter required it to see if the F-18 was tactically suitable, regardless of whether the aircraft met contractual specifications, many of which it did not. The Navy, knowing it would be criticized once the VX-4 results became public, began preparing for the conclusion of the

IOT&E test results, the criticism, and the most important of the three DSARC meetings, the DSARC III production decision. Sensing pressure from all quarters, the Navy began talking to itself, and the question it asked was "Where is Naval aviation going?"

Chapter 13

Quo Vadis Naval Air

March 10, 1981
The Tomcat and its integral Phoenix missiles are the only system in the free World capable of successfully engaging the Soviet Backfire *bomber.*

A few months later
The Hornet, armed with AIM-7F/M and AIM-9L missiles, can maintain a CAP station that will allow it to intercept and attrite the Backfire *bomber before it can reach its weapons release line.*

Vice Adm. Wesley McDonald, USN
DCNO (Air Warfare)

The Department of Defense approved the F-18 in June 1981 for the fighter mission. The Navy had finally gotten its way. However, in the six years since the Navy selected the F-18, its purpose appeared to have been lost. All of the large carriers would carry F-14s. The fighter mission for the F-18 in the Navy was disbanded except for two smaller carriers. The attack version of the F-18, scheduled for the Marine Corps, competed with the AV-8B and lost. Under the circumstances, it is easy to understand why the Navy created a program review of tactical air alternatives. The review, done in December 1980 by Capt. Frank Whittle, was dubbed "Quo Vadis Naval Aviation, Where Is Naval Aviation Going?"[1]

Essentially, Whittle showed how, with a given budget, the Navy could increase the total number of aircraft available for the 15 carrier fleet. It was a case of quantity versus quality all over again. Some congressmen, familiar with the Whittle Report, asked the Navy why it did not implement the options discussed in the report. Vice Admiral McDonald replied that the Whittle Report "was based on economic considerations, to acquire the maximum number of aircraft, rather than operational considerations that consider effectiveness as well as cost."[2]

In the spring of 1981—as the IOT&E test program was being completed—factions within the U.S. Navy generated reports unfavorable to the F-18. One of them was attributed to the Systems Analysis

Division of the Office of the Chief of Naval Operations.[3] The Whittle Report had questioned the economics of buying F-18s; the Systems Analysis paper attacked the very capability of the Hornet. The Navy claimed that the paper, untitled and undated, was an internal discussion paper only, generated by George Haering, a civilian analyst.

The Systems Analysis paper reviewed the F-18 program, summarizing the Navy's original desire for F-14s to replace F-4s and, thus, an all F-14 fighter force. In spite of DOD's desire to replace the expensive F-14s (which the paper added were modest by today's standards) with F-18s, the original intent of the Hornet appeared lost.

> To date, none of the expectations that were the basis for initiation and continuance of the program have been achieved.
>
> a. The CNO has recently stated that the large CVS will have an all F-14 fighter complement and that the ORISKANY is slated for an all-attack (A-4 or A-7) air wing.
>
> (1) Sea-Plan 2000 showed the F-14 to be three times more effective than the F-18 in the fleet defense role.
>
> (2) The ASOW Warfare Appraisal for POM 83 estimated that losses of attack aircraft are twice as great when the strike is escorted by F-18's vice F-14's.
>
> Thus, the large F-18 buy for the Navy fighter mission will not be made. The Navy has returned to its original position, that it needs an all F-14 fighter force and that position will probably be sustained.

The study paper continued with a comment on the increasing cost of the F-18, 75 to 80 percent of the F-14. The A-7, AV-8B and A-6 were, respectively, only 35, 50, and 95 percent of the cost of the Hornet.

The paper then compared the attack performance of the F-18 with existing attack aircraft.

> With F-18s designed payload, (4 Rockeyes) A-7 radius of action is twice as far. With four times the F-18s design load, the A-6 radius of action is twice as far. Many targets that might be critical in a Middle East/Persian Gulf/Indian Ocean scenario could not be reached with F-18s. For targets that the F-18 could reach, its smaller payload would require an increased number of sorties and more attack aircraft exposure to enemy defenses.

One will recall that the argument favoring the F-18 had been that it had greater penetration speed than either the A-7 or the A-6. But, as the Haering study went on, the Hornet is a supersonic aircraft loaded down with air-to-ground ordnance, which reduces its speed significantly.

> (Although the F-18 is faster [supersonic] in a fighter configuration than either A-6 or A-7, it is not supersonic nor significantly faster when

carrying weapons and, if adequate fuel is provided to allow the F-18 to leave the target at supersonic speeds after weapon delivery, the F-18s usable weapon payload is even further degraded.)

Having stated the case of a waning purpose for the F-18, the paper listed five alternatives. (1) The Navy could maintain the A-7E's and buy three more for the cost for each F-18. (2) It could replace A-7s with A-6s to take advantage of the weather for offensive strikes. (3) The Marine Corps could replace F-4s with the AV-8B. (4) The Marine Corps could also replace F-4s with new F-4s. (5) The final choice was based on the fact that the Marines would not be flying Navy aircraft, that is, AV-8B's only. The Study Paper suggested the Marine Corps procure F-16s.*

The common argument for continuing with the F-18 was based on the money already spent on the program. The study paper's concluding remark addressed this issue: "To counter sunk cost argument, the nose of the camel is $3B, the camel itself is $30B. Relatively small nose."

The Navy disavowed the report. Nevertheless, the arguments made in the study paper were the focus of many congressional questions for the Navy in the weeks before and after the DSARC meeting of March 17, 1981.

Shortly after the Initial Operational Test & Evaluation pilots from VX-4 finished on February 12, 1981, the Department of Defense prepared for the DSARC III decision to authorize the production version of the F-18.†[4] This DSARC III meeting originally scheduled for November 1980, had been rescheduled due to a delay in the F-18 program.

Capt. John Weaver, F-18 Program Manager from Naval Air Systems Command, briefed the group at the March 17, 1981 DSARC meeting. His comments were routine; the briefing from the VX-4 pilots, however, was not. They told DSARC that the F-18 was deficient in range, cycle time, strafing, and roll. They complained about the inability to track with some of the heads up display (HUD) symbology. But

*While this alternative was criticized because the F-16 was not carrier suitable, the Marine Corps flew most of World War II with a fighter, the F4U Corsair, which was not certified carrier suitable until nine months before the war ended. The Marines made the reputation of the Corsair, but as a land-based airplane.

†Originally there were three DSARC III decision points. DSARC IIIA was for the limited production aircraft, also called *Pilot Production Aircraft*. (These correspond somewhat to the "Y" designated aircraft which before and during World War II, were called "service test." DSARC IIIA was scheduled for March 1980. DSARC IIIB was originally scheduled for November 1980. It would have authorized F-18 production and low-rate A-18 production. The full production for the A-18 was originally scheduled with DSARC IIIC in January 1982. Once the F-18 and the A-18 were merged, these DSARC III distinctions were theoretically eliminated, since the airplane was identical for both missions.

the worst indictment against the Hornet was its faulty radar.

The VX-4 pilots claimed that when they changed from the high pulse repetition frequency (HPRF) to the shorter range medium PRF, they would lose up to a third of their targets. They complained that the radar was insufficient in the air-to-ground mode and that the built-in test (BIT) gave a 62-percent false alarm rate. As a result of the VX-4 comments, DSARC postponed its decision.[5]

Critics of the F-18 program claimed that the delay was prompted by the negative report by the VX-4 pilots, who represented the Commander, Operational Test and Evaluation Force. Navy representatives who defended the F-18 claimed that the DSARC delay was due not to technical issues, but to costs.

The DSARC received two briefings: one from the Naval Air Systems Command Program manager, Captain Weaver, and one from VX-4. After these two briefings, DSARC once again postponed the decision.

Navy officials on the program claimed that the decision to postpone approving full scale development was not due to the somewhat negative reports from VX-4, but because members of DSARC were from a new administration.

Other Department of Defense officials disagreed. They stated that due to the negative comments made by the VX-4 pilots to the DSARC, the program was in jeopardy. These officials stated that the pilots found the F-18's range to be deficient: with three external fuel tanks and 2 MK-84 bombs the airplane could fly a mission radius of only 320 nautical miles. The VX-4 pilots also expressed concern about the F-18's ability to make the 1-hour and 45 minute cycle time for carrier operations, to strafe accurately, and to roll. They complained about over-correction and inability to track with some of the symbology in the Heads Up Display (HUD).

There was further testimony about the F-18A flying against the F-14. Officials claimed that the VX-4 pilots who flew against the F-14 gained an initial advantage, but within 90 seconds relinquished the advantage to the F-14. A Navy F-18A program office official claimed that this was true, but that the difference was due to lack of recent dogfighting by the F-18 pilots, while the F-14 pilots had been practicing for two weeks.

As a result of the VX-4 and program manager's report, the DSARC began looking at alternatives. One that was favored by the Office of the Secretary of Defense (OSD) was to give the U.S. Marines F-16s and AV-8B's.

A Navy official disputed this report of problems with the technical capability of the airplane. He said, "There isn't any issue on the technical capability of the airplane. The only issue seems to be the price."

Whether it was the issue of cost or the technical capability of the F-18 is not clear, but the new Deputy Secretary of Defense, Frank Carlucci, directed the Navy to study some alternatives to the F-18, one of which was to give F-16s to the Navy for both land and carrier use. Carlucci also ordered the Navy to investigate ways to reduce the Hornet's cost.[6]

The decision memorandum, issued mid-April 1981, required the Navy to complete its review by June 18, 1981. At the same time, Carrlucci sent the House Appropriations Subcommittee on Defense a letter stating that he was unable to certify that significant deficiencies were corrected and tested.

The F-18 deficiencies continued to mount. The environmental test report of the Hornet's visit to the McKinley Climatic Laboratory at Eglin Air Force Base, Florida, was not favorable.[7] Environmental tests conducted between January 26 and April 3 disclosed 39 failures.

Furthermore, there was no restriction on putting smart weapons on the A-7, in which case the A-7 increased its maneuverability. A Vought Corporation proposal in the summer of 1981 included the reintroduction of the A-7 with twin F404 engines (which had been submitted every year since the 1975 hearings) and a new design that incorporated the F101 (13-1) engine in the A-7.

The Hornet's ability to fly at speeds equivalent to the fighter escort would help its survivability. If the carrier was working with its normal 1-hour and 45 minute cycle time, the F-18 would actually have more range because it could fly further during the same time as the A-7.[8]

The success rate of the F-18's missile firing was what one might expect: nineteen fired by the summer of 1981 and all either hit or passed within lethal radius. The driver behind the missiles was the sine qua non of the F-18, the radar. The Hughes APG-65 air-to-air and air-to-ground doppler radar had been acclaimed throughout the program. Lt. Col. Pete Field stated in an article that the false alarm rates were down and the detection ranges were up.

The radar was credited with some of the tracking problems during the summer of 1980. According to the specifications for the F-18, the false alarm rate could not exceed more than one false target per minute. Field was quick to point out that the specifications on the F-15 radar required no more than five false alarm targets per minute. As of the summer of 1981, the F-18 rate was down to three per minute.

Five and a half years had passed since the approval for full-scale development, yet the Hornet was still surrounded by controversy—controversy that many in the Navy claimed should not exist. Pilots that flew the F-18 loved it. But virtually all pilots feel that way about the airplanes they fly.

The real issue remained what it was in the beginning: Did the Navy need an airplane with a radar-guided missile? Now that it had one, was it getting what it paid for?

All of the F-18's problems were supposed to be behind it as of September 1981. The roll rate problem mentioned by VX-4 had been eliminated, according to Marine Lt. Col. Pete Field, the F-18 Program Manager at the Naval Air Test Center.[9] The airplane that the VX-4 pilots flew did not have the second roll rate fix involving the leading edge flaps; they were forced to fly the F-18 before the fix, Field claimed. The roll rate met the specifications at all points except at 0.95 to 1.0 Mach at 5,000 feet and below. Field said that the Navy was happy with the roll rate between 0.95 and 1.0 Mach and that it would not spend the money to force the contractor to fix the deficiency. The roll rate of 23 degrees can be generated at 0.7 Mach. Field said that the rate of roll was equal to the F-16's subsonically, and better than the F-16's supersonically. The only area that the F-16 was superior, he stated, was in the .95-1.0 region.

Field pointed out additional improvements. "The maintainability and reliability are almost unbelievable. The F-18 is five times more reliable than either the F-4 or the F-14 and three times more reliable than the A-7. It takes 13 F-4 Phantoms to support 4-6 F-18's as chase planes," he said. "We had 100 hours on one airplane without a down. It is not unusual to fly one of the F-18's six times a day for a week or two without a gripe."

During a reliability demonstration that lasted 100 hours, there were only 11 total failures and only two radar failures. An engine change was made in 16.3 minutes.

The range, according to Field, was still 8 percent below the specification. However, he pointed out that the F-14 was 17 percent below the specification, and the A-7 was 13 percent below. Field readily admitted that the F-18 had a slightly shorter range than the A-7 (approximately 10 percent) with the same payload. The greater survivability justified this.

The F-18 was sold as an attack aircraft—in spite of its lower payload capability—because of its alleged increase in survivability. The increased survivability was due to greater maneuverability and faster speed. However, the F-18 had a higher speed not because it could cruise significantly faster than the A-7, but because the F-18 carried a lighter payload. The smaller payloads were justified because they were smart bombs, which promised to yield higher accuracy when coupled with the sophisticated F-18 weapons system.

But the benefits of smart weapons require a trade off. In the case of the F-18, survivability was traded. Smart bombs required more time than iron bombs did to align the sights—regardless of whether the system was electro-optical, laser, etc. The increased time had to be flown straight and level. That made the F-18 more predictable over the target, thus taking away any maneuverability advantage over the A-7. "Attrition goes up exponentially with the length of straight tracking flight." One could argue that the F-18 flew through the target area faster than the A-7 and was, therefore, exposed for a shorter period of time. However, experience in southeast Asia showed that, for example, Walleye "sorties took four times as many hits as iron bomb sorties."

The F-18 DSARC IIIA—the session to approve the fighter portion of the Hornet—took place on June 18, 1981. The F-18 was approved for production, with the admonition that the Navy and the contractor had better watch their costs.

The F-18 was procured in large numbers. But would it stand the test of battle? It would have its chance, a little more than 10 years after its final approval, to join an air armada that would reign over the skies of Iraq.

Before the F-18 would get an opportunity to prove its merits, the U.S. Navy would have close to 36 squadrons, the U.S. Marine Corps 27 squadrons, the Berlin Wall would fall, and President Bush would eliminate tactical nuclear weapons from Europe and Asia. Canada, Spain, Australia, Kuwait, Switzerland, and Finland would procure the Hornet by the middle of the 1990s.

Chapter 14

Hornets in the Gulf

"Every Iraqi fixed-wing aircraft destroyed in air-to-air combat, including five Soviet-made MiG-29 Fulcrums, were downed by F-15C's."

"Airpower in Operation Desert Storm"
Air Force Public Affairs Fact Sheet 91-03, p. 5

Aircraft at two-two-five 30 from Manny. It's *hot* on you. . . ."

"Bandits on your zero-nine-zero from 6 miles westbound. . . ."

"400—bandits on your nose 15."

"400's radar contact on my nose. Mach at 28,000."

Lt. Nick "Mongo" Mongillo transitioned into the air-to-air mode.

"400. Bogies on the nose. 28,000 . . . 7 miles. MiG-21. . . ."

"VID. Targets lock. Kill sections stand by for VID. Coming down both sides, Mach."

"Mongo's locked."

"Trail section stand by for VID. Coming down my nose . . . both sides Mach."

"Bouncer's tally one."

"Mongo's tally one . . . Good sniff, MiG-21. . . ."

"Fox one, MiG-21 low."

Mongo pressed the button; the missile fired.

"Fox one. Good kill. That's a MiG-21 low. That's confirmed."

The F-18 got the first Navy Iraqi air-to-air kill of Desert Storm.*

Unfortunately, the F-18 also has the dubious dintinction of suffering the only air-to-air loss in the air war. It acquired this distinction in large part to the continued inability to acquire positive identification beyond visual range, the premise on which the Sparrow missile is based. The F-18 and its pilot was one of the first casualties in the Gulf War but the truth was a close second.[1]

*The false statement in the epigraph above by the U.S. Air Force, which claimed that F-15s got all the air-to-air kills, shows the brazenness of postwar falsifications.

The Navy entered the arena of the Gulf War with F-18s as part of its arsenal and found itself subservient to the U.S. Air Force. An Air Force lieutenant general was in charge of the air operations for both services. What the Air Force wanted to do in the Gulf War was demonstrate that strategic bombing as a concept was not only relevant in winning a war, but could be the exclusive option.* The U.S. Naval carrier forces, on the other hand, while always claiming to be virtually equal to the Air Force in strategic capability, were considered by many to be more ideally suited for providing tactical support for the U.S. Marine Corps. Unfortunately, the Navy no longer had some of its long loiter aircraft that were ideally suited for supporting the foot soldier.†

The Air Force's strategic bombing‡ advocates believed that the best method to subdue adversarial societies was through bombing—whether massive or precise.

If all electricity in a given community came from a single electric plant, destroying that plant would bring the society to a halt. But, if each home, industry, and business had its own generator, the destruction of a single electrical plant would not bring the society to its knees. Agrarian societies in Vietnam are more like the latter; industrial societies of the United States and western Europe are more like the former. The question that faced the military planners during the build up to Desert Storm was, where was Iraq on the evolutionary continuum?

Group decision-making tends to perpetuate conventional thinking regardless of new information. In a like manner, the planners of Operation Desert Storm generated a classic strategic bombing program that would have made Ira Eaker, the U.S. Army Air Force

*The strategic bombing target selection was a joint effort. The fact that the U.S. Navy felt that it was subservient was due to its continued resistance to take part in joint operations with other services. The Navy has always insisted on operating autonomously.

†Philip "Skip" Okamoto, who served in the Army Special Forces during Vietnam, said that he would forgo close air support in most cases unless the artillery coordinators could assure him that the aircraft was an A-1 Skyraider or other long loiter type. Okamoto not only wanted the loiter time, he also wanted the accuracy that came with the slower speed. While the Navy uses the expression "close air support" it does not have the capability to support U.S. Marines in the manner preferred by Okamoto. (Statement made to the author by Philip "Skip" Okamoto.)

‡Strategic bombing is defined by the *Air Force Dictionary* as, "The bombing of a selected target or targets vital to the war-making capacity of a nation." Tactical, when used in contrast to strategic, means: "Of or pertaining to tactics, i.e., to the arranging, positioning, or maneuvering of forces in contact, or near contact, with the enemy so as to achieve an objective or objectives in an air campaign, air battle, or surface battle."

general in charge of bombing Germany in World War II, quiver with envy.

The grand wizard of strategic bombing was an Italian named Guilio Douhet, who, as a result of the strategic bombings in World War I, wrote a book in 1921 entitled *Command of the Air.* In it he claimed that bombers would replace all other instruments of warfare.

As a result of Douhet's writing, most strategic bombing advocates believed that massive bombing on civilian and industrial targets would destroy the population's will to wage war, their ability to sustain it, and, as a result, eliminate the need to commit land troops. For the majority of air power theorists, ground troops were a threat but not to the enemy. They threatened funds destined for bombers because ground troops required aircraft to provide close air support, combat air patrols, and battlefield interdiction. Providing these services would have drawn on Army Air Force assets, but more disruptive would have been the confrontational self-assessment with the solifidian belief in strategic bombing's ability to "do it all."[2] But not all of the bombing advocates of World War II were convinced that the use of land troops could be avoided. Nevertheless, they believed that strategic bombing would achieve the first requisite for committing those troops, namely achieving air superiority through the destruction of enemy fighters from the fire power of the bombers and from the bombs themselves. They also believed that the strategic bombing campaign would tie up assets, and eliminate the fighters that would otherwise be available for Germany to throw against the invading troops that would eventually arrive on June 6, 1944, in Operation Overlord.

As to bombers' ability to destroy the war-making capability of the enemy, in the first raid on the Schweinfurt ball bearing factory, B-17s destroyed less than 4 percent of the equipment. More importantly, however, after a year of bombing Germany, the U.S. Army Air Force bombers averaged less than 5 percent destruction of equipment, and production capability was back to where it was prior to the first bomb strikes.

Despite these facts, the Chief of Staff of the U.S. Army Air Forces, General H. H. "Hap" Arnold, said shortly after the first deep bomber raid on Germany, "All five of the works at Schweinfurt were either completely or almost completely wiped out. Our attack was the most perfect example in history of accurate distribution of bombs over a target. It was an attack that will not have to be repeated for a very long time, if at all."

Another erroneous concept was that bombers were so fast, heavily armed, and armored that any enemy fighters that were caught were destroyed. On the contrary, at the end of the first strategic bomber raid, the United States lost 20 percent of its bombers—an experience which would be repeated and contradict the rhetoric of the day, that bombers had eliminated the need for fighter escort because they could defend themselves. The idea of the self-defending bomber formation died along with approximately 60 percent of the bombers on the first two long-range raids into the heart of Germany in late 1943. (Today's analogue is that F-117s cannot be seen on radar and, thus, do not require fighter cover. (See page 286 below.)

This bomber-belief system continued for more than 50 years, up through the Gulf War. Indeed, during part of the buildup phase, strategic bombing advocates promulgated a plan called Instant Thunder, which was designed "to shoot their wad" in Iraq so that the Army would not have to commit land troops. This plan became known around the Pentagon as "Instant Blunder."[3]

Unlike the planners of the strategic bombing campaigns in World War II, who quickly learned that the intrepid bomber crews faced the virtual certainty that German fighters and surface fire would splay 10 percent of them from the entrails of the B-17s and B-24s like adipose tissue from a surgeon's liposection, strategic bombing advocates learned in Iraq that they faced neither fighters nor a surface-to-air threat as they bombed with the same monthly intensity that they did in World War II. Nevertheless, they had to commit land troops. But groupthink dies hard. Chief of Staff of the U.S. Air Force Gen. Merrill McPeak said regarding the victory against Iraq: "My private conviction is that this is the first time in history that a field army has been defeated by airpower."[4] One can only wonder if General Schwarzkopf shared that belief.

The attempt to destroy Germany's war-making capability in World War II solely through airpower was a bust. Some have speculated that the Allied bombing of Germany transferred hatred of Hitler to the allied bombers and extended his time in power.*[5] In spite of the official position against waging war directly against civilians, Douhet's belief in civilian bombing was dominant in the plans of strategic bombing advocates in World War II. As a result, thousands died from direct or indiscriminate attacks.[6] Almost as many civilians died in the firebombing raid on Dresden as U.S. soldiers died in the

*Andrew and Leslie Cockburn, who filmed a documentary of the effects of strategic bombing in Iraq, told the author that there were indications of a similar transference of hostility among the Iraqis from hating Saddam Hussein to hating the Coalition bombers.

Vietnam War. Yet the Allied bombing campaign reduced neither Germany's ability to wage war nor its production. Since Germany was on the sophisticated end of the societal continuum, strategic bombing should have had an effect. But the more the Allies bombed Germany, the greater the output in fighters and bombers. Increased bombing was an unsuccessful attempt to reduce German production. Increased production occurred in spite of it. Not until the Allies committed land troops did the German industrial might come to a halt.

Now that the Gulf War is over, the military aviation community, led by the Air Force, wants observers to hang on to retinal images of video tapes showing guided munitions gliding precisely to their intended target. It is difficult, with such dramatic evidence, to challenge the Air Force on specific failures because failure knows no author in a victorious army.

One is tempted to capitulate to the military information officers because we won a partial victory in the Gulf. However, we must never forget that the same institution that withholds information from the press, ostensibility to preserve the lives of the operational warriors or the population at large, will wrap tactical, strategic, and procurement blunders in the same flag.

It would be wonderful if we could rely on the generals and admirals to tell us the truth about the results in Desert Storm. At first blush, there seems to be no reason for them to distort the truth. But deeper investigation tells a different story.

Several years ago I interviewed one general who was particularly adept at confusing patriots with partisans. During the interview this general told an absolute canard. He said that recent Sparrow missile tests had demonstrated excellent results.[7] The classified test report signed by this general described the test results as disastrous. When confronted with the inevitable question—are you lying now or were you lying when you signed the report—he replied: "O.K. I'll level with you. We have to lie. Don't you understand? If we tell Congress that these missiles aren't working, we won't get future funding in order to fix them."

Some of the weapons used in Desert Storm were operational for the first time. The careers of many of these technology advocates might suffer if the prewar claims turned out to be inaccurate. If generals can fabricate the truth about test results during peacetime to ensure continued funding, could they not falsify actual results under the euphoria of an advertised victory?

If military threats of treason and traitor don't eliminate probing questions, these gatekeepers resort to intimidation through arrogance. "How could you possibly question what we do when what we do is secret?" they say, with light reflecting off their victorious silver stars or gold braid. History does not support their condescension.

At Desert Storm press conferences, senior military officers paraded a small number of video clips of laser-guided bombs making direct hits on bridges. This high tech advantage began, they tell us, toward the end of the Vietnam War, when high technology destroyed the Than Hoa bridge in North Vietnam. For seven years we tried to take out that bridge with dumb bombs and failed, they say. Then proudly they will add, when we finally attacked it with laser-designated ordinance, we dropped it with a single bomb. This tactic is to generalize from a specific with dramatic evidence.

When this story is told by the gatekeepers—and it is told often—it is never told completely. These briefers never reveal that there were other bridges that were not dropped after repeated attempts with laser-guided bombs; they never tell you that the Than Hoa bridge could have been taken out in an afternoon with the USS *New Jersey*, a World War II battleship, (as could have 80 percent of all targets in Vietnam),[8] they never divulge that more than 70 aircraft were lost in an attempt to drop the bridge with dumb bombs, and most of them don't even know that once the Than Hoa bridge was dropped it proved to be of no strategic or tactical significance. The Viet Cong merely forded the river a short distance up stream.

In attempts to bolster its high tech claims in Iraq, the military showed video tapes of laser-guided bombs going down the smokestacks of strategic targets and other examples of apparent direct hits. But former Navy Secretary Lehman admitted that 40 percent of laser-guided bombs go ballistic,[9] the RAF admitted that one of its bombs went awry and hit an Iraqi bazaar;[10] the final report to Congress revealed that the LGB's were not 90 percent successful, but had, instead, a success rate closer to the 50 to 60 percent that Pierre Sprey indicated prior to the war;[11] and the Allied Forces averaged 72 sorties for each bridge destroyed, for a success rate of 1.5 percent.[12] We have to ask ourselves, how much has changed? As Sprey testified before Congress:

> This really points out just how shameless the censoring of the results for guided weapons was during the war. You remember seeing over and over again the same targets being blown up by the same missile. It looks like, for every missile that blew up a bridge, there were maybe 70 to 75 misses that nobody was showing. . . .
>
> The very shallow, tendentious picture of the Nintendo war that we

got from the TV coverage was false and not useful in making future defense decisions.[13]

Everyone has heard the story of how the Japanese sank the USS *Arizona* with a single bomb that went down one of its funnels. Should we conclude, therefore, that the Japanese had high technology too? One can only imagine what use was made of the movies showing the demise of the USS *Arizona* with a single bomb by the company that made the bombsight for the plane that dropped it. Truly, the elimination of a battleship worth hundreds of millions of dollars by a dumb bombsight eclipses any technological leverage the United States had in the Gulf War.

Even senior flag officers challenge the military assertions on what actually happened in Desert Storm as this statement by Brigadier General Hopgood illustrates. "Only limited antiair opposition was encountered, particularly from modern antiaircraft missiles. . . . Why Iraqi air and ground forces did not fight harder remains unclear."

If the tenacity with which the military sticks to its high-technology-will-save-us position comes as a surprise, then consider again the conclusion made by Maj. Gen. Perry McCoy Smith an on-air consultant for CNN News during the Gulf War. In his book, *The Air Force Plans for Peace*, Smith summarized the high tech gatekeepers' process. In light of the evolving information coming out of the Gulf War, his book is worth quoting from again.

> Once a military doctrine is established it is difficult to change, especially if technological advancements in weaponry seriously bring into question a doctrine upon which a specific military is based. . . . And if service doctrine is questioned by members of that service, there is a tendency for the leadership to brand the critics heretics, especially if the doctrine is ordinarily designed to justify fully the services's attempt to obtain or maintain exclusive control over certain missions. . . .
>
> When doctrine becomes dogma, all kinds of counter-dogma signals can be ignored. If the lessons of the Battle of Britain could be ignored, if the high losses in bombardment aircraft whenever they were seriously opposed by German fighters in the early, unescorted daylight raids in 1943 could be discounted, if it took the loss of 60 aircraft on a single mission over Schweinfurt in August 1943 and 60 more over Schweinfurt in October 1943 finally to convince all the Air Corps leaders that unescorted bombardment against defended targets was self-defeating as well as suicidal, then is there any reason to believe that attitudinal changes among the American public and in the War Department would have permitted a different Air Force to develop?

The military, like all organizations, is made up of individuals with various degrees of integrity, but it unquestionably has an abundance of men and women of high moral character. Undoubtedly those who attempt to fog the truth do so out of a motivation that springs from their interpretation of the best interests of the country. But one needs to make inquiries beyond their ostensible probity.

When the story of the general who lied about the test results of the Sparrow missile became known to one Navy pilot friend of the author, he related a similar story. On his aircraft carrier, the admiral briefed his crew with the same need to misinform a congressional delegation for the identical reasons. Is it any wonder that the military fosters lying as a form of patriotism?

Viewers of CNN during the Gulf War have not had the benefit of a thorough postwar analysis like that which came from the *Strategic Bombing Survey* after World War II. Nor are they likely to believe they need it. They saw precision bombing with their own eyes. The military establishment attempted to eliminate Saddam Hussein and failed, but it successfully suppressed the public's attempts at a timely postmortem of the results. But truth emerges slowly from the Gulf War. Evidence is creeping from faceless patriots that the high technology of the Gulf War did not always work as advertised.

Planning Desert Storm

Reasonable plans have criteria, usually called mission and goals, or objectives, by which they can be measured. Based on the Secretary of Defense's guidelines, General Schwartzkopf, Central Command (CENTCOM), developed the following mission statement:

- Neutralize Iraqi National Command Authority
- Eject Iraqi Armed Forces from Kuwait
- Destroy the Republican Guard
- Destroy Iraq's ballistic missile and nuclear, biological and chemi cal capability
- Assist in the restoration of the legitimate government of Kuwait[14]

From this mission statement came the military objectives in Central Command Operations Order 91-001, dated January 17, 1991.

- Attack Iraqi political-military leadaership and C^2 [command and control];
- Gain and maintain air superiority;
- Sever Iraqi supply lines;
- Destroy known nuclear, biological and chemical (NBC) production, storage and delivery capabilities;
- Destroy Republican Guard forces in the KTO [Kuwait Theater of Operations]; and
- Liberate Kuwait City.[15]

In Desert Storm the major goals were put in the form of Centers of Gravity. A center of gravity is "that point where the enemy is most vulnerable and the point where an attack will have the best chance of being decisive. The term is borrowed from mechanics, indicating a point against which a level of effort, such as a push, will accomplish more than the same level of effort could accomplish if applied elsewhere."[16]

The initial war plan juxtaposed in a matrix the three major centers of gravity—the national command authority; the nuclear, biological, and chemical weapons; and the Republican Guard—with the theater objectives. The objectives evolved into targets that originally numbered 84, but in true strategic bombing enthusiasm evolved to 800 and finally more than 3,000.[17]

Attached to each of these specific air campaign objectives were a series of target classes that, according to the Department of Defense, would, if destroyed, result in the attainment of the goals of the Gulf War.

- **Isolate and incapacitate the Iraqi regime.** (Leadership command facilities, electricity production facilities that power military and military-related industrial systems, and command, control and communications systems)
- **Gain and maintain air supremacy to permit unhindered air operations** (Strategic air defense systems including radar sites and air defense control centers, and airfields and air forces)
- **Destroy the known nuclear, biological, and chemical (NBC) warfare capability.** (NBC research, production, and storage facilities)
- **Eliminate Iraq's offensive military capability by destroying major portions of key military production, infrastructure, and power projection capabilities.** (Scud missile production and storage facilities, naval forces and port facilities, and oil refining and distribution facilities—as opposed to long-term production)
- **Render the Iraqi army in Kuwait ineffective, causing their collapse.** (Railroads and bridges connecting Iraqi military forces with their means of support, army units to Republican Guard forces in the KTO, and military storage sites.[18]

To determine what part the F-18 Hornet played and whether it was successful in playing that part, we must consider what, specifically, was its role and mission in the air plan.

General Air Plan

The Air Force was in charge of the overall air plan. The manifestation of these plans was reflected in the revised Air Force Manual 1-1 and Col. John A. Warden's *The Air Campaign.*[19] "Operation Desert Storm was based on a four phased plan. The phases were:

Figure 14-1
Centers of Gravity/Theater Objective Matrix

Theater Objectives	**Centers of Gravity:** Leadership (Saddam Hussein)*	Nuclear, Biological, Chemical	Republican Guard
Leadership/C 3			
Air Superiority			
Supply Lines			
Nuclear, Biological, Chemical			
Republican Guard			
Eject Iraq from Kuwait			

*The original draft of the war plan used Hussein's name.

SOURCE: Department of Defense

This matrix of centers of gravity and theater objectives is a rough approximation of what was in the war plan for Desert Storm. Note the duplication of leadership, nuclear, biological, chemical, and Republican Guard in both categories. This raises the obvious question, What is the difference between the centers of gravity and the theater objectives? Undoubtedly, this confusion led, in some part, to the failure to destroy many of both.

Strategic Air Campaign, Attainment of Air Supremacy in the Kuwait Theater of Operations (KTO), Battlefield Preparation, and Ground Offensive. The first three phases were executed almost concurrently because of the large number of available aircraft and early attainment of air supremacy." (See fig. 14-2).[20]

The Coalition, and the F-18 pilots along with them, faced what was advertised as a sophisticated integrated air defense system (IADS) designed to control the Iraqi defending fighter force and its low- and medium-altitude surface-to-air missiles. There is nothing unique in using both fighters and surface-to-air (SAM) missiles to defend a country. What distinguished the IADS was its ability to orchestrate, coordinate, and provide for mutual support.[21] As technology goes, the Iraqi system was from the 1970s, designed to repel relatively small attacks (raids of approximately 20 aircraft) from Israel in the west and Iran in the east. The system was weak in the south because when it was installed Saudi Arabia posed no potential threat. It was not designed to work with the massive aircraft raids that it eventually experienced in Desert Storm.

Phase 1 of the air plan required establishing air superiority. (See page 26 above for "air superiority" definition.)

Current tactical thinking states that the best way to achieve air superiority is to destroy any element that contributes to the enemy's

Figure 14-2

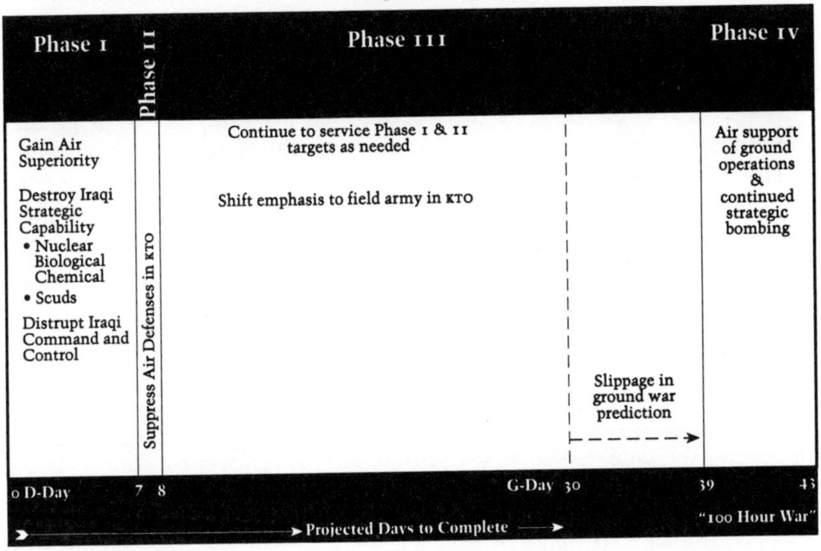

SOURCE: Title V Report
The Coalition air war was divided into four phases, shown here. Note that the ground war slipped from day 30 to day 39, because of, according to the Air Force, poor weather.

achievement of it by destroying their systems on the ground.* This called for the destruction of systems used to control the fighters and to lead them to the attacking Coalition aircraft, as well as the radars and surface-to-air missile sites. One instrument used to disrupt the Iraqi IADS was the electron jamming aircraft. The purpose of the now-famous first night attack on Iraq at 2:00 AM was to eliminate the various radar sites and control centers. The loss of this system, along with its long-range radar warning, would make Iraq blind to incoming attacks.

The Air Tasking Order (ATO)

The U.S. Air Force was responsible for controlling all the Coalition aircraft in Iraq and Kuwait (except for some of the U.S. Army aircraft). It attempted to do this with an integrated air plan, designed to focus and coordinate the efforts against the enemy, reduce the possibility of mid-air collisions, and prevent blue-on-blue kills (shooting down your own aircraft). By the end of the war, the plan had grown to more than 800 pages in length per day. At the end of the 43-day

*The penchant for wanting to establish air superiority through bombing is the result of the Douhet mentality combined with the rare successful strikes such as Pearl Harbor and the Israeli experience in the 1967 Six-Day War. The 1973 Arab-Israeli war showed that air superiority is not a prerequisite to launching a successful attack.

war, this computerized plan would, when printed, be more than 30,000 pages long.[22]

The Air Tasking Order (ATO) demanded adherence. Deviations invited collision or mistakes in judgment, common occurences when split-second decisions are required. The Air Tasking Order, originally conceived to fight a war in Europe, was the computerized replacement of the Vietnam Air War's "route packages," which were aircraft corridors with targets within them.[23] The Air Tasking Order was a clean, neat method of target assignment in a rigid, static world, but it was not fit for any environment other than the fixed, pitched battle plans of World War I. As it turned out, the Iraqi Army fought in the World War I manner. Even so, there were problems.

> Overall, the ATO system is ill-suited to targets that are fundamentally unpredictable, such as moving enemy ground forces or areas in which Scud launchers may or may not be found. The basic method of the ATO cannot be adjusted so that coordinated strikes occur in one area and tactically responsive ones occur somewhere else. Such variations merely invite catastrophe. . . .
>
> In the case of Iraq and Kuwait, the problem was that tactical and deep-strike areas could not be separated neatly. The relatively inflexible ATO had to cover most of the enemy's airspace, yet it had to deal with unpredictable mobile targets like enemy tanks and Scud launchers. The solution seems to have been twofold.
>
> One was to use the ATO method and to accept inefficiency. "Kill boxes" in areas of expected enemy vehicle concentrations were defined. Aircraft were timed to appear over the boxes, and given a limited time in which to find and destroy as many vehicles as they could. Attacks of this sort could be kept up as long as successive groups of airplanes were despatched to the "kill boxes." None of the fast tactical airplanes (which carried most of the bombs) could be allowed to stay in a box for very long; the set time above the "box" had to be estimated well in advance by a targeter. The entire philosophy of the ATO and of transient concentration would prohibit any attempt to hand over a kill box from one group of airplanes to the next. All strike groups had to operate independently. Only rarely would the same aircraft or the same squadron visit the same box on a regular basis. Moreover, because there was always a severe shortage of tactical reconnaissance airplanes, it was not easy to monitor any given box on a continuous basis.* One consequence was that the Iraqis were more successful than they should have been in decoying, for example, by fixing wrecked tanks just well enough to make them look operable (hence worth hitting). Similarly, wrecked or unserviceable aircraft were sometimes mocked up to appear viable. Throughout the air campaign against the Iraqi Army, there were considerable disagreements between CentCom and the U.S.-based analyst (who used satellite data) as to just how well the attack was proceeding.[24]

*The clearest evidence of a shortage of damage assessment resources is the extensive use of strike videos for bomb damage assessment.

There was no guarantee that upon arriving in a kill box the pilots would acquire the target within the allotted time. Thus, attacking tactical aircraft were not always able to expend their munitions.[25]

> The ATO system is effective only as long as the U.S. forces hold the initiative, because in that case pre-planning can be realistic. If the enemy moves quickly enough, the minimum 24- or 48-hour turn-around time inherent in the system makes it worse than inefficient; the system breaks down. It invites a classic application of the sort of blitzkrieg tactic described by retired air force Col. John Boyd. That actually happened at least once at the Air Force's tactical school, Red Flag. In Iraq and Kuwait the ATO worked well because the Iraqis were generally fairly passive, so that the United States determined the tempo and nature of the war.[26]

In theory the ATO was run by a joint command, but as one Navy Commander pointed out,

> the Black Hole was not really joint. While the Navy and the allies were represented, an overwhelming percentage of the staff was Air Force. . . . Interestingly, General Glosson [head of the target committee] was primarily air-to-air, not air-to-ground experienced. . . . Second, target intelligence support, even with available material, was less than it could have been. This was partially because of the physical separation of the intelligence targeting shop and the Black Hole, which made communication and interaction between them inconvenient at best. In addition, each facility had different paths of communication to the national intelligence community, and at times the Black Hole and targeting almost appeared to be working against each other.[27]

Had the Navy already been working with the Air Force, it would have had the ability to communicate. Because it had not, the Air Tasking Order had to be flown out each day to the aircraft carrier rather than sent electronically. The Navy's foot-dragging in the mid-1980s caused it to be the understudy in Desert Storm. The Navy's insistence on operating autonomously, even after the Goldwater-Nichols Amendment of 1986 (which was designed in large part to foster joint operations), perpetuated its isolation in the Gulf War. Although in the minds of some, the war with Iraq was a continential war, which meant that the Navy's role was collateral at best.

The Air Tasking Order was inconsistent with the AirLand Battle Doctrine which said that wars required the mutual involvement of both the Army and the Air Force. Clearly, the ATO was a reversion to the days of old when the Air Force believed it could "do it all" with strategic bombing. General Horner, to his credit, resisted the four-phase plan the Pentagon sent to Riyadh. He took seriously the Air Force commitment to the AirLand Battle Doctrine, which stated that the Air Force was to serve the needs of the Army and its land troops.

In the end, General Schwarzkopf approved the Pentagon plan, generated by a group known as Checkmate and led by Col. John Warden. The plan from Checkmate, which called for attacking centers

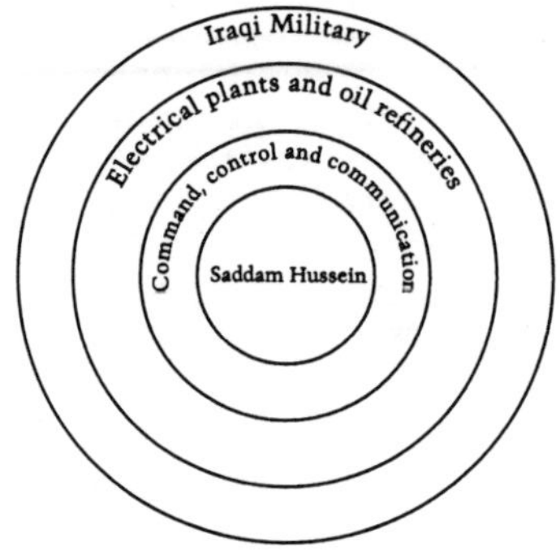

of gravity, defined Saddam Hussein as the center of the centers of gravity. Additional centers, as illustrated above, emanated from him.

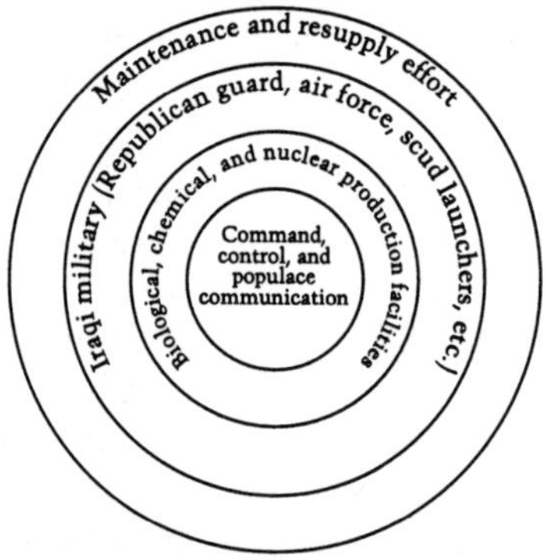

General Horner's chief lieutenant, Brig. Gen. Buster Glosson, defined the centers of gravity, shown above, differently.

SOURCE: *Triumph Without Victory*, 267

The Army defined the center of gravity like the circle above.

The Air Force did not live up to supporting the Army. "Glosson . . . had to be 'dragged kicking and screaming' by the ground commander into apportioning more air resources to bombing Iraq's ground forces."[28]

The Department of Defense, in its Interim Report to Congress, claimed the centers of gravity were a compromise between those of Checkmate and Gen. Glosson. Accomplishing these goals through air power would begin on January 17, 1991.

DESERT STORM RESULTS

Nothing the Iraqi's had was given more press than the alleged awesomeness of their Integrated Air Defense System. Nevertheless, the IADS was defeated by a superb plan that integrated deception, passive and active jamming, F-117 attacks under cover of this jamming, and collateral SEAD missions. Strategic bombing did not destroy the IADS. A well-orchestrated plan that implemented all the elements Col. John Boyd, USAF, had preached for the last two decades destroyed it. Ironically, the architects of the plan did not give credit to the quality of their plan, but to the technology available to them.

According to Sprey, great plan or not, the system was defeated the moment the Coalition sent large numbers of aircraft against it because the computer software could not cope with the overload of inputs: "When you cross tracks at shallow angles, there is no tracking algorithm in the world that can keep them from garbling track identity. None of the blips come with numbers. Tracking algorithms have to sort targets into tracks and each target has to be associated in memory. The uncertainty in the position of the airplane is of the same magnitude as the deviations of a straight line of a maneuvering target. All the algorithms are required to use straight line extrapolation."[29]

Sprey's contention was supported by Friedman: "The defense (particularly its longer-range elements) can handle only so many distinct targets at a time. . . . The Iraqis' integrated air-defense system apparently functioned initially, though unsuccessfully (strike aircraft could generally jam their way through where they had to). . . ."[30]

One Navy official credited the U.S. Navy's Tomahawk cruise missile with the defeat of the IADS. The missile contained, according to this official, microfine filaments, nano-inches in length, that could disrupt computers and electrical circuitry within a significant distance from the burst point. While filming the aftereffects of the bombing in August 1991, Andrew and Leslie Cockburn were shown these filaments by Fayik Moustafa, Director of the Al Doura electrical plant, a recipient of one of these cruise missile bursts. The Cockburns said that the filaments looked like glassy angel hair about 2 to 2 1/2 inches long. Moustafa told them that the filaments completely shut down the electrical generating plant, but only temporarily. The people at the electrical plant spent the day cleaning up all the angel hair. They were operating the next day. The plant had to be bombed before it was put out of operation. Perhaps more to the point was the interview the Cockburns had with the Minister of Industry who said that at least 50 percent of the cruise missiles missed their targets. Or, if they hit what they were aiming for, no one could understand why targets such as swimming pools and palm trees had been selected.[31]

The defeat of the Integrated Air Defense System may have had help from a computer virus. According to *U.S. News and World Report*, the National Security Agency designed a chip that contained a virus designed to disable the IADS's main computer. This chip was planted in a printer destined for Iraq shortly before the war began.[32]

Whether the IADS collapsed due to annihilation by the Coalition, sensory overload, the Tomahawk missile, or a computer virus remains unclear. In any case, the centralized IADS was rendered incapacitated from the beginning. The Army's antiaircraft (AAA) guns, on the other hand, were decentralized and required repeated attacks.[33]

The F-18 Mission

The Department of Defense defines the F-18's mission this way:

> The F/A-18, a multi-mission aircraft flown by the Navy and the Marine Corps, was one of many aircraft employed for the first time in combat during Desert Storm. The F/A-18 is capable of performing several missions: offensive air-to-air, interdiction, battlefield air interdiction, close air support, and suppression of enemy air defenses [SEAD]. This capability allowed the F/A-18 to execute interdiction strikes while providing its own air cover, thus eliminating the requirement for fighter escort. Not only did this multi-mission capability allow the Services to generate/support greater numbers of strike missions, but fewer support aircraft were required to fly into hostile enemy territory.
>
> No single event of the war demonstrated the value of multi-role capability more than the events of the first day when two F/A-18s from VFA-81, a fighter/attack squadron, embarked in USS *Saratoga* shot down two Iraqi MiG-21s. The F/A-18s were on a scheduled bombing mission against an Iraqi airfield when they detected the two "bogies" several miles away. They switched their weapons computer systems from the bombing mode to the air-to-air mode, confirmed the planes as hostiles and downed both MIGs using Sparrow and Sidewinder missiles. They then successfully completed their assigned mission of bombing in support of a coalition strike against an enemy airfield.[34]

There is a temptation to claim that the F-18 was a great fighter because of its successful encounter on the first day of the war. Before we examine this, let's give credit to the F-18 as it appears to have lived up to its promise as a maintainable airplane.* Indeed, Maj. Gen. Mike Sullivan USMC said that in over 600 hours flying the F-18, he had only one inoperative radar.[35]

Table 14-1
Mission Capable (MC) Rates
of Selected U.S. Fighter and Attack Aircraft

	Peacetime	Gulf War
A-10	90.4	95.5
F-4G	80.0	86.0
F-15C/D	85.1	93.7
F-15E	80.4	95.5
F-16	90.2	95.4
F-117	81.6	85.8
F-18	N/A	91.5

SOURCE: U.S. Department of Defense. U.S. Air Force. "Reaching Globally, Reaching Powerfully: The United States Air Force in the Gulf War." (A Report) n.p. September 1991 p. 29. F-18 rates are from a McDonnell Douglas briefing "F/A-18 Hornet: Operation Desert Shield/Desert Storm-The Strike Fighter War." n.p. n.d. slide GP12 0139 16 c/dmb.

The mission capable rates above show that, when supported, the modern aircraft has a better-than-average mission capable (MC) rate. Note that these rates are the mission capable (MC) rates and not the fully mission capable (FMC) rates of a totally ready aircraft.

Before we succumb to the trap of saying that the F-18 did a "fabulous" job in the Gulf, we have to ask ourselves: what did it do—really? To some, tonnage of bombs dropped is the measure of merit for a military aircraft. If that is true, then the F-18 was not meritorious. It spent a significant portion of its time on the suppression of enemy air defenses (SEAD) missions. This is not to say that SEAD missions were not important. But if bomb tonnage dropped is the measurement by which one evaluates a contribution, then the F-18 lacked, at the very least, the opportunity to show its stuff as a "fighter."[36] (See the discussion of the definition of a fighter on page 31 above.)

How did the F-18 compare to the B-17? B-17s in World War II could hold more than 17,000 pounds of bombs. But if they carried that much, their range was severely limited. Consequently, when they flew from England to targets in Germany, a range and altitude similar to those flown by the F-18s in the Gulf War, their average load was 4,000 to 5,000 pounds. Except for SEAD and the Fast FAC (forward air controller) missions, the F-18 flew at B-17 altitudes, carrying B-17 loads, with bombs as dumb as those on a B-17. It was unable to fly B-17 distances, with BDA so ineffective that accuracies

*The military makes a distinction between "fully mission capable" and "mission capable." Fully mission capable means that everything on the aircraft is working. A "mission capable" aircraft might be able to perform, for example, an air-to-air mission but not an air-to-ground mission.

no better than B-17s were unassailable, and had a cost in constant dollars that far exceeded the B-17.

What, if anything, made the F-18 great? According to the Department of Defense, it was the "technology." One has to assume that means the F-18's newer technology. But that implies that the older technology did not work or did not work as well. Yet the Secretary of Defense said, "much of the hardware that played such a crucial role in our victory over Saddam Hussein and the Iraqi forces was developed 20 and 30 years ago."[37] If we assume that the Secretary is correct, then based on the range and payload of the B-17, if it had flown, the Secretary of Defense Cheney could have said 50 years ago.

Was the F-18 particularly accurate with the dumb bombs that it carried? That is its manufacturer's claim and a claim made by many Navy defenders of the F-18. But there is little evidence of the F-18's accuracy in the Gulf War. As one F-18 squadron stated, "The traditional measurement of air-to-ground success is the number of tons of ordnance released by the air wing. But a true assessment of strike effectiveness can only be made by reviewing the target battle damage assessment (BDA). An impressive quantity of tonnage released on the target gave only an illusion of success."[38]

The Air Force admitted poor BDA. Claims that the F-18 exhibited fantastic accuracy in the Gulf War appear to be nothing more than a perpetuation of the promise made during development and tests. There was no way to verify the majority of the claims made. "Overall, BDA was a problem. It was not always timely. In addition, the Video Tape Recorders in many fighters did not have sufficient quality to permit accurate BDA. Less than half of all air-to-air kills could be confirmed through this system."[39]

What about the F-18's air-to-air engagement? F-18s did make two air-to-air kills on the first day in the Gulf War. But how did they do it? Was it with some new technology? No—it was with a visual identification and the heat-seeking Sidewinder missile. Furthermore, (as Myers pointed out on page 35 above) 97.2% of all contacts in Vietnam were from sources other than the aircraft's own radar, so too it was outside sources that alerted the F-18s that they were being approached by MiGs.

When the Department of Defense or the Navy provides information on what killed the first two Iraqi fighters, it credits one kill to a heat-seeking Sidewinder and one kill to a radar-guided Sparrow missile. This is another example of the military readjusting reality. Even if one of the Iraqi fighters was killed by the Sparrow (which it wasn't) the Sparrow was nevertheless fired within visual range. But what actually happened was that the F-18, in attempting to destroy the second Iraqi fighter, fired two missiles. The first was a heat-seeking Sidewinder, the second was a radar-guided Sparrow. The pilot thought he was firing his Sparrow with the first shot but his switches were in the Sidewinder mode. When he did not see the normal smoke associated with the Sparrow, he assumed the Sparrow malfunctioned and reset his switches to Sparrow. He fired again. The Sidewinder destroyed the Iraqi MiG—the Sparrow flew into the explosion.[40] But the official Navy position is that the Sparrow made the kill.

Air-to-Air Experience

To fairly assess the F-18's performance during Desert Storm, we should consider how it did relative to other aircraft. In the Gulf War the Coalition shot down 33 fixed-wing enemy aircraft—while losing one. As the F-18 received credit for the first Navy air-to-air kills in the war, air-to-air experience seems like a reasonable starting place.

Positive Identification

The entire concept of the radar-guided missile, the technology the Department of Defense claimed shot down the second MiG, is based on the ability to shoot down an incoming aircraft beyond visual range in any type of weather. In the Gulf War the ability to positively identify an aircraft as one that belonged to the enemy still did not exist. "Aircraft have been equipped with identification friend or foe (IFF) systems for years. IFF is becoming less practical for aircraft, the only systems where anything approaching a solution has ever been tried. . . . IFF systems are not all compatible, cannot support enough data to support large armadas like the Gulf War, and are easy to defeat."[41]

In spite of Gen. William Creech's admission in congressional testimony that IFF has never worked, the military claimed that it now had the ability to positively identify (ID) aircraft and that this ability was extant in the Gulf War.

The ability to recognize another aircraft beyond visual range falls under the generic title of Non Cooperative Target Recognition (NCTR). The system was historically know as TRISAT and more recently as Combat Tree. The system interrogrates the fan blades and receives indications from other sources to acquire a positive identification of the aircraft type, but only if the aircraft is within a few degrees of a head-on interrogation. While these positive ID systems can identify the *type* of aircraft, they cannot identify the *nationality* of the pilot. For example, in the Gulf War, both the Qataries and the Iraqis flew the same aircraft, the Mirage.

The concept of positive identification is not new according to Pierre Sprey. "The Germans were doing it against Allied bombers in World War II. The British had a study that showed that a bomber emits 8 different things, any one of which was enough to positive ID them. If positive ID didn't work, [in the Gulf War] it means that the MiGs turned off their radars, radios, and IFF."[42]

The ability to determine the type of aircraft in this way was confirmed by a still active U.S. Navy pilot. "There is more to detecting low radar-cross-section aircraft than the power-aperture product. The F-14D's high power output probably causes it to be detected passively by other aircraft."[43]

The Air Force had this positive identification system during the Gulf War, but the Navy did not. "The F-18 did not get it," Col. Manfred Reitsch, commanding officer of the land-based Marine F-18 air wing, speculated, "because of the dual role of the airplane."[44] To avoid accidents, the positive identification used by the U.S. Air Force, required two positive IDs. There were no air-to-air blue-on-blue kills in the Gulf, as there were in Vietnam, but the positive ID system was not trustworthy enough for at least one of the two F-18 pilots credited with a kill on the opening day of the Gulf War. Lt. Mark Fox, USN, who got the second kill, said he would have to have a visual identification.[45] Even Air Force pilots, some of whom had parts of the positive ID system, were not always sure if they had fired on their own aircraft.

> [The pilot] made up his mind fast. He pressed the trigger and fired one 12-foot long radar-guided missile. . . . [The pilot] suddenly was tense, worried and confused. The AWACS radar controller had been unable to confirm that the target . . . was an enemy jet. It was possible, though unlikely, that he had fired on another allied plane.[46]

Capt. Will Rogers of the USS *Vincennes,* who mistakenly shot down an Iranian airliner thinking it was an Iranian F-14, probably shared these misgivings. Rear Adm. John M. Luecke, USN, said, "it was amazing there was no air-to-air fratricide in Desert Storm."[47]

Air-to-Air Antiradiation Missiles

Not only has no new technology emerged that would permit the beyond-visual-range missile to work reliably, there has been no mention of the one technology that could end conventional radar-guided missile confrontations forever—the *air-to-air* antiradiation missile.

The concept of an air-to-*ground* antiradiation missile has been around since the Vietnam War. The idea is essentially this: if an enemy turns on his radar to launch surface-to-air missiles or radar-guided antiaircraft artillery (AAA), the air-to-ground antiradiation missile locks on his radar. The antiradiation missile follows the radar emissions to their source and explodes on impact.

The concept of an air-to-air antiradiation missile has been around since 1957 when John Boyles and Tom Amlie, using an AIM-9 Sidewinder hull, built one at China Lake. They called it the Ray-winder. "There was no interest in the concept," Amlie said, "because everyone said that Russian fighters don't use radar."

The military services and industry have been reluctant to build an air-to-air version of these air-to-ground antiradiation missiles because it would shut down an economic infrastructure that controls the building of these expensive complex radars and the larger-than-necessary aircraft required to hold them.

An air-to-air antiradiation missile was proposed during the late 1960s–early 1970s. Abe Buruna, an engineer at China Lake, developed interest with Liz Beggs, who worked in the Naval Air Systems Command. The concept missile was called Brazo, which is the Spanish word for "arm," the acronym for Anti-Radiation Missile (ARM). More recently the air-to-air ARM evolved from one or more programs, one of which was code-named Heavy Hammer and then Senior Blue. These missiles were available in the Gulf and were combat proven. There were also at least two incidents of an air-to-ground antiradiation missile attacking U.S. frigates.[48]

If antiradiation missiles become the arm of choice in air-to-air confrontations, then fighters would fly around with their radars turned off. If that were to happen, then the need for large radar antennas would disappear. Thus eliminated, the need for large cross-sectional frontal area fighter aircraft would also fade away. All of this evolution would result in air-to-air combat between smaller (some would say lightweight) fighters.

There are opponents to air-to-air antiradiation missiles. They claim that air-to-air ARMS are easy to defeat through Low Probability of Intercept Radars or LPIR. But Tom Amlie, a Ph.D. in radar technology and former director of China Lake, the Navy's incubator for missile concepts, disagrees. "Trying to build an LPIR is similar to trying to hide an elephant in a strawberry patch by painting its toenails red." (See Appendix C.)

Stealth—the Alleged New Technology

With all the commotion about stealth, one needs to ask, was the F-18 outdone by the stealthy F-117 or, more particularly, its stealthy characteristics? One must keep in mind that defense establishment proclamations do not equal truth. Stealth, or the viability of it, is a vivid example. The B-2 bomber, long held in strict secrecy because of its radar-evading technology, failed its own test to evade radar.[49] Indeed, even Air Force Chief of Staff Gen. Merrill McPeak admitted, after returning from a trip to the Soviet Union, that the Soviets could detect the B-2.[50]

But these revelations were made after the expenditure of billions of dollars were justified on the basis that the B-2 and the F-117 were virtually invisible to radar. And the Air Force is sensitive to the criticism. "Stealth does not deserve the bum rap it gets. It [the F-117] has been operating with impunity" over Iraq and Kuwait. "High technology works."[51] The Department of Defense Interim Report to Congress is also quick to defend stealth.

> The F-117, by virtue of its stealth characteristics, allowed operations without the full range of support assets required by non-stealth aircraft. By contrast, in one attack against one airfield, eight conventional (non-stealth) bombers required escort by 30 other aircraft to provide radar jamming, carry radar-homing missiles and provide force protection. Because stealth eliminated the need for suppression of enemy air defenses (SEAD) and force protection aircraft, fewer resources were required to attack each target. This freed up additional aircraft to attack additional targets, allowing coverage of a larger portion of the target base during one attack. Viewed in terms of total requirements to hit a target, stealth systems expose fewer lives, reduce total sorties, and reduce requirement for munitions, manpower, fuel and support infrastructure.[52]

The report also said that the F-117 was the only attacker allowed into central Baghdad and that not a single stealth aircraft was lost.[53]

Both of these statements are misleading. Recall that the coverage of the IADS was limited in the south. Consequently, prior to the original two F-117s going downtown, two Army helicopters blinded the IADS at a location just across Iraq's southern border. Three EF-111s were stationed to the northwest and southeast of Baghdad to blind whatever residual IADS radar capability existed.[54] What is fair to say is that the F-117 did not have any electronic or fighter cover flying directly on its wings. Due to the elegance of the plan, however, virtually any attack aircraft could have gone downtown that morning. Nevertheless, the F-117 was the right choice because it had the most accurate weapons system in the Tactical Air inventory. However, there was nothing in the F-117's bombing system to prevent its use in F-18s, or in F-4 Phantoms for that matter.

What of the claim that no F-117s were lost? Does this give evidence of the F-117's stealthiness? If so, does this mean that any airplane without losses is stealthy? No A-7s or F-111s were lost in the Gulf War. In fact we lost very few aircraft of any type. As the F-117 was a small percentage of the overall aircraft population and sortie rate, the probability that we would lose any F-117s was very low. Pierre Sprey's congressional testimony may offer the best clarification.

> MR. MCCRERY. How do you explain the fact that the F-117's were used disproportionately in the opening stages of the war, disproportionately in terms of the sorties they ran, compared to the number of aircraft they represented as a percentage of the whole, and knocked out some of the elements of the Iraqi Army that allowed us to establish air superiority, and yet we didn't lose a single 117?
>
> MR. SPREY. For the same reason that the other fighters that flew 10,000 feet and higher didn't get hit, either. That is not a tribute to the survivability of the airplane.
>
> It just means if you stay out of the close-in combat zone, it is not hard to survive. Every airplane in the war survived beautifully as long as they flew high. At high altitude there are no guns to reach you, and the radar missiles that can reach you are very easy to outmaneuver, with or without stealth.
>
> In general, in previous wars it has taken anywhere from 100 to 500 surface-to-air radar missiles to get a single kill. They are just not a big threat if you see them coming and if you fly high.
>
> So, the F-117 achieved the same thing as the F-16 or the F-15: when you flew high, you didn't get hit. There is no miracle there.[55]

What does it take to be stealthy? After all, A-1 Skyraiders flew with impunity from carriers in the Pacific to Las Vegas simulating incoming Russian bombers without being detected. The young German pilot Mathias Rust flew undetected from Germany into Red Square. Five Cubans defected in a Soviet-built Antonov AN-2 crop duster and avoided radar detection until they were within 10 miles of the Miami airport.[56] A MIG-23 landed in the United States without being detected. What does it take to defeat radar?

Defeating radar apparently does not require high technology or millions of dollars. It can be done with ease. In fact, there are cases where drug-running aircraft can defeat even the multimillion dollar AWACS on a regular basis.[57]

But has the F-117 been detected on a regular basis? "The F-117A is difficult to detect, but not impossible. F-117A pilots testified recently to Congress that special tactics, planned with prior knowledge of target's location, were required to minimize the chances of detection during the Gulf War."[58]

The U.S. Air Force always cites that first night of the war and the surprise that the F-117 gave the Iraqis. The surprise was due to the vast support of electron-emitting aircraft, such as the three EF-111 Ravens. "The reason you couldn't see the F-117 is because it was looking like a blip in the middle of a Milky Way. It was definitely not alone and unafraid."[59]

"General Dynamics/Grumman EF-111B Ravens opened a 'door' for the Stealth attack by bombarding Baghdad with an ultra-heavy ECM barrage that scrambled just about every piece of electronic equipment owned by the enemy."[60]

During the Gulf War, the F-117 was observed by E-2CS at 150 miles,[61] and by British ships at 80–100 miles.[62] More to the point, the Iraqis tracked the F-117s on a regular basis.[63] So we cannot be too critical of the F-18 for its lack of stealth. It appears to have the same relative observability as any other aircraft in the Gulf War.

If stealth worked neither side could pick up the other on radar. If that were true, then the radar-guided missile becomes less useful, forcing the fighters into the visual arena once again. Thus, eliminating all of the negatives in aircraft design associated with radar accommodation—large cross-sectional area, weight, and size—would result in a smaller, lighter aircraft. And one comes full circle to stare at the logic that created the Lightweight Fighter in the first place.

All-Weather Capability

For years TacAir has told Congress it needed enormous sums of money because of its need for all-weather capability. One could assume that if the F-18 had anything to be envious of it was the all-weather capability developed for other aircraft, such as the F-111 and the F-15E.

But the U.S. Marine Corps considers the F-18 an all-weather aircraft. No less than the Commandant of the Marine Corps stated, "Marine F/A-18s aren't just fighters. They can provide all-weather air defense around the clock if necessary, as they did throughout Desert Shield when aircraft carriers were considered too vulnerable in the northern Persian Gulf. But with the retirement of our A-6E Intruders, F/A-18s will also provide the bulk of our day/night attack capability, our only in-the-weather close air support capability. . . ."[64]

If one accepts the definition of "close air support" (page 298 below) then one can only imagine how the coordination between soldier and aircraft takes place as the F-18 descends through the clouds. If the F-18 was an all-weather aircraft, as was the F-15E, then weather should not have been a problem in Desert Storm. According to the Department of Defense, it was.

> Weather was a factor during all phases of the operation. Approximately 40% of all scheduled attack sorties during the first 10 days of the war were cancelled due to poor visibility or low overcast sky conditions in the KTO. Ceilings of 5,000 to 7,000 feet were not uncommon, especially during the last few days of the ground war. Coalition planners assumed the customary 13% cloud cover, typical for the region at that time of

year. In fact, the cloud cover measured 39%, the worst in 14 years and possibly longer.[65]

The Air Force claimed that the weather conditions in the Gulf were the functional equivalent of a European summer. "Cloud cover exceeded 25% at 10,000 feet over central Iraq on 31 days of the 43 day war; it exceeded 50% on 21 of those days, and 75% on 9 days."[66] But the F-15E was designed to operate in worse weather than the Middle East—the European winter.

> The premise for the *Strike Eagle* F-15 is that in Europe, where tactical air would get its biggest challenge, the weather will not allow "second echelon"* attacks against tanks and trucks. McDonnell Douglas has produced a report entitled *All-Weather Aircraft in Europe,* which says that in the winter months (from November through February) the visibility and ceilings are equal to or greater than 3,000 feet and three statute miles for only 37 percent of the time. Therefore, a clear-day-only fighter, the report states, could expect to be operational only 3.1 hours during a 24 hour period—as a result of both poor weather and the shorter daylight period. During other seasons, the day fighter would *still be limited* in operation to less than 31 percent of the time.
>
> *Second echelon is a somewhat nebulous term that basically refers to those areas in which the Air Force has the sole responsibility for selecting targets.[67]

During the last eight months of World War II, the Allies flew more than 762,000 sorties over northern Europe. The flights took place from September to May, the worst months for weather, and 265,200 of them were air-to-ground missions. This resulted in an average monthly sortie rate of 95,250 and an average air-to-ground sortie rate of 33,150.[68]

How does that compare with the monthly sortie rates from the Gulf War, where the U.S. flew 44,145 total combat sorties? The war lasted 43 days. The average monthly sortie rate was 30,798, slightly below what pilots flew in Europe in World War II during the worst weather. What, then, has the all-weather technology brought us?

It seems to have brought us an ability to give various twists on the perception of the situation. The Air Force claimed that the weather was bad, others had a different assessment.

> The bad weather was not really bad. The base of the clouds was pretty high, about 4,000 feet. No 500-knot fighters dared fly underneath, simply because of the guns. None of our thin-skinned jet fighters could fly in the *clear* weather under 4,000 feet, because the Iraqi gun defenses were too rough. At these altitudes, the AAA guns tore the unarmored jets apart.
>
> In a very real sense, the gun defense, as has been the case in every previous air war, dominated the air defense situation and caused a major degradation in the effectiveness of high-speed jets.[69]

There is a certain irony that weather would even be a factor in a discussion of the Gulf War. On page 169 above, Captain O'Rourke stated that the clear weather in the Middle East was not the kind in which the Navy would fight, which was why the Navy needed its all-weather capability.

Precision-Guided Munitions (PGMS)

Much was said about the precision-guided munitions (PGM) during the Gulf War. The U.S. Air Force, for example, dropped 6,660 tons, which amounted to 90 percent of all the precision-guided ordnance in the Gulf War (see fig. 14-4). Even so, the U.S. Air Force's *precision* ordnance amounted to only 7.9 percent of the total ordnance tonnage expended by the United States. Precision-guided munitions were less than 5 percent of the total of Coalition ordnance dropped. The F-18 used very few precision-guided munitions.* How could F-18s do otherwise when the total precision guided munitions used by the U.S. Navy and Marine Corps amounted to less than 740 tons out of a total of 84,200 tons dropped by U.S. aircraft for only 0.87 percent of the total ordnance dropped?

One of the PGMS that the F-18 was cleared for and able to drop was the AGM-62 Walleye. But only 131 of the Walleyes were dropped, no doubt due in part to their $46,746-price tag, for a total cost of $6,123,726. Only 7 AGM-84 SLAMS were dropped. Each SLAM had the same weight warhead as the 500-pound dumb MK-82. Unlike the MK-82, which cost $662 each, the SLAM had an FY1991 unit price of $1,127,000.

Interdiction Results

One of the three centers of gravity the United States wanted to eliminate was the Republican Guard. To accomplish this through air power alone, as claimed by Chief of Staff General McPeak (page 268 above), the U.S. tactical air forces would have had to isolate and prevent the movement of the Republican Guard. Interdiction, unlike strategic bombing, is designed to isolate and cut off an army's ability to retreat.†

*The precision munitions dropped by the F-18 were Precision Standoff Land Attack Missile (SLAM) Walleye, Maverick, and HARM. The nonprecision ordnance was the MK-80 series of dumb bombs and Rockeye.

†The *Air Force Dictionary* states that *interdict* means: "To stop, prevent, or hinder enemy *movement* or *lines of communication* on land, sea, or in the air; to impede an *enemy* in his movements; to isolate a particular *area* by gunfire, bombing, etc." (Italics in original.)

"Line of communication" in the military means "any land, air, or water route connecting a military force in the field with its supplying source or base of operations, and along which supplies and reinforcements move."

Figure 14-3
Coalition and U.S. Sorties During Desert Storm

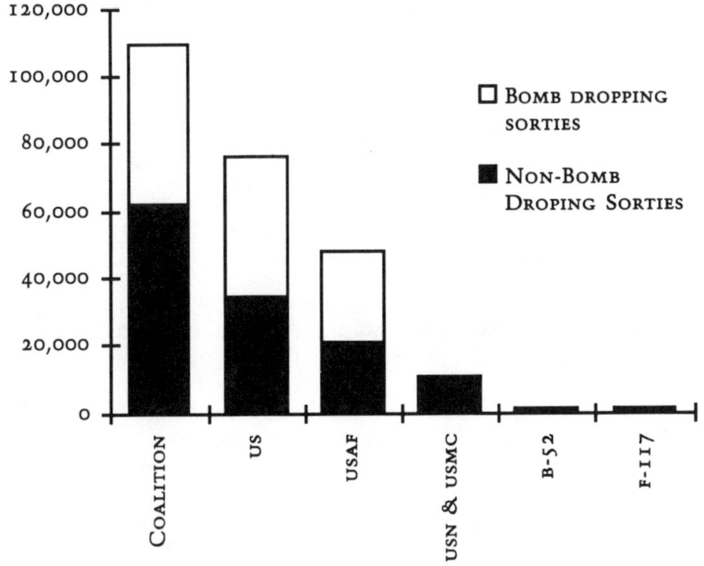

SOURCE: U.S. Army's Central Command, U.S. Air Force and U.S. Navy data
The number of sorties on this chart can be compared with the tonnage of bombs dropped, shown in fig. 14-4.

In order to simplify this mission, an air force would like to ask the enemy to group themselves into as tight a bunch as possible. Air Force Lt. Gen. Chuck Horner stated that the Iraqi army stayed tightly bunched, implying that Saddam Hussein, rather than Air Force's interdiction, was responsible for the guard's lack of movement.[70]

With this tight clustering, the Air Force should have managed easily in eliminating one of its three centers of gravity. However, as Brigadier General Hopgood stated, "Even though Coalition forces were able to bomb at will, main-force Republican Guard units were still more than 75 percent intact when the ground fighting started."

Air-to-Ground Success

The F-18 was able to switch effortlessly from its air-to-ground role to the air-to-air role. Merely the flip of some switches on the stick and throttle enabled the pilots to do that. But the F-18 got credit for only two kills out of a total of 33 fixed-wing aircraft. So if the F-18 was not a super star in the air-to-air arena, was the Hornet was more successful in the air-to-ground arena? "Navy F/A-18s (along with their A-7 progenitors) destroyed more Iraqi aircraft on the ground than the entire coalition forces combined destroyed in the air."[71]

Sounds wonderful. But the fact is that the author of that statement has no method of knowing whether it is true. There was a poor feedback system. The only real-time Bomb Damage Assessment (BDA) was the highly classified satellite system, which the keepers did not want to release. In one case, the photograph sent to the soldiers in the Kuwaiti Theater of Operations was intentionally fogged to avoid showing the level and quality of detail. As General Schwarzkopf stated to Congress:

> What we were lacking was a real-time ability of the theater commander to get the type of intelligence that needed to be made, that needed to be available to make the decisions that were going to occur within the next 24 hours. . . .
>
> We were sending aircraft out—this is when we were trying to destroy the Republican Guard, we were sending aircraft out against a target array and after a couple of weeks of doing this, the Air Force would go out against that target array, and it wouldn't be there.
>
> . . .Chuck Horner [the general in charge of the Gulf War air operations] said, in every war I ever fought until now, the pilot generally sat there with an aerial photo in his lap and that aerial photo was less than 24 hours old. . . .
>
> We didn't have that. We didn't have that available. . . . We were going back because of certain BDA assessments we were making, but we weren't getting them validated.[72]

Pilots were not assigned to the same zone more than once, which prevented them from reviewing their own results. This created several problems: pilots could not finish unfinished business; they could not provide their own BDA; and morale may have been lowered because pilots did not feel a sense of completion.[73] Even the official report admitted the problem.

> The battle damage assessment (BDA) necessary to judge the effectiveness of the air interdiction campaign was difficult to obtain because of reconnaissance systems limitations and adverse weather. Estimating attrition of Iraqi defensive forces was often more art than science. It was often impossible to confirm destruction of dug-in targets until Coalition forces arrived to see for themselves. Damage to vehicles caused by modern weapons and damage to troops often cannot be verified by imagery. General Schwarzkopf has commented that there was a problem if discrepancies between the BDA provided by the national intelligence was willing to confirm as opposed to the damage estimates developed in theater, based on national intelligence, theater reconnaissance, pilot reports, and other battlefield reports.[74]

Figure 14-4

Tons of Ordnance in Desert Storm by Service and Type

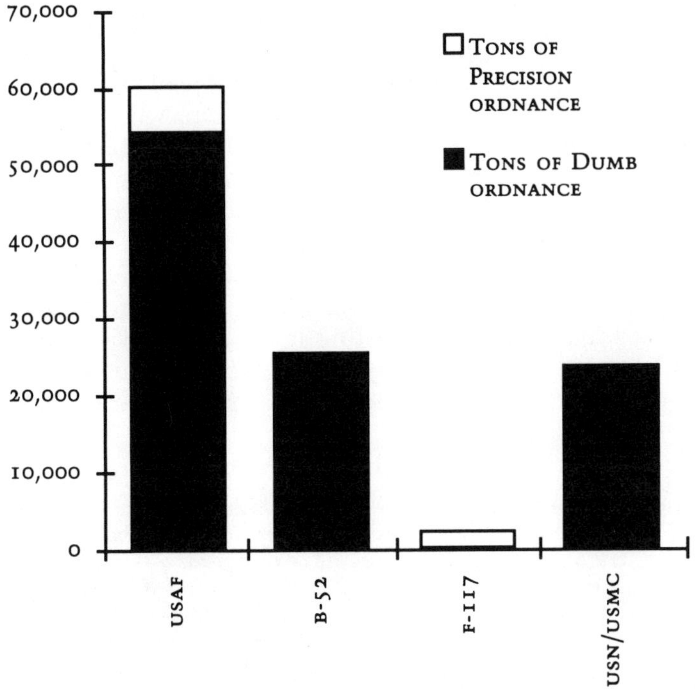

SOURCE: U.S. Army's Central Command, U.S. Air Force and U.S. Navy data

The bulk of the ordnance dropped by all services was as dumb as those dropped by B-17s in World War II. Less than 5 percent of the weapons the United States dropped were precision-guided munitions (PGMS), which amounted to less than 8 percent in tonnage. The navy dropped 740 tons of precision ordnance which is too small to register on this chart.

Sprey was blunter. He said that the military "didn't want to know how bad it was. The same thing happened in Vietnam. Once they found out how bad the A-6s were doing, they didn't want to know. They were doing CEPS* of 4,200 feet and the F-111s were getting 4,800 foot CEPS.[75]

At least one general agreed with Sprey. "War is incredibly complex. Information reported in the heat of battle can be downright wrong. It also can be deliberately skewed to bolster spirits at home or to

*CEP stands for "circular error probable." It means that 50 percent of the bombs fell within a circle of that size. It also means that the balance fell outside. According the Col. John Warden, the CEP of the B-17 was 3,300 feet. This would tend to indicate that bombing accuracy in Vietnam had not improved since World War II.

deceive the enemy. Press reports can be inaccurate and incomplete; they also can be circumscribed by the need to maintain secrecy.... Military men who should know better too often try to score postwar points with statistics that cannot survive careful scrutiny."[76]

In January 1993, Saddam Hussein began violating the 'no fly' zones set up in the northern and southern parts of Iraq. As a result, the U.S. flew air strikes against isolated targets using several types of aircraft. The F-18 was among them. The Department of Defense admitted that the F-18 destroyed only two out of six targets.

Pilots were faced with an approach-withdrawal conflict during the planning phase of the war. To bomb from medium or high altitude meant sanctuary from Iraqi low-altitude guns and missiles with a corresponding inability to bomb accurately. Flying low provided the ability to bomb more accurately, with a corresponding increase in the probability of getting shot down. Naval Intelligence officers briefed every U.S. Navy squadron on the intensity of the surface-to-air antiaircraft artillery (AAA) gunfire.[77] TacAir developed plans for initial low level penetration by U.S. Navy pilots, in spite of the briefings from Naval Intelligence recommending against it.

> After initial losses in low-altitude attacks, both U.S. Air Force and U.S. Navy aircraft were generally directed to attack from above about 10,000 ft. The B-52s, which made their first attack at 500 ft., switched to 20,000 to 30,000 ft. or more. These relative safe attack altitudes were not always practical. Airplanes could generally fly toward their targets at high enough altitudes to avoid any sort of damage en route, but in many cases (particularly when guided bombs or missiles were not available) accurate weapons delivery was impossible except at low altitude. Similarly, a Navy A-6 was lost delivering mines, which had to be laid precisely, that is at low altitude. No initial air offensive could have solved the low-altitude problem.[78]

After the initial loss of an F-18 flying at low altitudes, the Navy began bombing from medium altitudes, altitudes that had been the sanctuary of the B-17s and B-24s in World War II. The difference was that in World War II the enemy had AAA that could reach those altitudes. The Iraqis, who had relied on their surface-to-air missiles for altitudes above 10,000 feet, were without arsenal at medium altitudes. As a result at medium to high altitudes, with the exception of some AAA that went to 20,000 feet,[79] the Coalition loss rate was 0.3 per 1,000 sorties compared to Vietnam where the rates were 2.6 to 3. By comparison, the Navy's beginning loss rate, when they ingressed at low levels, was 2.7 per 1,000. That was the good news. The bad news was that at those higher altitudes U.S. and coalition aircraft suffered from gross inaccuracies, as F-18 pilots were quick to admit.

> To release weapons with accuracy, strike aircraft require airspace that is relatively free from enemy threat. Attaining such a sanctuary, whose location depends on enemy capabilities, was the object of intensive strike planning. Standoff distance and altitude are paramount factors for aircraft survival, but increasing the distance from the target makes it more difficult to locate that target and maneuver to a precise aimpoint. Iraqi tanks and troops were well dug-in and camouflaged, and were almost impossible to see from the sanctuaries available from Iraqi AAA and SAM sites. Continuous saturation bombardment served to demoralize the enemy, but it rarely destroyed targets. . . .
>
> The weapons and systems compatible with the Hornet were designed for visual acquisition of targets at low or medium altitudes, and not at the standoff distances or altitudes required in the Gulf War.[80]

The F-18's contribution would be laudable if, even at those higher altitudes, it launched the more accurate precision-guided bombs. But just as radar must exist in a fighter to guide the radar-guided missile, so must laser spot designators exist on the bombers so they can launch laser-guided bombs.

However, the F-18 "was not capable of attaining the precision associated with laser guided-bombs or the laser Maverick air-to-surface missile—'smart' weapons proved more than a decade ago—because the aircraft was not capable of designating the target by laser."[81]

The F-18s could not designate for themselves because the Navy failed to procure the laser spot designators that are required to tell the bombs where to go.* Not procuring the designators is the functional equivalent of sending fighters with Sparrow missiles into battle but failing to procure radar sets to guide them.† But again, we should not be too critical of the F-18's failure to make use of the laser guided ordnance, because, as General Hopgood stated, "Before we as a nation . . . attach too much importance to smart weapons (laser-guided bombs and missiles), we must remember that they are often prohibitively expensive—and, in the case of air-delivered smart weapons, require more sophisticated aircraft and air formations for their delivery."[82]

As a result of these omissions and the effective AAA gun fire, "Hornet pilots were limited . . . to MK-80 gravity bombs, released at high altitude. Unstable ballistics and unpredictable, erratic winds meant that several re-strikes were often required to score the required direct hits."[83] Laser-guided bombs have a similar limitation. As a result, contrary to the statement made (page 268 above) that it takes

*F-18s dropped a few laser-guided bombs with the help of some A-6s that were designating for the Hornets.

†The Navy did not begin operational test and evaluation of laser spot trackers until early 1993.

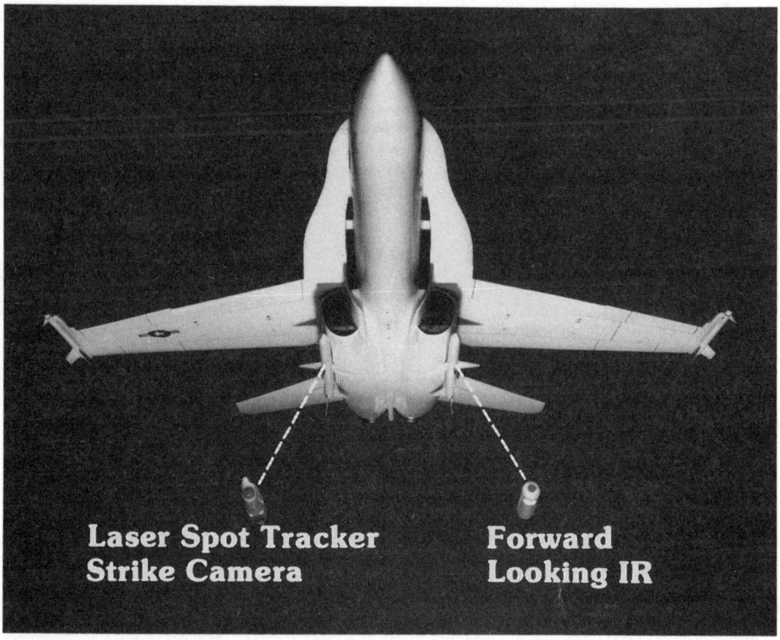

SOURCE: McDonnell Douglas
This marketing photo of laser spot trackers on the F-18 was created by McDonnell Douglas in 1978. Until the Navy began operational test and evaluation in early 1993, the F-18 had not method, short of using other aircraft, to employ laser-guided bombs. The Navy justified the F-18's smaller range/payload over the A-7 because of the Hornet's ability to use precision ordnance.

fewer F-117S to attack a target because of their single-shot capability, LGB's may actually increase the number needed.

> A bomber cannot drop more than one laser-guided bomb at a time, because the explosion and debris caused by the first explosion will throw off the guidance of the next; smoke and low clouds, which can also disrupt the laser bombs, do the same thing. Thus putting two or three laser-guided bombs on a given target may require either multiple passes by one bomber, or else attacks by two or three individual bombers, sequenced to arrive after the smoke from the preceding explosion.[84]

So, contrary to the F-18 shining as an example of high technology as the Department of Defense argued, the F-18 was hauling around, as one F-18 squadron wrote, technology from World War II.

> What the strike-fighter pilots saw on the television screen told them with painful clarity that they would be fighting the Gulf War with the tactics of the 1990s, in a front-line aircraft procured during the 1980s, using air-to-ground weapons designed, in some cases, as long ago as the 1950s. They would be going into combat carrying thousand of pounds of gravity bombs suspended from their aircraft, and they would be delivering those bombs by a method older than themselves. . . .

> Unable to paint targets by laser, the F/A-18 was essentially limited to the daylight-only Walleye and MK-80 gravity bombs, dropped at high altitude.[85]

Because F-18s were limited to dropping dumb bombs and SEAD electronic defense suppression, the question was, could it have been done less expensively with F-4 Phantoms or other reconstituted aircraft?

WHAT GOALS DID WE ACCOMPLISH IN THE GULF WAR?

The victory in Iraq was unprecedented. Never in the history of warfare have so many been defeated with the death or injury of so few. Fewer than 200 American lives were lost in the ejection of Iraqi troops from Kuwait, and some were taken by other Americans. The Department of Defense claimed that "technology did it." But a glance through the red, white, and blue picket fence called national security shows that everything did not work just as it was supposed to.

The U.S. Air Force claims that strategic bombing won the war. But evidence continues to unfold that suggests a different story. Keep in mind the definition of strategic bombing, "the bombing of a selected target or targets vital to the war-making capacity of a nation." According to a former Army intelligence officer who compared the Air Force target list with the actual damage in Iraq, the Coalition did not accomplish its mission: " 'The air war was clean on a strategic level, but irrelevant to the defeat of the Iraqi army.' "[86]

Contrary to the conventional wisdom that the strategic bombing campaign prevented the Iraqi army from communicating with its leadership, the Iraqi army said it failed to communicate with its leaders for fear signal intelligence would pinpoint their locations leading to bombing of their positions on a tactical level.

If we look at specific air campaign objectives (which follow the goals/objective matrix listed on page 274 above) that were designed to eliminate the centers of gravity, we find that the destruction of fuel supplies was clearly a target. Yet, as reported in *Aviation Week & Space Technology*, at one location, "only 10 of 100 oil storage tanks were destroyed, and postwar Iraqi fuel supplies are so great that gasoline is still cheap."[87] Can a strategic target exist that is more important than the elimination of an enemy's fuel supply?

Aviation Week went on to say that some of the strategic bombing accomplished nothing more than the postwar demise of health and food services for the civilian population. As a result, civilian death rates are continuing at a rate two to three times the death rate of the Iraqi army during the war.

It seems odd that the Department of Defense would claim that technology won the Iraqi war when 90 percent of the weapons were ancient technology.* B-52s, older than most of the pilots flying them, dropped 30 percent of the bombs, which was more than were dropped by the U.S. Navy and Marine Corps combined. Indeed, how much could the F-18 have done when, according to *Armed Forces Journal International*, all of the carriers in the Gulf were involved in only 17 percent of the attack missions?[88] According to some Iraqi officials quoted after the war, B-52s carpet bombing Bagdhad would have been more effective than the random precision bombing that took place.

The claim by the Department of Defense that technology was what saved us does not appear to be supported by the meager battle damage assessment available. As Sprey put it, "when laser-guided bombs get a 1.5 percent success rate against bridges, that is not my idea of reliability success."[89]

Some of the military and civilian defense technologists have pointed to the sortie rate as an example of the benefits of new technology. But again, as Sprey said, "As far as unprecedented sortie rates for airplanes, I don't find any evidence for that. We had 1,800 airplanes in the theater turning out 2,000 sorties a day. I don't know what is unprecedented about that; we did that well or better in Vietnam whenever we put on the pressure to produce sorties. . . . The only really remarkable result in aircraft reliability was the A-10 which really did fly between two and three sorties a day. The [other] jets didn't. It is that simple."[90]

Close Air Support and the A-10

It is not enough to fly around above the clouds, as the F-18s did, and claim that the aircraft is performing close air support.† Close

*The Air Force did not use B-1s in Desert Storm. The Air Force's failure to use them was due, no doubt, in part because B-52s can drop 8 different types of bombs while the B-1 can drop only 500-pound MK-80s bombs; the B-52 can be loaded in a couple of hours, while the B-1 takes over a day; the B-1 would require eight passes over a target compared to only one for the B-52; and the B-1 has less range than a B-52. (David Evans, "Costly B-1B bomber . . . ," *Chicago Tribune* (18 April 1993): 27).

†Close air support is defined by the U.S. Air Force Dictionary as the "air support or cooperation provided friendly surface forces, consisting of air attacks with guns, bombs, guided airborne missiles or rockets on hostile surface forces, their installations or vehicles [is] *so close to surface operations as to require detailed coordination between air and friendly surface forces.*" The February 1993 publication of the "Roles, missions, and Functions . . . ,"of the military services states that close air support is "Air action against hostile targets which are in close proximity to friendly forces and which require *detailed integration of each air mission* with the fire and movement of those forces." (Emphasis added.)

air support requires that pilots have the ability to distinguish a tank from a hot rock. They must get close enough to separate friend from foe. By definition they must fly at the same low altitudes that the F-18s avoided (as did all the other aircraft) after their initial losses told them this war, like Vietnam and others in between, would be lethal below 10,000 feet. While the Air Force will admit that the

Figure 14-3
A-10 and Maverick Time to Fire

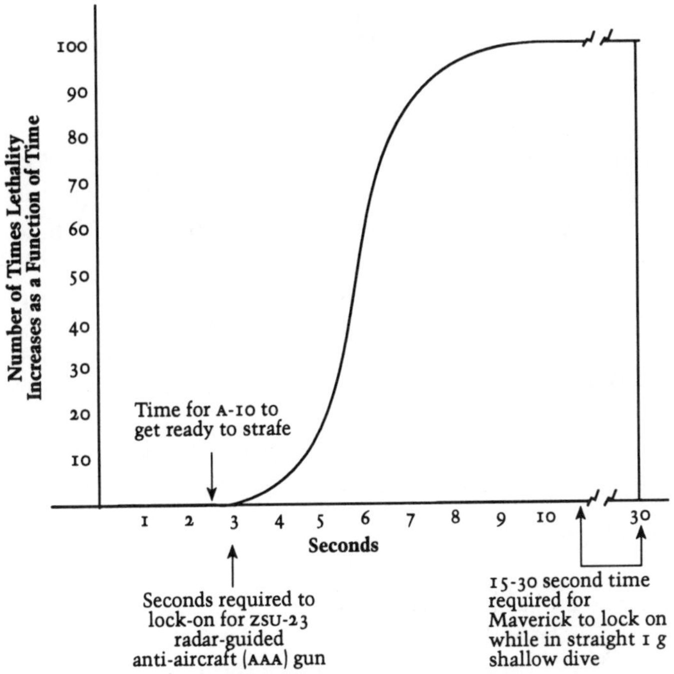

SOURCE: U.S. Congress. House. *The Impact of the Persian Gulf War. . . .*, p. 574
The A-10 can bring its gun up to firing readiness before the ZSU-23 radar-controlled AAA surface-to-air gun can fire. Launching Mavericks, on the other hand, requires flying in harm's way for at least 15 seconds before launching the missile. The A-10s flew most of the Maverick missions because A-10s were designed to absorb gunfire.

A-10 was somewhat helpful, its success is always attributed to the more complex technology in the Maverick missile.

> The Maverick is a very interesting question, and there are pluses and minuses to be said about the combat results. Very interesting is the fact that almost all the Mavericks were fired by A-10s. . . . Now, that is a fact of major significance, because one of the criticisms that we made of the Maverick, and one of the things that was very obvious from the operational tests was that Maverick would grossly increase the loss rate of any airplane launching it. . . .
>
> Everybody thought if the Maverick gives you standoff, and you are

> further from the target, you are safer. The opposite was true. It is much more dangerous to fire a Maverick than to fire a gun or drop a bomb. The Maverick requires you to approach the target at fairly low altitude, usually within gun envelope and fly straight and level for 15 to 30 seconds.
>
> Flying straight and level for 15 to 30 seconds, even in the presence of only machine guns is nearly suicidal in a standard thin-skinned jet, because the aim of the ground gunners gets much more accurate with every succeeding second of straight-line flight.
>
> Instead of flying straight for a 2 second strafing pass or 3 1/2 seconds for a bombing pass, you have to fly straight for 15 seconds with Maverick. That may cause you 100, perhaps 500 times as much attrition as a 3-second run. We established this in tests using actual Soviet anti-aircraft guns.[91]

General Schwarzkopf asked for the A-10s, well aware of their tank killing ability.[92] The Air Force, through Lieutenant General Horner, initially attempted to prevent the A-10s from going to the Gulf. It acquiesced only after General Schwarzkopf insisted and Cheney overruled the Air Force.[93] As a result, "the 144 A-10s in the Gulf [which represented 15 percent of the total aircraft] flew about a third of the total sorties but were responsible for more than half the confirmed bomb damage."[94] In other words, the 15 percent of the aircraft inventory that the A-10s represented created more damage to the Iraqis than the remaining 85 percent. Even General Horner is reported to have said, "I take back all the bad things I've ever said about the A-10's—I love them. They're saving our asses."[95]

Unprecedented Morale Collapse

In the spring and summer of 1991, the House Committee on Armed Services held hearings entitled *The Impact of the Persian Gulf War and the Decline on the Soviet Union on How the United States Does Its Defense Business.* During those hearings, Sprey raised many unconventional reasons for the victory over the Iraqi army. After all the positive comments by the high technology gurus, contrary comments by Pierre Sprey and others raised eyebrows on some and blood pressure in others. Representative Jim McCrery of Louisiana questioned Sprey:

> . . .To what do you attribute the overwhelming victory that we achieved?
>
> MR. SPREY. I attribute it to a high order of guts and skill and determination on our side, and almost total moral collapse on the other side, a collapse that I am not sure is very intimately connected with the bombing even with the clear inadequacies of their communications.
>
> [Morale] is the way wars are won and lost. They are won and lost by moral strength and moral collapse. . . .

To say it was because of the bombing I think is certainly premature, certainly when you look at the casualty numbers. Actual military casualties from bombing were astonishingly low. There must have been something other than their soldiers getting wounded and killed by bombing that prompted 200,000 of them to decide to walk out of the theater before the war began and to not fight. . . .

What really wins and loses wars is a much more dominant issue than all the technological differences we like to argue about so much. That is not an excuse for buying bad weapons. . . . If you study military history, it is people that win and lose wars primarily, and it is the things that affect their minds that allow you to win quickly and bloodlessly.

MR. MCCRERY. You don't think the fact we established air superiority in just a matter of a few days had anything to do with their state of mind?

MR. SPREY. I didn't say that. I told you I didn't know what the effect of the bombing was. I am raising the possibility the bombing didn't have nearly as powerful an effect as is generally believed.

I'll give you an example of something that might have had a very powerful effect indeed: . . . It looked like the Iraqis were battle weary. They fought for 8 years against the Iranians and, incidentally, they fought with great tenacity and courage and a half million of them died and were wounded during the course of that war. You can't make a blanket statement that Iraqis are cowards or unwilling to fight.

But a most significant event occurred in Iraq, an event people didn't make much of in this country: very soon after we started to build up the Desert Shield forces, Saddam Hussein turned around and made a very quick peace with the Iranians. He essentially gave away in a minute everything the Iraqis had bled and died for for 8 years, gave it all back to the Iranians. . . .

It is very possible the cost of that very expensive peace with Iran was the collapse of the morale of all those Iraqi soldiers that were faced with dying in Kuwait. . . .

THE CHAIRMAN. Pierre, I am surprised at your explanation. Why don't you as a military reformer explain the collapse of the Army forces in the John Boyd theory.

MR. SPREY. This is the John Boyd theory. The John Boyd theory holds that the mental and moral factors that drive people are the overwhelmingly important elements in winning and losing. You need to understand what causes the collapse of morale, no matter whether its due to politics, religion, starvation or military force.

THE CHAIRMAN. The explanation under Boyd theory would not necessarily be what happened with the Iran-Iraq war. We got inside their decision making. We did a big maneuver warfare operation way out to the west, and all of a sudden, we were in behind them.

That is pure John Boyd, at least the ground war was. The air war was just pounding them. . . .

MR. SPREY. I agree with you wholeheartedly. The air [war] was the same old classic attrition warfare, interdiction bombing stuff we did in WW-2. There were no new ideas in the actual strategy of the air war.

> There may have been some new tactics, particularly in the A-10 side, but basically the overall direction of the air war was the same old stuff that generals have been doing in picking bombing target list ssince 1942.
>
> The ground war was a brilliantly different plan of campaign. It reflects the fact there were a lot of young staff officers on the staff of General Schwarzkopf who heard and understood John Boyd's ideas. General Schwarzkopf saw the merit of those ideas and approved that plan.
>
> That doesn't mean that that plan won the war because, in fact, 100,000 to 200,000 Iraqi soldiers had already decided before day one of that plan that they weren't going to fight. . . . Understanding what caused that moral collapse is the heart of understanding why it was such an easy war.[96]

In a private moment, Sprey was more explicit. In discussing the value of air power in defeating the Iraqi Army, he said: "That's not the reason the Iraqi Army collapsed. That thing collapsed by itself without being attacked. A 400,000-man army was loaded in the front lines with approximately 200,000 Shi'ites and Kurds, Saddam's natural enemy. All we did was finish killing his enemy for him. They couldn't surrender fast enough."[97]

One might ask, how did Sprey's comments, and those of John Boyd, conform with the man in charge, General Schwarzkopf. The General was most disparaging about the Soviet equipment. "The Soviet equipment did not perform will against our equipment. . . . There is nothing on the battlefield that could stand up to anything we had."

Thus, this statement would seem to feed the technophilic belief that technology is what won the war. However, General Schwarzkopf said that people were the primary reason we won the war.[98] Fifth on his list were the weapons, weapons which Schwarzkopf said we could have traded with the Iraqis and had the same result.

All of this takes us back to the fundamental question: what goals or objectives were realized in the Gulf War? Clearly, the Coalition was successful in pushing the Iraqis out of Kuwait. But what about the three centers of gravity?

Incapacitate the Iraqi Regime

Saddam Hussein was able to communicate with his forces well enough for them to come to the cease-fire negotiations. And immediately after the cease-fire, he was able to put down two uprisings in two disparate parts of Iraq. So it is unclear exactly how well the Coalition did in neutralizing Iraq's national command authority. Furthermore, with articles more than a year after the war, such as "White House Seeks New Funds to Oust Hussein," there is not much doubt about the lack of success in eliminating Hussein during the Gulf War.[99] The ultimate irony is that Saddam Hussein outlasted President Bush.

Destruction of Nuclear, Biological, and Chemical Weapons

Based on postwar inspections, the destruction of the known nuclear, biological, and chemical (NBC) weapons was a failure, unless one were to use the chimerical excuse that we destroyed all we knew about and thus accomplished our goal. We failed to eliminate two of the three major centers of gravity. But what about the Republican Guard?

The Defeat of the Republican Guard?

The Republican Guard was made up of the elite army units whose allegiance to Saddam Hussein was strong. It was the group that he could trust. The United States wanted to defeat, preferably eliminate, it for two reasons. First, its members were the best trained and held the greatest threat to the ground forces. Second, they were the source of Saddam Hussein's power. Eliminate them and Hussein would become more malleable. Postwar Iraq without the Republican Guard would become a different negotiating ground.

Saddam Hussein held the Republican Guard in reserve at the northern side of Kuwait. Consequently, General Schwarzkopf sent one of his two best generals on a sweeping end-run to the west on the edge of Kuwait. The idea was to sneak around to the back door and keep the Republican Guard quarantined inside Kuwait.

Schwarzkopf told the world in his now-famous February 27, 1991, briefing that he had, indeed, cut off the head of the Iraqi Army and killed it as he had been instructed to do by the Chairman of the Joint Chiefs, Colin Powell. "There was nobody between us and Baghdad. . . . The gates are closed."[100]

Unknown to General Schwarzkopf, his end-run Commander, Lieutenant General Franks, was inhibited by a technological limitation and a preexisting paradigm. The general did not have fuel prepositioned for his trip to stymie the Republican Guard. This was no trivial matter as his M1 tanks used seven gallons of kerosene per mile. Second, while the Army had modified its field manual to eliminate the frontal assault and attrition mind-set, it had not eliminated a concept called "synchronization," which called for everyone converging together for the greatest firepower. This ran counter to John Boyd's teachings (page 45 above) on the value of operating at a faster tempo through the Observation-Orientation-Decision-Action (OODA) loop. Consequently, while General Schwartzkopf was saying that the Coalition Forces had bottled up the Republican Guard and there was no way it could escape, in true Pentagon Paradox fashion, the Republican Guard was escaping.[101]

All of this raises a very important question: If Lieutenant General Franks could not keep up the pace to cut off the Republican Guard, why did he not call up the A-10s, which had already demonstrated their ability to rout the regular Iraqi army on its attempt to flee Kuwait on the "Highway of Death"? If he did, why were they not successful? Nothing confirms the failure to destroy the Republican Guard better than the headine in the *Washington Post* more than a year after the war: "U.S. Is Said to Revise Strategy on Iraq: Plan to Oust Saddam Seen as Unfeasible."[102]

Chapter 15

The Mercurial F-19 Wasp

Do we want to live in a society where public officials can resort to deceit and manipulation whenever they decide that an exceptional crisis has arisen? Would we not, on balance, prefer to run the risk of failing to rise to a crisis honestly explained to us, from which the government might have saved us through manipulation? And what protection from abuse do we foresee should we surrender this choice?

Sissela Bok, *Lying*

There are only two phases to a big military program: Too early to tell, and too late to stop. Program advocates like to keep bad news covered up until they have spent so much money that they can advance the sunk-cost argument; that it's too late to cancel the program because we've spent too much already.

Fitzgerald's *First Law of Program Management*

In 1987, two years before the fall of the Berlin Wall, when the Soviet Union was still perceived as the Evil Empire, the Navy began to study a follow-on aircraft to the F-18, which they were calling the F-18E/F.[1]

By 1992, however, the result was a totally new airplane. As of March of that year plans called for the:

> leading-edge sweep . . . [to be] increased from 26.7 to 29.4 degrees, taper will be increased, twist will be removed, thickness to chord ratio will be increased, a snag on the outboard leading edge of the wing will be added, the ratio of exposed wing to total wing area will be shortened. . . .
>
> The fuselage will be lengthened almost three feet, but its width will remain the same. Thus, the F-18E will have an increased fineness ratio. . . . The air inlets to the engine will be much larger and the exterior shape will be changed from a semicircle dominated by smooth curves to a four-sided parallelogram dominated by straight lines and sharp angles [called a carret inlet which is a new design]. . . . The F-18E will use a new engine. The core will be derived from the engine used in the now defunct A-12 program and an afterburner will be added. . . . The composition of the empty weight [aircraft] will include a higher percentage (by weight) of composite materials used in the skin sections. . . . The cumulative effect of a new wing, new engines, new inlets, and new structures make the F-18E more like a *new airplane* than a modification of an existing airplane.[2]

On July 11, 1991, OSD and the Navy met to discuss the issues

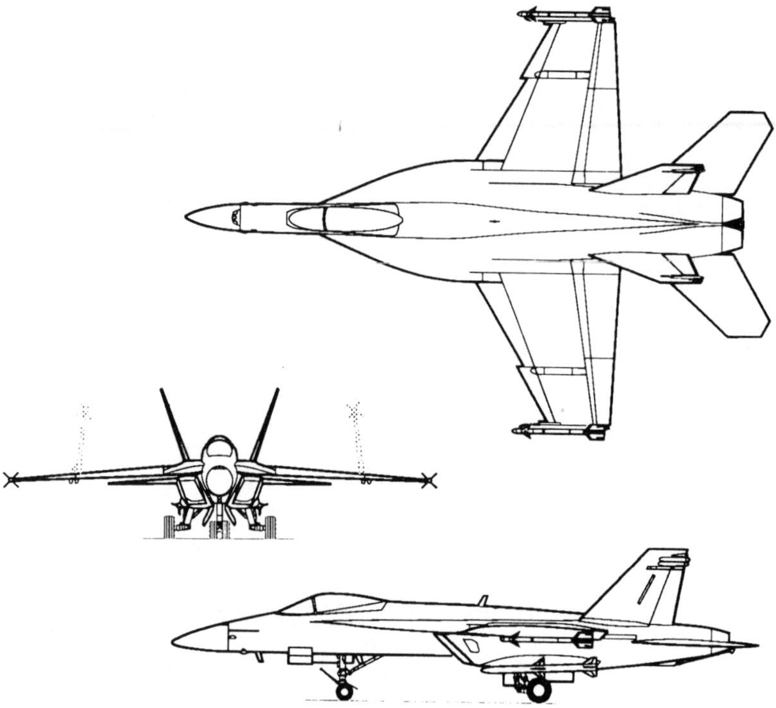

SOURCE: McDonnell Douglas
The configuration shown above represents the F-18E as of mid-1993.

that should be raised at the forthcoming Defense Acquisition Board (DAB) meeting, scheduled for January 1992.* The DAB was the final approval point to launch this new airplane. It was a critical meeting the Navy had to be well prepared for, because the Navy had received its comeuppance the previous January when Secretary Cheney canceled the A-12 Avenger II, the follow-on to the Navy's venerable A-6 Intruder.

In September 1991 Frank Kendall, OSD's top acquisition person for tactical systems, instructed the Navy to be prepared to discuss funding, avionics, acquisition strategies, exit criteria,† and test and evaluation of the F-18E/F. He also told the Navy that it would

*The Defense Acquisition Board (DAB) is a new name for a function virtually identical to that of the Defense Systems Acquisition Review Council (DSARC) process, which approved the earlier versions of the F-18.

†"Exit criteria are the specific minimum requirements that must be satisfactorily demonstrated before an effort or program can progress to the next acquisition phase. Failure to meet an exit criteria [*sic*] halts the progress of the system toward the next milestone decision point." But that is only in theory. U.S. Department of Defense. *DOD Directive 5000.1* (23 February 1991), p. II-A-7.

not be required to develop a "Cost and Operational Effectiveness Analysis" (COEA). In this memorandum, nine months after Desert Storm, and less than two years after the fall of the Berlin Wall, this new aircraft was being discussed as though it were a modification of an existing airplane.[3]

This E/F designation was an attempt to give a completely new fighter the appearance of a mere model change, in the tradition of renaming a cruiser a frigate. When one looks at the significant changes, the aircraft appears to deserve the designation F-19 Wasp.* The nickname Wasp is appropriate because wasps are known to kill their young. The added expense of the F-19 will have the equivalent effect on the F-18. All these changes raise the question, What quantity or quality of changes must take place in an aircraft to consider it a modification as opposed to a new aircraft?†

The Department of Defense has a six-step process by which it purchases weapons systems.[4] Each step has an associated milestone that is designed to investigate the progress of the previous phase and approve advancement to the next step (see fig. 15-1 below).

Mandatory and optional reports accompany each of these phases and milestones, to assist the DAB in its decision-making process. Many of the requirements of the phases and milestones are costly and time-consuming. As a result, contractors and weapons-system advocates within the services or Office of the Secretary of Defense interpret the regulations in a way that will minimize the paperwork, expedite the weapons system they advocate, and frustrate the purpose of the checks and balances in the process established to safeguard taxpayers' money from being spent recklessly.

The normal procedure for developing a new airplane would require that the Navy start at the beginning, as shown in fig. 15-1 below, at "Determination of Mission Needs." This step requires a Mission Need Statement (previously known as a Mission Element Need Statement, or MENS), which is the raison d'être of the aircraft. It identifies, among other things, "the projected threat environment."

Yet the Navy claimed, in its justification document for the F-18E/F,

*The F-18E/F should be designated the F-19 since it is the next available number in the fighter sequence. The F-18E/F was as great a departure from the F-18C/D as the F-18 was from the YF-17, and the Navy insisted on changing the F-17 to F-18. The F-19 designation was thought to be the designation for one of the stealth aircraft, since there are designations for the F-18, F-20, F-21, F-22, and YF-23. However, to date, no F-19 designation has surfaced; hence, the F-19 is the next available designation for the E/F version of the F-18.

†The Navy refers to the F-18E/F as a "modification." *The American Heritage Dictionary of the English Language* (Third Edition), 1992, p. 1,161 gives the following definition for modification: "A small alteration, adjustment, or limitation."

Figure 15-1

Acquisition Milestones & Phases

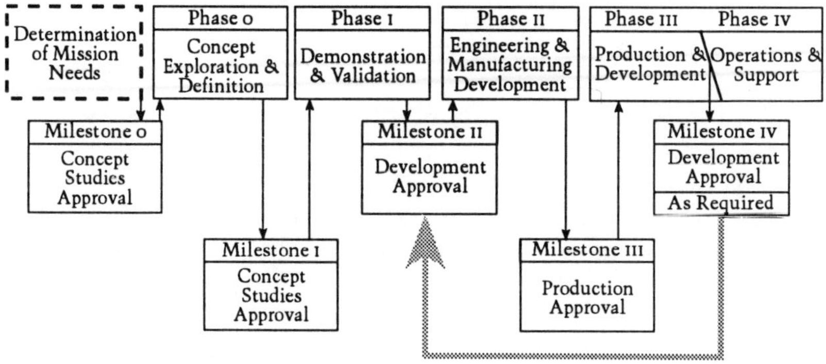

SOURCE: DOD Instruction 5000.2 Part 3 (23 Feb. 1991), pp. 3–4.

The six phases of the acquisition cycle with their associated milestones. The Navy and F-18E/F advocates attempted to bypass the process by beginning at Milestone IV to develop their new Hornet via the thicker gray arrow above.

that "the Mission Element Need Statement (MENS) of the F/A-18A/B is still applicable as the Mission Need Statement of the F/A-18E/F."[5] This admission is interesting in light of the fact that the MENS for the F-18A/B had to have been generated in the middle of the 1970s, at the height of the Cold War. However, because of shoddy oversight on the part of the office of the Secretary of Defense, this Cold War justification for the F-18E/F created not a ripple of opposition.

The Navy convinced the Office of the Secretary of Defense that the F-18E/F was a mere modification. It was thus able to jump to the head of the line and position the aircraft as a "Milestone IV/II; i.e., that the program would be reviewed at Milestone IV (Major Modification Approval) with plans to enter Phase II (Engineering and Manufacturing Development)."[6] Some members of the OSD staff believe that the Office of the Secretary of Defense failed to provide the necessary oversight on this process.

One of the more important documents in the justification process for a new aircraft is the "Cost and Operational Effectiveness Analysis," or COEA. "A COEA evaluates the costs and benefits of alternative courses of action to meet recognized Defense needs and determines the total life-cycle costs and operational effectiveness of alternative programs and the associated program for acquiring each alternative."[7]

The COEA is not optional for new programs. "Cost and operational effectiveness analyses shall be prepared and considered at milestone decision reviews of acquisition category I programs, beginning with Milestone I. . . ."[8] A COEA is required, even for the less ambitious

Milestone IV. "A Milestone IV decision addresses the need to initiate an upgrade or modification to a system currently in production. The analysis prepared for this milestone decision review should consider the costs and consequences of all alternatives to include maintaining the status quo."[9]

The Navy, in response to criticism from the Inspector General for its failure to develop a COEA for the F-18E/F, said that the COEA was optional for a Milestone IV evaluation. "DOD Instruction 5000.2 does not explicitly require that a COEA be done for a Milestone IV. Instead it states that the 'milestone decision authority *may* elect to require a cost and operational effectiveness analysis.' "[10] (Emphasis added.) The Inspector General took issue with the Navy's interpretation, primarily because "the program was slated for a combined Milestone IV/II review."[11]

Thus even if the Navy believed that it could avoid the COEA because the regulation used the word *may* during a Milestone IV meeting, according to the Inspector General, the COEA was not optional under Milestone II. But the Navy's interpretation of the option of the COEA is incorrect. Regulations have to be viewed in toto for a proper interpretation. DOD Instruction 5000.2 requires that each member of the DAB have a book with the appropriate documents and states what is required to be in it. For a Milestone IV review, the regulations clearly state that a COEA is required.[12] "The Navy and the Air Force have been disregarding COEAs for years," said Tom Christie. "They would simply just not do one. But the DABs would be held anyway."[13]

The Inspector General believed the Navy's failure to develop a COEA would result in the DAB's inability to view alternative candidates to the F-18E/F; would not reveal the fact that the Navy justified the F-18E/F based on threat analysis done at the height of the Cold War; and would expose the Navy's failure to list 25 years of life-cycle costs.[14]

The Navy's suppression of the excessive F-18E/F changes slid through the system. The F-18E/F alterations were significant from every measurement. The aerodynamic changes (see page 305 above) were substantial, as was the weight increase. The changes the Navy proposed prior to the critical Defense Acquisition Board meeting, scheduled for April 30, 1992, showed that by weight, only 16 percent of the E/F modification was common with the F-18C/D. An 84-percent change tends to indicate that this E/F was more than a mere modification.

The cost increases also showed that the E/F was more than a

modification. One would expect that a modification would cost some small percentage of the original. The development cost of the *original* F-18 was $1.43 billion in 1975 dollars (see page 223 above). The development costs of the E/F *modification* were advertised to cost, as of the fall of 1992, $4.88 billion in FY1990 dollars. Since these costs are from two different base years, they are not equivalent. In 1975, the Navy claimed that in 1990-year dollars, the original F-18 would cost $3.47 billion, or $1.41 billion less than the E/F modification.

In the fall of 1992 the Navy maintained that the $3.47 billion figure did not include "the cost of engine development or government furnished equipment (GFE)."[15] But according to the Lightweight Fighter hearings in the summer of 1975, these costs *were* included. During these hearings, the Navy testified that the total cost for research and development for the F-18 would be $1.43 billion in constant 1975-year dollars, as shown in table 11-3 (page 223).

In the fall of 1992 the Navy stated that rather than $3.47 billion, the original F-18 ultimately cost $4.815 billion in FY1990 dollars. They broke out the numbers in the following manner:

$3.781 billion for the airframe
$0.671 for the engine
$0.363 billion for GFE/in-house
$4.815 billion[16]

If these numbers are run through the DOD deflators, they equate to the following in 1975:

$1.557 billion for the airframe
$0.276 for the engine
$0.150 billion for GFE/in-house
$1.983 billion

Table 15-1 shows the original projections and the current claim in 1975 dollars.

Table 15-1
Original F-18 Research and Development Costs Compared (in Millions)

	1975 Estimate	1992 $	Difference	% ±
F404 development	$300.0	$276	$(24)	(8%)
Airframe & avionics	$765.0	$1,557	$792	203%
(GFE)	7.0			
Test, eval., management., & support	$358.0	$150	$(215)	(41%)
Total	$1,430.0	$1,983	$553	38%

SOURCE: Lightweight Fighter Hearings Summer 1975; 29 Oct. 92 Mixson to Stevenson letter

Thus, the Navy was either incorrect, and was asking to develop a "modification" that cost $1.41 billion more than the original F-18 projections, or it underestimated the development costs of the original F-18 by 38 percent. Assuming that the original F-18 did in fact cost

$4.815 billion, and one were to apply the 38-percent underestimation of the F-18A to the projected development costs of the F-18E/F, the *actual* development costs of the F-18E/F would be $6.7 billion. This figure approaches the $7.9 billion figure that was briefed within the Pentagon. Even if we assume that the Navy had developed its new estimates correctly, the cost still raises the issue, How can a modification cost anything close to the original?

The Navy claims that the increased weight of the F-18E/F contributes to its increased development cost. (This E/F *modification* weighs 50 percent more than the F-18A.) "The Navy estimates development *and* procurement cost based on aircraft weight (dollars per pound). Although the F/A-18E/F is a *modification* it weights more than the original and therefore will cost more."[17] (Emphasis added.)

Franklin "Chuck" Spinney, an analyst in the Office of the Secretary of Defense, takes exception to the Navy's claim. "That's hogwash. Weight is used to estimate procurement costs, *not* development costs. If the Navy's claim were true, they could develop an airplane for half the cost of the F-18 which could cruise at Mach 1.6 for 2,000 miles if it weighed half of what the F-18 weighs. That's just nonsense."[18]

Looking beyond the development costs (which are small compared to the procurement costs) the Navy said that the total program cost (defined on page 220 above) of the F-18E/F in constant FY1990 dollars would be $54 billion for 1,000 aircraft. This results in a program unit cost of $54 million per F-18E/F.[19] How well the Navy will predict the program unit costs of the F-18E/F is, in large measure, a function of how well it has predicted program unit costs in the past.

In 1975, three years before the F-18 made its first flight, the Navy estimated that the total program unit cost of the F-18 would be $9.6 million. The Navy subsequently increased the number of aircraft it planned to purchase by 70 percent, from 800 to 1,366. However, contrary to the usual claims that if quantities increase, unit prices decrease, the unit price of the F-18 actually *increased* 64 percent (see table 11-4, page 224). This phenomenon is know as the Quantity Discount Corollary to the Pentagon Paradox: The unit price is proportional to the number purchased. Or, stated differently, the more you buy, the more each one costs.

If we assume, for a moment, that the Navy will *not* increase the number of F-18E/FS it plans to buy (if for no other reason than to avoid the effects of the quantity discount corollary), what reasons would one have to assume that the F-18E/F unit price would not grow by the same percentage as the original F-18? After all, the

F-18E/F development cost increased $1.4 billion to $4.88 billion from the previous year.[20] If one further assumes that the Navy will do no better in controlling costs on the E/F version of the F-18 than they did on the original F-18, then the real program unit price for the F-18E/F (in 1990 dollars) would likely grow to at least $75 million. Since the F-18 average program unit price is approximately $32 million, what the Navy is proposing is to give the taxpayer a modification of the C/D for approximately twice the cost.[21]

What really illustrates the silliness of the claim that the F-18E/F is a "modification" is that the total cost for the Lightweight Fighter Program, from which the F-18 evolved, cost the taxpayer significantly less. Both contractors were allocated $45 million, with $8 million held in reserve. The remaining $16 million paid for government-furnished equipment (GFE). The total of $106 million equates to $330 million in FY1990 dollars for two YF-16s and two YF-17s, or $187 million for two YF-17s. These were not modifications of anything but two separate and original designs.

But the Navy wanted to avoid having the F-18E/F perceived as a new airplane. Otherwise, the F-18E/F would be subjected to a much greater degree of scrutiny, as required by DOD procurement regulations. The tougher inspection would raise issues that might threaten the existence of this new airplane.

The questioning of the Navy's modification proposal began with intensity by an employee of the Office of the Secretary of Defense, Chuck Spinney, who works in the Office of Program Analysis and Evaluation (PA&E).

Spinney and PA&E in the Pentagon function primarily to provide an alternate view and to attempt to keep the spending habits and inappropriate approaches of technologists in check.* As military aircraft approach the cost of gold per pound, Spinney attempts to convince the military services to use technology that works in combat.

Spinney has been a traditional devil's advocate toward all of the services. He was tenacious in his requirement that the services prepare their rationale and have honest, coherent arguments for wanting to spend taxpayers' money. The apex of his notoriety came when he was asked to appear before the Joint Hearing of the Senate Armed Services Committee and the Senate Budget Committee, to offer testimony as to why the military was understating its budgets.

*One employee in PA&E said, "In reality PA&E is nothing more than a speed bump in the procurement process."

Figure 15-2

F-18 Projected and Actual Learning Curve Costs

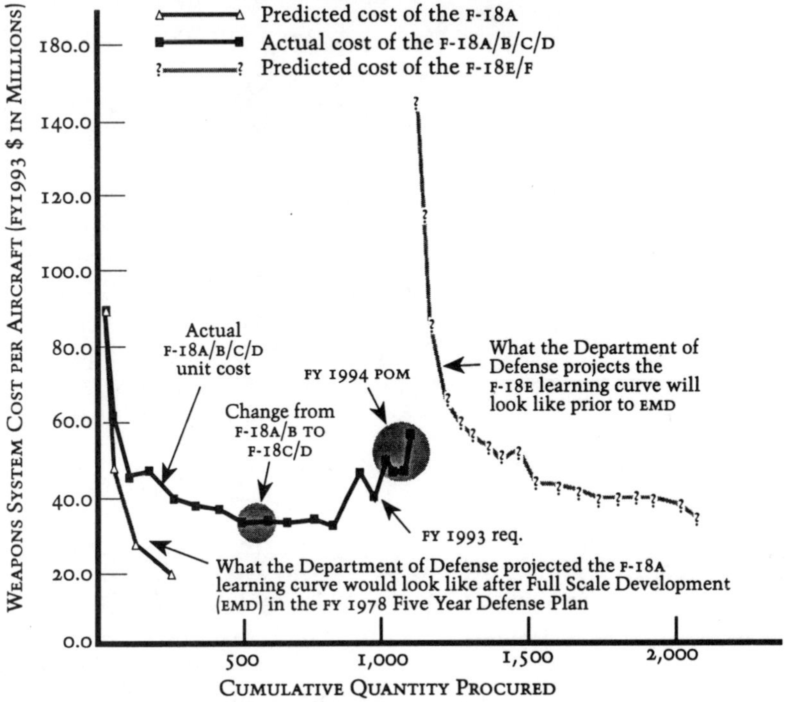

SOURCE: Spinney, "Memorandum for Mr. Puscheck . . . (2)," August 26, 1992, Tab 5. All data is approximate.

Both the Navy and McAir claim that the high initial costs of the F-18 are reduced over time. This results, they say, because as manufacturing efficiencies increase, unit price will decrease. A large input to these reductions in cost are the result, they maintain, to an increased knowledge of the workers on the assembly line. These cost reductions, which are supposed to take place over time, are called the "learning curve." These learning curves are used to justify initially high costs because they promise future reductions. The 1978 Five-Year Defense Plan (FYDP) reflected this promise to reduce the cost of the F-18A over time (see dark gray line above). In reality, the cost reductions did not take place, and in fact, in the case of the F-18C, increased. Ironically, the F-18C is the only true modification to the original F-18A. (See solid black line above.) The learning curve for the F-18E/F starts higher and remains higher than either the original F-18A promise or reality. (See dark gray line above.) One can only guess what the F-18E/F actual cost line will look like.

The Office of the Secretary of Defense refused to let Spinney appear; the Committee then threatened to subpoena him. In a countermove, Chairman Tower, a longtime friend of the military, scheduled the Committee meeting late Friday afternoon, so that Spinney's remarks would get as little media attention as possible.

With assurances that they had diffused Spinney's remarks, then-Secretary of Defense Weinberger's military aides boastfully reported

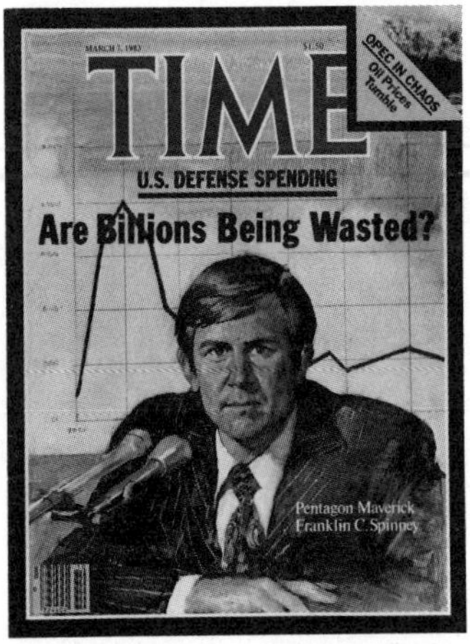

SOURCE: *Time* magazine
The assertions that Spinney made in 1983 have virtually all been validated.

words to this effect: "Well, we've taken care of Spinney. There was nothing of significance in the media over the weekend."

Unbeknownst to Weinberger, his aides, or anyone else in the defense establishment, a cover story in *Time* magazine on the decline in military readiness had been completed. In preparation for months, the article was ably assisted by Boyd, Sprey, and Dina Rasor. Boyd suggested to the *Time* writers that they look into Spinney's work on readiness and budget crises, which were reflected in his works, *Plans Reality Mismatch* and *Defense Facts of Life*. At Boyd's suggestion, *Time* put Spinney's picture on their March 7, 1983, cover.* The magazine was dropped on the Pentagon newsstands minutes after Weinberger's aides reported that Spinney was no longer an issue.

Just as Spinney would not go away on the budget issues in the early 1980s, he refused to go away on the F-18E/F. Spinney listened to internal Navy briefings in which the Navy promised, with this alleged modification, a 28-percent increase in combat radius. When he asked, "How are you going to get this increase?" the Navy initially replied that the increase would come from an increase in fuel, but otherwise the plane was a mirror image of the F-18C.[22]

Spinney did some simple estimates, using the Breguet range equation (see page 116 above). Two of the major factors in the formula are the fuel fraction (the weight of the fuel divided by the gross

*Spinney was aware that Boyd was working with *Time* magazine but was not privy to Boyd's encouragement that *Time* feature Spinney's picture on the cover until the last moment.

weight of the aircraft) multiplied by the engine's specific fuel consumption. Taking the Navy's claim that it would increase the F-18E's fuel fraction by about 5 percent and add engines that used more fuel than previous F-18 engines, Spinney became skeptical. This claim was aerodynamically incredible. Spinney said it was not clear "how the F-18E would achieve a 28% increase in combat radius, given only a 4.9% increase in fuel fraction, higher engine SFCS [Specific Fuel Consumption], similar wing loading, and lower thrust-to-weight ratios. . . ."[23]

As a result of the Navy's failure to tell him any more, Spinney attacked this claim verbally to smoke out additional information. His approach resulted in the sensitivity studies, using a Navy computer program, that showed that the fuel fraction only accounted for about half of the increase. This information led to Spinney's point paper (below) and recommendation to form a special study group.

Spinney, concerned that the DAB would meet without adequate information to make a coherent judgment, wrote an internal point paper on April 8, 1992, which said in part, "If all internal fuel were available for cruise, and assuming a 7% improvement in F-18E's L/D, then Breguet range eq. predicts that F-18E range > F-18C by only 7.3%. This implies the 18E's 28% increase in combat radius (OR=24%) *depends critically* on superior fuel consumption rates in non-cruise portions of mission (i.e., takeoff, climb, descent, combat, and landing) to free up fuel for cruise.

"The DAB has no insight into how this can be done, and OSD has not done an independent performance analysis to verify Navy/McAir #s."[24]

Spinney was justified in his skepticism. In 1975 the Navy claimed that for $1.43 billion it could develop an F-18 that could deliver four MK-83 1,000-pound bombs over 600 nautical miles from the aircraft carrier, then return. The Initial Operational Test and Evaluation squadron later revealed that the range was closer to the A-4's range of 345 miles, a range that was ratified by lot 14 F-18C models when the Navy said that the interdiction radius of action was 398 miles.[25] This range/payload reduction is, no doubt, the source of the F-18 slur heard among the NAS Miramar fighter community of "one pilot, one bomb, one hour," (see fig. 15-3 page 317).

Not only did the Navy fail to achieve the range objective, it also missed the cost goal. Now the Navy claims it will finally approach the 1975 range goal, if the taxpayer will just ante up an additional $4.88 billion to develop the F-18E. Since the Navy missed its range

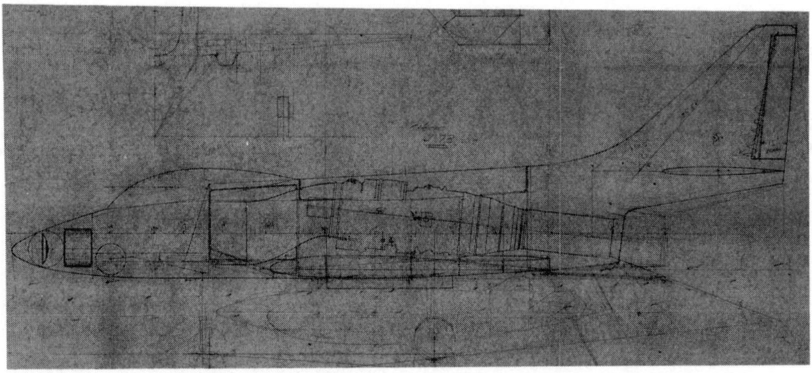

SOURCE: Ed Heinemann

The original drawing of the A-4 Skyhawk shows the compactness of the design.

goal by close to 40 percent and its development cost goal on the original F-18 by nearly 40 percent, it seems reasonable for Mr. Spinney to ask for something other than "trust me" from the Navy, when it is now saying it will finally miss the original range goal by only 20 percent by exceeding the original development cost by 200 percent.

An independent study group, recommended by Spinney, confirmed his suspicions that the increase in fuel fraction was not sufficient to account for the entire range increase.* In fact, almost half the increase came from the theoretical effects of a better lift-to-drag ratio of a totally new wing. It was this knowledge—that the F-18E was virtually a completely new design—that had not been made available to the Office of the Secretary of Defense (OSD), for whom Mr. Spinney works. The Navy initially withheld this information, no doubt, to avoid criticism that the F-18E was indeed a *new* airplane. Working from a different perspective, the Inspector General came to the same conclusion—the F-18E was a new aircraft. In fact, it was as different, when compared to the F-18A, as the Navy's 1950s-era Douglas F4D-2 was to the Douglas F4D-1 Skyray. It turns out that the Navy had previous experience in attempting to achieve increased range from a fighter by scaling up the basic design. Ed Heinemann, the F4D designer (and designer of attack aircraft from the SBD Dauntless to the A-4 Skyhawk), described the two planes. "[The Navy] . . . ordered two prototypes of what, at the time, was designated the F4D-2. The F4D-2 represented an attempt on our part to correct

*Oversight in this manner is supposed to come from other offices within OSD. Spinney did this on his own initiative, filling a void left by the responsible elements in the Office of the Secretary of Defense. The fact that an analyst working without portfolio smoked this out at the last minute says something about the current state of competence in the Office of the Secretary of Defense.

Figure 15-3
F-18 Range Degradation Over Time

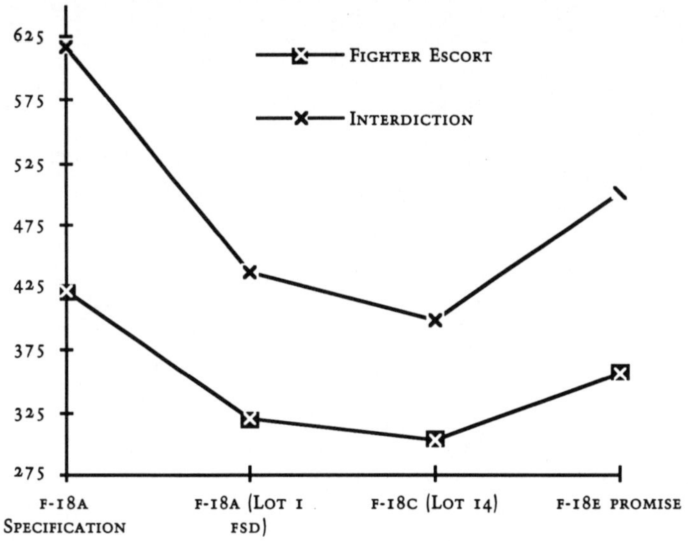

SOURCE: U.S. Department of Defense. Department of the Navy. Naval Air Systems Command. "Performance comparisons with F/A-18A (Lot I and Lot XIV) and F/A-18E specification Ground Rules," March 25, 1993.

Interdiction range for F-18A/B/C/D includes (4) MK-83LD (1,000-pound laser-designated bombs), FLIR/LDT, and (3) 330-gallon tanks dropped when empty. F-18E/F carries 45 percent more fuel in (3) external 480-gallon tanks. Fighter escort range based on internal fuel only and (2) AIM-7 sparrows or, in the case of F-18E/F, (4) AIM-120s.

This chart shows the range degradation in both fighter escort and interdiction missions for the various versions of the F-18.

the weaknesses of the F4D. . . . The F4D-2 gradually evolved as an entirely new aeroplane retaining nothing in common with the F4D-1, apart from the actual wing planform, and this development was, in consequence, to be redesignated F5D-1 [Skylancer]. . . . The F5D-1 had appreciably thinner wing sections; . . . lengthened fuselage . . . [and the] internal fuel capacity was markedly increased. . . ."[26]

Heinemann anticipated additional problems in the development of the F5D Skylancer. "As if we were not presenting ourselves with sufficient problems, we compounded them with a decision to use an entirely new . . . engine."[27] Spinney, aware that the F-18E would be, like the F5D, a complete redesign, and evolve with an undeveloped engine coupled with a new inlet design, thought these were reasons enough for him to recommend prototypes for the F-18E/F.

Spinney maintained that the F-18E/F was, in reality, a Milestone I/II program, and recommended that the "program . . . be re-configured

SOURCE: Naval Institute Collection
The F5D Skylancer (right) was a scaled-up version of the F4D Skyray.

as a fly-before-you-buy prototype program to conform with intent of the changes in acquisition policy announced by Secretary Cheney."[28] There were cogent reasons Spinney suggested for prototyping the F-18E/F.

> Prototyping['s] . . . goal is to work the bugs out of a design *before* a decision is made to expend substantial resources on its . . . production. . . .
>
> In contrast, an engineering and manufacturing development (EMD) strategy makes large financial commitments to production of a product *while* it is being designed. . . .
>
> While many Americans believe that a prototyping strategy increases development lead times, the Japanese auto manufacturers have demonstrated that prototyping, when combined with an early involvement of manufacturing engineers and a policy of rigorous testing, can be accompanied by greater product variety, shorter development lead times, and quicker transitions to high rate production.[29]

Furthermore, Spinney was advocating no more than the policy that Secretary of Defense Cheney had before the World Affairs Council of Northern California on February 12, 1992.

> "With the collapse of the Soviet Union, . . . the *need to produce new systems quickly is less urgent* now than it was in the past, and we can afford to take more time before we move systems into full scale production. . . . We can concentrate on R&D, on operational testing, and the *development of prototypes,* and the upgrade of existing systems to ensure that we maintain the technological edge our smaller forces will require. We'll move to large scale production of new weaponry *only* [when] *we get what we want at a cost we can afford.*"[30] (Emphasis in original.)

SOURCE: McDonnell Douglas and U.S. Navy.

The Navy calls the F-18E/F a "modification" of the F-18C/D. The size differences are shown above. The attempt to create the illusion that a new aircraft is a "modification" results from a desire to avoid new funding and performance milestones. The Navy has a history of this. It called F4D-2 a modification of the F4D-1 and the F2H-3 a modification of the F2H-2 (shown above left in the insert).

Spinney also suggested additional reasons for prototyping the new Hornet: this program was suitable; it would give the Navy freedom of action; and it would foster competition with all of its attendant benefits.[31]

The Navy was not interested, believing that Spinney's approach would cost too much and take too much time. Some of the more cynical critics believed the rush was an attempt to bail out McDonnell Douglas. The company was in severe financial trouble over the cancellation of the A-12, cost and performance overrun problems on the C-17, recovery from the problems it had with the T-45, and lagging commercial sales of the MD-11 (which failed to meet its range goals as well). The Air Force had advanced $442 million to McDonnell Douglas to help it appear healthy to potential creditors.[32] Nevertheless, the DAB approved the new F-18 plane on May 6, 1992, the last step before approval by the Secretary of Defense, which is, as in this case, virtually automatic. The Navy's next step was to convince Congress.

Not everyone at the Department of Defense, however, was convinced. The DOD's Inspector General took exception to the Navy's bypassing what he considered legally mandated steps toward procuring the F-18E/F. Specifically, he said "viable alternatives to this new development program may not be adequately assessed with regard to their relative cost and operational effectiveness."[33]

Bypassing the COEA was rationalized in part because the Navy said that with the elimination of the A-12, NATF (Navy Advanced Tactical Fighter), and the F-14D, there were not really any alternatives against which to do trade-off studies.[34]

Congress reacted to the F-18E/F debate within 15 days, no doubt partially because the Senate had mandated that a COEA be performed. In spite of this directive, the Navy chose to snub the Congress in the tradition of ignoring congressional language that mandated navalizing the winner of the Air Force's Air Combat Fighter Competition. And it would use the same technique—it would work the situation out with the staff. "Regarding . . . the 'COEA mandate imposed by Congress,' we are aware of the language contained in the Senate Appropriations Committee (SAC) report on the FY1992 Appropriations Act. It is our understanding that OSD has discussed this issue with the staff of the SAC and based on those discussions OSD intends to submit cost and effectiveness data which we think will be responsive to congressional direction."[35]

Figure 15-4

Tactical Aviation Modernization Plan

Service		Mission Area		
		Fighter	**Fighter/Attack**	**Attack**
USAF	**New Plane**	F-22	MRF	AX
	Would Replace	F-15	F-16	F-111, F-117, F-15E
USN/USMC	**New Plane**	[NONE]	F-18E/F	AX
	Would Replace	F-14	F-18A/B, F-18C/D	A-6

SOURCE: Congressional Research Service, "Tactical aircraft modernization: Issues for congress," p. 2.

Congress was evaluating the F-18E/F, along with the balance of the Tactical Aviation Modernization Plan presented by the Department of Defense. DOD was offering four aircraft at the same time, all of which it said were required to modernize TacAir: the Air Force needed the F-22 and the multirole fighter (MRF) and the Navy needed the F-18E/F and the AX.

The estimated cost for the four aircraft over the next 40 years was $320 billion in FY1993 dollars, or approximately $3,000 per taxpayer.[36] Partially as a result of the ever-increasing cost, some congressmen wanted to look at prototyping as a method of ensuring positive results. However, the senator from Missouri, in whose jurisdiction McDonnell Douglas is located, was not one of them. On May 21, 1992, in an attempt to force the issue, Senator Bond asked Secretary of Defense Cheney to discuss the prototype and range issues surrounding the F-18E/F.[37]

SENATOR BOND: Is there any reason why that should be prototyped, the E and F?

SECRETARY CHENEY: I know the House Armed Services Committee has recommended that. I think my view of it would be that we have flown millions of hours in the F/A-18 already, because it is of course operational, has been in operation with the fleet for a long time, and that prototyping is not necessarily something that we would want to do. But I would be guided by the judgment of our acquisition people. I have not had a chance to talk to them about it.

SENATOR BOND: What would prototyping do to the cost and to the planned acquisition strategy with your projections as to when the AX would come on line?

SECRETARY CHENEY: I would have to get that for the record, Senator. I could not tell you immediately what its consequences would be.[38]

Secretary Cheney's response contradicted his February comments in which he advocated prototyping. But this may have been as a result of his believing the F-18E/F to be a modification, like the C/D was to the A/B. F-18E/F advocates within the Office of the Secretary of Defense presented the following statement, in the name of Secretary Cheney, for the record, during the week of June 22, 1992.

> We do not believe that there is any good reason to pursue a prototype program for the F/A-18E/F. The F/A-18E/F is a true derivative of the C/D, thus *the A/B/C/D aircraft are the flying prototypes for the E/F*, with more than 1.5 million flight hours logged. Although *structural components have limited commonality*, the E/F is <u>very similar</u> <u>aerodynamically</u>, and E/F avionics subsystems are 90% common to the C/D, as is the support infrastructure. *The E/F engine is a derivative of the A-12 engine* which is already well into development. To add an unneeded prototype phase would significantly increase program cost and delay the schedule by 2-4 years with no real reduction in risk over the current plan.
>
> This extension to the schedule would be an unwarranted delay to the E/F development and would delay fleet introduction of this needed capability. Further, extending the E/F development would increase the concurrency between the E/F and A-X programs, and ultimately would place the two programs into competition for procurement funds in the future. We believe our current plan properly phases the two efforts, and would permit us to achieve both capabilities at the appropriate time. To prototype the E/F would not be a prudent use of taxpayer dollars.[39] (Underline in the original, italics added.)

Senator Bond also asked Secretary Cheney about the range issue.

SENATOR BOND: I might ask you one other question. Recently there was a great deal of discussion over range predictions and there was a study, citing the Breguet equation, showing that there would not be any significant extension of range in the E and F. Was that report accurate or was that report flawed? What can you tell us about why that has been such an item of discussion?

SECRETARY CHENEY: I do not have that information immediately available, Senator. I would be happy to provide it for the record.[40]

Secretary Cheney's clarification to the record was made during the week of June 22, 1992.

> The report you refer to was an independent paper written by an Analyst in the Program Analysis and Evaluation office. The analyst used some simplified calculations based on the Breguet range equation to *assert that the Navy could not achieve the range performance* being projected for the E/F aircraft. In an effort to review the situation, the Office of the Under Secretary of Defense (Acquisition)/Tactical Systems put together an independent team of experts from the Air Force and NASA to review and assess the Navy and McAir's aerodynamic characteristics predictions, engine performance predictions, and mission performance methodology and range predictions. After a thorough review of these areas, the independent assessment team validated the E/F aerodynamic predictions, verified the predicted propulsion performance and validated mission radius predictions. The bottom line of the assessment team's findings was that the E/F can meet the predicted performance. The Navy position is well supported and the difference with the PA&E analysis is understood. This is no longer an item of discussion.[41] (Emphasis added.)

These two submissions to the record continued the efforts of F-18E/F advocates within the Office of the Secretary of Defense to distort the facts surrounding the debate on the efficacy of the F-18E/F, as well as the benefits of prototyping it. These answers might have remained unchallenged had it not been for "a newspaper reporter who said a U.S. senator was passing them out to the media."[42] When Spinney heard this, he called a Senate Appropriations Committee staff member, who confirmed it. Spinney then mentioned these misrepresentations to Mr. Puscheck, his immediate supervisor's superior, who responded with "a sympathetic but frustrated shrug . . . [and suggested that] nothing could be done."[43] It was only after a failure to generate a verbal reaction that Spinney, on July 28, 1992, wrote a memorandum to Assistant Secretary of Defense for Program Analysis and Evaluation, Dr. David Chu, demanding an investigation by the Department of Defense's Inspector General. Spinney believed there had been a violation of the criminal statutes that prohibit false statements to Congress.* Spinney, in his mem-

*The first criminal statute that Spinney was referring to was 18 USC §1001, orandum to Dr. Chu, objected to the impression that these two submissions, taken as a whole, would give Congress.

> The first insert . . . claims that a prototype of the F-18E is not needed because the F-18A/B/C/D aircraft are its prototypes, but to justify this claim, it states falsely that the F-18E is very similar aerodynamically to the F-18C, it downplays the other changes in the F-18E, and ignores critical information that contradicts or undermines the validity of its claim.
>
> The second insert . . . reinforces the misrepresentations of the first insert by setting up a phony argument that distorts both the analysis and conclusions of my 8 April point paper [see page 315 above] . . . and ignores the findings and recommendations contained in my 29 April memorandum. It states falsely that my independent analysis (i.e., the 8 April point paper) used calculations based on the Breguet range equation to assert that the F-18E could not achieve its projected range performance, when in fact, the language in the point paper clearly shows that I used the Brequet calculation to focus the debate on the question of why the F-18E had superior performance in the non-cruise portion of its mission. It uses loaded words like "simplified" and "assert" to insinuate that I incorrectly applied the Brequet equation, when in fact the Navy's own calculations and conclusions were very close to and in substantial agree-

which was enacted during the Civil War "in the wake of a spate of frauds upon the Government," but when originated pertained only to "any person in the land or naval forces of the United States." *U.S.* v. *Bramblett* (1955) 348 US 503, 505; 12 STAT. 696.

18 USC §1001 STATEMENTS OR ENTRIES GENERALLY

Whoever, in any matter within the jurisdiction of any department or agency of the United States knowingly and willfully falsifies, conceals or covers up by any trick, scheme or device a material fact, or makes any false, fictitious or fraudulent statements or representations, or makes or uses any false writing or document knowing the same to contain any false, fictitious or fraudulent statement or entry shall be fined not more than $10,000 or imprisoned not more than five years, or both.

18 USC §1505 OBSTRUCTION OF PROCEEDINGS BEFORE DEPARTMENT, AGENCIES AND COMMITTEES

Whoever, with intent to avoid, evade, prevent, or obstruct compliance, in whole or in part, with any civil investigative demand duly and properly made under the Antitrust Civil Process Act, willfully withholds, misrepresents, removes from any place, conceals, covers up, destroys, mutilates, alters, or by other means falsifies any documentary material, answers to written interrogatories, or oral testimony which is the subject of such demand; or attempts to do so or solicits another to do so, or tempts to do so or solicits another to do so; or

Whoever corruptly, or by threats or force, or by any threatening letter or communication influences, obstructs, or impedes or endeavors to influence, obstruct, or impede the due and proper administration of the law under which any pending proceeding is being had before any department or agency of the United States, or the due and proper exercise of the power of inquiry under which any inquiry or investigation is being had by either House, or any committee of either House or any joint committee of the Congress—

Shall be fined not more that $5,000 or imprisoned not more than five years, or both.

ment with those of my point paper. By ignoring the contents of my 29 April memorandum . . . the language in the second insert reinforces the misrepresentations of the first insert and disregards completely the central finding of the range controversy: namely that the superior performance in the non-cruise portion of the F-18E's mission comes from the improved aerodynamics of a re-designed wing. In fact, the Navy predicts that the improved aerodynamics of the F-18E will account for 40 to 50 percent of the increase in its combat radius. An acknowledgment of this calculation, however, would unravel the claim made by the first insert—namely, that the F-18E is very similar aerodynamically to the F-18C.

Since there is a high probability that whoever prepared and approved these inserts understood their false, misleading, and dissembling nature beforehand, these statements may also constitute material violations of Title 18 (Crimes and Criminal Procedure) of the U.S. code, specifically 18 U.S.C. 1001. . . and 18 U.S.C. 1505. . . .[44]

It was Spinney's contention that "our legal system provides methods for challenging the Government's right to ask questions—lying is not one of them. A citizen may decline to answer a question, or answer it honestly, but he cannot, with impunity, knowingly and willfully, answer with a falsehood."[45] Evidently Spinney's superiors took his memorandum seriously. Within a month, they had taken an extraordinary action—they altered Secretary Cheney's remarks on the range and prototyping issues. Note the substantial differences between the *original* entry (page 322 above) submitted into the record and this *final* version below on range which was prepared as a direct result of Spinney's memorandum.

The report you refer to was an independent paper written by an analyst in the Program Analysis and Evaluation office. The analyst performed some basic calculations using the Brequet range equation and questioned whether the Navy could achieve the range performance being projected for the E/F aircraft based on the planned increase in fuel volume alone. The Department performed an independent review of the situation using technical experts from the Air Force and NASA. After thorough review, these independent experts showed that the increased fuel volume combined with projected improvements in aerodynamic and engine efficiencies will enable the F/A-18E/F to achieve the predicted performance. The question raised regarding range performance has been resolved and this is no longer an item of discussion.[46]

Note that there is no reference to a totally new wing. The final version regarding the need to prototype says even less than the original (page 321 above).

I don't think that there is. The F/A-18C/D seems to me to be more than a reasonable flying prototype for the F/A-18E/F with more than 1.5 million flight hours logged. While the airframe design has been modified to substantially increase the range, we have assessed the risk as being low to moderate. The E/F avionics subsystems are 90% common with the C/D, as is the support concept, infrastructure and support equipment. The E/F engine is a derivative of the A-12 engine which is already well into development.

To add an unneeded prototype phase for the E/F would significantly increase program cost and delay the schedule by 2-4 years, with no real reduction in risk over the current plan. Further, extending the E/F development would increase the scheduler [*sic*] overlap between the E/F and A-X programs, and ultimately would stress the declining Defense budget. Moreover, the timing of the program would not be responsive to force capability requirements. We believe our current plan properly phases the two efforts, and would permit us to achieve both capabilities at the appropriate time.[47]

When Spinney saw the distortions, he sent a third memorandum. In it, he showed the evolution of the changes that had taken place within OSD, which he believed showed the requisite intent to ask once again for an IG investigation. The first change, which never left OSD, was in the proper direction. (Spinney used strike-through to indicate deletions and bold italics for additions.)

1st Version Sent to Congress (10 June): [submitted week of 22 June]

We do not believe there is because . . . "Although structural components have limited commonality, the E/F is similar aerodynamically, and E/F avionics are 90% hardware common. . . ."

Change #1 (29 July):

We do not believe there is because . . . "***The flight experience gained with the F-18C/D has provided an extensive data base regarding its aerodynamic characteristics. As a result, the F-18E/F will benefit from significant aerodynamic improvements, particularly in wing design.*** Although structural components have limited commonality, the E/F is very similar ~~aerodynamically~~ ***in planform and the layout of aerodynamic components. Moreover, the*** E/F avionics are 90 % hardware common. . . ."

Change #2 (10 August)—2nd version sent to Congress:

I don't think there is. . . . ~~"The flight experience gained with the F-18C/D has provided an extensive data base regarding its aerodynamic characteristics. As a result, the F-18E/F will benefit from significant aerodynamic improvements, particularly in wing design. Although structural components have limited commonality, the E/F is very similar aerodynamically in planform and the layout of aerodynamic components. Moreover,~~ ***While the airframe design has been modified to substantially increase its range, we have assessed the risk to be low to moderate.*** The F/F avionics are 90% common hardware. . . ."[48]

Spinney was gracious toward the first change. He said that it removed the crucial false statement "very similar aerodynamically" and "makes the fact that the E/F has a significantly improved wing design evident to the reader." He went on:

> On the other hand, while Change #2 acknowledges that substantial changes were made to the design and is factually correct, the massive deletion denies the reader access to any information revealing that part of the range increase comes from the improved aerodynamics of a new wing.[49]

Spinney further analyzed the changes in Cheney's statement on the issue of prototyping. (The complete memoranda, minus attachments, are in appendix D.)

Despite the fact that his office was instrumental in making the changes to the original distortions, Spinney continued to press for an Inspector General's investigation for some cogent legal reasons.

> The fact that the Department took action to change the inserts and correct the record . . . amounts to an "adoptive admission" that serious misrepresentations did in fact occur. If any of these misrepresentations was intentional, a felony would have occurred (i.e., a violation of 18 U.S.C. Sections 1001 and/or 1505 . . .). If this is true, any person who worked on these changes would have committed another felony, if he perceived but did not report the original felony (. . . 18 U.S.C. Section 4, which say [*sic*] concealment of the commission of a felony is a felony). Moreover, since more than one individual was involved in these changes, several other criminal statutes could conceivably have been violated, if this matter was not promptly reported to the proper investigative authorities (18 U.S.C. Section 2 making it an offense to aid another in the commission of a criminal offense; 18 U.S.C. Section 3 making it an offense to assist an offender; and 18 U.S.C. Section 371 making it an offense to conspire to commit an offense).
>
> . . . We now know that the USD(A) staff analyst responsible for preparing and coordinating these inserts (1) has years of experience, (2) was fully aware that the inserts referred to work done in PA&E, . . . and (3) had unrestricted access to the information indicating that the language contained false, misleading, and incomplete statements.[50]

As of mid-1993, no request for an investigation had been made to the Inspector General. This matter is apparently destined to remain one more example of the course of conduct that gives Congress a fuzzy lens through which to provide oversight.

As the fall of 1992 approached, the Senate and House Appropriations Committees were in conflict as to how to proceed with the procurement of the F-18E/F. The House Bill wanted to prototype it and restrict funds for further engineering and manufacturing development (EMD) until the prototypes proved themselves. The Senate Bill wanted to take the Navy at its word, appropriated almost twice as much money as the House ($943.6 million versus $596.6 million) for fiscal year 1993, and let the Navy proceed. The Senate also wanted the F-18E/F to become the Air Force's answer to the multirole fighter

(MRF), which was a follow-on to the F-16.

As in most compromises, the final law was a tasteless broth from both stocks. It said the Secretary of the Navy "could not obligate any funds" until the Navy had "completed an early operational assessment of the aircraft design based in part on flight performance of not less than two *research and development* prototype aircraft. . . ."[51] (Emphasis added.) Furthermore, it added that only 65 percent of the funds appropriated for the three mainline tactical aircraft—the F-18E/F, F-22, and AX—could be spent until the Defense Science Board forwarded a report to the congressional committees on the technical risks of the F-18E/F and the other two aircraft.

Finally, the bill mandated that no development funds could be spent on the F-18E/F until the Secretary of Defense certified that the aircraft would cost no more that $4.88 billion in 1990 dollars; dictated that "the Department of Defense shall conduct an independent cost and effectiveness analysis (COEA); and that the flyaway cost of the F-18E/F not exceed 125 percent of the flyaway cost of the F-18C/D. But the bill left the Navy an escape clause—it said, "The conferees are open to reconsidering the flyaway cost cap if the Navy demonstrates the war fighting effectiveness that could be achieved at higher flyaway costs."[52]

Initially, the primary rationale for financing the F-18E/F was to increase the F-18's range.* But according to Manfred Reitsch, Marine Corps F-18 Wing Commander in Desert Storm, fuel was not a problem in the Gulf. "We had all the tankers we needed."[53] If this is true, why concern ourselves with fuel in the first place? Indeed, if the F-18 had access to tankers, why not rely on smaller, less expensive, and more agile fighters, which would permit the Navy to purchase more of them? The answer lies, of course, in the cost associated with the tanker. To truly understand the cost of a fighter, we must add the cost of its "dependence" aircraft. But the tanker is not the only supplemental equipment required for the F-18 to perform its mission.

The fact is, in Desert Storm the F-18 required tankers, AWACS, and E-2C aircraft to augment its radar, in addition to A-6s to serve as laser designators for the few laser-designated bombs it dropped. This all begs the question, What is the real cost of the aircraft? Or perhaps the better question is, If fighters are going to operate with all of

*Some would argue that the issue is not range but range/payload. However, all of the interdiction ranges used to compare the F-18E/F with the F-18A/B/C/D use the same four (4) MK-83 bombs. Consequently, increased radius of action is the real issue. Later the Navy added a litany of "increased survivability, weapons enhancement, additional weapon carrying capacity, and bring back capacity."

these junior partners absorbing collateral duties, would it not make sense to develop lightweight fighters in the first place?

The F-18E/F is far from the YF-17 lightweight fighter the F-18 evolved from. We find an F-18E/F that is admitting a thrust-to-weight and wing loading close to that which John Boyd rejected for the FX. The new F-18E/F will increase in size and weight, which will have

Figure 15-4
Expanded Military Aircraft Cost Definitions

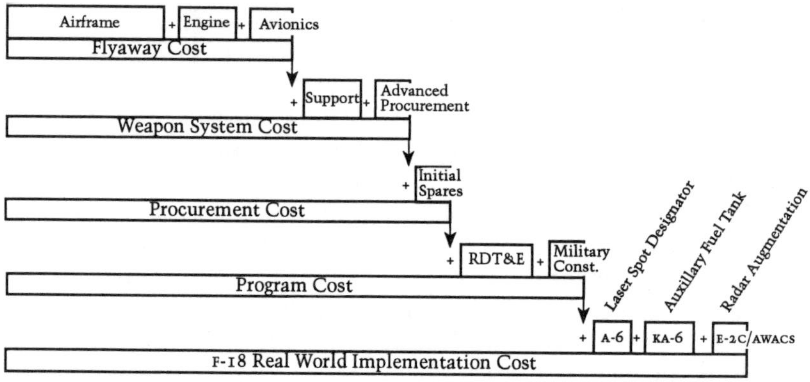

SOURCE: Flyaway costs through program cost, McDonnell Douglas

In an attempt to separate the real costs of military aircraft programs, the Department of Defense has developed various terms, such as "Flyaway Cost," "Procurement Cost," etc. However, the collateral aircraft, which are perceived as necessary to accomplish the mission, are not included in the "Total Program Cost." Even though the aircraft is sold to Congress as a capable self-contained fighting machine, experience in Desert Storm shows that without these dependence aircraft, the F-18 has difficulty in accomplishing the tasks for which it was purchased.

the same negative effects that were known as far back as World War II: "The most frequent reason why weight is added to a fighter airplane is to increase the military load. . . . Whatever form it takes, it harms the performance and it reduces the maneuverability."[54] (See page 65 above for a fuller summary.)

The F-18 was conceived as the consummate lightweight fighter, stripped of all but the barest essentials for air-to-air combat. It was taken to the Navy's hog farm, the procurement process, and fattened with requirements. The Navy told Congress that the F-18 could do the job of both the air-to-air role of the fighter and the attack role of the A-7. Now the Hornet is down on the farm again and is supposed to replace, on an interim basis, an even bigger attack mission, the venerable A-6 all-weather deep strike aircraft. No doubt the Navy would designate the F-18 as the F/A-18 with the A becoming as large as possible before it would admit that F-19 is the more appropriate designation.

This rush to procurement on the F-18E/F raises many moral and military questions: If the Iraqis had the fourth largest army in the world, not to mention one of the most modern, and if we could have traded our superior equipment for Iraq's inferior equipment and still won the Gulf War, why does the U.S. Navy need to develop a newer F-18? Does the Department of Defense, and specifically the Navy, anticipate a more potent potential threat than the Iraqis? If Iraq had the fourth largest army, do they anticipate going to war against the second or third largest armies in the world?

The Navy establishment answers that the aircraft carrier has to be prepared to operate around the clock, in all types of weather, as far inland as the technology will permit. A contrary view, one Chuck Myers wrote about and briefed on extensively during the late 1980s and early 1990s, was that the Navy should do what it can do best—maintain air superiority and close air support in the open ocean and along the "littorals" (the sand/sea interface that lies around the world). In the summer of 1992 Myers began his briefing with a photograph of the world taken at night, which vividly demonstrated that, indeed, the majority of the industrialized world lies within the littorals.*

One should recall that the purpose of the Lightweight Fighter Program was to solve the problem of dwindling numbers of aircraft and to supplement the F-14. The rationale was that the increased cost of the F-14 would reduce the number of aircraft available. If too few aircraft were available, the number of aircraft carriers would reduce. As recently as mid-1993 some senior naval officers thought the solution was to acquire more F-14s, in spite of the fact that the Navy had shut down the F-14 line altogether in 1992 because of its repeated deletion by the Secretary of Defense.

This force reduction is something that no institution would want, and it was particularly true of the U.S. Navy. Vice Adm. Richard Dunleavy, Deputy Chief of Naval Operations at the time, stated: "When you balance capabilities and costs, the F/A-18 compares favorably with the F-14D in most areas, is good enough in others, and is the most cost-effective overall. . . . In addition, the Tomcat is a single-mission aircraft, devoted primarily to air defense, at a time when power projection is receiving increased emphasis."[55]

*"Littorals" is defined as the area along the boundary where the occan and the land meet. *The American Heritage Dictionary of the English Language* (Third Edition), 1992, p. 1,052 gives the following definition: "Of or on a shore, especially a seashore." The argument for why the Navy should focus on the coastline is summarized in Chuck Myers's article, "Littoral Warfare: Back to the Future," *Naval Institute Proceedings* (November 1990), pp. 49–55.

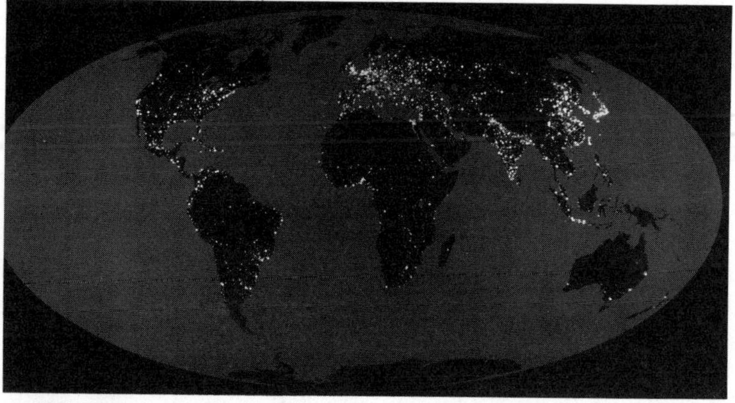

SOURCE: U.S. Navy

One glance shows that the majority of countries' population centers and targets of value are within easy reach of the area known as the littorals.

Vice Admiral Dunleavy's comments are a continuation of the waffling on the F-14 that we saw represented in the quotations at the heading of chapter 13.

The irony is that the F-18E/F does to the F-18C what the Navy claimed the continued purchases of F-14 would do to the Navy's tactical air force in general: reduce the number of individual aircraft below an acceptable quantity. For the cost of development of the F-18E/F, the Navy could procure more than 100 F-18C/DS. Or, put another way, the Navy could have enough F-18s to put two squadrons of F-18s on four aircraft carriers. According to Chuck Spinney, as the Navy's forecast stood in the spring of 1992, the Navy would have only enough aircraft projected to fill up seven carrier air wings and two Marine air wings by the year 2005 if everything worked perfectly, which it never has.*

*Spinney based his analysis on data presented to Congress in April 1992 by Vice Chief of Naval Operations Adm. Jerome L. "Jerry" Johnson. The data showed that the projected retirement rates coupled with the AX and F-18E/F acquisition rates would draw down to the equivalent of about seven carrier air wings and two Marine air wings by the year 2005. Vice Admiral Johnson's briefing included a massive increase in projected inventory by service life extension programs (SLEP) for F-18s but this SLEP program was neither funded nor defined. Indeed, its projected funding is based on the assumption that the budget will grow, an assumption that few are making in the post-war economy. Admiral Johnson's charts show that the SLEP programs contributed more airplanes than the F-18E/F program would until the year 2008. He also assumes the Navy's procurement account (APN) will have steady growth in R&D and procurement to the year 2010. This funding includes neither the SLEP program nor medium lift for the Marine Corps, considered by many to be the most pressing need in naval tactical air. U.S. Congress. House. Committee on Armed Forces. Subcommittee on Procurement and Nuclear Systems. *National Defense Authorization Act for Fiscal Year 1992*—H.R. 5006. 102d. Cong. 2d. sess. (Washington, D.C.: Government Printing Office, 1992), pp. 271–274.

The reduction in the number of aircraft available for the Navy's carriers is exceeded only by the reduction in the F-18E/F's performance. The two largest factors, thrust-to-weight and wing loading (page 28 above), have diminished at an unacceptable rate. The thrust-to-weight ratio, computed by dividing the thrust in pounds by the gross weight in pounds, is the primary factor in acceleration and P_s. The higher the thrust-to-weight, the faster the acceleration and the better the aircraft can climb in level and turning flight. A thrust-to-weight ratio greater than 1.0 means the aircraft can accelerate straight up. The F-15A, YF-16, and YF-17 were the first aircraft to have this advantage. The original FX (see page 351 below) had a T/W of 0.75. A desirable T/W ratio is above 0.9 (shown below on fig. 15-5 on the left-hand scale). Every pound of growth increases cost and lowers the thrust-to-weight ratio, which reduces acceleration.

Wing loading is one of the primary contributors to an aircraft's maneuverability. Wing loading is determined by dividing the weight of the airplane by the square feet of wing area. The fewer pounds each square foot has to support, the quicker the turn. Modern maneuverable fighters tend to have wing loadings in the 75-pounds-per-square-foot range and lower (see scale below on right).

John Boyd criticized the original FX because the wing loading was too high—it was close to 100 pounds per square foot. Note the evolution of the wing loading from the YF-17's close to 60 pounds per square foot to the 96 pounds per square foot in the F-18E/F proposal,which will likely reach 100 pounds per square foot.

We find, in the F-18E/F, an airplane that Boyd would have rejected. If the Navy would adhere to its own requirements, it would also reject the F-18E/F. First, the Navy is promising fighter escort and interdiction radii of action shorter than the original promise of the F-18. Second, this E/F modification had acceleration, specific excess power (P_s), and approach speed promises that do not equal the original F-18A promise. Third, the F-18E/F's spotting factor which was originally claimed to be 1.19, or 19 percent bigger than the original F-18A, has now grown to 1.24, or 24 percent larger than the F-18 that it is designed to replace. And that is against an F-18 that was 17 percent larger than the A-7 it replaced. The net result is that the Navy can fit fewer F-18E/FS on the carrier—which is lucky because with their increased cost, they will be able to buy fewer of them. Recall that the spotting factor was one of the requirements the Navy used to kill the navalized version of the YF-16—they said it was too big!

Lastly, the Navy permits a carrier approach speed in its exit criteria—the benchmark which, if it fails to meet, will result in the program's cancellation—of 150 knots. What makes this increased approach speed critical is the concept of momentum—mass times velocity. With the F-18E/F, we have a 50 percent increase in empty weight and over 15 percent increase in approach speed. This approach speed far exceeds the 115–124 knot approach speed that it required for, and used to eliminate, the navalized YF-16 candidates or the 130-knot approach speed used to cancel the F-111. More to the point, the 150-knot approach speed is greater than the 130–140 approach speed of the F-8 Crusader, one of the unsafest carrier aircraft. But the Navy, ever cautious of its carrier suitability problems with the F-18E/F, wants a high exit criteria for the first demonstrable phase of development, the TECHVAL phase. Once it has successfully demonstrated the 150-knot approach speed it wants the rules relaxed at the next phase, the NPE-1 demonstration, so that in order to receive funding it has to demonstrate only an 154-knot approach speed.

GROUPTHINK IS STILL AT WORK

In spite of this degradation of the Hornet's performance, the groupthink syndrome was in full force. One facet of the groupthink syndrome, "an unquestioned belief in the group's inherent morality, inclining the members to ignore the ethical or moral consequences of their decisions," was displayed by Capt. Craig Steidle, the F-18 program manager. He did this in response to the *Naval Institute Proceedings* (September 1992) adaptation of Chuck Spinney's 29 April memorandum, in which Spinney discussed the benefits of prototyping and questioned the F-18E/F's ability to meet its range, based on the information that the Navy had been providing.

Attorneys have an expression: when you are weak on the law, argue the facts; when you are weak on the facts, argue the law; when you are weak on both, attack your opponent personally. Instead of rebutting Spinney's arguments, Steidle attacked Spinney personally and accused him of wanting to reverse "the defense acquisition process" because Spinney "presented two papers opposing the planned program for the F/A-18E/F" and "asserted that the F/A-18E/F could not achieve its specified range." As a result of this assertion, Captain Steidle claimed, the Defense Acquisition Board decision was delayed to address Spinney's claim, only to have NASA experts prove Spinney wrong. Captain Steidle stated that in Spinney's second paper, he recommended that the F-18E/F go through a "more lengthy" prototype process. The inference is that prototyping is bad because it delays the acquisition process.

Figure 15-5
Thrust-to-Weight and Wing Loading of Recent Fighter Aircraft

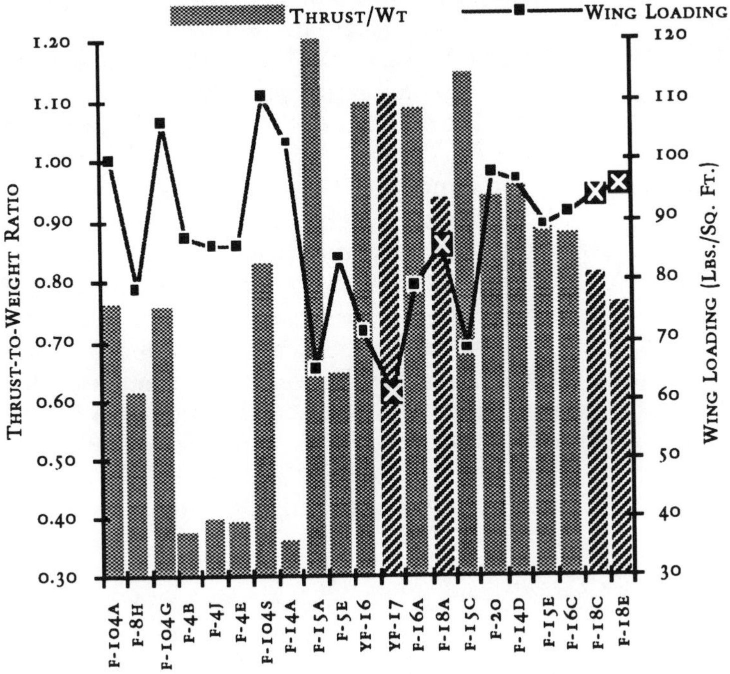

SOURCE: Northrop Corporation

The higher thrust-to-weight the better. The lower the wing loading the better. In the chart above, wing loadings are superimposed on thrust-to-weight ratios. Ideally, the T/W ratio (shown on the left axis) should be high, while the wing loading (W/L), shown on the right axis, should be low. An ideal example is the YF-17—thrust-to-weight is high, while wing loading is low. Note how the spread has collapsed over time as the weight of the F-18 has increased from the YF-17 to the F-18E/F.

Captain Steidle then dressed down Spinney by stating that, while Spinney's acting as the "devil's advocate" was worthwhile, he should have become a team player once a decision had been made and should have helped the Department of Defense acquire the F-18E/F. As evidence of Spinney's lack of team spirit, Steidle alleged that in 1983 Spinney suggested canceling the F-18 in favor of the A-7 and opposed the production of "an improved radar-guided Sparrow air-to-air missile, contending that the shorter-range, heat-seeking Sidewinder missile was adequate. . . . Had [Spinney's] advice been followed," Captain Steidle claimed, "the F/A-18 and improved Sparrows would not have been available during strikes against Libya or the Persian Gulf War."[56]

Steidle's unwillingness to address the substantive issues raised by Spinney precluded readers unfamiliar with the Pentagon from questioning Steidle's false assertions. Contrary to Captain Steidle's specious allegations, Spinney's memoranda never said that the F-18E/F could not make its range. In fact, Spinney said it was not clear "how the F-18E would achieve a 28% increase in combat radius, given only a 4.9 % increase in fuel fraction, higher engine SFCS [Specific Fuel Consumption], similar wing loading, and lower thrust-to-weight ratios. . . ."

Steidle's statements about Spinney's positions on the A-7 and Sparrows were pure fabrications. Spinney discussed neither the A-7 nor the Sparrow missile in the *Time* article, nor did he advocate the elimination of the F-18 or the advanced versions of the Sparrow missile in 1983 or at any other time. When Spinney confronted him with this fiction, Steidle said that "I *assumed* that *Time* was referring to you as one of the military reformers who cited numerous examples of 'gold-plated armaments bringing embarrassingly small improvements in fighting capability,' when it expanded on A-7 versus F/A-18 and Sidewinder versus Sparrow."[57] (Emphasis added.)

Steidle's assumption fits neatly within another aspect of the groupthink syndrome, which states that members of the group can have "an illusion of invulnerability . . . which creates excessive optimism and encourages taking extreme risks." The risk in this case is making libelous statements that could potentially subject Steidle to a lawsuit. Steidle's ability to ignore "the ethical or moral consequences of [his] decision" is found, most likely, in another part of his response to Spinney's demand for a retraction.*

Aside from the libelous aspects of his statements, Steidle raises an interesting issue on the A-7. The A-7 suffered no losses in the Gulf War, and when carrying identical bomb loads as the F-18, had a longer range. Even if the Sparrow missiles were not updated, the success rate of the missiles would not significantly have changed

*Spinney demanded a retraction from Steidle. Steidle offered to apologize, although he did not do so. As a result, Spinney wrote to Steidle again on January 5, 1993, and said:

"I did not ask you to apologize. My letter of November 30, 1992 . . . appealed to your sense of honor as a Naval officer and asked you to correct the written record. Your letter to *Proceedings* (page 16, November 1992 . . .) was an untruthful, personal attack aimed at discrediting my professional reputation. Although personal attacks are undignified distractions, I have learned to expect them, but you concocted phony examples and gross distortions to 'prove' your position, while ignoring completely the substance of my arguments concerning the desirability of prototyping the F-18E. . . . Last November, I challenged you to either back up your statements with supporting evidence or change the record. Unfortunately, the evasions contained in your letter of December 28 . . . suggest you do not intend to correct the record. What is even more incredible, your recent letter contains new information that indicates the false statements made in your letter to *Proceedings* were indeed premeditated."

the course of the war, which tends to be ratified by Secretary of Defense Cheney's statement that "much of the hardware that played such a crucial role in our victory over Saddam Hussein and the Iraqi forces was developed 20 or 30 years ago." Cheney's statement, coupled with General Schwarzkopf's that the United States could have traded equipment with the Iraqis and the outcome would have been the same, indicated that even if Mr. Spinney had made these statements in 1983, there would have been precious little difference in the Gulf War if his falsely attributed views had prevailed.

In view of the Navy's poor record in meeting its own specifications, Spinney's effort to have the Navy validate its claims with a prototype seems reasonable. One need only consider the $3 billion spent on the A-12, with nothing to show for it but a few parts and drawings (with the possible exception of the A-12 program manager's promotion to rear admiral), to understand a taxpayer's concerns.

There is little risk in advocating prototyping. Companies with effective management teams use prototyping regularly to reduce delays in production, lower costs, lower risk, and improve quality. One might argue against prototyping if the exigencies of war were upon us. However, never in the last 50 years have we had such a reduction in overall threat to the United States.

This threat reduction is a necessary input to the "roles and missions" statement required by the Goldwater-Nichols Act. However, the congressionally mandated, updated "roles and missions" statement was not published at the time of the F-18E/F appropriations hearings. A change in the Navy's role or mission could have adjusted the nature of carrier aircraft and most certainly affected the character and form of the F-18E/F. Accordingly, it seems that in light of the Navy's " . . . From the Sea" pronouncement, coupled with the unannounced definition of a possible new role for the Navy, a delay of a few months would have justified a pause in the rush to judgment on the F-18E/F.*

Steidle's false statement that Mr. Spinney "asserted that the F/A-18E/F could not achieve its specified range" is either an intentional attempt to obscure the truth or an opprobriously negligent reading of what Spinney actually wrote. However, since Steidle chose to roam that allotted territory, it should be noted that his language is virtually identical to the original fiction submitted in Mr. Cheney's

*The document, entitled "Roles, Missions and Functions of the Armed Forces of the United States," (February 1993), left the roles and missions of the services virtually unaltered. But if it took the Roman Catholic Church 350 years to admit that Galileo was correct, should it come as a surprise that the military services are unwilling to adapt to changing circumstances?

name to the congressional hearings in June 1992, which prompted Spinney to demand an IG investigation into possible false statements to Congress. Apparently Captain Steidle was not aware of the retraction or considered false statements to the *Proceedings* readers less egregious.

Captain Steidle chose to attack Spinney on fictitious positions concocted by Steidle, which even if true would have been inappropriate, off point, and irrelevant. Steidle reverted to the classic bureaucratic maneuver of making ad hominem attacks. These assaults were coupled with the shallow logic of argumentum intimidatum to shroud a nonsubstantive response. For these and previous efforts, Captain Steidle was promoted, like his A-12 program manager cohort, to the rank of rear admiral, proving that the Navy, like the Air Force with Larry Welch, will take care of defenders of the faith. Indeed, Steidle was unrelenting in his attempt to end Spinney's attempt to continue the debate. In private correspondence he persisted with Spinney. "Your article in the Proceedings . . . has the potential to damage the F/A-18E/F program and naval aviation by imposing endless delays while an advanced technology F/A-18C is re-analyzed, and/or an F/A-18E/F prototype program is substituted for Engineering and Manufacturing Development (EMD), and/or preliminary designs are produced 'for two new aircraft.' "[58]

Steidle's role as gatekeeper extended to an attempt to "review" this book. He wrote the Naval Institute Press on Navy stationary stating: "Pre-publication advertising for this book leads me to believe that it has the potential to perpetuate misleading and/or inaccurate information about the history and current status of the F/A-18 program. Consequently, I request that my office be given the opportunity to review the manuscript for factual content and technical accuracy prior to its submission for print." Steidle would be well served to follow the words of Chief Justice Rehnquist who said: "Ideas with which we disagree . . . should be confronted with argument and persuasion, not suppression."[59]

If the quality of Captain Steidle's logic and research for his attack on Spinney is indicative of the quality of the Navy's work on the F-18E/F, then Chuck Spinney did indeed have a duty to ask the Navy to reverse "the defense acquisition process" by going back to the process of prototyping. It was, after all, a prototype—the YF-17—from which the F-18 evolved. Both flying YF-17s cost the taxpayers less than $187 million in FY1990 dollars to develop. Consequently, for the Navy to prove its predictions with a $4.88 billion F-18E/F prototype development budget—a 2,600 percent increase in constant dollars over the YF-17—seems reasonable.

All of this takes us full circle. We began this story with the need for an air superiority fighter, which resulted in the F-15 replacing an F-111 follow-on, the FX, that weighed more than 60,000 pounds, had a thrust-to-weight below 0.75, and a wing loading close to 100 pounds per square foot. That design was rejected, and in its place appeared the F-15 Eagle, the first aircraft designed as a dogfighting aircraft. Even the F-15A was not small or inexpensive enough, so the Lightweight Fighter Mafia developed the YF-16 and YF-17 and converted them into real aircraft to supplement the declining number of aircraft in the tactical air community. This decline was a direct result of the increasing expense of the fighters. With the F-18E/F we are once again back to the future. However, instead of an aircraft conceived as the consummate follow-on to the *Air Force's* F-111 nuclear bomber, we have an aircraft designed to supplant the A-6, the *Navy's* consummate nuclear bomber.

F-18E/F Wasp Ignores What Works in Air-to-Air Combat

One question that is constantly asked is, "Is the F-18 a good airplane?" The answer ought to be, "Compared to what?" Is it a "good" airplane compared to other aircraft? Or is it a good airplane compared to what it could or should have been? If one accepts Pierre Sprey's criteria on what does and does not work in air-to-air combat, and if one defines a fighter as an aircraft designed to shoot down other aircraft in the sky, the F-18A/B/C/D emerges as more viable than the F-18E/F.

Figure 15-6

F-18 Acceleration Degrades from Original Promise to F-18E

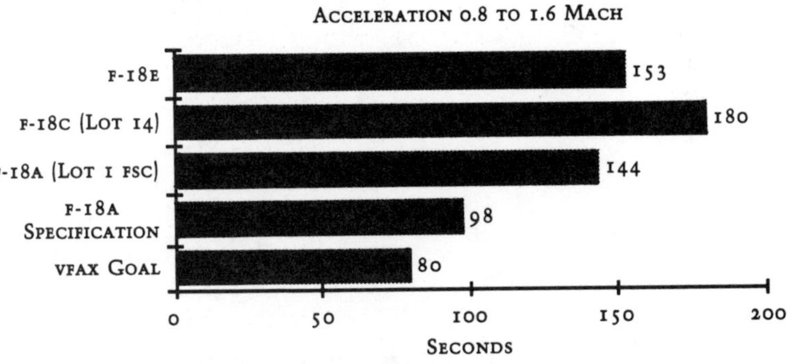

SOURCE: VFAX Presolicitation Notice. U.S. Department of Defense. Department of the Navy. Naval Air Systems Command. "Performance comparisons with F/A-18A (Lot I and Lot XIV) and F/A-18E specification Ground Rules," March 25, 1993.

Air-to-air capability is enhanced by quick acceleration. This quality, while promised, was never realized.

The F-18E/F, relative to the F-18A/B/C/D, violates at least three of the four criteria that Sprey set for what wins in air-to-air combat: (1) first sight, wins the fight; (2) outnumber the enemy in the air; (3) outmaneuver the adversary to gain gun firing solution; and (4) have a quick firing solution. Increasing the size of the F-18E/F Wasp will make it easier to see both visually and on radar, in spite of allegations of stealth enhancements. (See fig. 1-9 on page 34 for the growth in size of the F-18E from the F-18C.) Increasing the cost reduces the number that the Navy can purchase. The third criterion, maneuverability, is a function of the laws of physics. The bigger the object, the greater the inertia. Consequently, the size of the F-18E/F is going in the wrong direction to improve its maneuverability. Both the increase in wing loading (fig. 15-9) and the thrust-to-weight (fig. 15-7) have caused Sprey's third criterion to degrade even further. Acceleration has also degraded (see fig. 15-6).

The ability to generate a quick firing solution is a function of the switch technology in the cockpit and future solutions in the missile technology.

Figure 15-7
Evolution of the F-18 Thrust-to-Weight Ratio

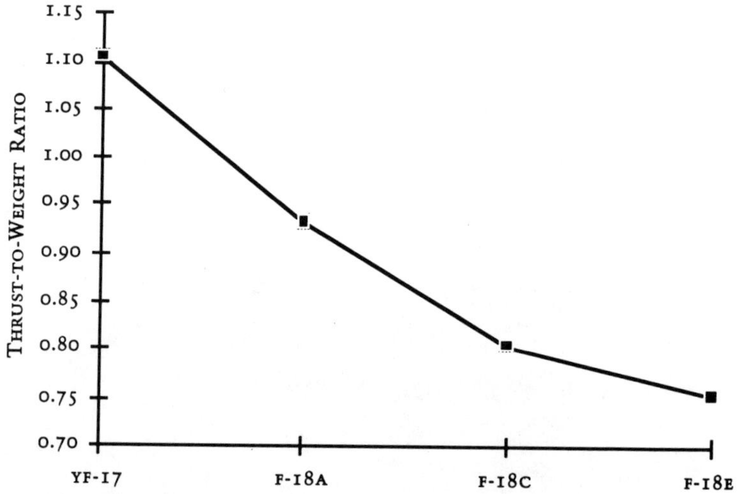

Source: Northrop Corporation

The F-18 thrust-to-weight, a primary factor in acceleration, has degraded over time.

One constant TACAIR liturgy is the need for long range for a fighter so that "we can take the fight to the enemy." Without addressing whether that is a valid benefit, proponents of the F-18E are advocates of the need for long range for the fighter escort mission. Fig. 15-8 below would tend to indicate that the need for long range for the fighter escort mission is not well served.

Figure 15-8

F-18A/B/C/D Escort and Interdiction Radius Degradation Compared with F-18E/F

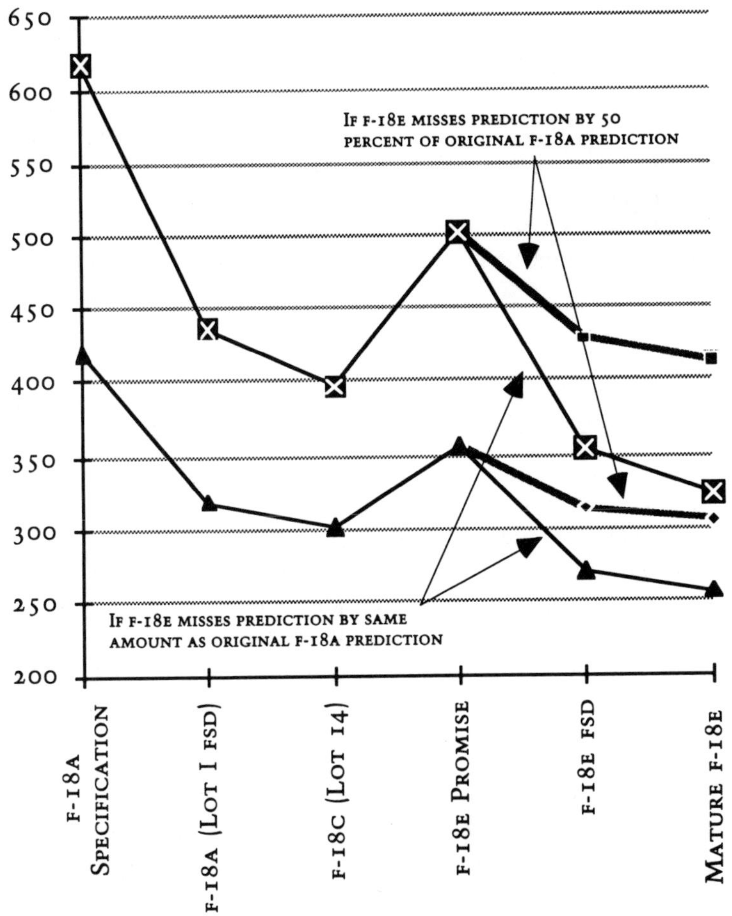

SOURCE: VFAX Presolicitation Notice. U.S. Department of Defense. Department of the Navy. Naval Air Systems Command. "Performance comparisons with F/A-18A (Lot I and Lot XIV) and F/A-18E specification Ground Rules," March 25, 1993.

Both the F-18 fighter escort (triangle line above) and interdiction radius of action have degraded over time. The gray line above shows what the radius would be for the F-18E over time if the Navy misses its prediction by only half as much as in the past.

Figure 15-9
Evolution of F-18 Wing Loading

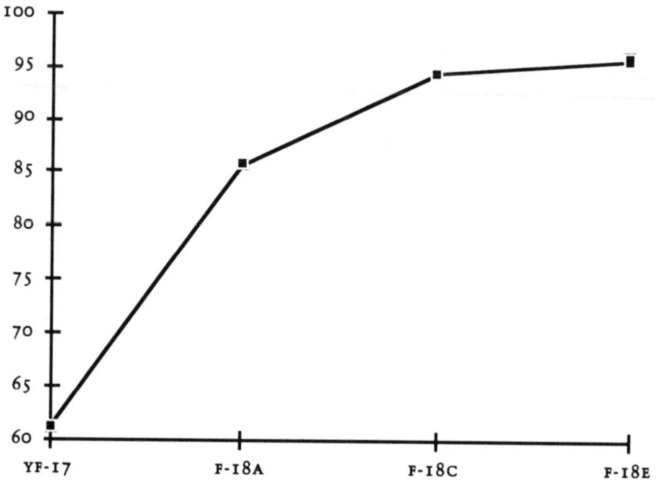

SOURCE: Northrop Corporation.
F-18 wing loading, the primary component in an aircraft's ability to turn quickly, has degraded over time.

F-18E/F Has Incremental Increase in Interdiction Range

But if one takes the position that what makes a great fighter is its air-to-ground capability, the F-18E/F fares no better. The Navy claims that the F-18E/F avionics are 90 percent common. Therefore, the added air-to-ground capability cannot come from the miracle of avionics. Recall that one of the arguments for the F-18 was its increased maneuverability when loaded with bombs. But fig. 15-9 shows that the wing loading, a major input into maneuverability, has degraded with the F-18E. For the F-18E/F to meet the claimed range increase in the interdiction mission, the Navy increased the size of the three external fuel tanks the F-18 carries. The F-18C/D uses three 330-gallon tanks, whereas in the F-18E/F interdiction role, the new tanks were increased to 480 gallons each. These larger external tanks give the F-18E a 45-percent increase in external fuel. One U.S. Navy flag officer expressed uncertainty about whether the F-18E/F Wasp could get off the carrier with the three 480-gallon tanks. According to this same Navy official, if the F-18C/D flew with these same 480-gallon tanks, the C/D version could fly within 50 nautical miles of the F-18E/F Wasp and have a loiter time within 10 percent of it, which McAir data tend to confirm.[60] Therefore, if this is true, even if the F-18E could get off the carrier, one has to question the benefit of spending $4.88 billion for such a small incremental benefit.

SOURCE: McDonnell Douglas
The F-18E/F was a substantially different design with different inlets, leading edge, engines, weight, and cost. To the layman, they were visually similar.

F-18E/F Carrier Suitability

In addition to the existing F-18C/D almost matching the range and loiter capability of the F-18E/F Wasp, at the beginning of February 1993 the F-18E/F was on its way to matching the aerodynamic problems the F-18 had with its original snagged leading-edge wing.

The YF-17's wing was designed with a straight leading edge. When McDonnell Douglas redesigned the YF-17 in order to generate more control authority at high angles of attack, it designed the F-18A with a snag on the leading edge. This acted as a vortex generator to create more lift at slow speeds. However, it also created 1-*g* side forces at the cockpit at the rate of up to 5.6 times per second. As a result the snag was removed.

McDonnell Douglas put the snag back into the leading edge of the F-18E/F. This was predictable, because at higher weights more lift is required. To the degree that the higher lift cannot be generated, the aircraft will land at higher speeds. It is for this reason that the exit criteria on the F-18E/F Wasp began approaching the landing speed of the F-8 Crusader, an airplane that first flew in the mid-1950s.

But the Navy declared in the mid-1970s that they could not accept the edict of Congress to navalize the F-16 because of its inferior carrier suitability, going so far as to state that "the NACF specifications are intended to advance Naval aviation, not to perpetuate old problems." But with the F-18E/F we have an old problem creeping back—high carrier approach speeds. In fact, the carrier suitability problems of the F-18E/F Wasp were severe enough that the ersatz COEA the Navy put together said that all development issues of the F-18E/F except one were low to moderate risk. The one exception was carrier suitability, which the spurious COEA said was high risk.[61]

The Navy defined high risk as "likely to cause significant, serious disruption of schedule, increase in cost, or degradation of performance even with special contractor emphasis and close government monitoring."[62] This high risk began showing itself in early February 1993 when the wind tunnel model of the F-18E/F Wasp at the NASA Ames wind tunnel began showing some longitudinal stability problems such that there was speculation that the vertical tail would need to be increased in size. The problem was severe enough that McDonnell Douglas took some of its engineers off the F/AX (née AX) program to attend to the problem. It was no surprise that neither Navy nor OSD officials charged with oversight came forth with this negative news.

Wake of False Statements

Congress has, with the passage of 18 USC 1001 ,made it a crime to make intentionally false statements to Congress or any other federal agency. To be subject to this statute, the person must "knowingly and willfully" falsify, conceal, or cover up "by any trick, scheme or device a material fact, or [make] any false, fictitious or fraudulent statement . . . or representation . . . , or make . . . or use . . . any false writing or document knowing the same to contain any false, fictitious or fraudulent statement or entry. . . ."

To be guilty of this crime a person must possess the intent to misrepresent as well as commit the act. Intent separates murder from manslaughter. However, specific intent of an individual's mental state is difficult to prove, especially where issues of policy and judgment may be involved.

Experience over the years demonstrates that 18 USC 1001 is not an effective guarantee that Congress will be given accurate testimony, especially on issues involving large sums of money. Consequently, inaccurate statements in front of Congress abound. Generals have admitted lying for such patriotic reason as needing money for repairs, while admirals encouraged others to lie for the same reason. Future costs and performance figures have been offered as recklessly as testimony from a mafia don in front of a paid-off judge. Billions were spent on stealth to make the B-2 bomber invisible to radar only to have the Air Force Chief of Staff admit that the Russians could see it. The Navy told Congress that the F-18 could meet the VFAX requirement, which it never came close to. The Navy assured

Congress on the F-18 range, loiter, and acceleration specification, only to reduce the specification requirements once the money was in hand. The Chief of Staff of the Air Force claimed that the Iraqi army was defeated by airpower alone, when in fact the Iraqi army never left Kuwait until land troops invaded. Some Sparrow missiles were credited with air-to-air kills, when the Sidewinder did the actual work. Videotapes of bridge kills were played repeatedly, while the real success rate was below 2 percent. The Air Force took credit for all air-to-air kills in the Gulf war, when the Navy got two on the first day. The Navy testified that the F-18 would replace the A-7 because the Navy was going away from gross tonnage of bombs, yet failed to procure the laser spot tracker required to implement its claim. In the mid-1970s, the CNO told Congress that at the pinnacle of naval aviation (which he claimed was 1946), the Navy used the F4U to prove the multirole fighter concept. But in fact the zenith of naval aviation was at the end of World War II, which found the Navy putting all its faith in the consummate single-purpose lightweight fighter, the F8F Bearcat. Sparrow missile claims were inflated, only to be exceeded by the AIM-82 heat-seeking missile claims of 955-to-1, which even internal high technology proponents could not stomach. The January 1993 incursion into the Iraqi no-fly zones gave the Air Force an opportunity to set up a canned situation for the AIM-120 (AMRAAM) radar-guided missiles that were fired with the radar assistance of an AWACS aircraft. While the AIM-120 successfully killed the Iraqi fighter, the kill was well within visual range and could as easily have been done with an AIM-9 Sidewinder.

Table 15-2

VFAX and F-18 A/B/C/D Performance Compared with F-18 E/F

	VFAX Goal	VFAX Threshold	F-18A Spec.	F-18A (Lot I FSD)	F-18C (Lot 14)	F-18E Promise
Fighter Escort (NM)	450	400	420	319	302	356
Interdiction (NM	N/A	550	618	437	398	501
External fuel (gals.)	900	900	900	990	990	1,440
Acceleration (sec.) 0.8 to 1.6 Mach	80	110	98	144	180	153
Specific Excess Power (P_s) (ft./sec)	850	750	753	617	584	637
Approach speed (kts.)	115	125	128	140	142	144

SOURCE: VFAX Presolicitation Notice. U.S. Department of Defense. Department of the Navy. Naval Air Systems Command. "Performance comparisons with F/A-18A (Lot I and Lot XIV) and F/A-18E specification Ground Rules," March 25, 1993. Committee on Armed Services. Subcommittee on Tactical Airpower. *F-18 Program*, 1975, p. 29.

The data in this chart compares the VFAX threshold & goal and F-18A specification with the subsequent F-18A, F-18C, and F-18E on an apples-to-apples comparison. This comparison was done so that the F-18E/F data would be standardized to the F-18A specification. It is for this reason that the F-18E/F does not show the 420 NM fighter escort radius and the 520 NM interdiction radius that the Navy heralded around the Pentagon during late 1992 and early 1993. For the interdiction mission the F-18A and F-18C have (3) 330-gallon tanks that are dropped when empty. The F-18E has 45 percent more external fuel in (3) 480-gallon tanks that are dropped when empty.

And in mid-1993, the Navy promised an 11.5 and 14.6 percent increase in the fighter escort and interdiction radius of action, respectively, of the F-18E/F—a paper airplane—over the demonstrated range of the original F-18A. For these and other promised benefits (see table 15-2 above) the taxpayer will pay $4.88 billion for development—more than the A-12 Avenger II contract development costs—and a total program unit cost of $54 million each in constant 1990 dollars, for a 67-percent increase over the average program unit cost of the F-18 it is designed to replace.

When the Navy compiled the data in table 15-2 above, they no doubt recognized that the F-18A missed its promised performance by substantial margins. (See table 15-3 below for the percentages.) In an attempt to mollify this revelation, the Navy incorporated the following note of explanation.

> Questions have been raised about the Navy confidence in achieving the performance capability specified for the F/A-18E when historically, on the F/A-18A, certain performance parameters were not met. With the enhanced technical information available high confidence that a similar deficiency in specification performance will not occur. . . .
>
> Lessons learned during the F/A-18A program have been utilized with great success in determining the range capabilities of all F/A-18s since lot #3. . . . The F/A-18E program further uses the extensive database developed from F/A-18A flight tests which included in-flight thrust measurements and represents 13 years of operational flight experience. Therefore, as previously stated, there is high confidence that a similar deficiency in specification performance will not occur. [63]

These assurances are reminiscent of similar guarantees the Navy gave during the Lightweight Fighter hearings in the mid- to late 1970s, where, among others, Vice Admiral Houser said that the F-18 met the VFAX requirement (see page 231 above). They based their self-confidence on the fact that they had a prototype, the YF-17, on which to base their calculations. But just as the Navy missed the

Table 15-3

F-18A/B/C/D Percentage Improvement or Degradation with F-18E/F

	F-18A Spec.	F-18A (Lot 1 FSD)	F-18C (Lot 14)	F-18E
Fighter Escort	100%	76%	72%	85%
Interdiction	100%	71%	64%	81%
External fuel	100%	110%	110%	160%
Acceleration 0.8 TO 1.6 Mach	100%	147%	184%	156%
Specific Excess Power (P_s)	100%	82%	78%	85%
Approach speed	100%	109%	111%	113%

SOURCE: VFAX Presolicitation Notice; U.S. Department of Defense. Department of the Navy. Naval Air Systems Command. "Performance comparisons with F/A-18A (Lot 1 and Lot XIV) and F/A-18E specification Ground Rules," March 25, 1993.

fighter escort range by 24 percent, the interdiction range by 29 percent, and the acceleration time from 0.8 TO 1.6 Mach by 47 percent, there is every reason to believe that they will miss it by an equal amount, if for no other reason than the fact that aerodynamically, the F-18E/F is a greater departure from the F-18C/D than the F-18A was from the YF-17. (Compare fig. 15-10 below with the drawing above on page 319 that compares the F-18C with the F-18E.)

Figure 15-10
Evolution of the YF-17 to the F-18A and Their Differences

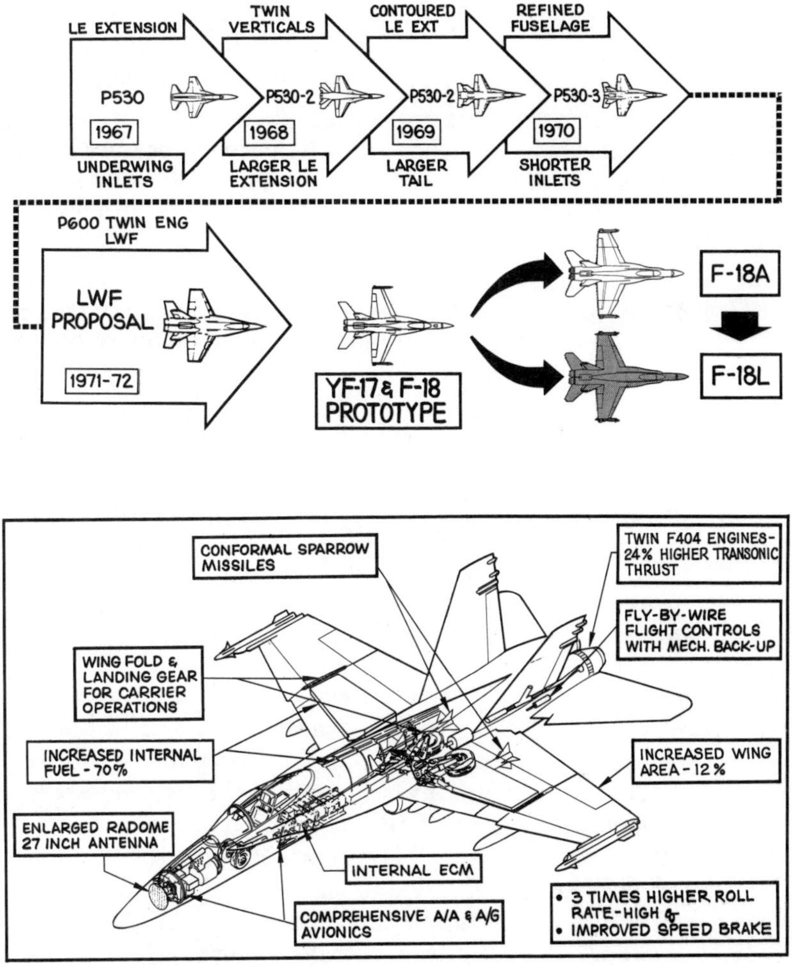

SOURCE: Northrop Corporation

The aeronautical differences between the YF-17 and the F-18A are significantly smaller than the differences between the F-18C and F-18E/F.

OSD Fails to Provide Oversight

The fact that Chuck Spinney could, within 30 minutes, smoke out the truth that the F-18E/F was a new airplane, coupled with the fact that Spinney was not in charge of overseeing the F-18, gives one an idea of the level of control exhibited within the Secretariat's office.

The U.S. Constitution is specific about civilian control over the military. The civilian-controlled Office of the Secretary of Defense (OSD) has the legislative duty to provide this civilian control. Unfortunately, it does not provide it. Its failure is evident in various ways. It failed in the planning process. How else could one explain such volatile planning numbers of F-14s (see page 152 above)? Malcolm Currie's failure to back down the Navy on the VFAX preliminary solicitation notice (PSN) is a graphic example of the civilian government's obsequious behavior. Indeed, Chuck Myers received a reprimand for his failure to get along better with the military, the same military he was legally obligated to oversee and to which Currie kowtowed.

But unquestionably, the best example of the failure to control the military is OSD's consummate failure to ensure accurate testimony to Congress. The military services are able to get away with these fallacies because as they shovel them across the hearing room tables they display maps showing the location—by congressional district—of the subcontracts that the weapons systems will bring to each senator or congressman they are addressing.

Even more egregious was the failure by the Office of the Secretary of Defense to ensure that Congress had the facts that would have allowed Congress to realize that the F-18 was a completely new airplane. We will never know whether or not the information was intentionally obscured initially because the Office of the Secretary of Defense failed to follow Spinney's advice to turn the issue over to the Inspector General. One could argue that it did in fact fix the error. However, there is not much doubt that it would not have without Spinney's intercession. The Office of the Secretary of Defense apparently believed that the investigation of the Tailhook scandal was more important because in that case it did intercede and took the investigation away from the Navy. Furthermore, the Department of Defense has become embroiled in the issue of whether to allow avowed homosexuals in the military—an issue that cannot equal the fiscal bondage the American taxpayers suffer at the hands of deceitful public servants charged with their protection.

It was, after all, taxation without representation that inspired the

American Republic in the first place. But this seminal principle is being distorted, according to Spinney, through what he calls "an evolved moral code that inspires intellectual corruption."[64]

> Our constitutional design for a representative democracy in which the people are sovereign (i.e., a government of the people, by the people, and for the people) rests on three ideas:
> (1) *Accountability*
> When the government produces delusionary, deceptive, or false information, the People or their Representatives will not understand what their government is doing, and they will have no basis for judging the soundness of their government's policies.
> (2) *Consent of the Governed*
> Delusionary and deceptive stratagems aimed at subverting Congress's power of the purse undermine what James Madison (Federalist NO. 58) called the "most complete and effectual weapon with which any constitution can arm the immediate representatives of the people" to redress grievances or effect salutary measures.
> (3) *Rule of Law*
> 18 U.S.C. 1001 makes it a felony to "knowingly & willfully falsify, conceal, or cover up by any trick, scheme or device a material fact" within the jurisdiction of any department or agency of the United States.[65]

Blatant violations of these three principles demonstrate that the military has, in the pursuit of gathering as large a share of the budget as possible, developed "an evolved moral code inspiring a pattern of intellectual corruption [which] subverts the spirit, if not the letter, of the Constitution's ideals, the concept of checks & balances, and the rule of law."[66]

The Navy's deceptions on the F-19, née F-18E/F, were designed to turn on the money spigot and lock it open. The Navy wrapped its efforts in the American flag, sprinkled them with holy water from the Persian Gulf, and reminded congressmen that in a declining economy it was in their best interest to support the Navy's efforts to keep their constituents employed. How does the fighter mafia feel? John Boyd summed it up best. After learning the total program unit cost of the F-18E/F and its incrementally small promised improvements, he said: "All this shows is the real Pentagon strategy: don't interrupt the money flow—add to it."[67]

Appendix A

An Evaluation of Lt. Col. John R. Boyd's Creative, Professional Contributions to the USAF

by Everest E. Riccioni

Shortly after his involvement in the Korean conflict, possessing the enriching experience of teaching tactics in a CCTU at Nellis and becoming a graduate of the Fighter Weapons School [FWS] (then) Capt. John R. Boyd was assigned to the FWS as an instructor. Here he made his first significant contribution to fighter operations. He wrote the Air Combat Training (ACT) manual used for instruction at Nellis. He created the attendant lesson and mission plans for the ACT program. His excellent analysis of modern flight maneuvers, the first such work, published in the June 1957 issue of the Fighter Weapons School (FWS) Newsletter, was to become an enduring classic.

Lt. Col. Boyd created many of the maneuvers included in the analysis. As a creative military analyst, he tried, developed, and evaluated many novel elements of Air Combat Maneuvering (ACM). For example, he was the first officer to formally isolate the adverse yaw problem in the F-100A, C aircraft. He had the answer (liberal use of rudder and very little aileron when at high angles of attack) and was teaching it before the test pilots of Edwards AFB isolated the problem. Lt. Col. Boyd was the first to question the use of very high G maneuvers so fashionable at Nellis during that period. He developed the "soft maneuver" analysis and started to explore and define the impact of the vertical dimension in fighter maneuvers.

In early 1959 Lt. Col. Boyd made his beginning analysis of pursuit curve trajectories. He found the mathematical reasons for the associated physical tracking problems. He published his results in the March 1959 issue of the FWS Newsletter—another classic. He was to continually build on these results in later years.

In 1959–1960 just before leaving Nellis, he wrote another enduring classic, his "Aerial Attack Study." This was the first formal analysis of fighter maneuvers in which he not only catalogued the repertoire of basic maneuvers and possible counter-maneuvers but he showed their relation to tactical doctrines. In presenting the doctrines and the rationale on which they were based, he offered the art of fighter tactics one of its most powerful ideas—that for a maneuver there is a counter-maneuver, for a tactical system there is a counter-system, and it is the understanding of maneuvers, tactical doctrines, and their possible options which will determine the outcome of airbattles. Incorporated within this study was Lt. Col. Boyd's analysis of the "Sidewinder" missile. He was the first to question the idea that missiles would bring an end to the maneuvering airbattle among fighters. Until Lt. Col. Boyd forced and indeed effected much of the analysis, the U.S. Navy had a dilettante's view of the successful delivery envelope for the missile. His work, represented by this singular study, was never matched by the contributions of other pilots at Nellis AFB.

Lt. Col. Boyd left Nellis in 1960 to go to Georgia Tech to get a Bachelor of Science Degree in Industrial Engineering. This education did nothing but bear more fruit in his ensuing work. He was next assigned to Eglin AFB.

At Eglin (then) Major Boyd was to initiate one of his most notorious, most widely accepted efforts—his Energy Maneuverability analyses. Despite the considerable strain of operating in a domain where few of his peers and commanders appreciated or understood the implications of this emerging work, he completed the famous work: TR-66-4 Energy Maneuverability, Vols. I and II.

This work has never been rivaled for excellence, comprehensiveness, and substantive contribution to the analysis of the performance and maneuverability of fighter (and other) aircraft. For the first time, Air Force Commanders had available a tool which would permit comparative evaluation of aircraft in a global presentation of its capabilities. His previous work on aircraft pursuit trajectories now gave additional fruit because he was the first to question (and answer) what happened to the successful delivery envelope of a missile aircraft attacking a target that uses "s" maneuvers for evasion. These envelopes developed disturbing holes which made them look like Swiss cheese. The results made all missile contractors review their previous overly optimistic analyses. The analysis contributed toward the development of anti-SAM operations in North Vietnam, but this is another example of a "Boyd First."

Lt. Col. Boyd, together with the now well known Mr. Thomas Christie, developed general missile simulation programs. He deepened and proliferated his Energy Maneuverability and Attack Geometry Analysis.

By this time, his work had made him famous and notorious among the engineering and military world. In 1965, he received the "AFSC [Air Force Systems Command] Scientific Achievement Award" at the 12th Annual Symposium for Science and Engineering for the best Engineering Analysis. In 1966, he received the Air Force "Research and Development Award" for Outstanding Contribution to Aeronautical Engineering. He received the Air Force Association "Citation of Honor" in 1969 for Pioneering Development in Fighter Tactics and Analysis Leading to Superior Combat Capability in Fighter Aviation and Fighter Aircraft Design.

In 1966, as a volunteer to fly F-4C's in Vietnam, because of his analytical expertise, he was reassigned to the FX project in AFRDQRT at the Pentagon. Here all his previous work fructified in new analyses which modified a (then) ineffectual solution to the FX ROC to that which eventually become the existing F-15. He developed, fostered, and forced new trade-off studies and techniques which eventually identified the proper engine cycle, engine size, wing configuration and wing loading for the F-15. This result together with his parametric trade-off techniques led eventually to the specific application of the selection of the best variable sweep wing for the FX and the best fixed wing. During this period he created his "Expanded Energy Maneuverability Concept" which used in combination with the trade-off techniques proved the logical basis for choosing the fixed wing over the variable sweep wing—quite an achievement in a period where the current fashion and pressures were all to use variable sweep wings. By October 1969, he had almost completed his "Fully Expanded Energy Maneuverability Concept." Results derived from this concept not only permitted aircraft evaluation but insights his curves displayed were very closely related to the air battle (dogfight). Now optimum fighter maneuvers were more derivable. A new reformulation of attack geometry analysis was developed to make more perspicuous the results of terminal attack maneuvers using both guns and missiles. These results will heavily impact analysis of the role, possible employment, and development of the Short Range Missile (SRM).

He early saw the need for the rational question that must be addressed by Air Force military planners—"What is the role of numbers, aircraft quality, and training effectiveness on the outcome of an air superiority war?" His work is the only significant analytical (formula) analysis of this kind developed since the celebrated (and inapplicable) Lanchester equations. Here he showed his breadth of scope and reiterated his creativity and combat relevance.

A more specific insight into this remarkable man comes from his work on the FX, F-15 project—a project he deeply loved and greatly served. When he came to the Air Staff, he was asked to evaluate the accepted solution and Air Staff position on the FX aircraft. This concept had been given an "optimum" solution culminating in a 62,500 lb aircraft and a thrust-to-weight ratio at take-off (T/W) of 0.75, a wing loading (W/S) equal to 100 lbs/ft², with a turbofan engine of 2.2 bypass ratio. He correctly saw that this would lead to a disaster both before the Congress and before the enemy. He held forth the results of his analysis (trade-off study) and the first cut was to modify the solution to a 40,000 lb aircraft with T/W at takeoff equal to 0.97, a W/S of 110/ft². He became suspicious of the effects of high wing loading so he made an intensive investigation of aircraft drag polars. The result of this analysis was to bring the wing loading down to 80 lbs/ft² and an engine bypass ratio of 0.9. Only with this progress did it become clear that at light wing loadings a fixed wing could become competitive with a variable sweep wing. Limited engine data provided by the contractors showed that the best value of engine bypass ratio was the least possible value, 0.6. He developed new EM analyses which gave new insights in mission analysis and developed new task-relevant rules for fuel budgeting. Now his tradeoff analyses in another iteration lead to a 40,000 lb aircraft with T/W= 1.1, and a W/S of 80 lbs/ft² for a variable sweep wing. His computations then revealed that a fixed wing of 60-65 lbs/sq ft had definite combat advantages over the fashionable variable sweep wing. This led to the definition of the F-15 as it is today. No one else in the USAF could have achieved these results.

It is interesting to realize that his achievements were not purely theoretical, analytical or military; his work was very pragmatic. He had the ethical integrity of backing his insights to save the FX concept from the original overweight, underwinged, overly expensive, overcomplex, ineffective 62,500 lbs solution proposed by others.

His wide range of insights and abilities led him to "anticipate" the Navy move to switch from a fighter attack VFAX to an air superiority F-14. He wrote a memo eliciting his prediction for General L. L. Wilson and prepared a briefing on methods for countering the Navy ploy. This was the second time he kept the USAF FX concept viable. His insights and abilities led him to "anticipate" the current budget squeeze on the defense establishment and he took the timely and forceful action to change some specifications for the F-15 plus suggesting a list of expensive (and relatively ineffective, if fashionable) equipment for removal. The list of his fruitful actions, analyses, and political insights into the F-15 is literally too great to present in complete detail. Let it be concluded that the F-15 could never have survived the congressional and Navy threats to its viability without Lt. Col. Boyd's selfless, outstanding, irreplaceable professional service.

Of late, he continues to guide the F-15 concept through the intricacies of the acquisition system and to deepen his theoretical contributions. His latest reanalysis of his own work has lead to ever more powerful results, ever more useful presentations. His EM work is at the point where it appears feasible to add instrumentation in the aircraft which will permit pilots knowledge of optimal energy management of the aircraft. He has never stopped producing.

IN SUMMARY—it is clear that Lt. Col. Boyd has an outstanding list of achievements.

- He developed and experimented with and contributed to ACM [Air Combat Maneuvering].
- He explored the limitations and capabilities of missiles as has no other individual, service, or corporation.
- He has created the complete analysis of pursuit curves and applied the results.
- He created the Energy Maneuverability Concept.
- He created the Expanded Energy Maneuverability Concept.
- He created new methods of trade-off analysis.
- He applies his results to combat problems.
- In creating his numbers—quality—trade-off analysis, he has developed a remarkable effective tool for force structure analysis.
- He has modified, optimized, guided, and (frequently) saved the F-15 concept and program.
- He has received many awards for his remarkable achievements.

He has seldom been understood or appreciated by his peers or commanders. They have frequently looked at his small human failings instead of his outstanding contributions. Despite being the most fruitful military and scientific contributor to fighter aviation in the history of TAC, he has been given rather ordinary OER's. His ratings were instrumental in retarding his progress, convincing him that he was unappreciated by the Air Force.

Lt. Col. Boyd has had an impeccable record of the highest professional integrity and he has had the courage of his convictions and the loyalty to his country to present them to all that were necessary, to do the right.

Fighter aviation can never be the same for the advent of Lt. Col. Boyd. Aircraft and battle analysis will never be the same. The entire spectrum of aircraft contractors has modified their analyses and presentations. Air combat tactics can never revert to the pre-Boyd era.

It is strongly recommended that every effort be expended to retain this officer in the Service. No effective organization can rationally allow itself to lose such a spectacular major contributor and expect to dominate the enemies of our country.

Aircraft Common to the U.S. Air Force and U.S. Navy

Air Force	**Navy**
Fighters	
P-1, P-2, P-3	BFC, BF2C, F7C, F11C
P-4	FB
P-5, P-6, P-11, P-17, P-20, P-21, P-22, P-23	BFC, BF2C, B7C, F11C
P-7	FB
P-8	F2B, F3B
P-12	F4B
P-15	F5B
P-35	FN
P-38	FO
P-39	FL
P-41	FN
P-43	FN
P-44	FN
P-49	FO
P-50	F5F
TF-51D-25-NT (44-84900)	***ETF-51D-25-NT***
P-58	FO
P-61	F2T-1N
P63	F2L
P-66	SNV
P-70	BD
F-80	TO-1, TV-1, TV-2, ***T2V***
F-86	***FJ***
F-110	F4H
YF-17	F-18
Bombers	
B-24	PB4Y
B-25	PBJ
B-66	A3D
Attack	
A-24	SBD
A-25	SB2C-1A
A-7	A-7

NOTE: ***Boldface italics*** aircraft indicate designs originated by the U.S. Air Force as land-based aircraft and subsequently *navalized* to land on board a carrier.

Appendix C

Low Probability of Intercept Radar

DEPARTMENT OF THE AIR FORCE
WASHINGTON, D.C. 20330
OFFICE OF THE ASSISTANT SECRETARY

19 June 1987

MEMORANDUM FOR MR. FITZGERALD

SUBJECT: Low-Probability-of-InterceptRadar (LPIR)

Over the years there have been several costly attempts to build radars which are truly difficult to detect. Inasmuch as the Soviets have been churning out various models of Anti-Radiation Missiles for almost 30 years, this is a very laudable goal.

It is the purpose of this memo to visit the basic physics of the problem and to attempt to establish an existence (or non-existence) theorem.

Let us examine a typical medium-sized Airborne Intercept (AI) radar. Assume a 24″ diameter antenna and 200 watts of average power. Thus, the effective area of the antenna is (assuming 70% efficiency)

$$A_r = (24)^2 \frac{\pi}{4} (.7) = 317 \text{ sq inches}$$

Assume operation centered @ 10 GHz so that $\lambda = 1.2''$

$$G_t = \frac{4\pi A_r}{\lambda^2} = 2763 \text{ or } 34.4 \text{ db}$$

Thus, the average Effective Radiated Power (ERP_{ave}) in the center of the beam is 556.6kw. At a distance of 20 km this gives a power density of

$$\frac{552{,}600}{4\pi\,(20{,}000)^2} = 110 \ \mu\omega/ \text{ sq meter}$$

Now assume a "sniffer" or ARM antenna 20 cm (8″) in diameter

$$A_r = \pi\,(.2)^2\,(0.7) = .022 \text{ sq m}$$

Average power Received is

$$P_{ave} = 110 \times .022 = 2.42\mu\omega = 56.2 \text{ dbw} = -26.2 \text{ dbm}$$

Assume that the "sniffer" has an effective bandwidth of 2GHz and a noise figure of 10 db. (This is very conservative.) Thus, receiver noise is given by

$$KTB (NF) = 1.38 \times 10^{-23} \times 300 \times 2 \times 10^{9} \times 10$$

$$= 8.28 \times 10^{-11} \text{ watts} = -101 \text{ dbw} = -71 \text{ dbm}$$

The signal to noise ratio if the radar is looking at the sniffer and the sniffer is looking at the radar is therefore 71 – 22.2= 48.8db. If we assume –30db sidelobes for the radar antenna/radar combination, the SNR is 18.8db in the sidelobes, enough for automatic detection.

The discussion here is related more to radio astronomy than to the usual radar equations. The sniffer "knows" there is something at a certain elevation and azimuth but it doesn't know what it is. The receiver is assumed to simply, by brute-force, integrate the signals it gets. It can be configured to angle-track the radar.

The above has implicitly assumed that the radar transmits full time (duty cycle 100%). Such a radar would not be particularly useful because a single-antenna radar that both transmits and receives full time is a very difficult, if not impossible, proposition, although many have tried.

If we assume a duty cycle of 10% for the transmitter and thresh-holding of the receiver in the sniffer/ARM so that much of the receiver noise is not integrated, the SNR would improve dramatically. It would seem that almost any radar one could conceive of could be detected at useful ranges by fairly rudimentary equipment. It should be noted that using spread spectrum techniques does make the radar harder to detect. A monochromatic radar with the antenna and power assumed above could be detected and identified at thousands of miles, even in the sidelobes, by a simple sniffer.

Note also that the above assumes a generic LPIR of 2 GHz bandwidth and does not specify modulation waveforms. Presumably one would use frequency hopping, chirp, and p-n noise modulation, probably in combination. All this would entail considerable expense and the radar would be easily detectable anyway.

There is yet another problem: We have invested vast sums in the "look-down shoot-down" weapons systems and have repeatedly assured the congress that the Republic is in great jeopardy if we don't have them. In theory, it is barely possible to build a radar with a 2GC or so bandwidth that has adequate pulse-doppler performance, but it's very costly.

In summary, trying to build an LPIR is similar to trying to hide an elephant in a strawberry patch by painting its toenails red.

THOMAS S. AMLIE

Appendix D

Spinney Memoranda

April 29, 1992

MEMORANDUM FOR THE RECORD

Subject: F-18E Performance Uncertainties and Program Recommendation[1]

(U) Attachment 1 is a point paper on the subject of the F-18E's performance. It expresses two concerns: first, it was not clear, based on the information given to PA&E by Navy officials, how the F-18E would achieve a 28% increase in combat radius, given only a 4.9% increase in fuel fraction, higher engine SFCs, similar wing loading, and lower thrust-to-weight ratios.[2] Second, even if the increase in radius was theoretically achievable, it appeared that the engineering margins were so tight that the normal possibilities for unexpected weight growth, aerodynamic degradations (i.e., drag increases or lift decreases), and engine degradations (in either weight, thrust, or SFC) exacerbated the technical risk surrounding this program. The point paper recommends that the decision to approve EMD of the F-18E be delayed for two to three months while an independent study group examined these issues. Such a group was formed but was given only two weeks to render a judgment. The collective opinion of its three members is that the Navy's

1. This memorandum states the author's opinion only; it should not be interpreted as being the position of any other person in PA&E or OSD. This memo is a refined version of an earlier draft, which was circulated within OSD on 28 April 92 so that interested officials could review its contents before the DAB convened on 30 April 92. [The DAB was canceled & rescheduled to early May, shortly after this memo was distributed (for unrelated reasons) on 4/30/92.]

2. During our discussions, I asked Navy officials to run two excursions of their performance model to test the sensitivity of the combat radius in the fighter escort mission to changes in fuel fraction. In the first case, starting with the F-18C, LOT XV (with a combat radius of 331 NM), assume the TOGW remained the same, but increase the fuel fraction to that of the F-18E, and calculate the radius. The answer turned out to be 374 NM, an increase of 43 NM but 49 NM short of the F-18E's goal of 423 NM. In the second case, starting with an F-18E (with a combat radius of 423 NM), assume TOGW remains the same but reduce its fuel fraction to that of the F-18C and calculate the radius. This resulted in 377 NM, a reduction of 46 NM but was still 46 NM greater than the radius of the F-18C. In other words, depending on how it was calculated, between 50% and 53% of the increase in combat radius could not be accounted for by the increase in fuel fraction. What was causing the other increase? I asked variations of this question repeatedly and was told that the increase came from better fuel controls and improved flap scheduling, with vague references to improved lift-to-drag ratios. At no time was I told that the bulk of the improvement came from the different aerodynamics of a redesigned wing.

range calculations are reasonable and that engineering margins are acceptable.[3]

(U) On Wednesday afternoon, 22 April 1992, I participated in a debriefing meeting with the members of the study group. Others present were Roy Hempley and Robert Croteau. I was impressed by their objectivity and professionalism, and I have no reason to doubt their findings; however, the peculiar circumstances of the handling of their findings compel me to make the following statements for the record. While Mr. Croteau, as a team observer, was given the opportunity to discuss the results with the team members before the CSC, I was not. I have not had the opportunity to study their report, because it is still in preparation, yet the DAB is scheduled for 30 April 1992. In my opinion, a decision-making milestone that will commit the government to spending billions of dollars to a concurrent engineering and manufacturing development program is being scheduled before officials in OSD have had the time to digest the implications of the study group's findings. I see no reason to justify a rush to judgement. We ought to take the time to study their written report and resolve any lingering questions.

(U) What follows is a description of my understanding of some of these findings. I think they raise new questions about how DOD should proceed with the development of the F-18E.

(U) The central question relating to the combat radius was whether or not the F-18E would have sufficiently superior performance in the non-cruise portion of the mission (warm-up, takeoff, climb, descent, combat turns, etc.) to free up enough fuel to make up for a marginally better performance during the cruise legs. Gary Erickson, the aerodynamics expert on the review team, believes this increase is theoretically possible, because the F-18E will have a *new wing* (a design that improves lift-to-drag by as much as 23% at 10,000 feet and 7% at cruise altitude). Mr. Erickson also believes the wind tunnel work done to date confirms that these improvements should be possible, and he presented an impressive analysis to back up his belief.

(U) At least the following changes have been made relative to the wing of the F-18C: leading-edge sweep will be increased from 26.7 to 29.4 degrees, taper will be increased, twist will be removed, thickness to chord ratio will be increased, a snag on the outboard leading edge of the wing will be added,

3. The adequacy of the margins is still an open question in my mind. While the members reported that they felt the margins were adequate, during our question and answer session, David LeMaster, the performance expert, seemed to agree that the structural weight margin (1050 lbs) was slim and that the contractor would have to be very careful with configuration changes. On the other hand, Jim Day, the propulsion expert, indicated that the engine margins were more than adequate, because the Navy used a "minimum engine" in their analysis. Day believed that the liberality of this margin might provide enough of an extra cushion to offset the slim structural margin. While this belief seems reasonable, they did not present a detailed analysis measuring the size of this cushion. The prototyping program recommended below, if approved, would render this issue moot.

the ratio of exposed wing to total wing area will be increased, and the leading edge extension along the fuselage will be shortened. Erickson believes these changes, while small individually, should combine with the effects of improved flap scheduling to dramatically change the aerodynamics of the F-18E—if the wind tunnel and theoretical calculations translate into real-world performance improvements.[4] He believes the wind tunnel work done to date is very conservative and should be reliable. It should be remembered, however, that data from the best wind tunnel models (particularly drag estimates) do not always scale exactly to real-world performance. The F-18A, for example, had more drag than predicted by similar but less complete analyses, and this was a reason why it did not meet its range goals.[5] Erickson made a persuasive case that aerodynamic risk has been reduced, but it will not be completely understood until we fly a full-sized F-18E.

(U) Moreover, this new and aerodynamically different wing should be placed in the context of four other changes: 1.) The fuselage will be lengthened almost three feet, but its width will remain the same. Thus, the F-18E will have an increased fineness ratio. 2.) The air inlets to the engine will be much larger and the exterior shape will be changed from a semicircle dominated by smooth curves to a four-sided parallelogram dominated by straight lines and sharp angles. 3.) The F-18E will use a new engine. The core will be derived from the engine used in the now defunct A-12 program and an afterburner will be added. 4.) The composition of the empty weight a/c will include a higher percentage (by weight) of composite materials used in the skin sections. While some of the avionics remain the same, and notwithstanding the fact that its design is technically a derivative of an existing airplane, the cumulative effect of a new wing, new engines, new inlets, and new structures makes the F-18E more like a *new airplane* than a modification of an existing airplane. This conclusion suggests that it would be more appropriate to consider the upcoming DAB decision as a *"new start"* (perhaps a hybrid Milestone I/II decision) rather than the curious Milestone IV/II hybrid that is now contemplated.

Recommendations:

(U) Being more appropriately categorized as a Milestone I/II decision, the F-18E program should be reconfigured into a fly-before-you-buy prototype program to conform with the intent of the changes in acquisition policy announced by Secretary Cheney. The objective of this program would be to develop 2 to 3 *combat-capable prototypes* and have a flyoff against the

4. I asked Mr. Erickson if he thought it was possible that anyone familiar with the design of the F-18E would not understand that a new wing design was responsible for the bulk of the unaccounted for increase in combat radius. His response was an unequivocal "no." I do not know why Navy officials did not tell us that a new wing was the prime source of the improved lift-to-drag ratios, but I find their omission troubling. Are there other parts of this program that we do not fully apprehend?

5. Mr. Erickson was confident that the experience with the F-18A and the subsequent calibration of the wind tunnels by comparing the F-18A flight test data to wind tunnel data provided a greater level of assurance that F-18E wind tunnel data would translate more closely to real-world flight test data than that of the F-18A.

F-18C to determine if the actual improvements are worth the added cost.

(U) The F-18E prototype program would be the centerpiece of a new, comprehensive, acquisition strategy intended to extract the Navy from the looming crisis in its tacair force structure. Figure 5 of Attachment 2 portrays the Navy's estimate of how its fighter/attack inventory will begin to collapse early in the next decade. It is crucial to understand that this meltdown is not the product of reductions in the budget. Figures 1 and 2 of Attachment 2 (and the accompanying text) show that the real source of this crisis is a 40 year mismatch between cost growth and budget growth. (The reader should note that, due to data limitations, Figures 1 and 2 describe this problem in terms of the Navy's entire aircraft procurement program.) As long as costs increase faster than budgets, increases in the budget will not produce proportional increases in the number of new aircraft purchased, and decreases in that budget will magnify the decline in that number. The only solution to this mismatch is to attack it at its source. If the Navy wants to remain viable in the next decade, it must figure out how to reduce its costs. The new acquisition strategy is designed to determine if this is possible.

(U) Its objective, therefore, would be to break the crisis by providing the Navy with options for reducing costs while adapting its capabilities to the new threats and budgets of the post-cold war world. The new strategy would include two hedging options to protect the Navy in case the F-18E fails to live up to expectations. First, recognizing that there is little maneuvering room during the immediate-term planning horizon, the F-18C would remain in production during the prototype development phase to make up for any lost production of the F-18E. Second, to provide longer-term protection, $100 to $150 million would be divided up among four to six contractors (awarded on the basis of competitive bids) for the purpose of producing preliminary designs for two new aircraft—one a conventional, carrier-based aircraft designed for direct support of Marines in a littoral scenario, and the other designed for local air superiority (with a secondary bombing capability) in the same scenario.[6] Current A-X plans would also continue to be refined. While these efforts were underway, the DON, JCS, OSD, and IDA would use these options—i.e., the F-18E, F-18C, A-X, the local air superiority fighter (ASF), and the direct support fighter (DSF)—as the building blocks to produce a series of independent studies, the objective of which would be to determine how the Navy/Marine tacair force structure should evolve during the post-

6. Although these design efforts would be aimed at tailoring aircraft to the unique capabilities of naval and marine forces to intervene in a variety of littoral scenarios (as opposed to duplicating the Air Force's deep interdiction bombing capabilities), they would also be aimed at determining if available technologies can be combined with improved acquisition strategies (a greater reliance on commercial specifications, for example) to reduce costs while increasing the variety of pragmatic modernization options. The money to fund the conceptual designs would come from the near-term savings resulting from conversion of the F-18E EMD program to a prototype program. Finally, it would be understood by all participants that these design efforts did not imply a commitment to future procurement.

cold war era. These studies would examine the force-mix tradeoffs of moving between two extremes: At one extreme would be a projection of the status quo (the mix of F-18CS, F-18ES, A-XS, F-14S, and A-6S as described in Attachment 2, Figure 7), and at the other extreme would be a force structure designed to project power in support of marine ground forces employed in a variety of littoral scenarios (e.g., some combination of F-18CS, DSFS, ASFS, and perhaps F-18ES). Intermediate points between these extremes would also be examined. These studies would set the stage for a true intellectual competition—a free trade in ideas, so to speak, premised on the theory that ". . . the best test of truth is the power of the thought to get itself accepted in the competition of the market."[7] The ultimate objective of this debate would be a realistically attainable, fiscally pragmatic, modernization plan—one that accounts for the threats, missions, force structures, and budgets that are likely to shape DON tactical aviation for the next 20–25 years.

Arguments Against Prototyping the F-18E:

(U) *Time*: The principal objection to this plan is that it would delay the introduction of the F-18E into the fleet. While this complaint is true, the consequences of a delay should be evaluated in the context of its effect on the Navy's capabilities and the limitations of its current plan. If a prototyping program is pursued vigorously and enthusiastically, it should only add about two or perhaps three years to the current program. During the interim, additional F-18C production would make up for any "losses" caused by the deferral of the F- 18E's production. Given the large number of DON aircraft, the substitution of a relatively small number of F-18CS for F-18ES would have a negligible effect on the composition of the inventory mix. In view of the diminishing threat and the superior performance demonstrated by our aircraft in the recent war with Iraq, the impact of this delay can not be deemed significant except under the most extreme and improbable situations. Moreover, even if the F-18E and A-X enter the inventory on schedule, and the Navy embarks on a massive service life extension program for its remaining aircraft, its current modernization plan does not produce enough aircraft to support the base-force inventory goal (see Attachment 2, Figures 6 & 7), and that plan is premised on two questionable economic assumptions—that the a/c modernization budgets (measured in constant dollars) will trend upward until the year 2010 and that the procurement quantities within these budgets can be determined by "rough order pricing only" (see Attachment 2, Figure 8). Taken together, a marginal impact on effectiveness and highly-uncertain budget assumptions suggest a delay accompanying a prototype program is an advantage, not a disadvantage. It would buy more time to generate more reliable information—time the Navy needs to sort out a strategy for achieving its force goals and reduce the unavoidable economic uncertainties undermining the realism of its plans.[8]

7. Oliver Wendell Holmes, *Abrams* v. *U.S.*, 250 U.S. 616, 630 (1919).

8. DOD's increasing dependence on long-term projections is one consequence of buying ever more complex weapons. The steady increases in costs and development

(U) *Cost (?)*: Some may argue that a prototype program will increase the cost of the F-18E over the long term. The first point to note in this regard is that prototypes are used to reduce costs in private industry. (Rigorous prototyping is a central strength of Japanese auto manufacturers, for example. Moreover, they also introduce new models more quickly than their competitors.) Long-term cost control is primarily a function of the management discipline imposed by the U.S. government. If we hold the contractor's feet to the fire, and we maintain options for alternative solutions, so that the threat of cancellation is real, should we deem his program to be undesirable, the contractor will be under tremendous competitive pressure to please us, and he will do his best to hold down costs while trying to meet design specifications. That is what competition is all about. On the other hand, by removing options at an early stage, concurrent engineering and manufacturing development programs create a situation where there are no alternatives when the "production design" is to be made. This hands the contractor power to squeeze the government, and therefore reduces his incentive to control costs.

Arguments for Prototyping the F-18E:

(U) *Policy*: Secretary Cheney has announced that it is DOD policy to use prototypes wherever possible. On 12 February 1992, for example, in a speech to the World Affairs Council of Northern California, he said, "With the collapse of the Soviet Union, . . . the *need to produce new systems quickly is less urgent* now than it was in the past, and we can afford to take more time before we move systems into full scale production. . . . we can concentrate on R&D, on operational testing, and the *development of prototypes*, and the upgrade of existing systems to ensure that we maintain the technological edge our smaller forces will require. We'll move to large scale production of new weaponry *only we get what we want at a cost we can afford*." [Emphasis added]

(U) *Suitability*: The F-18E is ideally suited for a combat-capable prototype program. While it is nearly a new aircraft from the perspective of aerodynamics and propulsion, the weapons system integration will make much use of existing F-18C's systems. Systems integration is normally a major impediment to prototyping combat capabilities, but in this case that impediment is not significant.

lead times force planners to decrease the variety of new weapons while projecting the consequences of their current decisions (budgets, costs, and procurement and inventory quantities) ever further into the future. Plans become more vulnerable to disruption because they are premised on fewer alternatives and increasingly uncertain economic assumptions. Figures 7 & 8 of Attachment 2 illustrate the result—to justify the commitment of resources in FY1992, planners must project the consequences of that decision out to FY 2010 in order to prove that their plan is "affordable." This is being done despite the fact that DOD has not successfully executed a single five-year plan for at least 15 years, and we are entering an era of unprecedented change. Does anyone really believe we can predict budgets and costs out to the year 2010? While uncertainty can never be eliminated, one advantage of prototyping is that it buys time to reduce its pernicious effects to more manageable levels. This idea will be developed more fully in the following pages.

(U) *Sound Engineering Practice:* Prototyping is preferred engineering practice and should always be used unless the pressures of time make the acceptance of the higher risks of concurrent engineering mandatory. It is important to understand that producing a prototype does not mean that production engineers are not involved in the product's design. They should be involved from day one to insure that the ultimate design is producible. But the goal of prototyping is to work the bugs out of a product before large dollar resources are committed to its production. Once a product is in serial production, the cost of fixing design flaws on work-in-process or fielded systems rapidly escalates, particularly if assembly line equipment must be changed. In contrast, prototypes are build under job-shop rules, where highly-skilled labor and general purpose machine tools are substituted for production workers, specialized machinery and specially designed factory layouts.

(U) *Freedom of Action*: This plan reduces the price of technical risk by increasing freedom of action over the long term. By avoiding the higher up-front costs of a concurrent engineering and manufacturing development program, a prototype program, coupled with the preservation of F-18C's manufacturing capability and the new design options, protects future decision makers from the possibility that high sunk costs and local economic pressures will force them to accept an aircraft that does not meet its performance specifications. Our acceptance of the reduced range specification of the C-17 is an example of the price we pay when we have no options.

(U) *Competition*: The existence of lower cost production options (i.e., the F-18C) and the exploration of new aircraft design options will put pressure on McDonnell-Douglas to hold down costs and meet the specifications of the F-18E. Moreover, by sponsoring preliminary design work in different companies, we are helping to preserve a perishable national resource—the preliminary design teams in the aircraft industry. These teams are the heart of a company's culture, they take years to build up, and they embody the spirit of each company's peculiar approach to aircraft design. They are the source of new ideas as well as what little competition remains in an increasingly bureaucratized industry. When they dissolve, the bonds of mutual understanding and outlook evaporate and can only be reconstructed at considerable cost over a long period of time.

(U) *Adaptability and Viability*: In contrast to the rigid commitments of an EMD program, a fly-before-you-buy prototype program for the F-18E, combined with the other facets of this recommendation, will provide the Navy with the flexibility it needs to sort out its plans as it moves into an era of unprecedented and programmatic confusion. It is no longer clear what future threats will exist, how large future budgets will be, or how the Navy should relate to this emerging world. Proponents of the F-18E have compounded this unavoidable uncertainty with confusion by making contradictory cases for buying the F-18E: One faction argues that the F-18E is the only solution to the Navy's looming force structure crisis, because a single multi-role fighter will cost less than a high-cost (read unaffordable)

F-14/A-X combination. Yet another faction argues that the F-18E is the only solution to the crisis, because it will provide a bridge to a future force structure based on the high cost A-X and perhaps a new fighter (the NATF or even a version of the F-14). While these agendas are based on mutually exclusive views of the future, neither faction has constructed a realistic strategy for reaching the base-force goal. In this regard, planners would do well to remember what happened after the F-18 program was sold to decision makers in the 1970s as the low-cost solution that would prevent the emerging crisis from occurring in the first place.[9]

(U) The F-18 program was conceived during the mid-70s as the centerpiece of a long-term plan to procure enough airplanes to avoid a force structure crisis during a force expansion. The intention was to produce the F-18 at high rates in order to compensate for the low-rate production of the F-14, AV-8, and A-6 aircraft. But when it became clear in the early 80s that the F-18 would cost much more than originally planned, the Navy chose not to cancel other programs to make enough money available in its annual budget requests to Congress to execute this strategy, and consequently the high rates predicted in the outyears of successive FYDP's never materialized, notwithstanding strong support from Congressional appropriators (see Attachment 2, Figures 3 & 4 and the accompanying text). The resulting inefficiencies of lower-than-planned production then kept costs higher then necessary (even after accounting for the cost growth), and by the 250th unit, the actual costs of the F-18 were exceeding planned costs by about 40%, after taking out the effects of inflation. A case can be made, therefore, that optimistic cost predictions, particularly those made when the program was being sold, and unrealistic outyear budget expectations reinforced each other to make the F-18 part of the problem rather than the solution.

(U) Now both factions in the force structure debate, for very different reasons, contend that an F-18 EMD program is the only solution to yet another looming crisis, but first we must *increase* its cost even further. If, like earlier F-18s, the actual costs of the F-18E turn out to be higher than predicted (remember, current plans assume the "rough order" prices of a pre-EMD estimate), or outyear budgets turn out to be less than predicted (remember, current plans are based on projections out to 2010), the result could be a force structure debacle, even if the F-18E performs as predicted. By closing out other options, I believe the agenda of either faction will lock us into a high risk strategy and repeat the formula that caused the problem. On the other hand, the strategy recommended in this paper is designed to reduce risk, preserve options, explore alternatives, and stimulate an open, vigorous debate over the effectiveness and affordability of these alternatives. I think it is a more pragmatic approach to increasing the Navy's viability as it moves into the next century.

Franklin C. Spinney

9. It should be remembered that the F-18 procurement was sold as being necessary to preserve a force structure of 14 to 16 carrier air wings, not the base force of 13 wings now contemplated.

2 Attachments
1. F-18 Performance Uncertainties, April 8, 1992.
2. A Brief Synopsis of the Crisis in Force Structure.

OFFICE OF THE ASSISTANT SECRETARY OF DEFENSE
PROGRAM ANALYSIS AND EVALUATION
WASHINGTON, DC 20301-1800

July 28, 1992

MEMORANDUM FOR	MR. CHU
THROUGH	MR. PUSCHECK
	MR. CROTEAU

SUBJECT:F-18E—Making False and Misleading Statements to Congress—
ACTION MEMORANDUM

On 21 May 1992, during a hearing of the Defense Subcommittee of the Senate Appropriations Committee, Senator Bond asked Secretary Cheney two questions relating the prototyping and range controversies surrounding the F-18E. Mr. Cheney did not have the information to answer these questions, so he agreed to provide written answers for the record at a later date. Tab 1 contains the transcript of Senator Bond's questions and the inserts for the record that respond to his questions. A member of the SAC staff confirmed that these inserts were submitted to the SAC for inclusion in the record of the 21 May hearing.

Since Senator Bond's questions and Mr. Cheney's answers refer to work I performed last March and April, I feel compelled to comment on their contents: By distorting the contents of my 8 April point paper, then ignoring the contents of my 29 April memorandum, these inserts work together to misrepresent the F-18E's range and prototyping controversies. The first insert (Tab 1, p. 2) claims that a prototype of the F-18E is not needed because the F-18A/B/C/D aircraft are its prototypes, but to justify this claim, it states falsely that the F-18E is very similar aerodynamically to the F-18C, it downplays the other changes in the F-18E, and it ignores critical information that contradicts or undermines the validity of its claim.

The second insert (Tab 1, p. 4) reinforces the misrepresentation of the first insert by setting up a phoney argument that distorts both the analysis and conclusions of my 8 April point paper (Tab 3, Atch. 1) and ignores the findings and recommendations contained in my 29 April memorandum (Tab 3). It states falsely that my independent analysis (i.e., the 8 April point paper) used calculations based on the Brequet range equation to assert that the F-18E could not achieve its projected range of performance, when in fact, the language in the point paper clearly shows that I used the Brequet calculation to focus the debate on the question of why the F-18E had superior performance in the non-cruise portions of its mission. It uses loaded words like "simplified" and "assert" to insinuate that I incorrectly applied the Brequet equation, when in fact the Navy's own calculations and conclusions were very close to and in substantial agreement with those of my point paper. By ignoring the contents of my 29 April memorandum (Tab 3), the language in the second insert reinforces the misrepresentations of the first insert and disregards completely the central finding of the range controversy: namely, that the superior performance in the non-cruise portion of the F-18E's mission comes from the improved aerodynamics of a re-designed wing. In fact, the Navy predicts that the improved aerodynamics of the F-18E will account for 40 to 50 percent of the increase in its combat radius. An acknowledgement of this calculation, however, would *unravel* the claim made in the first insert—namely, that the F-18E is very similar aerodynamically to the F-18C.

Since there is a high probability that whoever prepared and approved these inserts understood their false, misleading, and dissembling nature beforehand, these statements may also constitute material violations of Title 18 (Crimes and Criminal Procedure) of the U.S. Code, specifically, 18 U.S.C. 1001 (re: Tab 2, p.1—false statements generally) and/or 18 U.S.C. 1505 (re: Tab 2, pp. 2&3—obstruction of proceedings).

The remainder of this memorandum describes my reasons for making these statements, why I think this issue is important, and my recommendation for corrective action—namely, that you should forward this memo to the DOD IG and ask the IG to determine (1) if its contents are substantially accurate, (2) if so, who was responsible for preparing, coordinating, and approving these inserts, and (3) did any of these people have prior knowledge that they were placing false, misleading, or dissembling statements in the mouth of the Secretary of Defense.

Discussion

The following discussion aims to answer two questions in detail: First, what statements are either false, misleading, or omit pertinent information? Second, is there reason to believe that these statements were willfully and knowingly designed to create a false or misleading impression in the minds of the members of Congress? The first is a verifiable question of fact. The second is a question of motive as well as fact, and by its nature is more difficult to prove, because motives are often hidden. I will show, however, that a formal investigation by the Defense Department Inspector General is warranted, because there are sufficient reasons to suspect that the mix of false, true, and ambiguous statements and omitted information is the result of a carefully crafted strategy that is systematically contrived to create a misleading impression in the mind of the reader.

Before analyzing the language in Mr. Cheney's inserts, however, it is important to understand what is meant by prototyping. The next section is a short digression that explains the differences between a prototyping strategy and a conventional engineering and manufacturing development strategy.

Background: Prototyping versus EMD and the Question of Derivative Designs.

Prototyping is a sequential, decision-making strategy for reducing technical and economic risks while increasing management's freedom of action. Its goal is to work the bugs out of a design *before* a decision is made to expend substantial resources on its factors of production (manufacturing engineering, specialized machine tools, unique factory facilities, a network of supplier relationships, and the hiring of production workers). Production engineers should be deeply involved in a prototype's design to insure that the ultimate product is producible at a reasonable cost. Moreover, as more detailed information flows out of the design and testing activities, they should prepare for an orderly transition to efficient production by continuously refining their plans for factory layouts, machine tools, worker skills, subcontractors, etc. But under a prototyping strategy, the decision to commit resources to production would be deferred until rigorous testing demonstrated that the product met its specifications.[1] Prototyping also reduces risk because its lower up-front cost gives decision makers the flexibility to simultaneously explore multiple options, even during periods of declining budgets.[2]

In contrast, an engineering and manufacturing development (EMD) strategy makes large financial commitments to production of a product while it is being designed. This concurrent strategy purports to shorten development time, but it also increases rigidity and magnifies risk. The test program must use aircraft produced during the low rate initial production (LRIP) run of a working assembly line. In theory, if the airplane fails to meet its specifications during these tests, it would have to be re-designed during LRIP, or the program would be canceled. In reality, the cost of fixing major design flaws on airplanes moving down an assembly line can escalate rapidly to prohibitive levels, particularly if assembly line equipment or factory layouts must be changed, but cancellation is usually impossible, because LRIP permits the contractor to establish a powerful political base by hiring a large number of production workers and establishing a nationwide net of subcontractors. A second deterrent to cancellation stems from the high up-front cost of EMD—it forces decision makers to put all their eggs in one basket, and in contrast to a prototyping strategy, they can not afford to explore other options. So, in the real world of concurrent EMD programs,

1. While many Americans believe that a prototyping strategy increases development lead times, the Japanese auto manufacturers have demonstrated that prototyping, when combined with an early involvement of manufacturing engineers and a policy of rigorous testing, can be accompanied by greater product variety, shorter development lead times, and quicker transitions to high rate production.

2. The YA-9 vs. YA-10, the YF-16 vs. YF-17, and the YC-14 vs. YC-15 competitive prototype programs all took place within a few years of each other, during the post-Vietnam budget crunch.

when a product fails to meet its performance specifications or cost goals, specifications are reduced, large cost increases are accepted as inevitable, schedules are slipped, and for reasons of affordability, production quantities are cut back. The practice of waiving specifications and goals is known among defense contractors as managing to a rubber baseline.[3]

An F-18E prototyping strategy would aim to reduce the risk of being boxed in by a rubber baseline. But to maximize risk reduction, the prototype should be as close to being a fully combat-capable replica of the eventual production item as is possible. The YA-10 prototype of the A-10 is the closest and most successful approach to this ideal of any aircraft produced since 1970.[4] The multi-role F-16 and F-18 fighters, in contrast, turned out to be substantially different from the single-mission YF-16 and YF-17 air combat fighter prototypes, with design changes resulting in unexpected performance degradations and cost increases to both aircraft.[5] While these aircraft were *derived* from the YF-16/YF-17 designs, the YF models were not true prototypes of the F-16A/F-18A.[6]

3. The reduced range specifications, cost increases, production cutbacks, and schedule delays of the C-17 program are prime examples illustrating this practice.

4. The A-10 was a very successful program. It did not suffer from a rubber baseline; its deficiencies—e.g., low thrust-to-weight ratio, large size, and (some would argue) the lack of sophisticated avionics—relate to the specification of its original design goals, not a failure to meet those goals. The bulk of the program was produced within cost targets [In a subsequent conversation with Spinney, he indicated that the earliest cost target was unrealistically low, reflecting the habitual DOD practice of a "buyin," but deviations from cost estimates completed after engineering development were very small], at high production rates, with almost no slippage, and production shut down after only a few years of congressionally imposed extensions. Finally, notwithstanding the claims of its many detractors, it proved to be one of the most effective aircraft employed in the Persian Gulf war.

5. After the YF-16 won the competitive flyoff, the Air Force initiated a full-scale engineering development (FSED) program (the equivalent of EMD) for a multi-role *derivative* of the YF-16 design. The result was a larger airplane with more complex avionics, and the performance of early production aircraft suffered, because, compared to the YF-16, the F-16 had lower thrust- to-weight, a lower fuel fraction, and a higher wing loading. Design problems also required a redesign of the F-16's tail. Subsequent weight growth in the F-16C degraded performance further. In the case of the F-18, the FSED changes were even more extreme (because, in addition to being changed into a much heavier multi-role fighter, its design had to be converted to maritime operations), initial technical problems were more severe, and the impact of subsequent weight growth forced serious cutbacks in range (see Tab 4).

6. Once the decision was made to convert the *single-purpose* YF-16/YF-17 designs into heavier, *multi-role* fighters, prototypes of these *new* aircraft (a YF-16A and a YF-18A) could have been built before DOD committed substantial resources to manufacturing development. While this strategy might have taken a few years longer, it would have reduced risks and might have been cheaper in the long run. Flight tests of the prototypes would have revealed at least two problems that were too expensive to fix once these aircraft entered production—namely, (1) that the increase in the size of the F-16's wing was not sufficient to compensate for its weight growth and (2) that the F-18 could not meet its range goals—not to mention the technical problems that were fixed at considerable cost—e.g., the F-16's tail and the F-18's early structural problems.

So, when evaluating the need for a prototype in the case of a derivative design, like that of the F-18E, the crucial question becomes: *How different is the new, derivative design from the earlier design?* The following discussion will show that, contrary to the assertions contained in Mr. Cheney's inserts, the F-18E is so different from the earlier versions of the F-18 that, from the perspective of engineering development and program costs, it should be considered a new airplane. Its design goals include significant improvements to its aerodynamics, a higher-thrust engine which itself is still in development, and major changes to its structure and electromechanical systems, but the F-18E will use much of the F-18C's avionics. Normally, avionics integration would be a major impediment to prototyping full combat capabilities, but in this case it is not significant. Thus, although the F-18E program incorporates large changes, it is also unusually suitable for prototyping. A YF-18E prototype program, therefore, offers a splendid opportunity to reduce the risk of a rubber baseline by returning to the prototyping ideal exemplified by the philosophy of the YA-10. My 29 April memo (Tab 3, pp. 4–8) explains other pros and cons of prototyping the F-18E.

With this background in mind, let us now return to the main thrust of this memo. Two conventions will be used to distinguish quotations in the following discussion: direct quotations from the transcript or inserts will be written in "***bold italics***" while quotations from substantiating documents will be written in "*plain italics.*"

False and Misleading Statements, Partial Truths, and Critical Omissions:

1. *Are the F-18a/b/c/d Aircraft Prototypes of the F-18E?*

Senator Bond asked Mr. Cheney if there was any reason why the F-18E should be prototyped. Mr. Cheney's said he was not familiar with the issue and would be guided by "***the judgement of our acquisitions people.***" Senator Bond then expanded the question to include the issues of cost and acquisition strategy (Tab 1, p. 1, which is page 84 of the transcript). Mr. Cheney responded by saying he would supply the answer for the record. Note also that on the following page of the transcript (Tab 1, top of p. 3), Mr. Cheney reinforced his determination to rely on the judgement of subordinates.

Mr. Cheney's written response to these questions (Tab 1, p. 2) says the F-18E should not be prototyped for the following reasons:

a.) The program has already been prototyped: He says "***. . . the F-18A/B/C/D aircraft are* the *flying prototypes . . .***" [emphasis in original] of the F-18E, because the F-18E is a "***true derivative***" of these aircraft. Simply being a derivative design is not a sufficient reason to justify this conclusion, however. The crucial question is: How different is the derivative design from the earlier design? Mr. Cheney's insert explores these differences with the following compound argument:

b.) "***Although the structural components have limited commonality . . .***" *True*. In other words, the structure is different. While this clause acknowledges that fact, note how the positive spin to the phraseology and limited information mitigate the sense of difference. Much is left unsaid. While many of the load paths in the structure are similar to those of the F-18C, the F- 18E's design includes a much higher percentage of composite materials (by weight) in its skin structure, has a different wing, a fuselage that has been stretched more than three feet, different air inlets, and incorporates substantial changes to its electro-mechanical systems (a higher pressure hydraulic system, a more powerful environmental control system, and different landing gear, for example). The table in Tab 9 breaks out the main structural components of the F-18E/F by the weight in terms of those items in common with the F-18C and those peculiar to the F-18E/F (Source: page 8 of the F/A-18E/F Cost Analysis Requirements Description—CARD 92-01, prepared by the Navy's F-18E program office). It shows that 84% (92% of the structure, 98% of the landing/arrest gear, and 65% of the subsystems) by weight will in fact be *unique* to the F-18E. The phrase ***"limited commonality"*** provides no hint of the extent of these differences.

c.) ***". . . the E/F is very similar aerodynamically, . . ."*** *False*. This is the crucial misstatement. In fact, the Navy believes that 40 to 50 percent of the increase in combat radius (relative to the F-18C) will come from the *substantially improved* aerodynamics of the F-18E. More precisely, the Navy predicts the lift-to-drag (L/D) ratio of the F-18E will improve significantly (from 7 to 23 percent) across a wide range of altitude and Mach numbers, if the results of its wind tunnel experiments and theoretical calculations can be translated into a real-world airplane. In fact, the question of what caused these improved aerodynamics was the heart of the F-18E's range controversy. The cumulative effect of the changes in the design of its wing was not made clear to the OSD staff until the members of the Conventional Systems Committee were briefed by the independent team of experts in late April, 1992. Nevertheless, as the following four examples show, there can be no question about the Navy asserting that the F-18E would have an improved L/D ratio, or that this assertion was widely known, if not understood, by officials throughout the Pentagon well before Mr. Cheney's testimony on 21 May 1992.

- *Example 1:* Tab 6 is a copy of a briefing presented to Frank Kendall, USDA(A) for Tactical Systems, on 25 March 1992. The range controversy was the reason for including the discussion of the F-18E's fuel fraction (see title page of brief, Tab 6, p. 1). Page 11 of Tab 6 is a slide that depicts the results of a scaling analysis that was designed to explain the sources of the increase in F-18's combat radius. It is important to understand that this is a theoretical calculation. It is designed to show how the separate changes in the F-18E's design should increase its combat radius over that of the F-18C Lot XV when flown in the fighter escort mission. The data on page 11 say that the combat radius of the F-18E would be 92 miles longer than that of the F-18C (423-331=92), and of this increase, 374–331=43 miles (or 46% of the 92 miles) would come from the increased fuel fraction of the F-18E, 420-374=46 miles (or 50% of the total increase) would come from its improved L/D, and

423-420=3 miles would come the F-18E's engine SFCS.

- *Example 2*: Tab 7 is an extract from a 2 April 1992 briefing that was designed to explain the F-18E's performance improvements to senior Navy officials. In this case, Page 4 of Tab 7 shows that the Navy revised its calculation to show that the L/D improvements resulted in an increase of 411-374=37 miles, or 40% of the range increase—a change of 10% which, incidentally, illustrates the uncertainty that inevitably surrounds such theoretical calculations.
- *Example 3:* Tab 3 is my memorandum for the record (MFR) of 29 April 1992. The improved aerodynamics of the F-18E are referred to repeatedly in the paragraphs and footnotes of the first three pages. In fact, the wing change was the crucial factor shaping the recommendation to build a combat-capable prototype of the F-18E before committing to a manufacturing development program. This reasoning was widely known throughout the Pentagon by the time the insert was written, because I distributed a large number of copies to staff members in ASD(PA&E), USD(A), ASD(C), and the DON.
- *Example 4:* Tab 8 is the report prepared by Gary Erickson (Senior Research Engineer, Transonic Aerodynamics Branch, NASA, Langley), the aerodynamics specialist n the independent team of experts. On page 7, he concluded that "*The increased lift-to-drag ratios* of the F-18E relative to the F-18C are maintained through the lift coefficient and Mach number encompassing the fighter escort mission. Factors contributing to the *improved aerodynamics* of the F-18E are increased wing thickness, increased ratio of exposed wing area to total wing area, and elimination of wing twist. [Emphasis added.] (See page [above] for a more extensive explanation.) As I indicated in the 29 April 1992 memo (Tab 3), Erickson has a high confidence in this conclusion, but it must be remembered that it is based on an analysis of wind tunnel data and theoretical calculations, not a real airplane.

So, by 21 May 1992 it was widely known to competent officials throughout the Navy and the Office of the Secretary of Defense that almost half of the predicted increase in the combat radius of the F-18E was the result of its redesigned wing. Unless the term ***"very similar"*** in Mr. Cheney's insert means *substantially improved*, his statement is false and misleading.

d.) ***"E/F avionics subsystems are 90% hardware common to the C/D . . ."*** *Probably True*. (I have not verified this statement.)

e.) ***"The E/F engine is a derivative of the A-12 engine which is already well into development."*** *True*. In other words, the F-18E will have a new engine. While its core will be derived from the F-18's F-404 engine, larger airflows, a higher fan pressure ratio, changes in the combustor, a hotter maximum turbine temperature, and other changes will improve component efficiencies, increase the engine thrust-to-weight ratio, and generate substantially more thrust. Normally, one would expect that the cumulative effect of these changes would make the case for prototyping even stronger because of the risks inherent in engine development and engine-airframe integration. It is my understanding, moreover, that this engine has been tested at the component level, but it has not been tested in its full-up configuration with an afterburner. So, notwithstanding the fact that its development risk was found to be low to moderate by the independent team of experts, some development risk remains. Moreover, even if the engine performs on a test stand as predicted, there will always be a risk it will not perform as well when it is integrated with a new airframe that includes the different airflows of new inlets and the different aerodynamics of a new wing.

The net effect of this mix of true, false, and partial statements creates a misleading picture that downplays the differences between the F-18E and the F-18A/B/C/D. The insert uses this misleading picture to conclude that ***". . .an unneeded prototype would significantly increase program cost . . . with no real reduction in risk over the current plan"*** [emphasis added] (Tab 1, p. 2).

Mr. Cheney's insert says *nothing* about the program cost or the risk of the current plan, yet it concludes that a prototype will increase costs and produce no ***"real reduction in risk"*** to that plan. Not only does this sweeping leap of faith violate generally accepted canons of sound engineering economics, without additional information, it is logically an unsubstantiated assertion. If the F-18A/B/C/D aircraft were indeed true prototypes of the F-18E, then all of the experience derived from their development and production would be relevant to an assessment of the risk embodied in the F-18E's current plan. Let's compare that experience to the *"current plan"* to see if it provides any insight into the cost and program risks of the F-18E.

The Navy plans to procure 1000 F-18ES for about $49 billion (weapon system procurement cost, FY93$). Figure 1 compares this plan to the early plan and actual history of the F-18 A/B/C/D. It uses a learning curve format to show the relation between average unit costs and the cumulative quantity procured. The effects of inflation have been removed. The first point to note is that the Navy's plan for the F-18E is costed out as if it were a *new and different airplane, not a modification to an existing airplane.* The initial costs of the E/F are much higher than those of the first F-18A/BS, and the projected rate of decline is even more extreme in the early part of the production run. This is a typical pattern for a new, more expensive aircraft made on a new production line. Moreover, the curve for the F-18E predicts that costs will continue to decline smoothly as production increases, as if no further modifications will occur. Thus, like its predecessor, this plan predicts that most of the F-18ES will be bought at costs much lower than the early costs. This pattern of decreasing costs will happen despite the fact that the Navy's current plan projects a lower maximum production rate (72/yr) than that actually achieved for the A/B/C/D aircraft (84/yr) and much lower than that projected in early plans for the A/B/C/D (120/yr in the last year of the 78-82FYDP). Finally, all the F-18E's cost improvements will take place in a factory where overhead rates are likely to increase because of lower total plant utilization. Taken together, these observations suggest that the F-18E's plan may be optimistic like that of its predecessor—i.e., the 78-82 FYDP pre-production prediction for the F-18A. (Tab 5 contains a larger scale version of Figure 1.)

Once the Defense Department bought into the rosy predictions of the 78-82 FYDP and locked the early F-18s into production, the actual cost to buy them turned out to be much higher than hoped for, notwithstanding strong support from Congress in an era of unprecedented budget growth. (This point is explained in the 29 April memo, Tab 3, Atch. 2). The FY 78-82 FYDP shown in Figure 1 was the last FYDP produced before production of the F-18A/B began. It should be remembered that its cost predictions were based on the detailed design information produced by an almost completed engineering development program—which presumably included a complete materials list as well as a work breakdown structure. Nevertheless, the actual costs of the F-18A/B/C/D program exceeded these predictions by well over 40 percent in constant dollars. On the other hand, the learning curve for the F-18E, shown in Figure 1, is based on the more general and less reliable information of a pre-engineering development estimate. In fact, the $5 billion engineering and manufacturing development (EMD) program for the F-18E would produce the same kind of detailed engineering data that resulted in the overly optimistic cost estimates of the FY 78-82 FYDP.

If the F-18E program repeats the experience of its so-called prototype, its average weapon system unit cost could increase from $49 million per aircraft (i.e., the average cost for the 1000 plane program shown in Figure 1) to over $70 million per aircraft, and the peak production rate could be less than half of that currently predicted—a bleak possibility made more likely by the prospect of declining budgets. If history repeats itself, and the *"current plan"* for the F-18E also succumbs to the imperatives of the rubber baseline, the very existence of Naval tactical aviation would be placed at risk. So, even a small probability of such an outcome would be a very large risk. On the other hand, the knowledge gained from designing, building, and flying a prototype can be used to reduce this risk without a harmful delay or an excessive increase in cost (see my 29 April memo, Tab 3, pp. 4–8).

Unexpected cost growth and cutbacks in production rates were not the only unforeseen risks that forced a rubber baseline into the plans of the early F-18s. Even after the first production lot did not meet the original range requirement, the Navy's subsequent contract specifications approved a steady diet of additional weight increases and range decreases. (Tab 4 displays the GAO's analysis of this result.) Mr. Cheney's statement does not explain why this risk does not apply to the range goals of the F-18E.[7] The next section examines what his statements do say about the range controversy.

2. *F-18E Range Predictions:*

7. F-18E range goals approximate the never-achieved F-18A range goals.

Senator Bond also asked Secretary Cheney about the controversy surrounding the F-18E's range predictions (Tab 1, p.3). Mr. Cheney's insert (Tab 1, p. 4) clearly refers to the point paper entitled "F-18E Performance Uncertainties" which I prepared on 8 April 1992 (Tab 3, Atch. 1). Let's compare some of the statements made in this insert to what was said in the point paper:

a.) ***"The report you refer to was an independent paper written by an analyst in the Program Analysis and Evaluation office. The analyst used some simplified calculations based on the Brequet range equation to assert that the Navy could not meet the range performance being projected for the E/F aircraft."*** [Emphasis added.] *False.*

The independent paper (Tab 3, Atch. 1) does not assert that the E/F can not meet its range goals. It states clearly that OSD can not answer the following question: "Can a 0.014 (4.9%) increase in Fuel Fraction be converted into a 29% increase in combat radius?" It then uses information provided by the Navy to do an analysis that concluded that the range increase "*depends critically*" [emphasis in original] on superior fuel consumption rates in the non-cruise portion of the mission and that the "DAB has no insight into how this can be done . . ."

The false statement in this insert is an oversimplification that distorts the essence of the F-18E's range controversy. I used the Brequet equation to highlight the importance of the non-cruise portions of the mission to the radius calculation. Note that the Brequet calculation is referred to as a "1st cut" (Tab 3, Atch. 1, p. 3). The Navy performance engineers understood the structure of this argument from the very beginning. In fact, in their own analyses, the Navy engineers came to the *same conclusion*: The 25 March briefing to Mr. Kendall (Tab 6, p. 12) says *"Differences in mission radius can also be attributed to non-cruise segments . . ."* About one week later, in their internal briefing to senior Navy officials, the Navy engineers strengthened their conclusion to say (re. Tab 7, p. 3) *"Differences in mission radius are directly attributable to non-cruise segments. . . ."* (Incidentally, note how close the results of the Brequet calculation are to those of the Navy's computerized performance model, Tab 7, p. 3.)

Furthermore, the idea of using a scaling analyses [*sic*] to determine how the increase in fuel fraction would increase the combat radius was first done by the Navy at my request. The Navy engineers then expanded this approach to identify the separate effects of the L/D improvements and the engine change. These efforts resulted in the data depicted in Tab 6, p.11 and Tab 7, p. 4. Once the Navy analyses *confirmed* my suspicion that the increase in fuel fraction was not sufficient to account for all of the increase in the mission radius, the question of *what design changes accounted for the increase in l/d became the central issue in the radius controversy* (see footnote 2 of the April 29 memo—Tab 3, p. 1). As Attachment 1 of Tab 3 indicates, our lack of insight into this question was the first reason why the 8 April point paper recommended that a team of independent experts examine the range issue.

b.) ***"In an effort to review the situation, the Office of the Under Secretary of Defense (Acquisition)/Tactical Systems put together a team of independent experts from the Air Force and NASA to review and assess the Navy and McAir's aerodynamic characteristics predictions, and mission performance methodology and range predictions."*** *True.*

Since the 8 April point paper recommended forming such a team, the fact that it was formed would seem to be a confirmation of the paper's conclusion—namely, that the DAB had no insight into what was causing the superior performance in the non-cruise portions of the mission.

c.) ***"After a thorough review of these areas, the independent assessment team validated the E/F aerodynamic predictions, verified predicted engine performance and validated mission*** **and** ***radius predictions. The bottom line of the assessment teams findings was that the E/F can meet predicted performance, the Navy position is well supported and the difference with the PA&E analysis is understood. This is no longer an item of discussion."*** *Technically true but misleading because it omits material facts.*

When this passage is evaluated in conjunction with the false statement that the independent analysis asserted the F-18E could not meet its range specifications (para. 2.a. above), it implies that the 8 April 1992 point paper was in error. Moreover, this false and deceptive conclusion is reinforced by what this passage does not say. Mr. Cheney's statement does not say what the ***"difference"*** with the PA&E analysis was or what new information made this ***"difference"*** understandable.

To the extent that there was a difference with the PA&E analysis, it was on the question: Why was the F-18E's performance superior in the non-cruise portions of the mission? This is clearly evident from reading my 8 April 1992 point paper (Tab 3, Atch. 1) as well as the first and fourth paragraphs and Footnote # 2 of my 29 April MFR (Tab 3). Bear in mind that it was the Navy's analysis that said the increase in L/D would account for 40 to 50 percent of the radius increase. Every time I asked why this increase was expected to occur, I was given answers (e.g., mounting antennas internally to increase L/D by decreasing drag, better flap scheduling, etc.) that simply did not seem significant enough to explain so large an effect. As Footnotes 2&4 of that MFR indicate, the Navy officials never told me that the main contributor to the improved L/D ratio was the result of a redesigned wing. The effect of the wing changes only became clear when the team of independent experts reported its results.

The new information that made the *"difference"* understandable was that the *F-18E would have a new wing with a substantially improved lift-to-drag ratio.* While its wind tunnel tests seem reliable, this new piece of information puts the program in a different light. Note how this finding contrasts with the false claim made in the previous insert. The F-18E is *not* ***"very similar"*** aerodynamically to the A/B/C/D. In fact, the aerodynamic dissimilarity is the major reason why it is prudent to reduce risk with a fly-before-you-buy prototype program (see Tab 3, p.3).

It appears, therefore, that the false information and critical omissions of the second insert were deliberately contrived to support the false claim made in the first insert.

The Question of Motive:

Is there reason to believe that these false, incomplete, and misleading statements were willfully and knowingly designed to create a false and misleading impression in the minds of the members of Congress?

We have seen that the first insert states falsely that the F-18E is very similar aerodynamically to the F-18C, that it downplays the other changes in the F-18E, and that it omits pertinent information that undermines its claim that F-18A/B/C/D are prototypes of the F-18E. We have seen how the second insert sets up a phoney strawman to discredit the PA&E analysis and distract attention away from the central finding of the range controversy—namely, that the F-18E will have a new and aerodynamically superior wing. Finally, we have seen how these false statements and omissions work together to systematically deny the reader access to information that suggests the F-18E is very different from the F-18A/B/C/D, particularly the crucial fact that 40 to 50 percent of the predicted increase in radius would result from the improved aerodynamics of a redesigned wing.

Can this situation be an accident due to ignorance?

While Mr. Cheney is technically responsible for making these false statements, his testimony indicates he was unfamiliar with the specifics of the F-18E controversy. On two occasions he said he would rely on his staff for the information requested. On the other hand, given the wide distribution of Tabs 3, 6, and 7, as well as the extensive publicity surrounding this issue, it is almost inconceivable that a member of Mr. Cheney's staff, who was competent to prepare or approve the answers to Senator Bond's questions, would be ignorant of the F-18E's improved aerodynamics by 21 May 1992. There is a strong possibility, therefore, that one or more of the people who wrote, coordinated, or approved these statements understood their misleading character before the fact and willfully places Mr. Cheney in this embarrassing position.

Why would someone want to mislead Congress in this matter?

At least one possibility comes to mind. If one admits that the F-18E has a new wing and that the predicted effects of this wing are based on theoretical scaling calculations of wind tunnel tests, then the argument for a risk-reducing prototype program in lieu of a higher-risk concurrent EMD program becomes much stronger, particularly when one considers the F-18E's other differences (new engines and different inlets, structures, and electro-mechanical systems) and the reduced threat facing our naval forces (which makes a short delay militarily acceptable). Moreover, Mr. Cheney indicated in recent speeches that his new acquisition policy will include an increased emphasis on prototypes. Nevertheless, the Navy requested and the DAB approved a concurrent EMD program for the F-18E in early May. Shortly thereafter, on 19 May, the House Armed Services Committee reported its determination to reduce the F-18E's budget request by $535 million and convert its development strategy to a prototype program—a position that was later sustained by the full House. The Senate has not yet acted on this matter. It is possible, given these stakes, that Senator Bond's question (on 21 May) provided an advocate of the F-18E EMD program with an opening to influence the outcome of the Senate's upcoming vote, but to make the case against prototyping, he found it necessary to make false statements and omit pertinent information.

If true, there is a real possibility that this action is a violation of the obstruction of proceedings clause of 18 U.S.C. 1505 as well as the more obvious violation of 18 U.S.C. 1001 (false statements, generally).

CONCLUSIONS AND SIGNIFICANCE

I want to stress that I do not know how or why the false statements were included in the inserts. I do not know who is responsible for them. My goal has been to show that they were made, that there is a high probability that whoever made and approved them knew they were false before the fact, and that there is at least one plausible explanation why someone might want to create a false impression in the minds of the members of Congress.

Some people may attack my motives for raising this issue by saying I favor prototyping the F-18E and the DAB chose to go in the other direction. Others may say that the question of prototyping is a political matter, that the two inserts will probably not be read, or be of any significance in a political debate involving the disposition of $535 million.

Both attacks miss a very important point: It is a felony to make false statements to or obstruct the proceedings of Congress. 18 U.S.C. 1001 has a maximum penalty of a $10,000 fine and five years in prison and 18 U.S.C. 1505 has a maximum penalty of a $5,000 fine and five years in prison. Making false statements to Congress is a serious crime because our constitutional system of shared power, checks and balances, and public accountability depends crucially upon the transfer of truthful information between the different branches of government. A willful corruption of that information flow subverts the checks and balances and should not be tolerated by anyone who has taken an oath to uphold the Constitution.

I respectfully request that you immediately forward this memorandum to the Defense Department Inspector General with the recommendation that he make a formal determination of whether its contents are accurate in substance, and if so, who was responsible for preparing and approving (informally as well as formally) the inserts, and did any of these people have prior knowledge that they were placing false and misleading statements into the formal testimony of the Secretary of Defense. Please inform me of your action at your earliest convenience.

Franklin C. Spinney

This memo contains the following nine attachments:

Tab 1 Pages 84 and 85 of the transcript of Secretary Cheney's testimony before the Defense Subcommittee of the Senate Appropriations Committee on May 21, 1992 and two inserts for the record made in response to the questions contained on these pages.

Tab 2 Copies of Title 18, Sections 1001 and 1505 of the U.S. Code.

Tab 3 29 April 1992 Memorandum for the Record, "F-18E Performance Uncertainties and Program Recommendations," with attachments (written by this author).

Tab 4 F/A-18 specification Radius History (GAO, 5/11/92).

Tab 5 Chart entitled "F-18: Plans vs. Reality" (prepared by this author). Data source: F-18E—cost estimates provided to OSD by Navy program office; F-18A/B/C/D historical record (P1s and FYDP data base).

Tab 6 F/A-18 Briefing on JIAWG and Fuel Fraction for Mr. Frank Kendall, Director, Tactical Warfare Programs, 25 March 1992.

Tab 7 F/A-18E Performance Briefing, 2 April 1992 (internal Navy briefing, selected pages only).

Tab 8 Section 2(a). Aerodynamics. Report of Gary Erickson, Senior Research Engineer, Transonic Aerodynamics Branch, NASA Langley, member of the independent team of experts.

Tab 9 Page 8 of the F/A-18E/F cost Analysis Requirements Description, CARD 92-01, prepared by NAVAIR F-18E/F program office, 12-20-91.

OFFICE OF THE ASSISTANT SECRETARY OF DEFENSE
PROGRAM ANALYSIS AND EVALUATION
WASHINGTON, DC 20301-1800

August 26, 1992

MEMORANDUM FOR MR. PUSCHECK
THROUGH MR. CROTEAU

SUBJECT: F-18E—False and Misleading Statements to Congress (2)

This memo responds to the question raised in your 30 July 92 note to Mr. Croteau on the subject of the F-18E/F inserts for the record (Attachment 1). It also states why I still feel strongly that an IG investigation in this affair is necessary, notwithstanding the Department's efforts to correct the record.

Your note indicates that you are under the impression that the inserts in question were draft inserts, still in coordination and open to change via normal staffing procedures. It also says you are troubled, because I did not promptly bring this issue to Mr. Croteau's and your attention, so we could correct the false statements, before I devoted several days to writing my 28 July 92 memo requesting an IG investigation (Attachment 2). While these concerns are understandable, both are mistaken.

The inserts were not drafts—they were officially approved and submitted to Congress without PA&E's coordination. I first learned about the inserts from a newspaper reporter who said a U.S. senator was passing them out to the media. I then called a staff member of the Defense Subcommittee of the Senate Appropriations Committee, and he confirmed that the two inserts had been officially received for inclusion in the public record of the hearings. As soon as I obtained copies of the inserts, I brought them to Mr. Croteau's attention. He was disturbed by their contents, but after determining that they had been officially submitted without our coordination, he believed there was nothing we could do to correct them. A few days later, I mentioned the inserts to you while you were walking past my office. Your response (a sympathetic but frustrated shrug) suggested to me that you also believed nothing could be done. It was only later that it became apparent that the inserts had not yet been published by Congress and that the Department could take action to correct the record during its editorial review of the galley proofs.

There are at least three reasons why I was justified in taking the time to carefully prepare the 28 July memo. First, any memorandum suggesting that the DOD Inspector General investigate a possible conspiracy to involve the Secretary of Defense in the commission of a felony (making false statements to Congress) is a very serious matter and should never be prepared frivolously. Second, these inserts deal with a question of great consequence (i.e., the F-18E prototyping controversy), involving a potential budget change of as much as $535 million in FY93 and the overall direction of a program which will cost more than $50 billion in procurement and R&D. Third, I had a legal obligation to bring this matter to the attention of my superiors. Under the terms of the "Code of Ethics for Government Service," 5 U.S.C. Section 7301, any person in government service has an affirmative duty to uphold the laws and regulations of the United States, never be a party to their evasion, and expose corruption whenever discovered.

The fact that the Department took action to change the inserts and correct the record makes it more important that the Inspector General conduct a formal investigation of the entire affair. The extraordinary action to change the record amounts to an "adoptive admission" that serious misrepresentation did in fact occur. If any of these misrepresentations was intentional, a felony would have occurred (i.e., a violation of 18 U.S.C. Sections 1001 and/or 1505 as explained in my 28 July memorandum). If this is true, any person who worked on these changes would have committed another felony, if he perceived but did not report the original felony (by violating 18 U.S.C. Section 4, which says concealment of the commission of a felony is itself a felony). Moreover, since more than one individual was involved in these changes, several other criminal statutes could conceivably have been violated, if this matter was not promptly reported to the proper investigative authorities (18 U.S.C. Section 2 making it an offense to aid another in the commission of a criminal offense; 18 U.S.C. Section 3 making it an offense to assist an offender; and 18 U.S.C. Section 371 making it an offense to conspire to commit offense). Attachment 3 contains copies of all the cited statutes arranged in ascending numerical order.

I think it is unlikely that PA&E was cut out of the coordination loop by accident, because we now know that the USD(A) staff analyst responsible for preparing and coordinating these inserts (1) has years of experience, (2) was fully aware that the inserts referred to work done in PA&E (one insert even mentions PA&E), and (3) had unrestricted access to the information indicating that the language contained false, misleading, and incomplete statements. It is more likely, therefore, that PA&E was deliberately cut out of the coordination loop. If this is true, it was a breach of bureaucratic courtesy that bespeaks contempt for our organization, not to mention a possible violation of one or more criminal statutes. If we allow such arrogant behavior to pass unchallenged, we can expect it to recur with increasing frequency, and PA&E will become even more marginalized.

One final comment. The rewritten inserts (i.e., the 10 Aug. versions) do not contain any false factual statements, to the best of my knowledge. Nevertheless, they are not, in my opinion, responsive to Senator Bond's questions, because they do not contain enough detail for the reader to make an informed judgement about the issues raised by those questions.

I respectfully request that you forward this entire package to the Inspector General in accordance with the recommendation contained in my 28 July memorandum.

Franklin C. Spinney

Staff Analyst, Tacair Division

3 Attachments:

1. 30 July 92 note from Mr. Puscheck to Mr. Croteau, subject "F/A-18E/F Inserts."
2. 28 July 92 action memorandum from Mr. Spinney to Mr. Chu, subject "F-18E—Making False and Misleading Statements to Congress."
3. Copies of cited statutes (5 U.S.C. 7301, 18 U.S.C. 2, 3, 4, & 371).

OFFICE OF THE SECRETARY OF DEFENSE

July 30, 1992
MEMO FOR Bob Croteau

SUBJECT: F/A-18 E/F INSERTS

I have forwarded Chuck's memorandum and your note (which I received yesterday) to David.

I can understand how, on occasion, draft inserts are not as complete as they ought to be. Our DOD process for coordinating draft inserts should be improved. Thanks for correcting these specific inserts.

What troubles me most is that Chuck considered the drafts of these two inserts to be fundamentally in error—a point not everyone shares—but he did not promptly bring this to our attention. Instead he took what may have been a considerable period to write a 15 page memorandum and assemble a lengthy package. I appreciate his insights, but why did he not try to correct what he considered to be in error?

Herb [Puscheck]

C: F. C. Spinney

OFFICE OF THE ASSISTANT SECRETARY OF DEFENSE
PROGRAM ANALYSIS AND EVALUATION
WASHINGTON, DC 20301-1800

September 14, 1992

MEMORANDUM TO MR. PUSCHECK
THROUGH MR. CROTEAU

SUBJECT: F-18E—Making False Statements to Congress (3)

On 4 September, L/C James Durham sent you a memorandum containing a history of the changes to the F-18E inserts for the record. This memo places these changes in context of the concerns raised in my memos of 28 July and 26 August.

My 28 July memorandum concluded its analysis by saying there is a "high probability" that whoever prepared or coordinated on the original inserts knew they were false before the fact, and, if this happened, some person or persons would have committed at least one felony. (18 U.S.C. 1001 makes it a crime to lie to Congress and 18 U.S.C. 1505 makes it a crime to obstruct the proceedings of Congress.) My 26 August memorandum said the fact that we changed the inserts amounts to an admission that false statements were made. While it was appropriate to remove the false statements from the record, that action did not negate the fact that they were made in the first place. (To argue otherwise would be tantamount to saying a bank robbery did not occur if the thief returned the money.) It is, therefore, even more important to forward this entire matter to the proper investigative authority (i.e., the IG) to determine, if, in fact, a crime occurred, and if so, who was responsible. A failure to do so, moreover, could risk embroiling members of PA&E (up to this point, innocent parties) in a conspiracy to violate several additional criminal statutes (e.g., 18 U.S.C. 2, 3, & 4).

This memorandum provides added weight to these earlier recommendations, because it will show that the sequence of changes to the language of the inserts reveals a pattern that first illuminates (Change #1), then suppresses (Change #2) critical information. Although the discussion will concentrate on the essential elements of and changes to each question and answer, please bear in mind that the legal concept of truth includes the ideas of the truth, the whole truth, and nothing but the truth. The fact that this memo does not discuss the impact of other critical omissions (e.g., the relation of program and cost risk to the prototyping question—see pp. 8–9 of my 28 July memorandum) should not be construed to mean that those concerns are now immaterial. Each incremental change from the preceding version of the insert will be highlighted in ***bold italics***, and each deletion will be highlighted by a ~~strikeout~~. L/C Durham's package is attached, if you desire to examine the language in its entirety.

Question #1: Is there "any" reason to prototype the F-18E?

1st Version Sent to Congress (10 June):

We do not believe there is because . . . "Although structural components have limited commonality, the E/F is very similar aerodynamically, and E/F avionics are 90% hardware common. . . ."

Change #1 (29 July):

We do not believe there is because . . . ***"The flight experience gained with the F-18C/D has provided an extensive data base regarding its aerodynamic characteristics. As a result, the F-18E/F will benefit from significant aerodynamic improvements, particularly in wing design.*** Although structural components have limited commonality, the E/F is very similar ~~aerodynamically~~ ***in planform and the layout of aerodynamic components. More-***

over, the E/F avionics are 90% hardware common. . . ."

Change #2 (10 August)—2nd Version Sent to Congress:

I don't think there is. . . . ~~"The flight experience gained with the F-18C/D has provided an extensive data base regarding its aerodynamic characteristics. As a result, the F-18E/F will benefit from significant aerodynamic improvements, particularly in wing design. Although structural components have limited commonality, the E/F is very similar in planform and the layout of aerodynamic components. Moreover,~~ ***While the airframe design has been modified to substantially increase its range, we have assessed the risk to be low to moderate.*** The E/F avionics are 90% hardware common. . . ."

Analysis:

Change #1 removes the crucial false statement "very similar aerodynamically" and makes the fact that the E/F has a significantly improved wing design evident to the reader. On the other hand, while Change #2 acknowledges that substantial changes were made to the design and is factually correct, the massive deletion denies the reader access to any information revealing that part of the range increase comes from the improved aerodynamics of a new wing.

Senator Bond asked if there was "*any*" reason to build a prototype. The importance of the new wing to this question can not be overstated. Its existence was the crucial finding that emerged during the F-18E's range controversy last April. According to the Navy's calculations, the improved lift-to-drag (L/D) ratio accounts for 40 to 50 percent of the range increase. Since the source of the L/D improvements was at the center of the range controversy, and it was the resolution of this controversy that prompted the prototyping issue (see my 29 April memorandum), as well as Senator Bond's questions, the deletions of Change #2 are very significant. Even when technical risk is "low to moderate," there is always a non-trivial possibility that lift and drag coefficients derived from wind tunnel data will not translate exactly into real-world flight data. This is a fact of life. It is absurd to argue that building a prototype would not reduce this risk. Since Change 2 hid all references to the existence of the new wing, its dismissal of design risk is disingenuous, because it violates the principle of the "whole truth."

It would have been more truthful to acknowledge that the wing has been redesigned, that we believed the wind tunnel data is very reliable, and that we were willing to take a risk, because saving two years is more important than reducing that risk via a prototyping strategy. While I do not agree with this trade off between risk and time, this acknowledgement would explain the rationale behind this decision in terms that reasonable people could understand.

Question #2: "Was that report [the independent PA&E analysis] accurate or was that report flawed?"

As I showed in my 28 July memorandum (pp. 10–12) the 10 June version used loaded words, like simplified and assert, to insinuate that I incorrectly applied the Breguet range equation, when, in fact, this was not the case. The crucial statements in this regard are compared below:

1st Version Sent to Congress (prepared on 10 June):

". . . The analyst used some simplified calculations based on the Breguet range equation to assert the Navy could not achieve the range performance being predicted for the E/F. . . . The bottom line of the assessment team's findings was that the E/F can meet predicted performance, the Navy's position is well supported and the difference with the PA&E analysis is understood. . . ."

Change #1 (29 July):

"The analyst ~~used~~ ***performed*** some ~~simplified~~ ***basic*** calculations ~~based on~~ ***using*** the Breguet range equation to assert the Navy could not achieve the range performance being projected for the E/F a/c ***based on the planned increase in fuel volume alone. This suggested that other unspecified inefficiencies in aerodynamics or engine performance were major contributors.*** . . . The bottom line of the assessment team's findings was that ***the increased fuel volume combined with projected improvements in aerodynamic and engine efficiencies will enable the F-18E/F to achieve*** ~~the E/F can meet~~ the predicted performance; the Navy position is well supported and ~~the difference with the PA&E analysis is understood~~ ***questions regarding the range performance and the E/F design have been resolved. . . .***"

Change #2 (10 August)—2nd Version Sent to Congress:

"The analyst performed some basic calculations using the Breguet range equation ~~to assert~~ ***and questioned whether*** the Navy could ~~not~~ achieve the range performance being projected for the E/F a/c based on the planned increase in fuel volume alone. ~~This suggested that other unspecified efficiencies in aerodynamics or engine performance were major contributors. . . . The bottom line of the assessment team's findings was that~~ ***After a thorough review, these independent experts*** showed the increased fuel volume combined with projected improvements in aerodynamic and engine efficiencies will enable the F-18E/F to achieve the predicted performance. ~~the Navy position is well supported and~~ The questions regarding range performance ~~and the E/F design~~ have been resolved. . . ."

Analysis:

The original insert falsely insinuated that the PA&E analysis was wrong. Change 1 corrected this but did not directly answer Senator Bond's question. It did, however, introduce two crucial facts: (1) that the PA&E analysis served to focus attention on the possibility that there existed changes to the F-18E/F's wing design that were not understood by members of OSD (i.e., by inserting the reference to "unspecified efficiencies in aerodynamics"), and (2) that the independent assessment team's finding that a new wing (i.e., "improvements in aerodynamic . . . efficiencies") was a major contributor to the range increase. Change 1 did not acknowledge that it was the PA&E analysis which first recommended the formation of the independent assessment team to resolve this issue.

Change 2 still does not answer Senator Bond's question. Moreover, by deleting the reference to "unspecified efficiencies," Change 2 obscures the essentially constructive role played by the PA&E analysis in the resolution of the controversy, namely, that it was the recommendation of the PA&E analysis to form a special team of experts, because senior OSD management had no insight into why the "unspecified efficiencies" were producing superior performance in the non-cruise portions of the mission (see my 28 July memorandum, pp. 10–12). Change 2 retained an oblique reference to the importance of the new wing, when it said the E/F would meet its performance predictions because of the combination of the fuel increase and the "*improved aerodynamic* and engine efficiencies." But as shown above, this crucial point was deleted in Change 2 of the insert dealing with the question of prototyping.

Summing up, the second set of inserts forwarded to Congress are factually truthful, but they do not tell the whole truth. Moreover, the pattern of change reveals a systematic effort to remove or obscure specific references to the contribution of the re-designed wing to the performance calculation. While the wind tunnel data was found to be conservative, as I indicated in my 29 April memorandum, the existence of the new wing is a reason for prototyping. To hide the wing's existence with partial or oblique references to it and then say there are no reasons to build a prototype is disingenuous, if not deceptive. This conclusion makes it even more important to forward all the information relating to this affair to the IG for an official determination of which, if any, laws were violated.

Franklin C. Spinney

Staff Analyst

1 Attachment:

Memorandum from L/C Durham, "F-18E/F Inserts for the Record," September 4, 1992 (w/September 11 Amendment).

OFFICE OF THE ASSISTANT SECRETARY OF DEFENSE
WASHINGTON, D.C. 20301-1800

September 11, 1992

MEMORANDUM FOR Mr. Puscheck
THROUGH Mr. Croteau

SUBJECT: Update to My Memorandum—F/A-18E/F Inserts for the Record—INFORMATION MEMORANDUM

This is an update to my Memorandum of September 4, 1992 concerning F/A-18 E/F Inserts for the record. Attached is a copy of the final version of the second Insert as promised in my Memorandum. Additionally, I have been informed that the Original Inserts that were submitted to Congress and referred to in Mr. Spinney's letter of 28 July 1992 were intended to be the final OSD position, normally reflecting full OSD coordination. The Inserts that we "coordinated" on were the final Galley proofs for the record.

James M. Durham

Staff Analyst

OFFICE OF THE ASSISTANT SECRETARY OF DEFENSE
WASHINGTON, D.C. 20301-1800

September 4, 1992

MEMORANDUM FOR Mr. Chu
THROUGH Mr. Puscheck
Mr. Croteau—copy provided

SUBJECT: F/A-18E/F Inserts for the Record—INFORMATION MEMORANDUM

Mr. Croteau asked me to provide you a history of the Inserts for the Record that Mr. Spinney asserts are false and misleading. According to the records that I have the history is:

- Original Inserts as they appeared in Mr. Spinney's letter of 28 July 1992. They had not been sent to PA&E for coordination. (TAB A)
- On 29 July, PA&E verified that the final versions of the Inserts had not been submitted to Congress. The original Inserts prepared on 10 June by OUSD(A) were then sent to PA&E by the Comptroller for coordination. This copy shows Mr. Croteau's comments on July 29, 1992. After some discussion between Mr. Croteau and Dr. Pallas this insert was rejected by both OUSD(A) and PA&E in favor of a new insert which could be more appropriate. (TAB B)

- New Inserts generated by OUSD(A) on 10 August 1992, coordinated by PA&E, accepted by OUSD(A) and forwarded to Comptroller. (TAB C)
- One coordinated Insert was forwarded and accepted by OUSD(A). The second Insert was amended by the Comptroller on 21 August 1992. (TAB D)
- Final insert as coordinated by PA&E, OUSD(A), and the Comptroller. (TAB E)

> Note: The final version of the second insert is not available at this time, however the Comptroller has assured me that it was submitted to Congress exactly as coordinated by PA&E and OUSD(A). A hard copy will be available next week.

James M. Durham

Staff Analyst

Appendix E

Responses from Various Air Force Commands to Headquarters Air Force Request for Comments on New IR Missile

(Nov. 1973)

1. What are the dimensions of the IR Arena?

TAC *[Tactical Air Command]*

Rear quadrant of hostile aircraft between radar missile envelope and gun envelope. With sufficient overlap, usually 1,000 to 18,000 feet.

USAFE *[United States Air Forces Europe]*

IR Missile should be confined to rear quadrant. Envelope should be large enough to miss targets between radar missile envelope and gun envelope.

PACAF *[Pacific Air Forces]*

Aft of beam –60 –90° are around IR source, range 500–1,000 ft. out to 2–3 miles, Sea Level to 25,000 feet.

AAC *[Alaska Air Command]*

1,000–15,000 ft.

2. Is a head-on capability an absolute requirement?

TAC

Not required. Spending scarce defense dollars on duplicating AIM-7 should not be considered.

USAFE

Not a requirement. It should in no way drive complexity nor cost of the IR missile. Any expandability other than rear quadrant should be a spin-off.

PACAF

"Although head-on opportunities will certainly occur in the dogfight arena, this capability is not in consonance with a low cost, unsophisticated concept for IR Missiles."

AAC

Not required. 180°–135° aspect capability.

3. Should all-aspect with associated sophistication, hence high cost, be the driver in our missile program?

TAC

All-aspect not required.

USAFE

Sophistication necessary to achieve an all-aspect capability tends to result in missiles which are expensive to buy, complex to maintain, and difficult to employ. Tracking and hitting targets from other than the rear quadrant aspects tend to drive the cost of these missiles out of reach of the user. Efforts to develop an all-aspect IR missile have a high propensity to end up with a missile which compromises rather than optimizes the desired missile envelope and usually with poorer Pks. Moreover, as a result of this increased complexity, there appears to be a direct decrease in missile reliability.

PACAF

"No attempt should be made to expand the envelope at the expense of reliability."

AAC

Cost should be low enough that crews can fire at least two missiles per year for training.

4. Command Comments

TAC

Tactical Air Command's primary objective to ensure fighter forces with sufficient missile with reliability. Number one criterion is sufficient numbers of missiles to counter threat. Past missile problems of function of too many different models or types. Ease of employment overriding consideration.

USAFE

"It is our opinion that the Air Force can achieve a greatly enhanced capability with relatively unsophisticated IR Missile."

PACAF

". . . future efforts in IR missile development must stress simplicity, reliability and maintainability. "The basic philosophy of employing specialized armament as specific envelopes are traversed while maneuvering for an ultimate gun kill, become more viable with the advent of more maneuverable aircraft." Simplicity, ease of maintenance, low cost, simple switchology.

AAC

Present quick launch procedures are satisfactory.

Source: Responses to Chief of Staff Messages CSAF/XOO 1218422 Nov. 73

Notes

Chapter 1
A Frame of Reference

1. Schemmer, "USAF's Fighter Crews Train," 30.

2. Anderton, *Hellcat,* 5.

3. Story confirmed by numerous individuals present at the meeting, including Larry Welch, John Boyd, and Everest Riccioni.

4. Kross, *Military Reform,* 24.

5. Russ, "Tactical Fighter Development," 33.

6. Statement made by C. E. Myers, Jr. to the author.

7. Goartz, "An Analysis of Air-to-Air Missile,"1–2.

8. Some prominent examples are Spinney, *Defense Facts of Life*, Gabriel, *Military Incompetence*, and Goodwin, *Brotherhood of Arms*. For an overview of the defense reformers, see Clark, et al., eds., *The Defense Reform Debate*. And for an alleged rebuttal that tends to make the reformers' point, see Kross, *Military Reform*. The bellwether publication that unleashed the reformers can probably be attributed to Fallows, *National Defense.* To understand fully the degree of the problem from the reformers' point of view, see Rasor, *The Pentagon Underground.*

9. The *Aerospace America* article has been preceded by numerous articles by members of the press and the military's own. For example, see Alexander Cockburn, "The Real AWACS Secret: It Doesn't Work," *The Wall Street Journal* (24 September 1981): 25; and Lake, "The U.S. Navy: Can Ships Survive?" 83–85.

10. Tasini, "Putting the Pentagon to the Test," 6.

11. See also, Hart, *America Can Win.*

12. Overy, *The Air War*, generally chapter 5.

13. Smith, "Some Thoughts on Clausewitz and Airplanes," 52–57, citing from Hansell, "The Development of the United States Concept," 13.

14. Spinney, *Defense Facts of Life,* 83–99.

15. For a discussion of the argument that civilians did not let the military win the war in Vietnam, see Schlight, "Civilian Control of the Military in Southeast Asia," 56–69. See also Halberstam, *The Best and the Brightest.*

16. See, generally, Hughes, *To the Maginot Line.*

17. Department of the Air Force, "Report of F-105D Configuration Board Proceedings."
18. Russ, "Tactical Fighter Development," 33.
19. Statement made by Larry Welch to author.
20. Ibid.
21. Ibid.
22. Russ, "Tactical Fighter Development," 31.
23. Statement made by Larry Welch to author.
24. Department of the Air Force, *The Development of Air Doctrine,* 66.
25. O'Rourke, "Lightweights and Heavyweights," 28–29.
26. Senate Committee on Armed Forces. *Department of Defense Authorization for Appropriations for Fiscal Year 1980,* 2300–2301. For a definitive analysis on the effectiveness of avionics, see Sprey, "The Impact of Avionics on the Effectiveness of Tactical Air."
27. White, *U.S. Tactical Air Power,* 47–48.
28. Statement made by C. E. Myers, Jr. to author.
29. Ibid.
30. Ibid. Some of the aces in attendance were: Brig. Gen. Harry Thyng, Col. G. Gabreski, Col. Bones Marshall, Col. Woody Davis, Brig. Gen. William Dunham, Col. George Laven, Lt. Col. J. J. Burns, and Lt. Col. Holly. See C. E. Myers, Jr., "FX Review."
31. Reed to Walker, 17 March 1965, author's collection.
32. Agan, letter to Mr. C. E. Meyers [*sic*], 6 May 1965.
33. Department of the Air Force, J. S. McConnell, "Air Superiority," 3 May 1965, author's collection.
34. C. E. Myers, Jr., "Combat Aircraft Grading by Mission," 1966.
35. Statement made by C. E. Myers, Jr. to author.
36. This summary of the components of Clausewitz's friction is from Watts, *The Foundations of U.S. Air Doctrine,* 2. Watts's book is the definitive work on U.S. Air Force doctrine and offers insights into the TACAIR mind-set. Watts's references to Clausewitz come from Clausewitz, *On War,* 2.
37. Watts, *Foundations of U.S. Air Doctrine,* 114–15, 127.
38. AFR-82-1 (18 May 1990), AR 70–50, and NAVAIRINST 8800.3.
39. Sprey, "The Century Series and Beyond." See also Sprey [E. E. Riccioni], "The Nature of a Fighter Aircraft," 145–47. Riccioni actually wrote the article but submitted it under Sprey's name because of his employer's restrictions. Myers adds that much of this material was garnered from Col. Jim Hagerstrom, USAF, a triple ace from World War II and Korea. Statement made by C. E. Myers, Jr., to author.

40. V. Dubrov, "How Has Air Combat Changed?" 277.

41. Statement made by E. E. Riccioni to author.

42. Ferris, "The Keith Ferris Deceptive Aircraft Paint System," 11–17.

43. See Ethell and Price, *Air War South Atlantic,* 19. In this example, a British pilot flew his aircraft ". . .with the radar switched off to avoid alerting the prey."

44. V. Dubrov, "How Has Air Combat Changed?" 277.

45. Ibid., 278.

46. Myers told the author that he got this number from the Red Baron Reports.

47. Statement made by James G. Burton to author.

48. Holloway, "Air Superiority in Tactical Air Warfare," 14. Adolf Galland, the Chief of the Luftwaffe, echoes Holloway's comment regarding the situation in World War II. "The problem of fighter aviation . . . which the Americans have created is simply one of air superiority. Developments as they are proceeding now already border on air supremacy. The ratio of numbers which we fight in the day time is approximately between 1:6 and 1:8." See Galland, *The First and the Last,* 339.

49. Senate Committee on Armed Services, *Department of Defense Authorization for Appropriations for Fiscal Year 1979*, 5204.

50. Ibid., 5213.

51. Statement by James McKinney to author.

52. See Barnard and Stevenson, "Fighter Procurement: Is the Hard Evidence Ignored, Asks Addabbo," 4–5.

53. Ulsamer, "Airpower—NATO's Foremost Deterrent," 27.

54. Senate Committee on Armed Services, *Department of Defense Authorization for Appropriations for Fiscal Year 1979*, 5211.

55. Kross, *Military Reform,* 96–97.

56. "The Adder Affair," *Air Force Flying Review,* 19.

57. Galland, *The First and the Last,* 330.

58. Statement made by Larry Welch to author.

59. From an interview between Jeff Ethell and Benjamin Kelsey.

60. Perry, "The Interaction of Technology and Doctrine," 387.

61. U.S. Strategic Bombing Survey. *The United States,* 22.

62. Kross, *Military Reform,* 97.

63. Statement made by numerous fighter pilots to author.

64. Griffiths, "F-15 Pilots Cite Need," 52.

65. "The New Defense Posture," 76–77.

66. Statement made by Larry Welch to author.

67. Smith, *The Air Force Plans for Peace,* 30, 120.

68. Department of the Air Force, *Civil Air Patrol,* 2.

69. Departments of the Army and the Air Force, National Guard Bureau, *Vista 1999,* 46.

70. Ibid., 66.

Chapter 2

The U.S. Navy Mission

1. House Committee on Appropriations. Subcommittee on Department of Defense, *Department of the Navy Appropriations for 1956,* 118.

2. Senate Committee on Appropriations, *Department of Defense Appropriations for Fiscal Year 1981,* 121–22.

3. Ibid. See also National Security Act of 1947; Key West Agreement 1948; 10 USC 5012; DOD Instruction 5100.1, December 1958; JCS Publication 1; JCS Publication 2 (Updated 1 Oct. 1974); and SECNAV Instruction 5410.85.

4. See Sherrod, *History of Marine Corps Aviation,* 325–26.

5. Holmquist, "Developments and Problems in Carrier-Based Fighter Aircraft," 233.

6. "Task Force Defense Fighter."

7. Brownlow, "Navy Stresses Simplicity, Reliability to Ease Budget Pinch," 78. The Request for Proposal was (PR AER-2477-0).

8. Senate Committee on Government Operations. Permanent Subcommittee on Investigations. *TFX Contract Investigation,* 1382.

9. Holmquist, "Developments and Problems in Carrier-Based Fighter Aircraft," 249.

10. Brownlow, "Navy Stresses Simplicity, Reliability to Ease Budget Pinch," 79.

11. Senate Committee on Government Operations. Permanent Subcommittee on Investigations. *TFX Contract Investigation,* 1382.

12. "F6D Mission Capabilities Presentation," n.p.

13. MacDonald, "The F-111B: Can It Do the Navy's Job?" 38.

14. Coulam, *Illusions of Choice,* 233, 285.

15. Wilson, "Variable-Geometry F-4 Proposed to Navy," 30–31.

16. Statement made to author by Adm. Elmo Zumwalt, USN.

17. Ibid.

18. Coulam, *Illusions of Choice,* 75–76.

19. Senate Armed Services Committee. *Statement of Secretary of Defense Robert S. McNamara,* 120.

20. Senate Armed Services Committee, *Authorization for Military Pro-*

curement, Research and Development, Fiscal Year 1969, 426.

21. *Authorization for Military Procurement, Research and Development, Fiscal Year 1969*, 477.
22. Coulam, *Illusions of Choice*, 303.
23. Christiansen, "F-14—Weapon System in Search," 103–5.
24. Coulam, *Illusions of Choice*, 246–50.
25. Ibid., 249–50.

Chapter 3

Cost, Numbers, and the Lightweight Fighter Concept

1. Holley, *Buying Aircraft*, 194.
2. Ibid., 3–4.
3. Ibid., 4, citing from the 1938 Annual Report of the Secretary of War, 34.
4. Stark, "Why Military Airplanes Cost So Much," 94.
5. White, *U.S. Tactical Air Power*, 43.
6. Lee, *Fighter Facts and Fallacies*, 33–35.
7. Galland, *The First and the Last*, 330.
8. Sims, *Fighter Tactics*, 181–82.
9. Ibid.
10. Stansfield Turner, "The B–1 is a Bummer," *Washington Post* (Editorial Page), 13 March 1981. Early advocates of putting guns on airplanes prior to and during the early part of World War I were either ordered to take them off or forced out of the military. See Munson, *Fighters Attack and Training Aircraft 1914–1919*. The submarine, the M16 rifle, and the P-51 are all examples of innovation that were discovered by outsiders and resisted by the military.
11. Statement made by Ed Schmued to author.

Chapter 4

Vietnam: Old Lessons Relearned

1. C. E. Myers, Jr., "FX Review," February 1968.
2. The early history of the F-15 is well documented. See Neufeld "The F-15 Eagle"; see also Stevenson, *The McDonnell Douglas F-15 Eagle*; and Ethell, *F-15 Eagle*.
3. C. E. Myers, Jr., "FX Review," October 1969 addendum.
4. Boyd, "Aerial Attack Study."
5. Sprey, "F-XX AND VF-XX— Feasible High Performance, Low Cost Fighter Alternatives."
6. Ibid., 2.
7. Ibid., 3.

8. Sprey added: "The usefulness of these devices is a strong justifcation against the active guided weapons dependent on high power level radars, since preparation to employ such weapons will alert an otherwise unaware adversary." See Sprey, "F-XX AND VF-XX—Feasible High Performance, Low Cost Fighter Alternatives," 4. See also Amlie, "Radar: Shield or Target?" 6.
9. Sprey, "F-XX AND VF-XX—Feasible High Performance, Low Cost Fighter Alternatives," 7 n.
10. Ibid.
11. Ibid., 9 n.

Chapter 5

The Aborted Navy Lightweight Fighter

1. Sprey, "Land-Based Tactical Aviation," 36.
2. Wheaton and Hinman, "A Proposal to Conduct a Conceptual Study."
3. Ibid., 1–1.
4. Statement made by Capt. "Tooter" Teague to author.
5. F. S. Teague, "Southeast Asian Aerial Combat Environment."
6. Ibid.
7. Statement made by Bob Thompson to author.
8. Statement made by Ernie Waller to author.
9. Hinman, Adcock [and Wheaton], "A Conceptual Study of Navy Advanced Fighter Alternatives."

Chapter 6

The Air Force Lightweight Fighter

1. Gentry, "Evolution of the F-16 Multinational Fighter," 26.
2. Ibid.
3. Memorandum, Riccioni to Gen. D. Smith, 29 March 1970.
4. Statement made by Pierre Sprey to author.
5. Gentry, "Evolution of the F-16 Multinational Fighter," 27–28.
6. Ibid., 20; Neufeld, "The F-15 Eagle," 46–48.
7. Kissinger, *White House Years*, 225.
8. Gentry, "Evolution of the F-16 Multinational Fighter," 22–23. See also Knaack, *Encyclopedia of U.S. Air Force Aircraft and Missile Systems*, 292.
9. Gentry, "Evolution of the F-16 Multinational Fighter," 24; Knaack, *Encyclopedia of U.S. Air Force Aircraft and Missile Systems*, 293.
10. See Senate Committee on Appropriations, *Department of Defense Appropriations for Fiscal Year 1971*, 306.
11. Statement made by former Air Force Secretary Robert Seamans to

author.

12. Statement made by Lt. Gen. Otto Glasser, USAF (Ret.), to author.

13. Statement made by C. L. "Kelly" Johnson to author.

14. Ibid.

15. For a complete history of the various proposals that the Department of Defense received, see Gentry, "Evolution of the F-16 Multinational Fighter," 24; Knaack, *Encyclopedia of U.S. Air Force Aircraft and Missile Systems.*

16. Gentry, "Evolution of the F-16 Multinational Fighter," 46 citing from Dr. John S. Foster, Director, Defense Research and Engineering, "Aircraft Prototype," memorandum to David Packard, DEPECDEF, 12 February 1971.

17. For a more complete history of the name, see Stevenson, "How the Fighting Falcon Was Named," 5.

18. Statement made by E. E. Riccioni to the author.

19. Cincinnatus, *Self Destruction*, 54.

20. Statement made by Allan Simon to author.

21. Ibid.

22. Ibid.

23. Gentry, "Evolution of the F-16 Multinational Fighter," 48–49.

24. E. E. Riccioni, "US Navy Progress with the Complementary Fighter Program."

25. Gentry, "Evolution of the F-16 Multinational Fighter," 38.

26. Statement made by C. E. Myers, Jr. to author.

27. Statement made by David Packard to author.

28. Gentry, "Evolution of the F-16 Multinational Fighter," 51.

29. Ibid., 51–52.

30. DoD Directive 5000.1, 13 July 1971, 2.

31. "Report on the F-14 and F-15 Tactical Fighters" ([Washington, D.C.: Members of Congress for Peace Through Law), n.d.

32. Statement made by John Boyd to author. See also Gentry, "Evolution of the F-16 Multinational Fighter," 56.

33. Gentry, "Evolution of the F-16 Multinational Fighter," 53–54.

34. NAVAIRNOTE 13010, AIR-103A, 22 June 1971.

35. See generally the following articles from *Armed Forces Journal*: Nihart, "Air Capable Ships and Through Deck Cruisers," 31–33; "Intent for Sea Control Ship Firm," 17; and "Sea Control Ship," 22. See also Zumwalt, *On Watch.*

36. LTV news release and Fact Sheet, "Vought-1100—Lightweight Fighter

Prototype." See also Gentry, "Evolution of the F-16 Multinational Fighter," 52.

37. Statement made by Allan Simon to author.

38. This and the preceding statements made to author attributed to Dr. Robert Frosch.

39. Senate Committee on Armed Services. *Fiscal Year 1972 Authorization for Military Procurement . . . ABM and Reserve Strength,* 3964.

40. Gentry, "Evolution of the F-16 Multinational Fighter," 57; statement made by David Packard to author.

41. Naval Weapon's Center (NWC) letter on NWC position paper of VFA/VSTOL.

42. "Memo," *Armed Forces Journal* (August 1971): 12.

43. Gentry, "Evolution of the F-16 Multinational Fighter," 57.

44. Naval Weapon's Center (NWC) letter on NWC position paper of VFA/VSTOL, Figure 1.

45. Gentry, "Evolution of the F-16 Multinational Fighter," 58; Senate Armed Services Committee, *Advanced Prototype,* 34.

46. Statement made by David Packard to author.

47. Statement made by Riccioni to author.

48. Gentry, "Evolution of the F-16 Multinational Fighter," 58.

49. Senate Armed Services Committee, *Advanced Prototype,* 4–5, 36.

50. Ibid., 40.

51. Ibid., 4.

52. Holmquist, "Developments and Problems in Carrier-Based Fighter Aircraft," 252.

53. Senate Armed Services Committee *Advanced Prototype,* 11–14.

54. *Congressional Record,* 93d Cong., 1st sess., 23 September 1971, 33111.

55. *Congressional Record,* 93d Cong., 1st sess., 23 November 1971, 42951.

56. Senate Committee on Armed Services, *Weapon Systems Acquisition Process,* 254.

57. Ibid., 242.

58. Sprey developed this material from the Korean War GUN-VAL work done by the University of Chicago. See Department of the Air Force, *Project Gun-Val.*

59. Senate Committee on Armed Services. *Weapon Systems Acquisition Process,* 245–46.

60. Ibid., 259.

61. Ibid., 276–77.

62. Ibid., 277–78.

63. Ibid., 281–83.

64. Statement made by Don Madonna to author. Madonna was the former Commanding Officer of the Air Force aggressor squadron.

65. Cincinnatus, *Self Destruction*, 54.

66. Ibid., 288.

67. Ibid., 286–88.

68. Gentry, "Evolution of the F-16 Multinational Fighter," 62.

Chapter 7

The Lightweight Fighter Program

1. Gentry, "Evolution of the F-16 Multinational Fighter," 59–60.

2. Senate Committee on Armed Services, *Fiscal Year 1973 Authorization for Military Procurement*, 2064.

3. Ibid., 3575.

4. Statement made by John Boyd to author describing his maneuvers in getting the F-15 union to focus on a defect that did not exist.

5. Senate Committee on Armed Services. *Fiscal Year 1973 Authorization for Military Procurement*, Part 4, 2064–65.

6. Ibid., Part 6, 3583.

7. Ibid.

8. Ibid., Part 4, 2086.

9. *Webster's Third International Dictionary*.

10. Air Force contract no. F33657-72-R-0235.

11. Senate Committee on Armed Services, *Fiscal Year 1973 Authorization for Military Procurement*, Part 6, 3575.

12. Ibid., Part 4, 2067.

13. Ibid., Part 6, 3586.

14. Statement made by Bud Nelson to author. Boyd, in an earlier comment, stated that "what Nelson is saying here was picked up by the evaluators at Wright-Patterson."

15. "Flexibility Is Key to Management," 101.

16. Statement made by C. L. "Kelly" Johnson to the author.

17. Statement made by a former Lockheed marketeer on the basis that he remain anonymous.

18. Statement made by James Stewart to author.

19. Statement made by Robert Seamans to author.

20. Statement made by James Stewart to author.

21. Anthony, "The Influence of Natural Fligh,t" 22–23, 83.

22. Statement made by Harry Hillaker to author.

23. Statement made by Pierre Sprey and Harry Hillaker to author.

24. Senate Armed Services Committee, *Fiscal Year 1975 Authorization for Military Procurement*, Part 8. "Tactical Air Power," 4553. For more information on the VFA V/STOL program see Schemmer, "Navy's Choice of North American V/STOL Fighter," 36–39.

25. *Congressional Record*, 93d Cong., 1st sess., 25 September 1973, 31232.

26. See ibid., 31219–36 for a general discussion of the status of the F-14.

27. Ibid., 31228.

28. Ibid., 31229.

29. Ibid., 31232.

30. Statement made by Richard Hallock to author.

31. Statement made by James Schlesinger to author.

32. Morris, "Perspectives on the Air Force Lightweight Fighter Program," 32, citing from Senate Committee on Armed Services, *Tactical Air Power*, Part 8, 4176; Part 9, 4581.

33. Ibid.

34. Weisner, "CEB Report of Cost Analysis and Cost Management."

35. Morris, "Perspectives on the Air Force Lightweight Fighter Program," 30.

36. Ibid., 31.

37. Ibid., 26.

38. Ibid., 31.

39. "Navy Air Combat Fighter," briefing, 15 May 1975.

40. Statement made by C. E. Myers, Jr. to author.

41. Letter from Senator Howard Cannon to William P. Clements, 24 April 1974.

42. See Spinney, "Defense Facts of Life," cited in Senate Committee on Armed Services. Subcommittee on Manpower and Personnel, *Impact of Technology on Military Requirements, Readiness and Operations*, 95. See also Coulam, *Illusions of Choice*, 130.

43. C. E. Myers, Jr., "Discussion of the Effort to Establish a Lower Cost Complement of Carrier Based Fighter/Interceptor Aircraft."

44. The Navy was represented by Dr. Potter, Under Secretary of the Navy for Research & Development, Admiral Moran, and Admiral Carr. Lt. Col. Harry Dunn, a Congressional Liaison, also attended the breakfast meeting.

45. C. E. Myers, Jr., "Memorandum for Record—Discussion of VFX Program Situation."

46. Senate Armed Services Committee, *Fiscal Year 1975 Authorization for Military Procurement, Research and Development*, Part 9, "Tactical Air Power," 5094.

47. Ibid., 5115.

48. Ibid., 5114.

49. Ibid., 5118.

50. Statement made by C. E. Myers, Jr. to the author.

51. Senate Armed Services Committee, *Fiscal Year 1975 Authorization for Military Procurement, Research and Development*, Part 9, "Tactical Air Power," 5125-26.

52. Ibid., 5128.

53. Ibid., 5129.

54. Ibid., 5130.

55. Morris, "Perspectives on the Air Force Lightweight Fighter Program," 32, citing from Senate Committee on Armed Services, *Tactical Air Power* hearings, Part 8, 4176; Part 9, 4581.

56. Statement made by C. E. Myers, Jr. to author.

57. Ibid.

58. Statement made by Gerry O'Rourke to author.

59. Department of the Navy, "Presolicitation Notice for Development of a New Navy Strike Fighter (VFAX)," 6 June 1974.

60. Ibid.

61. Morris, "Perspectives on the Air Force Lightweight Fighter Program," 33–34.

62. Clements, "The Lightweight Multinational Fighter Aircraft Program," memorandum, 11 July 1974.

63. C. E. Myers, Jr., "The Basis for Twenty-Six Wings." Unpublished paper in which Myers cites from the Program Decision Memorandum (PDM) and other documents to justify the position that the Air Force increased its force structure as a result of the Air Combat Fighter.

64. Department of Defense, "Development Concept Paper (DCP) for VFAX," 6 August 1974.

65. Morris, "Perspectives on the Air Force Lightweight Fighter Program," 36.

66. VFAX Draws Interest in Europe," 12–13.

67. "F-16 Gains Advantage in the Market," 12–18.

68. Morris, "Perspectives on the Air Force Lightweight Fighter Program," 39–40.

69. Ibid., 35.

70. H.R. Rep. No. 93–1363, 93d Cong., 2d sess., 1974, 27.

71. Affidavit of David S. Lewis, 10 July 1975, 2.

72. Affidavit of W. Paul Thayer, 8 July 1975, 1.

73. "Weapons Systems Procurement Uncertain," 17.

74. The RFQ contained two enclosures: the Criteria for Evaluation and Source Selection and the Request for Proposal for the VFAX Weapon System.

Chapter 8

Winner Take All

1. Senate. Report No. 93-1104, 93d Cong., 2d sess., 16 August 1974.
2. Statement made by Tom Christie to the author.
3. "Sen. Chiles Challenges F-16 Choice," 17.
4. Hughes, "The Congress and Lightweight Fighter Commonality."
5. Statement made by James Schlesinger to author.
6. Statement made by Jack Welch to author.
7. Hughes, "The Congress and Lightweight Fighter Commonality," 5.
8. Ibid.
9. Statement made by Robert Parker to author. Parker was unresponsive as to the merits of a common F-17 being more expensive.
10. Senate Committee on Government Operations. Permanent Subcommittee on Investigations, *TFX Contract Investigation.*
11. Statement made by Tom Christie to author.
12. Statement made by C. E. Myers, Jr., to author.
13. C. E. Myers, Jr., "Prospects for Air Combat Effectiveness of a Cannon/Sidewinder-Equipped Fighter."
14. Ibid. See also Robinson, "Two Strategic Programs Key to Air Force," 25; "Anti-Radar Weapon Development Pushed," 107.
15. Statement made by Tom Christie to author.
16. House Committee on Appropriations, *Department of Defense Appropriations for 1976,* Part 4, "Research, Development, Test, and Evaluation," 647.
17. Ibid., Part 2, 118.
18. Senate Committee on Armed Services, *Fiscal Year 1976 and July–September 1976 Transition Period Authorization . . . and Civilian Personnel Strengths,* Part 9, "Tactical Air Power," 4583.
19. "Navy Expects to Make Decision in March on Air Combat Fighter," 11.
20. Senate Committee on Appropriations, *Lightweight Fighter Aircraft Program,* 101; Hughes, "The Congress and Lightweight Fighter Commonality," 8; Senate Committee on Armed Services, Subcommittee on Tactical Airpower, *F-18 Program,* 19.

Chapter 9

The Air Combat Fighter Evaluation

1. Department of Defense. Public Affairs Office, Press release, 13 January 1975.
2. Statement made by Lee Begin to author.
3. Statement made by Lt. Gen. James Stewart to author.
4. Statement made by Lee Begin to author.
5. Statement made by Walt Fellers to author.
6. Ibid.
7. Statement made by Lee Begin to author.
8. Statement made by Walt Fellers to author.
9. Statement made by Lt. Gen. James Stewart to author.
10. Ibid.
11. Statement made by Lee Begin to author.
12. Statement made by Lt. Gen. James Stewart to author.
13. Ibid.
14. Ibid.
15. Cdr. Ron "Mugs" McKeown, USN, evaluated the YF-16 and YF-17 in January 1975 to assess their fighter capability. See Senate Committee on Armed Services, Subcommittee on Tactical Airpower, *F-18 Program*, 69–71.
16. Statement made by Ron "Mugs" McKeown to author.
17. Statement made by Mike Loh to author.

Chapter 10

The Navy Buys Another Air Force Airplane

1. Statement made by V. Adm. Ray Peet to author. The guided missile frigates were later redesignated as guided missile cruisers.
2. Statement made by R. W. McDonald to author.
3. Senate Committee on Appropriations. *F-18 Navy Air Combat Fighter*, 77–78.
4. Ibid., 77–78; and Senate Committee on Appropriations, *Lightweight Fighter Aircraft Program*, 33.
5. Senate Committee on Armed Services, Subcommittee on Tactical Airpower, *F-18 Program*; Senate Committee on Appropriations, *F-18 Navy Air Combat Fighter*; Senate Committee on Appropriations, *Lightweight Fighter Aircraft Program*; Senate Committee on Government Operations, Subcommittee on Federal Spending Practices, *Major Systems Acquisition Reform*, Part 1, "Air Combat Fighter Program"; and House Committee on Appropriations, Subcommittee on the Department of

Defense, *Department of Defense Appropriations for 1976*, Part 9, "Lightweight Fighter Aircraft Program."

6. House Committee on Appropriations, *Department of Defense Appropriations for 1976*, 274.
7. Senate Committee on Appropriations, *Lightweight Fighter Aircraft Program*, 13.
8. Ibid.
9. Senate Committee on Government Operations, *Major System Acquisition Reform*, 117, testimony of V. Adm. Lee, Commander, Naval Air Systems Command. See also Senate Committee on Government Operations, *Major System Acquisition Reform*, 165; Senate Committee on Appropriations, *Lightweight Fighter Aircraft Program*, 16.
10. Senate Committee on Government Operations, *Major System Acquisition Reform*, 165, 170.
11. Ibid., 177.
12. Ibid., 171.
13. Ibid., 173–74.
14. Ibid., 174.
15. Ibid., 175.
16. Ibid., 181.
17. Ibid., 138.
18. House Committee on Appropriations, *Department of Defense Appropriations for 1976*, 304; Senate Committee on Appropriations, *F-18 Navy Air Combat Fighter*, 105.
19. Senate Committee on Government Operations, *Major System Acquisition Reform*, 179.
20. Ibid., 184.
21. House Committee on Appropriations, *Department of Defense Appropriations for 1976*, 382. See also Senate Committee on Appropriations, *F-18 Navy Air Combat Fighter*, 88.
22. House Committee on Appropriations, *Department of Defense Appropriations for 1976*, 306.
23. For other performance reductions, see Wagner, *The North American Sabre*, 96–98, 143, 147.
24. See Craven and Cate, eds., *The Army Air Forces in World War II*, 462.
25. Coulam, *Illusions of Choice*.
26. Fallows, *National Defense*, 76–95.

Chapter 11

Costs, Mission, and the Promised Performance

1. Senate Committee on Appropriations, *Lightweight Fighter Aircraft*

Program, 6.

2. Ibid., 40.

3. Ibid., 61.

4. Senate Committee on Armed Services, *F-18 Program*, 37–38.

5. House Committee on Appropriations, *Department of Defense Appropriations for 1976*, 295.

6. Senate Committee on Armed Services, *F-18 Program*, 57, 59.

7. Ibid., 160.

8. Ibid., 58–59.

9. Cooper, *The F/A-18: Background Analysis of the Navy/Marine Corps F/A-18 Fighter Attack Program*, 42.

10. For this and the preceding quote, see Senate Subcommittee on Tactical Airpower, *F-18 Program*, 90.

11. Anderton, *Hellcat*, 5.

12. Dean, "Taming the Big-Tailed Beast," 62.

13. For further information on the SB2C Helldiver, see Mizrahi, "The Eagles of the Sea," 50; Bowers, *Curtiss Aircraft 1907–1947*, 423–33; and Trimble, "Big-Assed Bird," 12–23.

14. *Naval Aviation 1943*, 15.

15. Holmquist, "Developments and Problems in Carrier-Based Fighter Aircraft," 229.

16. Ibid.

17. Terzibaschitsch, *Aircraft Carriers of the U.S. Navy*, 282.

18. Stevenson, "TAC Brass Try Pep Talks to Boost F-16 Pilots' Morale," 5.

19. Senate Committee on Appropriations, *Lightweight Fighter Aircraft Program*, 35–36; Senate Committee on Armed Forces, *F-18 Program*, 14.

20. Senate Committee on Armed Services, *F-18 Program*, 67; House Committee on Appropriations, *Department of Defense Appropriations for 1976*, 327; Robinson, "Navy Plans Two Distinct F-18 Versions," 14.

21. Senate Committee on Armed Services, *F-18 Program*, 166.

22. Ibid., 93.

23. Ibid., 94–95, 176.

24. Ibid., 169.

25. Ibid., 166.

26. Ibid., 100–101.

27. Ibid., 170.

28. See Francillion, *McDonnell Douglas Aircraft Since 1920*, 514.

29. House Committee on Appropriations, *Department of Defense Appropriations for 1976*, 318.
30. Senate Committee on Armed Services, *F-18 Program*, 103.
31. Ibid., 137–38.
32. Ibid., 60.
33. Ibid., 154.
34. Ibid., 109.
35. Ibid., 150–51.
36. Ibid., 150–53.
37. Senate Committee on Appropriations, *F-18 Navy Air Combat Fighter*, 51.
38. Ibid.
39. The LTV protest is reprinted in Senate Committee on Government Operations. Subcommittee on Federal Spending Practices, *Major Systems Acquisition Reform*, 8–38. The 1 October 1975 Government Accounting Office decision is reprinted in *Congressional Record* (daily ed.), 94th Cong., 1st sess., Vol. 11, pt. 24, 1 October 1975, H9397–H9405; 55 *Comp. Gen.* 307 (1975).
40. For a succinct summary of the arguments and rebuttals, see Rich, *Competition in the Acquisition of Major Weapon Systems*, 65–70.

Chapter 12

The Promise and the Reality

1. "Operation Short Look II: F-15 European Tour," 2.
2. "Operational FASTPAC."
3. "F-15 Eagle: 'Maximum Availability,' "4.
4. Ibid., 4.
5. Cathey, "The Tactical Air Forces: Outlook," 1.
6. Walter S. Mossberg, "Many Air Force Planes Often Can't Be Flown for Lack of Spare Parts," *Wall Street Journal* (1 June 1981), 1.
7. Ibid.; "F-15 Eagle: 'Maximum Availability,' "4.
8. Department of the Navy, "Initial Operational Evaluation of the F/A-18 Naval Strike Fighter," 1.
9. Walter S. Mossberg, "Many Air Force Planes Often Can't Be Flown for Lack of Spare Parts," *Wall Street Journal* (1 June 1981), 1.
10. Government Accounting Office, "F/A-18 Naval Strike Fighter: Its Effectiveness Is Uncertain."
11. Ibid.; Government Accounting Office, "F/A-18 Naval Strike Fighter: Progress Has Been Made."
12. Statement made by Bill Brinks to author.

13. House Committee on Appropriations, *Department of Defense Appropriations for 1982*, 529.

14. Department of the Navy, "Initial Operational Evaluation of the F/A-18 Naval Strike Fighter," 15.

15. Ibid., 11.

16. Statement made by Bill Brinks to author.

Chapter 13

Quo Vadis Naval Air

1. House Committee on Appropriations, *Department of Defense Appropriations for 1982*, 489.

2. Ibid., 537.

3. For a detailed review of the various studies and reports see Cooper, "The Navy/Marine Corps F/A-18 Aircraft," 24–27.

4. See House Committee on the Budget, Task Force on National Security and International Affairs, *Tactical Air Warfare*, 77–78.

5. For more details see Barnard, "DSARC Delays Full Production of F-18," 1.

6. Barnard, "Carlucci Orders Review of F/A-18," 2.

7. "Fair-Weather Fighter," 1.

8. See, generally, Sprey, "The Impact of Avionics on the Effectiveness of Tactical Air."

Chapter 14

Hornets in the Gulf

1. Mark Crispin Miller, "Death of a Fighter Pilot," *The New York Times* (15 September 1992), A19.

2. McFarland and Newton, *To Command the Sky*, 6.

3. Statement made by senior Department of Defense official who made the statement on the basis of non-attribution.

4. Department of the Air Force, "Air Power Desert Storm: Backgrounder," n.p., n.d., 7.

5. Summers, *A Critical Analysis of the Gulf War*, 10.

6. McFarland and Newton, *To Command the Sky*, 3.

7. Department of the Air Force, "Combat Echo Weapon System Evaluation Program."

8. See C. E. Myers, Jr., "Interdiction for Sea-Based Power Projection," 103–6.

9. CNN interview, 24 January 1991; Fred Kaplan, "Laser Bombs Hit Targets 60 Percent of the Time, Officials Say," *Boston Globe* (20 January 1991), 2; and "Questions Surround a Precision Bombing," *Boston Globe* (14 February 1991), 10.

10. "Tactical Bombing of Iraqi Forces Outstripped Value of Strategic Hits, Analyst Contends," 63.
11. Friedman, "World Naval Developments: LGB Success Rate Revised," 107.
12. Fred Kaplan, "Laser Bombs Hit Targets 60 Percent of the Time, Officials Say," *Boston Globe* (20 January 1991), 2 and "Questions Surround a Precision Bombing," *Boston Globe* (14 February 1991), 10.
13. House Committee on Armed Services, *The Impact of the Persian Gulf War*, 550.
14. Department of Defense, *Conduct of the Persian Gulf War. Final Report to Congress*, 96.
15. Ibid., 96–97.
16. Warden, *The Air Campaign*, 7.
17. Statement made by senior Department of Defense official who made the statement on the basis of non-attribution.
18. Department of Defense, *Conduct of the Persian Gulf War. Final Report to Congress*, 2-6.
19. Department of the Air Force, "Reaching Globally, Reaching Powerfully," 11.
20. Department of Defense, *Conduct of the Persian Gulf War: Final Report to Congress*, 25-1.
21. Friedman, *Desert Victory*, 149.
22. Statement made by senior Department of Defense official who made the statement on the basis of non-attribution.
23. Friedman, *Desert Victory*, 174–75.
24. Ibid., 171, 175.
25. Ibid., 176.
26. Ibid., 178.
27. Muir, "A View from the Black Hole," 86.
28. *Triumph Without Victory*, 267.
29. Statement made by Pierre Sprey to author.
30. Friedman, *Desert Victory*, 158, 171.
31. Statement made by Andrew and Leslie Cockburn to author.
32. "The Gulf War Flu," 50.
33. Friedman, *Desert Victory*, 152.
34. Department of Defense, *Conduct of the Persian Gulf Conflict*, 6-3.
35. Statement made by Maj. Gen. Mike Sullivan to author.
36. Friedman, *Desert Victory*, 161; see also 401, note 28.
37. Cheney editorial, *Aviation Week*, 11.

38. Strike Fighter Squadron 87, "Aircraft—Yes . . . ," 57.
39. Department of the Air Force, "Air Force Performance in Desert Storm," 14.
40. The evidence for this is available on a videotape that was publicly displayed at the 1991 Tailhook Symposium at Las Vegas, Nevada.
41. Friedman, "World Naval Developments," October 1991, 125.
42. Statement made by Pierre Sprey to author.
43. Williams, "Comment & Discussion," 26.
44. Statement made by Col. Reitsch to author.
45. Statement made by Mark Foxx to the author at the 1991 Tailhook Symposium.
46. "The Air War," *U.S. News & World Report*, 47.
47. Dornheim, "Desert Storm Experience," 61.
48. Friedman, "World Naval Developments," *Naval Institute Proceedings* (October 1991), 125.
49. Ralph Vartabedian, "B-2 Bomber Fails Tests of Ability to Evade Radar," *Los Angeles Times* (12 September 1991), A-1.
50. Starr, "Soviets Can Detect B-2, Says McPeak," 693.
51. Kolcum, "Gulf War Reinforces Value of U.S. Stealth," 40.
52. Department of Defense, *Conduct of the Persian Gulf Conflict*, 6-2.
53. Ibid., 1-2, 4-3.
54. See also "Air Force Released Misleading Chart," 237.
55. House Armed Services Committee, *The Impact of the Persian Gulf War*, 582.
56. "Five Cubans Defect in a Biplane," *The New York Times* (21 June 1991), A7.
57. Senate Committee on Foreign Relations, Subcommittee on Terrorism, Narcotics and International Communications, *Drugs, Law Enforcement, and Foreign Policy*, 273–74.
58. White, "Comment & Discussion," 28.
59. Statement made by senior Department of Defense official who made the statement on the basis of non-attribution.
60. O'Leary, "Nighthawks Return Home," 35.
61. Statement made by Jeff Ethell to author as a result of conversation with U.S.S. *America* pilots who observed F-117s during the Gulf War.
62. Friedman, "World Naval Developments," September 1991, 124.
63. Statement made by senior Department of Defense official who made the statement on the basis of non-attribution. See also Friedman, "World Naval Development: LGB Success Rate," 107.

64. Mundy, "Comment & Discussion," 16.

65. Department of Defense, *Conduct of the Persian Gulf Conflict,* 4-6.

66. Department of the Air Force, *Reaching Globally, Reaching Powerfully,* 23.

67. Stevenson, "Strike Eagle Soars at Farnborough," 6.

68. Ibid., 7, citing from Institute for Defense Analysis, "Air-to-Air Combat in World War II."

69. House Armed Services Committee, *The Impact of the Persian Gulf War,* 573.

70. Burton, *The Pentagon Wars: Reformers Challenge the Old Guard.* See chapter entitled "Pushing Them Out the Back Door."

71. LeFong, "Comment & Discussion," 95.

72. House Armed Services Committee, *The Impact of the Persian Gulf War,* 960.

73. Statement made by senior Department of Defense official who made the statement on the basis of non-attribution.

74. Department of Defense, *Conduct of the Persian Gulf Conflict,* 25-1.

75. Statement made by Pierre Sprey to author.

76. Hopgood, "Experience: Handle with Care," 82.

77. Statement made to audience of U.S. Navy and civilian audience at September 1991 Tailhook Symposium.

78. Friedman, *Desert Victory,* 166.

79. "The Invisible Weapons of the Air War," 78.

80. Strike Fighter Squadron 87, "Aircraft—Yes . . . ," 56.

81. Ibid. See also McDonnell Douglas news release 93-187, "F/A-18s Use New Laser Target Designator/Ranger to Successfully Hit Targets with Laser-Guided Bombs," 19 July 1993.

82. Hopgood, "Experience: Handle with Care," 81.

83. Strike Fighter Squadron 87, "Aircraft—Yes . . . ," 56.

84. Friedman, "World Naval Developments: LGB Success Rate Revised," 107.

85. Strike Fighter Squadron 87, "Aircraft—Yes . . . ," 55–56.

86. "Tactical Bombing of Iraqi Forces Outstripped," 62.

87. Ibid.

88. Schemmer, "Six Navy Carriers Launch Only 17% of Attack Missions," 12.

89. House Armed Services Committee, *The Impact of the Persian Gulf War,* 576.

90. Ibid., 574.

91. Ibid.
92. John Fialka, "A-10 'Warthog' a Gulf War Hero, Would Fly to Scrap Heap If Air Force Brass Has Its Way," *The Wall Street Journal* (29 March 1991), A10.
93. Jack Anderson, "The Hero That Almost Missed the War," *The Washington Post* (5 March 1991), C9.
94. Joby Warrick, "Air Force Gives Itself an A Plus on War Role," *Air Force Times* (13 May 1991), 25.
95. Battle Staff Directive No. 7 DTG. 20 Jan 91/0500L, n.p.
96. House Armed Services Committee, *The Impact of the Persian Gulf War*, 581–82.
97. Statement made to the author by Pierre Sprey.
98. House Armed Services Committee, *The Impact of the Persian Gulf War*, 920–21.
99. Robin Wright, "White House Seeks New Funds to Oust Hussein," *Los Angeles Times* (31 May 1992), 1.
100. Richard Pyle, *Schwarzkopf in His Own Words*, 246–47.
101. Burton, "Pushing Them Out the Back Door," 37. See also Burton, *The Pentagon Wars: Reformers Challenge the Old Guard.*
102. Caryle Murphy and R. J. Smith, "U.S. Is Said . . . ," *Washington Post* (20 June 1992), A13.

Chapter 15

The Mercurial F-19 Wasp

1. Department of Defense, Office of the Inspector General, "F/A-18E/F Program," 1.
2. Spinney, "F-18E Performance Uncertainties," 2–3.
3. "The Navy Awarded McDonnell Douglas $25 Million Cost-plus-fix Fee Contract," 26; "Kendall memo on F/A-18E/F DAB," 13.
4. DoD Instruction 5000.1 (23 February 1991).
5. Department of the Navy, "Integrated Program Summary for F/A-18E/F Hornet," 1.
6. "Cann Letter to Rep. Ireland on F/A-18E/F COEA," 12.
7. Department of Defense, Office of the Inspector General, "F/A-18E/F Program," 5.
8. DoD Instruction 5000.2, 4-E-1.
9. DoD Instruction 5000.2–M (February 1991), pt. 8, 8–10.
10. "Cann Letter to Rep. Ireland on F/A-18E/F COEA," 12.
11. Department of Defense, Office of the Inspector General, "F/A-18E/F Program," 14.

12. DoD Instruction 5000.2, pt. 13, sec. B, 13-B-5, 13-B-2-1.
13. Statement made by Tom Christie to author.
14. Department of Defense, Office of the Inspector General, "F/A-18E/F Program," 6–7, 9–10, 44.
15. Mixson to Stevenson, 29 October 1992.
16. Mixson to Stevenson, 29 November 1992.
17. Ibid.
18. Statement made by Franklin C. Spinney to author.
19. Department of Defense.,"Selected Acquisition Reports," various dates.
20. Andy Pasztor, "Navy Is Forced to Cut Long-term Plans to Buy Aircraft For All of Its Carriers," *The Wall Street Journal* (10 March 1992), A20. See also "Navy Failed to Perform Detailed Cost Analysis," 4.
21. "SARS Reflect $6.9 Billion Increase," 270.
22. Statement made by Franklin C. Spinney to author.
23. Spinney, "Memorandum for the Record," 1.
24. Spinney, "F-18E Performance Uncertainties," 1.
25. Department of the Navy, Naval Air Systems Command, Attachment to: "Performance Comparisons with F/A-18A."
26. Heinemann, "A Veteran Designer's Thoughts on Fighters," 180–81.
27. Ibid.
28. Spinney, "Memorandum for the Record," 2.
29. Spinney, "Memorandum for Mr. Chu," 2–3.
30. Spinney, "Memorandum for the Record," 6.
31. Ibid., 6–7.
32. Thomas E. Ricks, "McDonnell Got Improper Aid, Report Finds," *The Wall Street Journal* (27 January 1993), A3.
33. Department of Defense, Office of the Inspector General, "F/A-18E/F Program," 1.
34. Ibid., 38–39.
35. "Cann Letter to Rep. Ireland on F/A-18E/F COEA," 12.
36. Congressional Research Service, "Tactical Aircraft Modernization Issues for Congress," 2–3. Partially as a result of the ever-increasing cost, some congressmen wanted to look at prototyping.
37. Spinney, "Memorandum for Mr. Chu," 1.
38. Ibid., Tab 1, 1 of 4.
39. Ibid., Tab 1, 2 of 4; see also "F/A-18E/F Prototypes Would Result in 'Unwarranted Delay,' Cheney Says," 4–5.
40. Spinney, "Memorandum for Mr. Chu," Tab 1, 3 of 4.

41. Ibid., Tab 1, 4 of 4.

42. Spinney, "Memorandum to Mr. Puscheck through Mr. Croteau: F-18E —Making False Statements to Congress (2)," 1.

43. Ibid.

44. Spinney, "Memorandum for Mr. Chu," 1–2.

45. *Bryson* v. *U.S.* (1969), 396 US 71, 73.

46. Spinney, "Memorandum to Mr. Puscheck through Mr. Croteau: F-18E —Making False Statements to Congress (3)," Tab E.

47. Ibid.

48. Ibid.

49. Ibid., 3.

50. Spinney, "Memorandum to Mr. Puscheck through Mr. Croteau: F-18E —Making False Statements to Congress (2)," 2.

51. *Congressional Record,* 102d Cong., 1st sess., 1 October 1992, H10224.

52. Ibid., H10345.

53. Statement made by Col. Manfred Reitsch to author.

54. Lee, *Fighter Facts and Fallacies,* 33–35.

55. Dunleavy, "Myths vs. Facts," 70.

56. Steidle, "Fly Off F/A-18E vs. 18C," 16.

57. Letter from Steidle to Spinney, PMA265/3082, 28 December 1992.

58. Ibid.

59. Lorraine Adams, "Rehnquist Talks on Free Speech in GMU Address," *The Washington Post* (23 May 1993), B5.

60. "The F/A-18 Hornet Multimission Strike Fighter," 3–2.

61. Department of the Navy, Naval Air Systems Command, "Integrated Program Summary, Annex D," 2, 5.

62. Ibid., 1.

63. Department of the Navy, Naval Air Systems Command, "Department of Defense Information Paper: RDT&D, Navy (PE 0204136N)."

64. Spinney, "Anatomy of Decline."

65. Ibid.

66. Ibid.

67. Statement made by John Boyd to author.

Bibliography

"The Adder Affair." *Air Force Flying Review* (November 1956): 19.

Agan, Arthur C., Jr. Letter to Mr. C. E. Meyers [*sic*], 6 May 1965. Author's collection.

"Air Force Released Misleading Chart to 'Sell' Stealth." *Aerospace Daily* (13 November 1991): 237.

"The Air War." *U.S. News & World Report* (20 January 1992): 47.

The American Heritage Dictionary (3rd ed.). Boston: Houghton Mifflin Co., 1992.

Amlie, Tom. "Radar: Shield or Target?" *Spectrum.* (April 1982): 6.

Anderton, David A. *Hellcat.* New York: Crown Books, 1981.

Anthony, Michael. "The Influence of Natural Flight." *Air Travel News* (September 1929): 22–23, 83.

Barnard, Richard. "Carlucci Orders Review of F/A-18." *Defense Week* (27 April 1981): 2.

——— "DSARC Delays Full Production of F-18." *Defense Week* (23 March 1981): 1.

Barnard, R., and J. Stevenson. "Fighter Procurement: Is the Hard Evidence Ignored, Asks Addabbo." *Defense Week* (30 June 1980): 4–5.

Bowers, Peter M. *Curtiss Aircraft 1907–1947.* London: Putnam, 1979.

Boyd, John R. "Aerial Attack Study." U.S. Air Force 50–10–6C. Nellis Air Force Base, Nev.: Air Force Fighter Weapons School, 11 August 1964.

Brownlow, C. "Navy Stresses Simplicity, Reliability to Ease Budget Pinch." *Aviation Week & Space Technology* (9 March 1959): 78.

Burton, James G. "Pushing Them Out the Back Door." *Naval Institute Proceedings* (June 1993): 37–45.

Burton, James G. *The Pentagon Wars: Reformers Challenge the Old Guard.* Annapolis, Md.: Naval Institute Press, 1993.

"Cann Letter to Rep. Ireland on F/A-18E/F COEA." *Inside the Navy* (6 July 1992): 12.

Cannon, Howard. Letter to Wm. P. Clements, 24 April 1974.

Cathey, Carl H. "The Tactical Air Forces: Outlook for the Next Decade." Frontiers of Achievement, AIAA–81–0932. New York: American Institute of Aeronautics and Astronautics, 1981, 1.

Cheney, Dick. Editorial. *Aviation Week & Space Technology* (9 September 1991): 11.

Christiansen, John S. "F-14—Weapon System in Search of an Engine." *Naval Institute Proceedings* (December 1976): 103–5.

Cincinnatus. *Self Destruction: The Disintegration and Decay of the United States Army during the Vietnam Era.* New York: Norton, 1981.

Clark, Asa A., et al., eds. *The Defense Reform Debate: Issues and Analysis.* Baltimore: Johns Hopkins Univ. Press, 1984.

Clausewitz, Carl von, *On War*. Edited and translated by Michael Howard and Peter Paret. Princeton: Princeton Univ. Press, 1976.

Clements, William P. "The Lightweight Multinational Fighter Aircraft Program." Memorandum for the Chairman, Multinational Fighter Committee, 11 July 1974.

Cooper, Bert H. "Tactical Aircraft Modernization Issues for Congress." Washington, D.C.: Congressional Research Service, 1992.

———. The F/A-18: Background Analysis of the Navy/Marine Corps F/A-18 Fighter Attack Program. Washington, D.C.: Congressional Research Service, 15 December 1978.

———. "The Navy/Marine Corps F/A-18 Aircraft: A Survey of Major Issues." Washington, D.C.: Congressional Research Service, 18 November 1981.

Coulam, Robert F. *The Illusions of Choice: The F-111 and the Problem of Weapons Acquisition Reform.* Princeton: Princeton Univ. Press, 1977.

Craven, Wesley F., and J. L. Cate, eds. *The Army Air Forces in World War II.* Vol. 1, *Plans and Early Operations, January 1939 to August 1942.* Chicago: Univ. of Chicago Press, 1948.

Dean, Jack. "Taming the Big-Tailed Beast." *Wings* (August 1971): 37–38, 40–41, 46–47, 62–63.

Dornheim, Michael A. "Desert Storm Experience Spurs Joint Development." *Aviation Week and Space Technology* (2 February 1992): 61.

Dubrov. V. "How Has Air Combat Changed?" *Aviatsya i Klosmonautika* (*Aviation and Cosmonautics*). Translated in *Soviet Press: Selected Translations.* Washington, D.C.: Air Force Intelligence Service (September 1978): 276–80.

Dunleavy, Richard M., "Myths vs. Facts." *Naval Institute Proceedings* (February 1992): 70.

Ethell, Jeffrey, *F-15 Eagle*. London: Ian Allen, 1981.

Ethell, Jeffrey and Alfred Price. *Air War South Atlantic.* New York: Macmillan, 1983.

"The F/A-18 Hornet Multimission Strike Fighter." McAir Report B1361, revision A. 2 January 1990.

"Fair-Weather Fighter: Report Bashes the F/A-18." *Defense Week* (20 April

1981): 1.

Fallows, James. *National Defense*. New York: Random House, 1981.

Ferris, Keith. "The Keith Ferris Deceptive Aircraft Paint System: Another Nickel on the Grass?" *Topgun Journal* 1, no. 2 (Spring 1976): 11–17.

"Flexibility Is Key to Management." *Aviation Week & Space Technology*. N.d., 101.

Foster, Dr. John S. Director, Defense Research and Engineering (DDR&E), "Aircraft Prototype." Memorandum to David Packard, DEPSECDEF, 12 February 1971.

Francillion, René. *McDonnell Douglas Aircraft Since 1920*. London: Putnam, 1980.

Friedman, Norman. "World Naval Developments." *Naval Institute Proceedings* (September 1991): 124.

———. "World Naval Developments." *Naval Institute Proceedings* (October 1991): 125.

———. "World Naval Developments: LGB Success Rate Revised." *Naval Institute Proceedings* (June 1992): 107.

"F-15 Eagle: 'Maximum Availability . . . Minimum Maintenance.' " [St. Louis, Mo.]: McDonnell Aircraft Co. (P.S. 838) 1 October 1976.

"F-16 Gains Advantage in the Market." *Aviation Week & Space Technology* (20 January 1975): 12–18.

"F/A-18E/F Prototypes Would Result in 'Unwarranted Delay,' Cheney Says." *Inside the Navy* (29 June 1992): 4–5.

"F6D Mission Capabilities Presentation." Report NO. AD-51003-AC-1. El Segundo, Calif.: Douglas Aircraft Co., 25 February 1961.

Gabriel, Richard A. *Military Incompetence: Why the American Military Doesn't Win*. New York: Hill and Wang, 1985.

Galland, Adolf, *The First and the Last: The German Fighter Force in World War II*. London: Methuen & Co., 1955.

Gentry, Jerauld R. "Evolution of the F-16 Multinational Fighter," Student Research Report No. 163. Washington, D.C.: Industrial College of the Armed Forces, 1976.

Goartz, Robert D. "An Analysis of Air-to-Air Missile Capability in Southeast Asia." Montgomery, Ala.: Maxwell Air Force Base, June 1968.

Goodwin, Jacob. *Brotherhood of Arms*. New York: Times Books. 1985.

Griffiths, David R. "F-15 Pilots Cite Need for New Air-to-Air Missile." *Aviation Week & Space Technology* (2 November 1981): 52.

"The Gulf War Flu." *U.S. News & World Report* (20 January 1992): 50.

Halberstam, David. *The Best and the Brightest*. New York: Random House, 1972.

Halleland, H. L. "Navy Air Combat Fighter (NACF)." Briefing by PMA 265 given at DDR&E (TWP), 15 May 1975.

Hansell, Haywood S. "The Development of the United States Concept of Bombardment Operations." Lecture presented at the Air War College, 19 September 1951. (Available in Simpson Historical Research Center, file K239.766251–76, p. 13.)

Hart, Gary. *America Can Win: The Case for Military Reform.* Bethesda, Md.: Adler & Adler, 1986.

Heinemann, Edward H. "A Veteran Designer's Thoughts on Fighters." *Air International* (October 1982): 180–81.

Hinman, K. R., C. L. Adcock, [and David J. Wheaton]. "A Conceptual Study of Navy Advanced Fighter Alternatives." Report NO. GDCA–DDM71-001 San Diego, Calif.: General Dynamics Convair, 18 January 1971.

Hinsley, F. H. *British Intelligence in the Second World War: Its Influence on Strategy and Operations.* Vol. 3, Part 1. New York: Cambridge Univ. Press, 1984.

Holley, Irving B., Jr. *Buying Aircraft: Material Procurement for the Army Air Forces.* United States Army in World War II, Special Studies. Washington, D.C.: Office of the Chief of Military History, United States Army, 1964.

Holloway, Bruce K. "Air Superiority in Tactical Air Warfare." *Air University Review* (March–April 1968): 14.

Holmquist, Carl O. "Developments and Problems in Carrier-Based Fighter Aircraft." *Naval Institute Proceedings* (May 1970): 229.

Hopgood, M. T., Jr. "Experience: Handle with Care." *Naval Institute Proceedings* (October 1991): 82.

Hughes, Judith M. *To the Maginot Line: The Politics of French Military Preparation in the 1920s.* Cambridge: Harvard Univ. Press, 1971.

Hughes, Phillip G. "The Congress and Lightweight Fighter Commonality (B)." Draft II. Cambridge, Mass.: Harvard Univ. School of Business Administration, March 1979.

Institute for Defense Analysis. "Air-to-Air Combat in World War II: A Quantitative History." Economic and Political Studies Division. Research paper P–345, November 1966.

"The Invisible Weapons of the Air War." *U.S. News & World Report* (20 January 1992): 78.

Janis, Irving L. *Groupthink: Psychological Studies of Policy Decisions and Fiascoes* (2d ed.). Boston: Houghton Mifflin Co., 1982.

"Kendall Memo on F/A-18E/F DAB." *Inside the Navy* (6 July 1992): 13.

Kissinger, Henry. *White House Years.* Boston: Little, Brown & Co., 1979.

Knaack, Marcelle Size. *Encyclopedia of U.S. Air Force Aircraft and Missile Systems.* Vol. 1, *Post-World War II Fighters 1945–1973.* Washington,

D.C.: Office of Air Force History, 1978.

Kolcum, Edward H. "Gulf War Reinforces Value of U.S. Stealth Technologies." *Aviation Week & Space Technology* (18 February 1991): 40.

Kross, Walter. *Military Reform: The High-Tech Debate in Tactical Air Forces.* Washington, D.C.: National Defense Univ. Press, 1985.

Lake, Julian. "The U.S. Navy: Can Ships Survive?" *Spectrum.* (October 1982): 83–85.

Lee, G. John. *Fighter Facts and Fallacies.* New York: William Morrow, 1942.

LeFong, Carroll F. "Comment & Discussion." *Naval Institute Proceedings* (October 1991): 95.

Lerner, Eric J. "Avionics Unreliability Turns Fighters into Shop Queens." *Aerospace America* (August 1985): 68–70.

Lewis, David S. Affidavit, 10 July 1975.

MacDonald, Scott. "The F-111B: Can It Do the Navy's Job?" *Armed Forces Management* (December 1966): 38.

McConnell, J. S. "Air Superiority." Memorandum to All Major Commands. Department of the Air Force, Office of the Chief of Staff, 3 May 1965.

McFarland, Stephen Lee, and Wesley Phillips Newton. *To Command the Sky: The Battle for Air Superiority over Germany, 1942–1944.* Washington, D.C.: Smithsonian Institution Press, 1991.

"Memo." *Armed Forces Journal* (August 1971): 12.

Mixson, Riley. Letter to Stevenson, 18 November 1992.

———. Letter to Stevenson, 29 October 1992.

Mizrahi, Joe. "The Eagles of the Sea." *Wings* (October 1980): 50.

Morris, Frederick A. "Perspectives on the Air Force Lightweight Fighter Program." Unpublished paper. Santa Monica, Calif.: Rand Corporation, February 1977.

Muir, Daniel J. "A View from the Black Hole." *Naval Institute Proceedings* (October 1991): 86.

Mundy, Carl E., Jr. "Comment & Discussion." *Naval Institute Proceedings* (January 1992): 16.

Munson, Kenneth. *Fighters Attack and Training Aircraft 1914–1919. The Pocket Encyclopaedia of World Aircraft in Color.* New York: Macmillan, 1968.

Myers, C. E., Jr. "The Basis for Twenty-Six Wings." Unpublished paper, n.d.

———. "Discussion of the Effort to Establish a Lower Cost Complement of Carrier Based Fighter/Interceptor Aircraft." Memorandum to Director, DDR&E through DD(TWP). n.d.

———. "Interdiction for Sea-Based Power Projection." *Naval Institute Proceedings* (November 1979): 103–6.

———. "Littoral Warfare: Back to the Future." *Naval Institute Proceedings* (November 1990): 48–55.

———. "Memorandum for Record—Discussion of VFX Program Situation." AD(AW) (11 June 1974).

———. "Prospects for Air Combat Effectiveness of a Cannon/Sidewinder-Equipped Fighter." Washington, D.C.: Office of the Director of Defense Research & Engineering (29 March 1974).

———. "Time to Fold 'em." *Naval Institute Proceedings* (July 1991): 37–41.

Naval Aviation 1943. Annapolis, Md.: Naval Institute Press, 1943.

"The Navy Awarded McDonnell Douglas $25 Million Cost-plus-fix Fee Contract of Re-engineering Studies for Proposed E/F Upgrade." *Aviation Week & Space Technology* (9 September 1991): 26.

"Navy Expects to Make Decision in March on Air Combat Fighter." *Aviation Week & Space Technology* (3 February 1975): 15–16.

"Navy Failed to Perform Detailed Cost Analysis in Initial $3.3 Billion E/F Estimate." *Inside the Navy* (29 June 1992): 4

Neufeld, Jacob. "The F-15 Eagle: Origins and Development 1964–1972." [Washington, D.C.]: Office of Air Force History, 1974.

"The New Defense Posture: Missiles, Missiles, and Missiles." *Business Week* (11 August 1980): 76–77.

Nihart, Brook. "Air Capable Ships and Through Deck Cruisers: Sea-Air on the Cheap." *Armed Forces Journal International* (19 April 1971): 31–33.

———. "Intent for Sea Control Ship Firm: Interim SCS Imminent." *Armed Forces Journal International* (7 June 1971): 17.

———. "Sea Control Ship."*Armed Forces Journal International* (February 1972): 22.

O'Leary, Michael. "Nighthawks Return Home." *Air Combat* (June 1991): 35.

"Operational FASTPAC." [St. Louis, Mo.]: McDonnell Douglas Corp., February 1977.

"Operation Short Look II: 'F-15 European Tour,' August 24, 1974–October 5, 1974." St. Louis, Mo.: McDonnell Douglas Corp, 1974.

O'Rourke, G. G. "Lightweights and Heavyweights." *Naval Institute Proceedings* (February 1973): 28–29.

Overy, R. J. *The Air War: 1939–1945*. New York: Stein and Day, 1981.

Pasztor, Andy. "Navy Is Forced to Cut Long-term Plans to Buy Aircraft for All of Its Carriers." *The Wall Street Journal* (10 March 1992): A20.

The Oxford English Dictionary. New York: Oxford Univ. Press, 1993.

Perry, Robert. "The Interaction of Technology and Doctrine in the USAF." In *Air Power and Warfare* (Proceedings of the Eighth Military History Symposium: USAF Academy 1978). Washington, D.C.: Office of Air Force History, 1979.

Pyle, Richard. *Schwarzkopf in His Own Words: The Man, the Mission, the Triumph.* New York: Signet, 1991.

Raffe, Joseph P. "F/A-18 Range Issues." Government Accounting Office. National Security and International Affairs Division (11 May 1992).

The Random House Dictionary. New York: Random House, 1983.

Rasor, Dina. *The Pentagon Underground.* New York: Times Books, 1985.

Reed, William S., to Thomas J. Walker. Letter, 17 March 1965.

Riccioni to Gen. D. Smith, 29 March 1970.

Riccioni, Everest. E. "U.S. Navy Progress with the Complementary Fighter Program." U.S. Department of the Air Force. Memorandum, 6 April 1971.

Rich, Michael D. *Competition in the Acquisition of Major Weapon Systems: Legislative Perspectives*. Santa Monica, Calif: The Rand Corporation, November 1976.

Robinson, Clarence A. "Anti-Radar Weapon Development Pushed." *Aviation Week & Space Technology* (27 January 1975): 107.

———. "Navy Plans Two Distinct F-18 Versions." *Aviation Week and Space Technology* (26 May 1975): 14.

———. "Two Strategic Programs Key to Air Force." *Aviation Week & Space Technology* (17 March 1975): 25.

———. "VFAX Draws Interest in Europe." *Aviation Week & Space Technology* (16 September 1974): 12–13.

Russ, Robert D. "Tactical Fighter Development: We Have Debated Long Enough." *Air Force Magazine* (April 1981): 33.

"SARS Reflect $6.9 Billion Increase over Previous Quarter." *Aerospace Daily* (19 August 1991): 270.

Schemmer, Benjamin F. "Navy's Choice of North American V/STOL Fighter Stirs Intra-Service, Technical, and Industry Debate." *Armed Forces Journal International* (July 1972): 36–39.

———. "Six Navy Carriers Launch Only 17% of Attack Missions in Desert Storm." *Armed Forces Journal International* (January 1992): 12.

———. "USAF's Fighter Crews Train to Win in TAC's Air Combat Program." *Armed Forces Journal International* (May 1974): 30.

Schlight, John. "Civilian Control of the Military in Southeast Asia." *Air University Review* 32 (November–December 1980): 56–69.

"Sen. Chiles Challenges F-16 Choice." *Aviation Week & Space Technology* (20 January 1975): 17.

Sherrod, Robert. *History of Marine Corps Aviation in World War II.* San Rafael, Calif.: Presidio Press, 1980.

Sims, Edward H. *Fighter Tactics and Strategy 1914–1970.* New York: Harper & Row, 1972.

Smith, James B. "Some Thoughts on Clausewitz and Airplanes." *Air University Review* (May–June 1986): 52–57.

Smith, Perry McCoy. *The Air Force Plans for Peace: 1943–1945.* Baltimore: Johns Hopkins Univ. Press, 1970.

Spangenberg, George A. and A. E. Waller. "Light Fighters for the USN." *Flight International* (1 August 1974): 113–14.

Spinney, Franklin C. "Anatomy of Decline: Why Today's Decisions Are Setting the Stage for a 'Hollow' Military or Higher Defense Budgets in the Mid–to–Late 1990s." Briefing [May 1993], n.p.

———. *Defense Facts of Life: The Plans/Reality Mismatch.* Boulder, Colo.: Westview Press, 1985.

———. "F-18E Performance Uncertainties and Program Recommendation." Washington, D.C.: Office of the Secretary of Defense, Program Analysis & Evaluation, 8 April 1992.

———. "Fly Off F/A-18E vs. 18C." *Naval Institute Proceedings* (September 1992): 41–46.

———. "Memorandum for the Record." Washington, D.C.: Office of the Secretary of Defense, Program Analysis & Evaluation, 29 April 1992.

———. "Memorandum to Mr. Puscheck through Mr. Croteau: F-18E—Making False Statements to Congress (2)." Washington, D.C.: Office of the Secretary of Defense, Program Analysis & Evaluation, 26 August 1992.

———. "Memorandum to Mr. Puscheck through Mr. Croteau: F-18E—Making False Statements to Congress (3)." Washington, D.C.: Office of the Secretary of Defense, Program Analysis & Evaluation, 14 September 1992.

———. "Memorandum for Mr. Chu through Mr. Puscheck, Mr. Croteau: F-18E—Making False Statements to Congress—Action Memorandum." Washington, D.C.: Office of the Assistant Secretary of Defense, Program Analysis & Evaluation, 28 July 1992.

Sprey, Pierre M. "The Century Series & Beyond." Briefing, Processed, n.d.

———. "F-XX and VF-XX—Feasible High Performance, Low Cost Fighter Alternatives." Staff Study (Washington, D.C.): Office of the Assistant Secretary of Defense, Systems Analysis, 9 June 1969.

———. "The Impact of Avionics on the Effectiveness of Tactical Air." Staff Study, Processed. Washington, D.C.: Office of the Assistant Secretary of Defense, Systems Analysis, June 1968.

———. "Land-Based Tactical Aviation." In *Critical Issues: Reforming the Military.* Ed. Jeffrey G. Barlow. Washington, D.C.: Heritage Foundation,

1981.

———. [E. E. Riccioni]. "The Nature of a Fighter Aircraft." *Interavia* (February 1973): 145–47.

Stark, Frederick T. "Why Military Airplanes Cost So Much and What Can Be Done About It." *Air University Review* 25 (November–December 1973): 94.

Starr, Barbara. "Soviets Can Detect B-2, Says McPeak." *Jane's Defence Weekly* (19 October 1991): 693.

Steidle, Craig. "Fly Off F/A-18E vs. 18C." *Naval Institute Proceedings* (November 1992): 16.

Stevenson, James P. "Fly Off F/A-18E vs. 18C." *Naval Institute Proceedings* (January 1993): 22.

———. "How the Fighting Falcon Was Named." *Defense Week* (28 July 1980): 5.

———. *The McDonnell Douglas F-15 Eagle.* Fallbrook, Calif.: Aero Publishers, 1978.

———. "TAC Brass Try Pep Talks to Boost F-16 Pilot's Morale." *Defense Week* (6 October 1980): 5.

———. "Strike Eagle Soars at Farnborough." *Defense Week* (1 September 1980): 6–7.

Strike Fighter Squadron 87. "Aircraft—Yes, Tactics—Yes, Weapons—No." *Naval Institute Proceedings* (November 1991): 56–57.

Summers, Harry. *On Strategy II: A Critical Analysis of the Gulf War.* New York: Dell, 1992.

"Tactical Bombing of Iraqi Forces Outstripped Value of Strategic Hits, Analyst Contends." *Aviation Week & Space Technology* (27 January 1992): 62.

"Task Force Defense Fighter." Report PDR-118-5. Bethpage, N.Y.: Grumman Aircraft Co., December 1955.

Teague, F. S. "Southeast Asian Aerial Combat Environment." Processed. n.p., n.d.

Terzibaschitsch, Stefan. *Aircraft Carriers of the U.S. Navy.* Annapolis, Md: Naval Institute Press, 1980.

Thayer, Paul, W. Affidavit, 8 July 1975.

Trimble, Robert L. "Big-Assed Bird." *Air Classics* (May 1981): 12–23.

Triumph Without Victory: The Unreported History of the Persian Gulf War. New York: Times Books, 1992.

Ulsamer, Edgar. "Airpower—NATO's Foremost Deterrent." *Air Force Magazine* (April 1978): 27.

U.S. Congress. *Congressional Record.* 94th Cong., 1 sess. Vol. 121, pt. 24.

Washington, D.C.: Government Printing Office, 1 October 1975.

———. *Congressional Record.* 102d Cong., 2d sess. Vol. 138, pt. 11. Washington D.C.: Government Printing Office, 1 October 1992.

———. *Congressional Record.* 92d Cong., 1st sess. Vol. 117, pt. 33. Washington D.C.: Government Printing Office, 23 November 1971.

———. *Congressional Record.* 93d Cong., Vol. 119, pt. 24. Washington D.C.: Government Printing Office, 25 September 1973.

———. *Congressional Record.* Vol. 117, pt. 24. Washington D.C.: Government Printing Office, 23 September 1971.

U.S. Congress. Government Accounting Office. "F/A-18 Naval Strike Fighter: Its Effectiveness Is Uncertain." PSAD-80-24. Washington, D.C.: Government Printing Office, 14 February 1980.

———. Government Accounting Office. "F/A-18 Naval Strike Fighter: Progress Has Been Made But Problems and Concerns Continue." MASAD-81-3. Washington, D.C.: Government Printing Office, 18 February 1981.

U.S. Congress. House. Committee on Appropriations. *Department of Defense Appropriations for 1982.* Hearings. Part 6. 97th Cong., 1st. sess. Washington, D.C.: Government Printing Office, 1981.

———. *Department of Defense Appropriations for 1976.* Hearings. Part 4. "Research, Development, Test, and Evaluation." 94th Cong., 1st sess. Washington, D.C.: Government Printing Office, 1975.

———. Subcommittee on Department of Defense. *Department of the Navy Appropriations for 1956.* Hearings. 84th Cong., 1st sess. Washington, D.C.: Government Printing Office, 1955.

———. *Department of Defense Appropriations for 1976.* Hearings. Part 9. "Lightweight Fighter Aircraft Program." 94th Cong., 1st sess. Washington, D.C.: Government Printing Office, 1975.

———. House. Committee on Armed Services. Subcommittee on Procurement and Nuclear Systems. *National Defense Authorization Act for Fiscal year 1992—H.R. 5006.* 102d Cong., 2d sess. Washington, D.C.: Government Printing Office, 1992.

———. *The Impact of the Persian Gulf War and the Decline of the Soviet Union on How the United States Does Its Defense Business.* Hearings. 102d Cong., 1st sess. Washington, D.C.: Government Printing Office, 1991.

———. House. Committee on the Budget. Task Force on National Security and International Affairs. *Tactical Air Warfare.* Hearings. 95th Cong., 1st sess. Washington, D.C.: Government Printing Office, 1977.

———. House. Rep. No. 93–1363, 93d Cong., 2d sess. Washington, D.C.: Government Printing Office, 1974.

———. Senate Committee on Appropriations. *F-18 Navy Air Combat Fighter.*

Hearings on H.R. 9861. 94th Cong., 1st sess. Washington, D.C.: Government Printing Office, 1975.

———. Senate. Armed Services Committee. *Advanced Prototype.* 92d Cong., 1st sess. Washington, D.C.: Government Printing Office, 1971.

———. *Fiscal Year 1975 Authorization for Military Procurement, Research and Development, and Active Duty. Selected Reserve and Civilian Personnel Strengths.* Hearings on S. 3000 Part 8. "Tactical Air Power." 93rd Cong., 2d sess. Washington, D.C.: Government Printing Office, 1974.

———. Part 9. "Tactical Air Power." 93d Cong., 2d sess. Washington, D.C.: Government Printing Office, 1974.

———. *Statement of Secretary of Defense Robert S. McNamara Before the Senate Armed Services Committee on the Fiscal Year 1969–1973 Defense Program and 1969 Defense Budget.* Washington, D.C.: Government Printing Office, 1968.

———. Senate. Committee on Armed Services. *Authorization for Military Procurement, Research and Development, Fiscal Year 1969, and Reserve Strength.* Hearings on S. 3293. 90th Cong., 2d sess. Washington, D.C.: Government Printing Office, 1968.

———. Senate. Committee on Government Operations. Subcommittee on Federal Spending Practices, Efficiency, and Open Government. *Major Systems Acquisition Reform.* Hearings 94th Cong., 1st sess. Part 1. Washington, D.C.: Government Printing Office, 1975.

———. Senate. Committee on Appropriations. *Department of Defense Appropriations for Fiscal Year 1981.* Hearings. 96th Cong., 2d sess. "Part 1—Posture Statement." Washington, D.C.: Government Printing Office, 1980.

———. Senate. Committee on Appropriations. *Lightweight Fighter Aircraft Program.* Hearings. 94th Cong., 1st sess. Washington, D.C.: Government Printing Office, 1975.

———. Senate. Committee on Armed Services. *Department of Defense Authorization for Appropriations for Fiscal Year 1980.* Part V. "General Procurement." 96th Cong., 1st sess., on S. 428. April 6, 9–11, 23, 1979. Washington, D.C.: Government Printing Office, 1979.

———. *Tactical Air Power.* Hearings, Part 8. Washington, D.C.: Government Printing Office, 1975.

———. *Tactical Air Power.* Hearings, Part 9. Washington, D.C.: Government Printing Office, 1975.

———. *Weapon Systems Acquisition Process.* Hearings. 92d Cong., 1st sess. Washington, D.C.: Government Printing Office, 1972.

———. *Department of Defense Authorization for Appropriations for Fiscal Year 1979.* Hearings on S. 2571. Part 7. "Tactical Air." 95th Cong., 2d sess. Washington, D.C.: Government Printing Office, 1978.

———. *Fiscal Year 1973 Authorization for Military Procurement, Research and Development . . . and Active Duty and Selected Reserve Strengths.* Hearings on S. 3108. Part 4. "Research and Development." 92nd Cong., 2d sess. Washington, D.C.: Government Printing Office, 1972.

———. Part 6. "Research and Development." 92nd Cong., 2d sess. Washington, D.C.: Government Printing Office, 1972.

———. *Fiscal Year 1976 and July–September 1976 Transition Period Authorization . . . and Civilian Personnel Strengths.* Hearings on S. 920. 94th Cong., 1st sess. Part 9. "Tactical Air Power." Washington, D.C.: Government Printing Office, 1975.

———. Subcommittee on Manpower and Personnel. *Impact of Technology on Military Requirements, Readiness and Operations.* Hearings. 96th Cong., 2d sess. Washington, D.C.: Government Printing Office, 1981.

———. Senate. Subcommittee on Tactical Airpower. *F-18 Program.* Hearings. 94th Cong., 1st sess. Washington, D.C.: Government Printing Office, 1975.

———. Senate. Committee on Foreign Relations. Subcommittee on Terrorism, Narcotics and International Communications. *Drugs, Law Enforcement, and Foreign Policy.* Hearings. Part 3. "The Cartel, Haiti, and Central America." 100th Cong., 2d sess. Washington, D.C.: Government Printing Office, 1988.

———. Senate. Committee on Government Operations. Permanent Subcommittee on Investigations. *TFX Contract Investigation.* Hearings. 88th Cong., 1st sess. Part 6. Washington, D.C.: Government Printing Office, 1963.

———. Senate. Committee on Armed Services. *Fiscal Year 1972 Authorization for Military Procurement . . . ABM and Reserve Strengths.* Hearings. 92d Cong., 1st sess. S. 939 (H.R. 8687). Part 5. "Bomber Defense . . . and Tactical Air Defense." Washington, D.C.: Government Printing Office, 1971.

———. Senate. Report No. 93–1104, 93rd Cong., 2d sess. Washington, D.C.: Government Printing Office, 1974.

———. Senate. Committee on Governmental Affairs. Subcommittee on Federal Spending Practices . . . Government. *Major Systems Acquisition Reform.* Hearing. Part 1. "Air Combat Fighter Program." 94th Cong., 1st sess. Washington, D.C.: Government Printing Office, 1975.

U.S. Department of Defense. DOD Instruction 5000.2.

———. "Development Concept Paper (DCP) for VFAX." Memorandum for the Assistant Secretary of the Navy (Research & Development), 6 August 1974.

———. "DOD Directive 5000.1." 13 July 1971.

———. "DOD Instruction 5000.1." 23 February 1991.

———. "DOD Instruction 5000.2–M." February 1991.

———. "DOD Instruction 5100.1." December 1958.

———. *Conduct of the Persian Gulf War. Final Report to Congress.* (Pursuant to Title V of the Persian Gulf Conflict Supplemental Authorization and Personnel Benefits Act 1991 [Public Law 102–25]) Chapters I through VIII. Washington, D.C.: Government Printing Office, April 1992.

———. Department of the Air Force. "Air Force Performance in Desert Storm." April 1991.

———. "Air Power Desert Storm: Backgrounder." N.p., n.d.

———. "Report of F-105D Configuration Board Proceedings." Mimeographed. Langley Air Force Base, Va.: Headquarters Tactical Air Command, 21 November 1959.

———. *Civil Air Patrol Aerospace Doctrine.* N.p., 1966.

———. *Combat Echo Weapon System Evaluation Program.* TAC Project 73E–134T Statistical Summary Report. Eglin AFB, Fla.: U.S. Air Force. TAWC [Tactical Air Weapons Center], 1 October 1978–30 September 1979.

———. Office of the Chief of Staff. "Air Superiority." Memorandum to all major commands from J. S. McConnell. Washington, D.C.: processed, 3 May 1965.

———. *Project Gun-Val.* Air Research and Development Command, Test Directive no. 5033-E1. Eglin Air Force Base, Fla.: Air Force Armament Center, 13 May 1952.

———. *Reaching Globally, Reaching Powerfully: The United States Air Force in the Gulf War* (A Report). Washington, D.C.: U.S. Air Force, September 1991.

———. *The Development of Air Doctrine in the Army Air Arm, 1917–1941.* Thomas H. Greer. Washington, D.C.: Office of Air Force History, 1985.

———. *U.S. Air Force Dictionary.* Woodford Agee Heflin, ed. Maxwell Air Force Base, Ala.: Air Univ. Press, 1956.

———. Department of the Navy. "Initial Operational Evaluation of the F/A-18 Naval Strike Fighter (OPNAV Report Symbol 3960-12)." Norfolk, Va.: Commander Operational Test and Evaluation Force, 16 June 1981.

———. "Integrated Program Summary for F/A-18E/F Hornet." Washington, D.C.: [Naval Air Systems Command], 8 January 1992.

———. "Presolicitation Notice for Development of a New Navy Strike Fighter (VFAX)." (Ser. C202 PMA265:HGH). Enclosure 9, 6 June 1974.

———. Naval Air Systems Command. "Integrated Program Summary, Annex.

D: Risk Assessment of the F/A-18E/F Hornet." Washington, D.C.: Naval Air Systems Command, January 1992.

———. Naval Air Systems Command. "Performance Comparisons with F/A-18A (Lot I and Lot XIV) and F/A-18E Specification Ground Rules." 25 March 1993.

———. Naval Air Systems Command. "Department of Defense Information Paper: RDT&D, NAVY (PE 0204136N)." Attachment to: "Performance comparisons with F/A-18A (Lot I and lot XIV) and F/A-18E Specification Ground Rules." 25 March 1993.

———. Departments of the Army and the Air Force. National Guard Bureau. *Vista 1999: A Long-Range Look at the Future of the Army and Air National Guard.* Washington, D.C.: n.p., 8 March 1982.

———. Joint Chiefs of Staff. *Roles, Missions, and Functions of the Armed Forces of the United States.* Transcript of Press Conference. Colin Powell, Chairman, JCS and Lt. Gen. Edwin Leland [Washington, D.C.: Government Printing Office], 12 February 1993.

———. Joint Chiefs of Staff. *Roles, Missions, and Functions of the Armed Forces of the United States.* Washington, D.C.: Government Printing Office, February 1993.

———. Office of the Inspector General. "F/A-18E/F Program as a Part of the Audit of the Effectiveness of the Defense Acquisition Board Review Process—FY 1992." Audit Report (Report Number 92–097), 5 June 1992.

U.S. Strategic Bombing Survey. *The United States Strategic Bombing Survey: Over-all Report (European War).* Washington, D.C.: Government Printing Office, 30 September 1945.

"Vought-1100—Lightweight Fighter Prototype." LTV news release and fact sheet. Arlington, Tex.: LTV Corporation, 1975.

Wagner, Ray. *The North American Sabre.* London: MacDonald, 1963.

Warden, John A. III. *The Air Campaign: Planning for Combat.* Washington, D.C.: Pergamon-Brassey, 1989.

Warrick, Joby. "Air Force Gives Itself an A Plus on War Role." *Air Force Times* (13 May 1991): 25.

"Washington Roundup." *Aviation Week & Space Technology* 102 (3 March 1975): 11.

Watts, Barry. *The Foundations of U.S. Air Doctrine: The Problem of Friction in War.* Maxwell Air Force Base, Ala.: Air University Press, 1984.

"Weapons Systems Procurement Uncertain." *Aviation Week & Space Technology* 101 (7 October 1974): 17.

Webster's Third International Dictionary (3d ed.). Springfield, Mass.: G. & C. Merriam Co., 1981.

Weisner, M. F. "CEB Report of Cost Analysis and Cost Management." 23 October 1972.

Wheaton, David, and Ken Hinman. "A Proposal to Conduct a Conceptual Study of Navy Advanced Fighter Alternatives." Vol. 1, Report no. GDC PIN 69–726A. San Diego, Calif.: General Dynamics, Convair Division, December 1969.

White, T. G. "Comment and Discussion." *Naval Institute Proceedings* (November 1991): 28.

White, William D. *U.S. Tactical Air Power: Missions, Forces, and Costs.* Washington, D.C.: The Brookings Institution, 1974.

Williams, John B. "Comment & Discussion." *Naval Institute Proceedings* (November 1991): 26.

Wilson, George C. "Variable-Geometry F-4 Proposed to Navy." *Aviation Week & Space Technology* (11 July 1966):30–31.

Zumwalt, Elmo. *On Watch.* New York: Quadrangle, 1976.

Index

About the Author

James P. Stevenson is the author of *McDonnell Douglas* F-15 *Eagle, Grumman* F-14 *Tomcat,* and *A Step Ahead*, a history of the F100 engine. Formerly the editor of the Navy Fighter Weapons School's *Topgun Journal* and a writer for *Defense Week*, he is also the author of numerous articles on tactical aviation for professional journals and the popular press.

For the last ten years Stevenson has served as a consultant to the aerospace industry and worked with various television networks producing military documentaries. He lives in Bethesda, Maryland, where he is writing his next book for the Naval Institute Press, a procurement history of the ill-fated A-12 Avenger II.